Grape Pest Management

THIRD EDITION

Larry J. Bettiga
Technical Editor

UNIVERSITY OF CALIFORNIA
AGRICULTURE AND NATURAL RESOURCES
OAKLAND, CALIFORNIA

PUBLICATION 3343

To order or obtain ANR publications and other products, visit the ANR Communication Services online catalog at http://anrcatalog.ucdavis.edu or phone 1-800-994-8849. You can also place orders by mail or FAX, or request a printed catalog of our products from

University of California
Agriculture and Natural Resources
Communication Services
1301 S. 46th Street
Building 478 - MC 3580
Richmond, CA 94804-4600

Telephone 1-800-994-8849
510-665-2195
FAX 510-665-3427
E-mail: anrcatalog@ucdavis.edu

Publication 3343
ISBN-13: 978-1-60107-800-1

Library of Congress Cataloging-in-Publication Data

Grape pest management / Larry J. Bettiga, technical editor. -- Third edition.

pages cm -- (Publication ; 3343)

Includes bibliographical references and index.

ISBN 978-1-60107-800-1

1. Grapes--Diseases and pests--Integrated control--California.
2. Grapes--Diseases and pests--California. 3. Viticulture--California.
I. Bettiga, Larry J. II. Series: Publication (University of California (System). Division of Agriculture and Natural Resources) ; 3343.

SB608.G7G74 2013

634.8'2--dc23

2013035836

Editing: Stephen Barnett. Design: Robin Walton. Illustrations: Will Suckow, except as noted in the captions. Proofreading and indexing: Hazel White. Editorial assistance: Sueanne Johnson. Photo research: Evett Kilmartin. Photo credits are given in the captions. Grape leaf photos on pages 1, 47, 69, 175, 433, 447, 471, 497, and 539 by Jack Kelly Clark. Front cover photo by Larry J. Bettiga; back cover photo by Elëna Zhukova.

To simplify information, trade names of products have been used. No endorsement of named or illustrated products is intended, nor is criticism implied of similar products that are not mentioned or illustrated.

 This publication has been anonymously peer reviewed for technical accuracy by University of California scientists and other qualified professionals. This review process was managed by ANR Associate Editors for Pest Management Joe Nunez and Mary Louise Flint.

Printed in the Unites States of America on recycled paper

5m-pr-11/13-SB/RW

WARNING ON THE USE OF CHEMICALS

Pesticides are poisonous. Always read and carefully follow all precautions and safety recommendations given on the container label. Store all chemicals in their original labeled containers in a locked cabinet or shed, away from foods or feeds, and out of the reach of children, unauthorized persons, pets, and livestock.

Recommendations are based on the best information currently available, and treatments based on them should not leave residues exceeding the tolerance established for any particular chemical. Confine chemicals to the area being treated. THE GROWER IS LEGALLY RESPONSIBLE for residues on the grower's crops as well as for problems caused by drift from the grower's property to other properties or crops.

Consult your county agricultural commissioner for correct methods of disposing of leftover spray materials and empty containers. **Never burn pesticide containers.**

PHYTOTOXICITY: Certain chemicals may cause plant injury if used at the wrong stage of plant development or when temperatures are too high. Injury may also result from excessive amounts or the wrong formulation or from mixing incompatible materials. Inert ingredients, such as wetters, spreaders, emulsifiers, diluents, and solvents, can cause plant injury. Since formulations are often changed by manufacturers, it is possible that plant injury may occur, even though no injury was noted in previous seasons.

Contents

FUNGAL DISEASES

Editors and Authors

TECHNICAL EDITOR

Larry J. Bettiga
*Viticulture Farm Advisor, UC Cooperative Extension,
Monterey County*

ENTOMOLOGY EDITORS

Walter J. Bentley
*Area IPM Entomology Advisor Emeritus, UC Cooperative
Extension, Kearney Agricultural Center, Parlier*

Philip A. Phillips
*Area IPM Entomology Advisor Emeritus, UC Cooperative
Extension, Ventura County*

Lucia G. Varela
*Area IPM Entomology Advisor, UC Cooperative Extension,
Sonoma County*

PLANT PATHOLOGY EDITORS

W. Douglas Gubler
*Plant Pathologist, UC Cooperative Extension, Plant Pathology,
UC Davis*

George M. Leavitt
*Viticulture Farm Advisor Emeritus, UC Cooperative Extension,
Madera County*

CONTRIBUTING AUTHORS

Rodrigo Almeida
*Professor, Environmental Science, Policy and Management,
UC Berkeley*

Mark Battany
*Viticulture Farm Advisor, UC Cooperative Extension,
San Luis Obispo County*

Kendra Baumgartner
*Research Plant Pathologist, USDA-ARS, Plant Pathology,
UC Davis*

Larry J. Bettiga
*Viticulture Farm Advisor, UC Cooperative Extension,
Monterey County*

Walter J. Bentley
*Area IPM Advisor Emeritus, UC Cooperative Extension,
Kearney Agricultural Center, Parlier*

Gregory T. Browne
*Research Plant Pathologist, USDA- ARS, Plant Pathology,
UC Davis*

Monica L. Cooper
*Viticulture Farm Advisor, UC Cooperative Extension,
Napa County*

Richard L. Coviello
*Entomology Farm Advisor Emeritus, UC Cooperative Extension,
Fresno County*

Jodi E. Creasap Gee
*Viticulture Extension Associate, Lake Erie Regional Grape
Program, Cornell Cooperative Extension*

Kent M. Daane
*Entomologist, UC Cooperative Extension, Environmental Science,
Policy and Management, UC Berkeley and Kearney Agricultural
Center, Parlier*

Joseph M. DiTomaso
*Weed Specialist, UC Cooperative Extension, Plant Sciences,
UC Davis*

Akif Eskalen
*Plant Pathologist, UC Cooperative Extension, Plant Pathology,
UC Riverside*

Matthew W. Fidelibus
*Viticulture Specialist, UC Cooperative Extension, Viticulture &
Enology, UC Davis, Kearney Agricultural Center, Parlier*

Carmen Gispert
*Area Viticulture Advisor, UC Cooperative Extension,
Riverside County*

Deborah A. Golino
*Plant Pathologist, Director of Foundation Plant Services,
UC Davis*

Elizabeth E. Grafton-Cardwell
*Entomologist, UC Cooperative Extension, Entomology,
UC Riverside, Kearney Agricultural Center, Parlier*

Jeffrey Granett
Professor Emeritus, Entomology, UC Davis

W. Douglas Gubler
*Plant Pathologist, UC Cooperative Extension, Plant Pathology,
UC Davis*

David R. Haviland
*Entomology Farm Advisor, UC Cooperative Extension,
Kern County*

Jennifer M. Hashim
*Former Viticulture Farm Advisor, UC Cooperative Extension,
Kern County*

Kurt J. Hembree
*Weed Management Farm Advisor, UC Cooperative Extension,
Fresno County*

EDITORS AND AUTHORS

Pedro Hernandez
Product Development Representative, Nichino America, Inc.

Chuck A. Ingels
Farm Advisor, UC Cooperative Extension, Sacramento County

Judy A. Johnson
Research Entomologist, USDA – ARS, San Joaquin Valley Agricultural Sciences Center, Parlier

Lee F. Johnson
Research Scientist, Science & Environmental Policy, CSU Monterey Bay, NASA Ames Research Center

Bruce C. Kirkpatrick
Professor, Plant Pathology, UC Davis

John H. Klotz
Entomologist, UC Cooperative Extension, Entomology, UC Riverside

W. Thomas Lanini
Weed Ecologist, UC Cooperative Extension, Plant Sciences, UC Davis

Andrew Lawson
Professor, Plant Sciences, CSU Fresno

George M. Leavitt
Viticulture Farm Advisor Emeritus, UC Cooperative Extension, Madera County

Glenn T. McGourty
Viticulture & Plant Science Advisor, UC Cooperative Extension, Mendocino County

Michael V. McKenry
Nematologist Emeritus, UC Cooperative Extension, Nematology, UC Riverside, Kearney Agricultural Center, Parlier

Rex E. Marsh
Wildlife Specialist Emeritus, Wildlife, Fish & Conservation Biology, UC Davis

Rick Melnicoe
Director, Pesticide Information & Coordination, UC Davis

Themis J. Michailides
Plant Pathologist, Plant Pathology, UC Davis, Kearney Agricultural Center, Parlier

Jocelyn G. Millar
Professor, Entomology, UC Riverside

Eric C. Mussen
Apiculturist, UC Cooperative Extension, Entomology, UC Davis

Maxwell V. Norton
Farm Advisor, UC Cooperative Extension, Merced County

William L. Peacock
Viticulture Farm Advisor Emeritus, UC Cooperative Extension, Tulare County

Thomas M. Perring
Professor, Entomology, UC Riverside

Elsa L. Petit
Plant Pathologist, Amherst College

Philip A. Phillips
Area IPM Advisor Emeritus, UC Cooperative Extension, Ventura County

Alexander H. Purcell
Professor Emeritus, Environmental Science, Policy and Management, UC Berkeley

David M. Rizzo
Professor, Plant Pathology, UC Davis

Philippe Rolshausen
Subtropical Crop Specialist, UC Cooperative Extension, Botany and Plant Sciences, UC Riverside

Suzanne Rooney Latham
Plant Pathologist, Plant Pest Diagnostics Branch, CDFA

Jay A. Rosenheim
Professor, Entomology, UC Davis

Adib Rowhani
Plant Pathology Specialist, Foundation Plant Services, UC Davis

Michael K. Rust
Professor, Entomology, UC Riverside

Terrell P. Salmon
County Director and Wildlife Specialist Emeritus, UC Cooperative Extension, San Diego County

Lawrence J. Schwankl
Irrigation Specialist, UC Cooperative Extension, Land, Air & Water Resources, UC Davis, Kearney Agricultural Center, Parlier

Anil Shrestha
Professor, Plant Sciences, CSU Fresno

David Smart
Professor, Viticulture & Enology, UC Davis

Joseph L. Smilanick
Research Plant Pathologist, USDA – ARS, San Joaquin Valley Agricultural Sciences Center, Parlier

Rhonda J. Smith
Viticulture Farm Advisor, UC Cooperative Extension Sonoma County

Richard Smith
Weed Science Farm Advisor, UC Cooperative Extension, Monterey County

Charles G. Summers
Entomologist Emeritus, Entomology, UC Davis, Kearney Agricultural Center, Parlier

Serguei V. Triapitsyn
Principal Museum Scientist, Entomology, UC Riverside

Florent Trouillas
Former Postdoctoral Researcher, Plant Pathology, UC Davis

José R. Úrbez-Torres
Plant Pathologist, Pacific Agri-Food Research Centre, Agriculture and Agri-Food Canada

Jerry K. Uyemoto
Research Plant Pathologist Emeritus, USDA-ARS, Plant Pathology, UC Davis

Lucia G. Varela
Area IPM Advisor, UC Cooperative Extension, Sonoma County

Ronald N. Vargas
County Director & Farm Advisor Emeritus, UC Cooperative Extension, Madera County

Stephen J. Vasquez
Former Viticulture Farm Advisor, UC Cooperative Extension, Fresno County

Paul S. Verdegaal
Farm Advisor, UC Cooperative Extension, San Joaquin County

M. Andrew Walker
Professor, Viticulture & Enology, UC Davis

Edward A. Weber
Former County Director and Viticulture Farm Advisor (deceased), UC Cooperative Extension, Napa County

James Wolpert
Specialist Emeritus, UC Cooperative Extension, Viticulture & Enology, UC Davis

Lynn R. Wunderlich
Farm Advisor, UC Cooperative Extension, El Dorado County

Glen Yokota
Staff Research Associate, Kearney Agricultural Center, Parlier

Frank G. Zalom
Professor and Entomologist, UC Cooperative Extension, Entomology, UC Davis

Acknowledgments

The editors wish to thank all the authors for their contributions of writing and photography for this third edition. We also thank the University of California Division of Agriculture and Natural Resources for support and contributions to the continued development of *Grape Pest Management*.

As with the past editions, improvements in our understanding the biology of pest organisms and application of integrated approaches to reduce the economic impact of pest populations are based on the dedication of research scientists, Cooperative Extension specialists and farm advisors, growers, and pest control advisers who have conducted the studies to develop and evaluate grape pest management solutions. Over 70 contributors were involved in the third revision of *Grape Pest Management*. It is important to remember the significant individual research and writing contributions to the previous two editions. We are especially grateful to Donald L. Flaherty for his dedication and leadership as Technical Editor Chairman in successfully developing the first edition published in 1981 and the revision published in 1992.

We express our gratitude to the contributions of the following authors of the first and second editions, who laid the foundation for this revision.

Harry S. Agamalian
Weed Control Farm Advisor Emeritus, UC Cooperative Extension, Monterey County

Harry L. Andris
Farm Advisor Emeritus, UC Cooperative Extension, Fresno County

Martin M. Barnes
Professor Emeritus, Entomology, UC Riverside

William W. Barnett
Area IPM Advisor Emeritus, UC Cooperative Extension, Kearney Agricultural Center

Warren E. Bendixen
Field Crops Farm Advisor Emeritus, UC Cooperative Extension, Santa Barbara County

Andrew M. Bledsoe
Former Director of Viticulture, Robert Mondavi Winery, Napa

Sue L. Blodgett
Former Area IPM Advisor, UC Cooperative Extension, Sonoma County

Keith W. Bowers
Viticulture Farm Advisor Emeritus, Extension, Napa County

L. Peter Christensen
Viticulture Specialist Emeritus, UC Cooperative Extension, Viticulture & Enology, UC Davis, Kearney Agricultural Center

Dell O. Clark
Program Supervisor (retired), Control and Eradication, CDFA

William R. Clark
Deputy Agricultural Commissioner (retired), Agricultural Commissioner Office, Tulare County

A. Charles Crabb
Professor Emeritus, CSU Chico

Charles E. Curtis
Research Entomologist (retired), USDA-ARS, Stored Products Lab, Fresno

John E. Dibble
Entomology Specialist Emeritus, UC Cooperative Extension, Kearney Agricultural Center

Dean R. Donaldson
Environmental Farm Advisor Emeritus, UC Cooperative Extension, Napa County

Robert V. Dowell
Senior Economic Entomologist, Pest Detection, CDFA

Clyde L. Elmore
Weed Science Specialist Emeritus, UC Cooperative Extension, Plant Sciences, UC Davis

James T. English
Professor, Plant Pathology, University of Missouri

Bill B. Fisher
Weed Control Farm Advisor Emeritus, UC Cooperative Extension, Fresno County

Donald L. Flaherty
Entomology Farm Advisor Emeritus, UC Cooperative Extension, Tulare County

John H. Foott
Horticulture Farm Advisor Emeritus, Extension, San Luis Obispo

Austin C. Goheen
Plant Pathologist, USDA-ARS, Plant Pathology, UC Davis

Paul Goodwin
Plant Pathologist, Environmental Biology, University of Guelph

Walter L. Graves
Natural Resources Management Farm Advisor Emeritus, UC Cooperative Extension, San Diego

Rachid Hanna
Former Entomologist, Entomology, UC Davis

Donna Hirschfelt
Viticulture Farm Advisor (retired), UC Cooperative Extension, Amador County

Marjorie A. Hoy
Professor, Entomology and Nematology, University of Florida

Frederik L. Jensen
Viticulture Specialist Emeritus, UC Cooperative Extension, Kearney Agricultural Center

Johannes L. Joos
Entomology Farm Advisor, UC Cooperative Extension, Sonoma County

Amand N. Kasimatis
Viticulture Specialist Emeritus, UC Cooperative Extension, Viticulture & Enology, UC Davis

Kathleen M. Kelley
Horticulture Farm Advisor, UC Cooperative Extension, Stanislaus County

Harold M. Kempen
Weed Control Farm Advisor Emeritus, UC Cooperative Extension, Kern County

Hiroshi Kido
Staff Research Associate (retired), Entomology, UC Davis

James J. Kissler
Viticulture Farm Advisor Emeritus, UC Cooperative Extension, San Joaquin County

Conrad J. Krass
Primary State Plant Pathologist and Nematologist (retired), CDFA

Arthur H. Lange
Weed Specialist Emeritus, UC Cooperative Extension, Kearney Agricultural Center

E. F. Legner
Professor Emeritus, Entomology, UC Riverside

James E. Lindegren
Research Entomologist (retired), USDA-ARS, Stored Products Laboratory, Fresno

Donald A. Luvisi
Viticulture Farm Advisor Emeritus, UC Cooperative Extension, Kern County

Curtis D. Lynn
Viticulture Farm Advisor Emeritus, UC Cooperative Extension, Tulare County

Norman F. McCalley
Entomology Farm Advisor Emeritus, UC Cooperative Extension, Monterey County

Patrick J. Marer
Pesticide Training Coordinator (retired), IPM Education and Publications, UC Davis

James J. Marois
Professor, Plant Pathology, University of Florida

William J. Moller
Plant Pathologist, UC Cooperative Extension, Plant Pathology, UC Davis

Rudy A. Neja
Viticulture Farm Advisor (retired), UC Cooperative Extension, Riverside County

John D. Radewald
Nematologist Emeritus, UC Cooperative Extension, Nematology, UC Riverside

Mary Ann Sall
Former Professor, Plant Pathology, UC Davis

Steve D. Savage
Plant Pathologist

William Schnathorst
Staff Research Associate (retired), USDA-ARS, Plant Pathology, UC Davis

Milton N. Schroth
Professor Emeritus, Plant Pathology, UC Berkeley

Edwin L. Soderstrom
Research Entomologist (retired), USDA-ARS, Stored Products Laboratory, Fresno

Garth H. Spitler
Entomologist (retired), USDA-ARS, Stored Products Laboratory, Fresno

William Steinke
Former Agricultural Engineer, UC Cooperative Extension, UC Davis

Vernon M. Stern
Professor Emeritus, Entomology, UC Riverside

Michael W. Stimmann
Pesticide Specialist and Statewide Pesticide Coordinator Emeritus, Environmental Toxicology, UC Davis

Beth L. Teviodale
Plant Pathologist Emeritus, UC Cooperative Extension, Plant Pathology, UC Davis

Stephen C. Welter
Professor, Environmental Science, Policy and Management, UC Berkeley

William E. Wildman
Soil and Water Specialist Emeritus, UC Cooperative Extension, Land, Air & Water Resources, UC Davis

Lloyd T. Wilson
Professor, Entomology, Texas A&M University

Donald Flaherty (left) and Larry Bettiga at The Monterey Vineyard winery, now operated by Constellation Wines. *Photo*: Jack Kelly Clark.

Introduction

When *Grape Pest Management* was first published in 1981, it consolidated into one source our knowledge of the biology and management of the pests affecting California wine, raisin, and table grape vineyards. The book helped growers and pest control advisers apply the principles of integrated pest management (IPM) to vineyards growing under the diverse site and pest conditions found in the state.

Grape IPM is an approach that seeks to manage pest populations below an established economic injury level. Key components of this approach are correct identification of the pest, established monitoring techniques, and treatment thresholds that determine when control practices are appropriate. IPM considers all control techniques that are appropriate for a given pest complex and combines biological control, mating disruption, habitat modification, cultural practices, pest-resistant rootstocks, and certified virus-tested plant material. Pesticides are applied only when monitoring indicates they are needed and are chosen to control the target pest while minimizing the risk to human health, beneficial and nontarget organisms, and the environment.

Pest management is constantly changing. To convey new information on introduced pest species, improved sampling and monitoring techniques, pesticide resistance issues, pest biology and epidemiology, and management practices, the book was revised and published as a second edition in 1992.

For this third edition of *Grape Pest Management,* we have added several invasive species that have become major grape pests, including vine mealybug and glassy-winged sharpshooter, as well as recent introductions such as Virginia creeper leafhopper, light brown apple moth, and European grapevine moth. We also added pests such as brown marmorated stink bug and spotted wing drosophila that may soon become pests in California. University of California research has significantly advanced our understanding of the bacterium *Xylella fastidiosa,* which causes Pierce's disease, as well as the fungal organisms that cause canker diseases and esca (black measles). We have also updated the biology of grape powdery mildew and introduced a risk assessment index model that allows vineyard managers to choose and time control options based on local disease severity. Vineyard floor management now includes the impact of cover cropping on pest populations, as well as shifts in weed populations due to control practices and herbicide resistance. The information on pesticide handling and application has been specifically related to application in vineyards, and new sections on diagnosing problems in the field and laboratory testing have been added.

Although control options are discussed, specific pesticide recommendations are not given in this book because pesticide registrations and labels change frequently. For current control options, see the current *UC IPM Grape Pest Management Guidelines:* on the Web at www.ipm.ucdavis.edu. Check with your local UCCE Farm Advisor or pest control adviser for the latest control recommendations. At the UC IPM website you can also download useful publications such as *Fungicides, Bactericides, and Biologicals for Deciduous Tree Fruit, Nut, Strawberry, and Vine Crops* and *Year-Round IPM Programs for Wine and Raisin or Table Grapes.*

As site conditions, pest complexes, and economics can vary greatly for different grape growing regions, we must emphasize that this book is to be used as a guide for grape IPM. Growers and pest control advisers must still determine for themselves the procedures most applicable to their vineyard situations.

Part 1

General Viticulture

Barbera

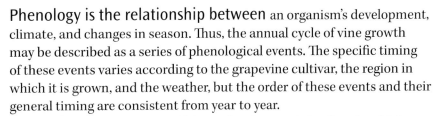

1 ANNUAL GROWTH CYCLE OF A GRAPEVINE

Matthew W. Fidelibus, David Smart, and James Wolpert

Figure 1.1 Dormant bud. *Photo*: J. K. Clark.

Phenology is the relationship between an organism's development, climate, and changes in season. Thus, the annual cycle of vine growth may be described as a series of phenological events. The specific timing of these events varies according to the grapevine cultivar, the region in which it is grown, and the weather, but the order of these events and their general timing are consistent from year to year.

The first obvious event within a calendar year is budbreak, which occurs in late winter or spring, depending on the geographic location where the grapes are being grown (see Section 2, "Calendar of Events"). Soon after, there is the "grand period of growth," when shoot extension and canopy development are rapid. Flower clusters are visible soon after rapid growth commences, with flower opening (anthesis) and berry set occurring in late spring. Fruit maturation begins in midsummer after veraison (when the berries begin to soften and those of black-fruited cultivars begin to change color). In late summer or fall, fruit reach their proper maturity and are harvested. Leaf senescence begins in late summer or fall, and the vines enter dormancy after the first fall frost.

BUDBREAK

Grapevines, like most deciduous fruit crops, require exposure to chilling temperatures during dormancy for optimal budbreak. Because their chilling requirement is relatively low, about 250 hours at less than 7°C (45°F), inadequate chilling is rarely a problem for grapevines in California, except in the Coachella Valley. Budbreak begins in spring, generally after mean daily temperatures exceed 10°C (50°F) (figs. 1.1–1.3).

Figure 1.2 Swollen bud. *Photo*: J. K. Clark.

Figure 1.3 Budbreak. *Photo*: J. K. Clark.

CANOPY DEVELOPMENT

After budbreak, canopy development, shoot elongation, and leaf area expansion can proceed rapidly and as a function of heat units. In most years, heat units accumulate slowly at first, so shoot growth is initially slow; as temperatures increase, so too does the shoot growth rate. The grand period of growth continues through bloom, but the rate of shoot growth begins to slow after fruit set (figs. 1.4– 1.9). Growth is indeterminate in grapevines, so primary shoots and lateral shoots may continue to grow after berry set, depending on water availability. The rate of canopy development, and its eventual density, may profoundly affect the potential for pest problems and their management.

Figure 1.4 Early shoot growth. *Photo*: J. K. Clark.

Figure 1.5 Flat leaf stage. *Photo*: J. K. Clark.

Figure 1.6 Six-inch shoot stage. *Photo*: J. K. Clark.

Figure 1.7 Twelve-inch growth stage. *Photo*: J. K. Clark.

Figure 1.8 Twelve-inch growth stage showing early development of axillary buds that form lateral shoots. *Photo*: J. K. Clark.

Figure 1.9 Vine growth at the beginning of bloom; shoots are as long as 1 m (3 ft). *Photo*: J. K. Clark.

FLOWERING AND FRUIT SET

Anthesis occurs from mid-May to early June (figs. 1.10–1.12). At this time, a calyptra, or cap, of fused petals detaches from each flower exposing the flower's male organs (stamens) and female organ (pistil).

Structures at the tip of the stamens, anthers, release pollen at or after cap fall. Pollen may be deposited onto the pistil's receptive tissue, the stigma, without the action of insects or wind, so grape flowers are considered to be self-pollinating. Soon after anthesis, berry set occurs for flowers that were pollinated (fig. 1.13). At about this time, less photosynthates are allocated to the shoot tips and more resources are invested in the developing berries. Consequently, the rate of shoot growth typically declines after fruit set.

Figure 1.10 Flower cluster just before bloom (A). The calyptra is beginning to dehisce on flower in (B). *Photos*: J. K. Clark.

Figure 1.11 Flower cluster with 10% of calyptras off. In (B) calyptra is in the last stage of dehiscing; after dehiscence, stamens begin to spread. *Photos*: J. K. Clark.

Figure 1.12 Flower cluster with 85% of calyptras off. In (B) a flower shows five stamens spread out and the stigma on tip of the ovary. Note dehiscing calyptra. *Photos*: J. K. Clark.

Figure 1.13 Fruit cluster with an early stage of berry development after set (A), with a close-up of a berry (B). *Photos*: J. K. Clark.

Berry growth is similar to that of other fruit and exhibits three distinct stages characterized by a double S-shaped curve (fig. 1.14). The three stages are recognized as (1) an initial period of rapid growth, due mostly to cell divisions; (2) a short lag phase during which there is almost no gain in volume or weight; and (3) a rapid increase in size and soluble sugars due to cell enlargement (fig. 1.15). The term veraison is used to describe the initiation of stage 3 (figs. 1.16–1.17). Soluble sugar accumulation and cell enlargement achieve a plateau at fruit maturity (fig. 1.18).

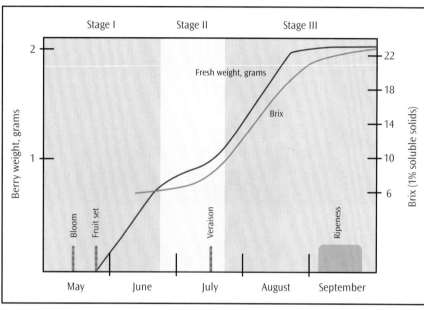

Figure 1.14 Growth of a grape berry.

Figure 1.15 Fruit cluster when the berries have grown to 8 to 10 mm (0.3 to 0.4 in) in diameter. *Photo*: J. K. Clark.

Figure 1.16 Fruit cluster of a white cultivar at veraison, or the beginning of ripening, when berries begin to turn soft and lose their green color. *Photo*: J. K. Clark.

Figure 1.17 Fruit cluster of a black cultivar at veraison showing the development of color. *Photo*: L. J. Bettiga.

Figure 1.18 Fruit cluster at harvest time, with a soluble solids reading of 21.5 Brix. *Photo*: J. K. Clark.

Shoot Development

In the final stages of fruit ripening, the shoots develop periderm and are said to ripen. Formation of periderm begins at the base of the cane and proceeds toward the tip, causing the shoot to change color from green to yellow and, finally, to brown (figs. 1.19–1.21). Periderm color is often characteristic of the cultivar. A well-developed periderm may help protect shoots from cold injury, and a poorly developed periderm can be a sign of Pierce's disease or of poor nutrient or canopy management.

After the fruit have matured, most photosynthates are directed to the arms, trunk, and roots as stored carbohydrates. These reserves are essential to the vine's survival during extreme cold temperatures in winter. They are also essential to early development of new shoots as vines break dormancy in late winter or spring.

Figure 1.19 Vine growth and canopy appearance at harvest. *Photo*: J. K. Clark.

Figure 1.20 Early stages of defoliation showing the loss of basal leaves. Note the brown, lignified canes indicating wood maturity. *Photo*: J. K. Clark.

Figure 1.21 In autumn the leaves turn yellow and fall to the ground. *Photo*: J. K. Clark.

PART 1: GENERAL VITICULTURE

ROOT DEVELOPMENT

Root development is less well understood than shoot development because roots are much harder to observe. However, evidence suggests that root development can be characterized by two growth flushes. The major flush occurs just after shoot growth peaks in mid-May to early June. At this time, there is sufficient photosynthetic activity in the shoots, and there is generally ample soil water to drive root growth and development. A second smaller root flush appears to occur after fruit harvest. This flush is surrounded by some controversy because it is so much smaller than the spring flush and the extent of growth depends on water availability and the general health of the vines.

Root distribution in the soil is most strongly affected by the soil's physical properties. With ample water available and no impediments to root growth such as soil compaction, grapevine roots will proliferate extensively and to very deep depths in the soil profile. Irrigation type, planting density, and rootstock characteristics also affect root proliferation, but to a much smaller degree than do soil physical properties. Root development and distribution are important to soil pest management, as in the case of nematodes and phylloxera, but not nearly as important as is selection of an appropriate resistant rootstock genotype. Nematodes and phylloxera are sensitive to soil physical properties such as texture (sand, silt, and clay content),

and the severity of infestation can depend on where roots are growing in the profile.

REFERENCES

Mullins, M. G., A. Bouquet, and L. E. Williams. 1992. Biology of the grapevine. Cambridge, UK: Cambridge University Press.

Pearce, I., and B. G. Coombe. 2005. Grapevine phenology. In P. R. Dry and B. G. Coombe, eds., Viticulture. Vol. 1, Resources. Adelaide, Australia: Winetitles. 150–166.

Winkler, A. J., J. A. Cook, W. M. Kliewer, and L. A. Lider. 1974. General viticulture. Berkeley: University of California Press.

2 IMPORTANT STRUCTURES AND FEATURES OF GRAPEVINES

Larry J. Bettiga, Paul S. Verdegaal, and Matthew W. Fidelibus

SHOOTS

The succulent new growths that extend from each bud are called shoots. By fall, mature, woody shoots that dropped their leaves and entered dormancy are called canes. The length of grapevine shoots and canes is partitioned, alternately, into nodes and internodes (fig. 2.1).

Figure 2.1 Main features of a grapevine shoot after fruit set.

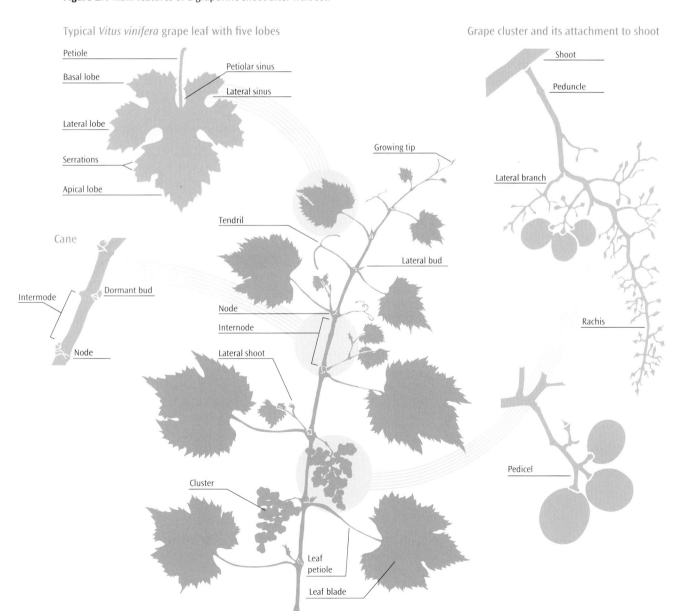

Typical *Vitus vinifera* grape leaf with five lobes

- Petiole
- Basal lobe
- Petiolar sinus
- Lateral sinus
- Lateral lobe
- Serrations
- Apical lobe

Cane
- Intermode
- Dormant bud
- Node

- Tendril
- Growing tip
- Lateral bud
- Node
- Internode
- Lateral shoot
- Cluster
- Leaf petiole
- Leaf blade

Grape cluster and its attachment to shoot
- Shoot
- Peduncle
- Lateral branch
- Rachis
- Pedicel

Nodes are the thickened sections that have buds from which new shoots may arise. Internodes are the smaller-diameter sections between each node. Each cluster is borne opposite a leaf on nodes near the base of a shoot. Tendrils, which replace clusters on more apical nodes, occur in an alternating pattern so that a tendril is formed opposite each of two adjacent leaves but not formed opposite the third leaf. This pattern is observed for all grapevines except *Vitis labrusca,* which has tendrils on most nodes.

Cells that compose new leaves, clusters, tendrils, and other tissues are formed by division of the apical meristem at the tip of each actively growing shoot. Newly formed cells then differentiate and expand, so that young leaves and other organs appear to unfold from the shoot tip.

The shoot growth rate depends on environmental conditions. Unlike many deciduous plants, grapevine shoots do not form terminal buds. Shoot growth will continue if there is sufficient heat and an abundance of moisture in the soil.

BUDS

As shoots develop, two types of buds are formed at each node in the leaf axil at the base of the petiole. Lateral, or prompt, buds are formed first. Prompt buds are so named because lateral shoots arise from them in the season the buds are formed; these shoots are also referred to as summer laterals. Lateral shoots may be very short or quite long. Most of the short lateral shoots fail to lignify and drop from canes during dormancy.

Regardless of its length or persistence, each lateral shoot will form a latent bud in its first leaf axil; this leaf is reduced to a prophyll, a bract or scalelike structure. This latent bud may also be referred to as a compound bud or an eye. Latent buds generally contain three growing points, each with partially developed shoots, including rudimentary leaves, tendrils, and flower clusters. A compound bud generally remains dormant after it has formed until the following spring. Then, in most instances, only the middle, or primary, growing point will emerge (fig. 2.2). Death or injury to the primary bud or some environmental conditions can result in the growing of secondary or tertiary buds, or both. Secondary and tertiary buds are generally less fruitful than the primary bud.

Figure 2.2 At left, a cross-section of a dormant grape bud attached to a cane, with internal features and the position of leaf petiole attachment. At right, a shoot showing a lateral shoot that has grown from the leaf axil and a latent bud.

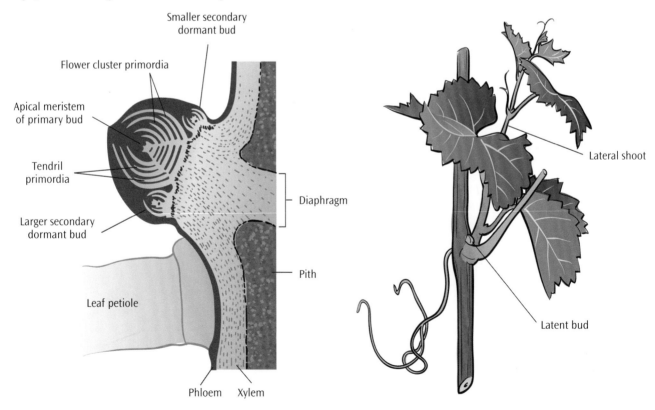

Leaf

The grape leaf consists of a blade (or lamina), the petiole, and a pair of stipules at the base of the petiole (see fig. 2.1). Full expansion of the mature leaf blade occurs 30 to 40 days after it unfolds from the shoot tip. The upper surface contains very few stomata; it may have epicuticular hairs, and it has a well-differentiated layer of epicuticular wax consisting of overlapping platelets. The lower surface lacks a wax layer but can contain epidermal hairs of various types (woolly, glandular, thorny), depending on the cultivar. The lower surface has many stomata arranged in a random nature. There are approximately 170 stomata per mm^2 (110,000 per in^2). The leaf blade has five main veins that arise from the petiole at the same point.

In spring under conditions of high temperature and humidity, grape leaves and shoots can produce natural exudates that form sap balls on the underside of leaves, on petioles, and on shoots; these balls can be confused with insect or mite eggs (fig. 2.3).

Figure 2.3 Sap balls, or pearls, are a natural exudate and may be found on the underside of grape leaves in spring; they are not to be confused with insect or mite eggs. *Photo*: J. K. Clark.

Flowers and Fruit

Grapevines have small flowers, typically 4 to 5 mm (0.17 to 0.20 in) long, that are grouped together in a cluster, or inflorescence. Before bloom the calyptra, a cap of fused petals, encloses the other flower parts. Each calyptra detaches from its base at bloom, exposing pollen-bearing stamens and a pistil with the ovary, the enlarged basal portion (fig. 2.4). If pollinated, the ovary of each flower may grow and develop into a berry.

Each cluster is attached to a shoot by a peduncle; the entire length of the main cluster stem framework is referred to as the rachis, with individual berries being attached to the rachis by a pedicel, sometimes referred to as a cap stem (see fig. 2.1). Clusters vary widely in shape and size, depending on the grapevine variety and by the position of the cluster on the shoot. Common cluster shapes are shown in figure 2.5. The classification depends on the number and length of the lateral branches of the cluster stem. Clusters with several well-developed laterals near the peduncle are called shouldered. When the first lateral developing from the peduncle is large and separate from the cluster, it is referred to as a wing.

Grapevine Structure

Cultivated grapevines are trained into various forms with the aid of a trellis system that helps support the permanent vine structures, the annual canopy, and the fruit. The main aboveground structures are the trunk, head, cordons, arms, spurs, and canes. The trunk branches into arms or cordons, depending on the training system. From these arise fruiting wood, 1-year-old dormant wood. This wood may be retained each year as spurs, canes, or both, depending on the grapevine variety and on the cultural practices the vines may be subjected to. Spurs are short fruiting units, 1 to 4 nodes long, with 2 node spurs being the most common. Canes are longer fruiting units that are typically 8 to 15 nodes long. The four main training and pruning systems are shown in figure 2.6.

References

Mullins, M. G., A. Bouquet, and L. E. Williams. 1992. Biology of the grapevine. Cambridge, UK: Cambridge University Press.

Pratt, C. 1971. Reproductive anatomy in cultivated grapes: A review. American Journal of Enology and Viticulture 22: 92–109.

———. 1974. Vegetative anatomy of cultivated grapes — a review. American Journal of Enology and Viticulture 25(3):131–150.

Winkler, A. J., J. A. Cook, W. M. Kliewer, and L. A. Lider. 1974. General viticulture. Berkeley: University of California Press.

Figure 2.4 Stages of grape flower bloom. (1) Grape flower not yet in bloom with cap attached. (2) Flower in early bloom with cap dehiscing. (3) Flower in complete bloom showing ovary and stamens. (4) Pollination and fertilization of a grape flower.

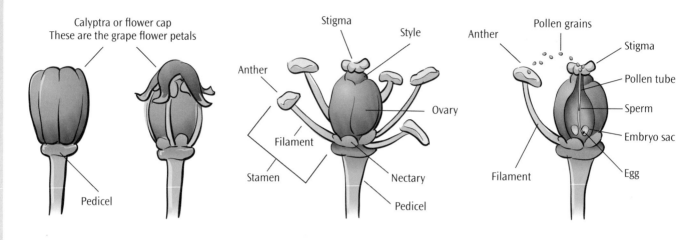

Figure 2.5 Common grape cluster shapes.

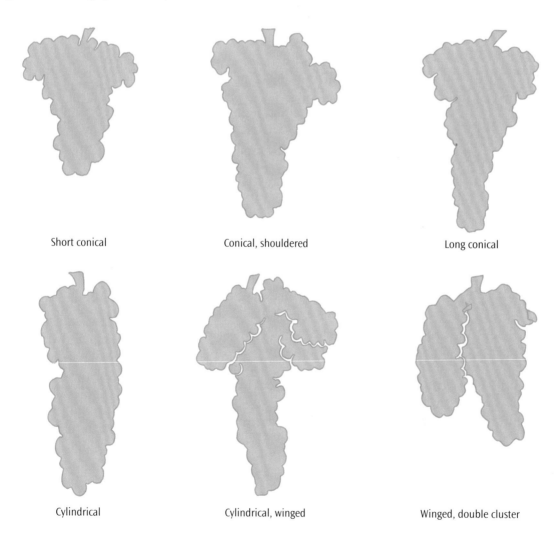

Short conical

Conical, shouldered

Long conical

Cylindrical

Cylindrical, winged

Winged, double cluster

Figure 2.6 Training and pruning systems.

A head-trained vine with spur pruning

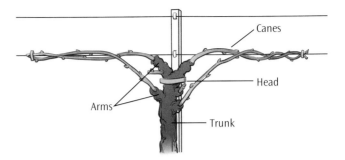

A head-trained vine with cane pruning

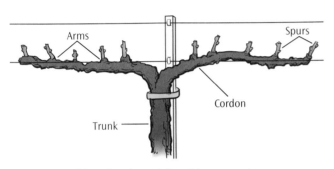

Bi-lateral cordon training with spur pruning

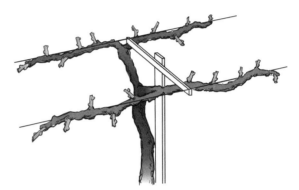

Quadra-lateral cordon training with spur pruning

3 CALENDARS OF EVENTS FOR VITICULTURE PRACTICES

Effective, practical pest management in the six major grape-growing areas of California requires close coordination between vineyard operations and pest control practices. The following pages contain calendars of management operations for all six areas of the state (fig. 3.1). Each calendar offers the grower and pest control adviser information about timing basic viticulture practices with monitoring and treating pests. The calendar of events for the vineyards located in the Sierra foothill areas would most closely follow the calendar for the northern San Joaquin Valley. For additional information, consult your local UC Cooperative Extension farm advisor and the UC IPM Pest Management Guidelines and Year-Round IPM Program at www.ipm.ucdavis.edu/PMG/.

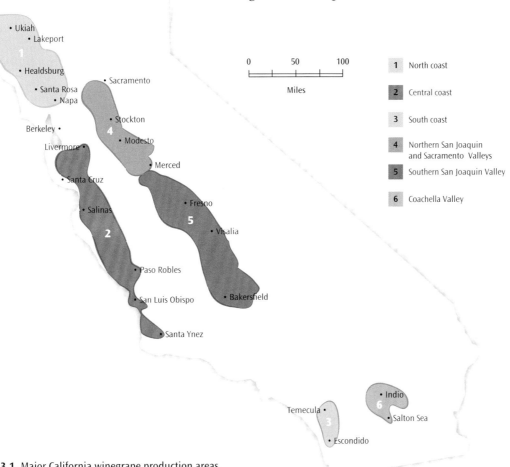

| 0 | 50 | 100 |

Miles

1	North coast
2	Central coast
3	South coast
4	Northern San Joaquin and Sacramento Valleys
5	Southern San Joaquin Valley
6	Coachella Valley

Figure 3.1. Major California winegrape production areas.

1. CALENDAR OF EVENTS FOR VINEYARD AND PEST MANAGEMENT: NORTH COAST

Rhonda J. Smith, Edward A. Weber, and Glenn T. McGourty

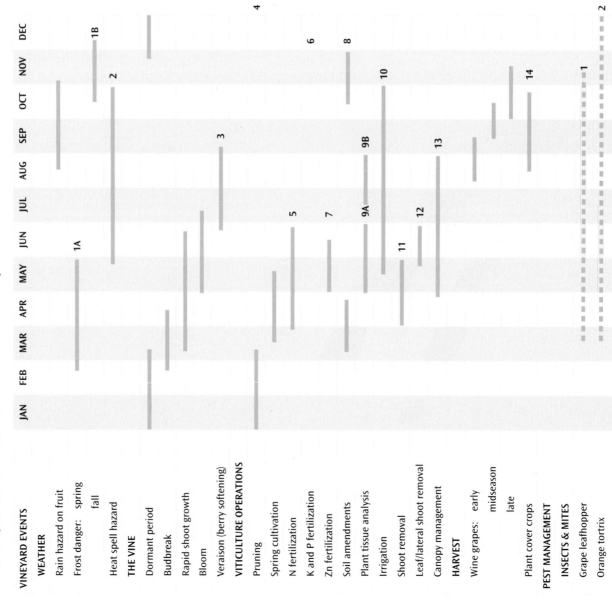

VINEYARD MANAGEMENT NOTES: NORTH COAST

1. Frost danger: (A) Spring: Mow or disk ground cover before frost period (allows time for winter rains to re-wet freshly disked ground). (B) Fall: Severe frost may defoliate vines and damage fruit, and may injure young vines with poor wood maturity.

2. Heat spell hazard: 2 or 3 days of high temperatures in bloom period can cause poor fruit set. Temperatures near or above 40.5°C (105°F) after set through ripening can damage fruit, depending on level of sunlight exposure.

3. Veraison (onset of ripening): Berries soften and sugar accumulation begins (8 to 10 Brix). Berries are no longer susceptible to new powdery mildew infection.

4. Pruning: Pre-pruning after leaf fall when followed by a final pruning near budbreak may reduce the incidence of pruning wound fungal infections.

5. Nitrogen (N) fertilization: Fertilize according to vineyard needs as judged by vine vigor and petiole nitrate-N level. In drip-irrigated vineyards, apply 1 month after budbreak and/or just after fruit set. In dry-farmed vineyards, apply so that spring rains can move N into root zone; avoid off-site N movement.

6. Potassium (K) and phosphorous (P) fertilization: If needed, apply K through the drip system for maintenance applications in summer, or per vine as a dry material in fall to correct a moderate or severe deficiency. Apply P in a similar manner, if needed.

7. Zinc fertilization: If needed, apply foliar sprays before or during bloom.

8. Soil amendments: Spread compost in spring or fall. Apply dry amendments in fall prior to winter rainfall.

9. Plant tissue analysis: (A) For bloom-time petiole analysis, sample 75 to 100 petioles opposite the flower clusters to assess macro- and micronutrient status. Nitrate-N levels give a general view of N status. (B) Petioles collected after veraison from recently matured leaves more accurately estimate vine potassium status.

10. Irrigation: Irrigate young bearing vineyards beginning in late spring (depending on rainfall) through harvest. Start irrigation in mature vineyards according to shoot growth, plant water status or available soil water. Avoid excessive spring shoot growth and preharvest leaf drop. Midseason (when shoot growth slows) and late-season (preharvest) applied water volumes may be similar. Apply a postharvest irrigation to maintain canopy until first frost. Vines entering dormancy under dry conditions are less cold hardy. Some mature vineyards on deep soils are not irrigated.

11. Shoot removal: Remove unwanted shoots from vine base to head; also along cordons. Remove excess shoots from count buds to adjust crop level and reduce canopy congestion.

12. Leaf and/or lateral shoot removal: Exposing clusters may reduce Botrytis bunch rot and improve spray coverage. Grape quality will be influenced with increased exposure. Accomplish just after fruit set; late cluster exposure may cause sunburn.

13. Canopy management: Move trellis wires for positioned canopies. Hedge to maintain canopy shape, to shoot tip, or to facilitate cultivation and mechanization.

14. Plant cover crops: Plant after harvest if possible, but early enough to have seed germination before the onset of heavy winter rains. Select cover crops for erosion control and/or soil-building characteristics.

PEST MANAGEMENT NOTES: NORTH COAST

Many north coast vineyards seldom require treatment for insect and mite pests, but all vineyards require control measures for disease management. The following pests and diseases may require control in specific years or specific areas of the region:

1. Grape leafhopper: Rarely warrants treatment. To influence treatment decisions, monitor to include *Anagrus* activity (red eggs).

2. Orange tortrix: If Botrytis bunch rot was common the previous year, inspect weeds and leaves near shoot tips prior to bloom. Monitor clusters from bloom to before bunch closure. If treatment is required, complete before bunch closure.

3. Spider mites: No prescribed treatment time. Treat as necessary, taking into account damage and predacious mite distribution. Populations may be high in May, and again later in the season starting in July.

4. Cutworm, false chinch bug: Spot treatments may be needed.

5. Thrips: Stunted shoots with bronzing in early season prior to bloom indicate damaging thrips populations. Control measures may be needed in cool springs. Damage to shoot tips or leaves in summer rarely warrants treatment.

6. Branch and twig borer: Remove dead wood at pruning and shred. Burn brush or woodpiles before larvae hatch in March. Chemical control is often ineffective.

7. *Pseudococcus* mealybugs: Monitor spurs and canes at budbreak. If possible, prune to reduce contact of ripening clusters with woody parts of vine. Ant control alone may eliminate the need for a treatment directed toward *Pseudococcus* mealybugs. Reduce spread with sanitation practices.

8. Vine mealybug: Use pheromone traps to detect males from June through October. Treat prior to harvest to prevent canopy and cluster infestations at harvest. With severe late-season infestations, take measures that will reduce the spread during harvest activities. Reduce spread with sanitation practices at all times.

9. Sharpshooters: Sharpshooter feeding does not damage vines, but sharpshooters can transmit bacteria that cause Pierce's disease. If Pierce's disease exists in the area, reduce the spring movement of blue-green sharpshooters from overwintering sites into the vineyard using vegetation management. Spot spray adjacent vines to prevent sharpshooter feeding. Use yellow sticky traps starting prior to budbreak to detect movement and to time treatments.

10. European fruit lecanium scale: Moderate to severe infestations occur in some areas. Time treatments after egg hatch of first generation in the spring.

11. Phylloxera: Use resistant rootstocks for control.

12. Nematodes: Preplant fumigation may be necessary. Nematodes are usually not significant pests in most north coast vineyards. However, nematodes of concern include *Xiphinema index*, which transmits grapevine fanleaf virus, and ring nematode.

13. Powdery mildew: Control depends on reducing early-season inoculum and subsequent infection. Monitor and use the UC Davis risk assessment model to determine spray intervals and material selection.

14. Botrytis bunch rot: In susceptible cultivars, make a bloom application, especially if wet conditions are present. In cool, damp growing conditions, an application just prior to bunch closure may be needed. Apply preharvest treatments before rainfall. Removing leaves to expose clusters and thinning clusters to prevent fruit clumping may be beneficial. See 11 and 12 under "Vineyard Management Notes," above.

15. Eutypa/Botryosphaeria dieback: The fungi that cause cankers can be found in most vineyards. If possible prune late (February–March) to reduce susceptibility of pruning wounds to some canker-producing fungi. Treat pruning wounds to prevent infection. See 4 under "Vineyard Management Notes," above.

16. Esca: The fungi that cause these diseases can be found in most vineyards. Spores are released during periods of high moisture and subsequent drying. Spores can enter vines through pruning wounds.

17. Pierce's disease: Removing diseased vines to eliminate sources of bacteria that can be acquired by insect vectors may be effective, depending on vector type and site. Replant vines to maintain production.

18. Birds: Prevent crop loss by netting vines.

19. Rodents: Includes gophers, voles (meadow mice), rabbits, and ground squirrels. Set traps or bait regularly when vine damage occurs. Be sure to identify endangered species in your area prior to trapping or baiting. Exclude rabbits in newly planted vineyards with fencing or vine shelters.

20. Deer: Exclude deer year-round with fencing.

21. Weeds: Time application of most preemergence herbicides before winter rains and seed germination. In high-rainfall areas, preemergence materials may be applied in early spring. Tank mixing with postemergence herbicides may be necessary. Weed size and growth stage affect the efficacy of postemergence herbicides. Mechanical weed control in the vine row is effective when weeds are small and soil moisture is optimal for the device used. Monitor weed species and populations to evaluate the success of weed control strategies.

Row	No.
Spider mites	3
Cutworm	
False chinch bug	
Thrips	5
Branch and twig borer	6
Pseudococcus mealybugs	7
Vine mealybug	8
Sharpshooters	9
European fruit lecanium scale	10
Phylloxera	11
NEMATODES	12
DISEASES	
Powdery mildew	13
Botrytis bunch rot	14
Eutypa/Botryosphaeria dieback	15
Esca	16
Armillaria root rot	
Pierce's disease	17
VERTEBRATES	
Birds	18
Rodents	19
Deer	20
WEEDS	
Preemergence herbicides	
In-row tillage	21
Postemergence herbicides	

KEY:

Timing of viticulture operations

Pest active or symptoms present

Critical monitoring period

Preferred timing of control

2. CALENDAR OF EVENTS FOR VINEYARD AND PEST MANAGEMENT: CENTRAL COAST

Larry J. Bettiga and Mark Battany

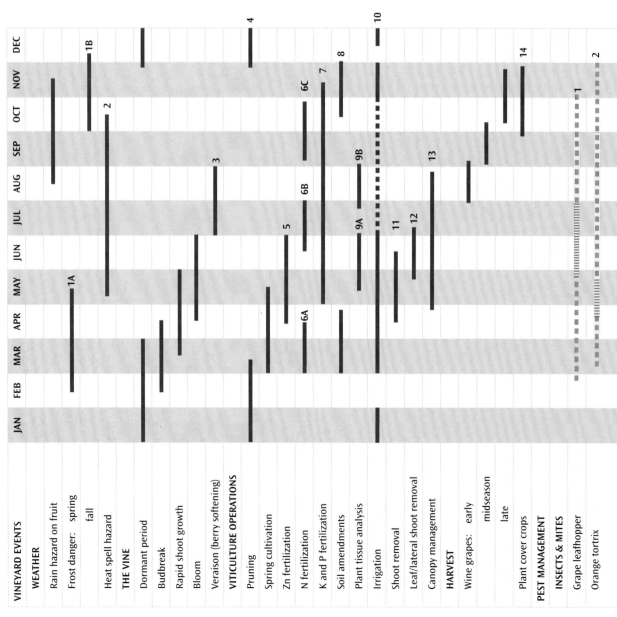

VINEYARD MANAGEMENT NOTES: CENTRAL COAST

1. Frost danger: (A) Spring: Mow or disk ground cover before frost period (allows time for winter rains to re-wet freshly disked ground). (B) Fall: Severe frost may defoliate vines and damage fruit, and may injure young vines and vines with poor wood maturity.

2. Heat spell hazard: 2 or 3 days of high temperatures in bloom period can cause poor fruit set. Temperatures near or above 40.5°C (105°F) after set through ripening period can damage fruit, depending on sunlight exposure.

3. Veraison (onset of ripening): Berries soften and sugar accumulation begins (8 to 10 Brix). Berries are no longer susceptible to new powdery mildew infection.

4. Pruning: Pre-pruning after leaf fall when followed by a final pruning near budbreak may reduce the incidence of pruning wound fungal infections.

5. Zinc fertilization: If needed, apply foliar sprays before or during bloom. For severe deficiencies, make one or more foliar applications before bloom and another after bloom for shoot growth.

6. Nitrogen (N) fertilization: If needed, apply according to vine vigor. (A) Apply after heavy rains to avoid excessive leaching. (B) Do not apply high N rates before bloom to avoid shatter due to excessive tissue N. Early-summer applications have greater uptake efficiency than those in early spring. (C) Fall, postharvest applications may be warranted in shallow soil and in sandy or low-vigor areas to increase vine-stored N. Do not apply postharvest N if excessive defoliation has occurred.

7. Potassium (K) and phosphorous (P) fertilization: If needed, apply K through the drip system for maintenance applications in summer, or apply per vine as a dry material in fall to correct a moderate or severe deficiency. Apply P in a similar manner, if needed.

8. Soil amendments: Spread compost in fall or spring. Apply dry amendments in the fall prior to winter rains.

9. Plant tissue analysis: (A) For bloom-time petiole analysis, sample 75 to 100 petioles opposite the flower clusters to assess macro- and micronutrient status. Nitrate-N levels give a general view of N status. (B) Petioles collected after veraison from recently matured leaves more accurately estimate vine potassium status.

10. Irrigation: (A) Begin season by leaching root zone of excessive salt and filling root zone to field capacity. Irrigate during December and January if rainfall is inadequate. (B) Provide adequate moisture level during rapid shoot growth through bloom. (C) Reduce volume applied once adequate canopy develops; allow soils to dry down sufficiently to stop tip growth (June–July). Provide adequate moisture to prevent defoliation prior to harvest. (D) Apply irrigation postharvest to maintain leaf area until frost. Vines entering dormancy under dry conditions are more susceptible to cold damage and delayed spring growth. Irrigate dry soil in early dormancy.

11. Shoot removal: Remove unwanted shoots from vine base to head; also along cordons. Remove excess shoots from count buds to adjust crop level and reduce canopy congestion.

12. Leaf and/or lateral shoot removal: Cluster exposure may reduce Botrytis bunch rot and improve spray coverage. Grape quality will be influenced with increased exposure. Accomplish just after fruit set; late cluster exposure may cause sunburn.

13. Canopy management: Move trellis wires for positioned canopies. Hedge to maintain canopy shape, to shoot tip, or to facilitate cultivation and mechanization.

14. Plant cover crops: Plant after harvest if possible, but early enough to have seed germination before the onset of heavy winter rains. Select cover crops for erosion control and/or soil-building characteristics.

PEST MANAGEMENT NOTES: CENTRAL COAST

Many central coast vineyards seldom require treatment for insect and mite pests, but all vineyards require control measures for disease management. The following pests and diseases may require control in specific years or specific areas of the region:

1. Grape leafhopper: Sometimes warrants treatment, particularly in warmer interior districts.

2. Orange tortrix: If Botrytis bunch rot was common the previous year, inspect weeds and leaves near shoot tips prior to bloom. Monitor clusters from bloom to before bunch closure. If treatment is required, complete before bunch closure.

3. Spider mites: Identify species; Willamette and/or Pacific mite may be present. Treat as necessary, taking into account damage and predacious mite distribution.

4. Cutworm, false chinch bug: Spot treatment may be needed.

5. Thrips: Wine grapes are rarely damaged sufficiently to warrant pesticide use. During prolonged cool spells in spring, high populations may cause stunting of shoots. However, when weather warms shortly after treatment, untreated vines do about as well as treated vines. Summer populations of grape thrips can cause significant bronzing of leaves, but damage is rarely of economic significance.

6. Branch and twig borer: Remove dead wood at pruning and shred. Burn brush or woodpiles before larvae hatch in March. Chemical control is often ineffective.

7. Pseudococcus mealybugs: Three species may be present in central coast vineyards. If present, identification is necessary to select proper management practices. Reduce spread with sanitation practices.

8. Vine mealybug: Use pheromone traps to detect males from June through October. Treat prior to harvest to prevent canopy and cluster infestations at harvest. With severe late-season infestations, take measures that will reduce the spread during harvest activities. Reduce spread with sanitation practices at all times.

9. Sharpshooters: Sharpshooter feeding does not damage vines, but sharpshooters can transmit bacteria that cause Pierce's disease. If Pierce's disease exists in the area, reduce the spring movement of blue-green sharpshooters from overwintering sites into the vineyard using vegetation management. Spot spray adjacent vines to prevent sharpshooter feeding. Use yellow sticky traps starting prior to budbreak to detect movement and to time treatments.

10. European fruit lecanium scale: Moderate to severe infestations occur in some areas. Time treatments with egg hatch of first generation in the spring.

11. Phylloxera and nematodes: Use resistant rootstock for control. Preplant fumigation may be necessary.

12. Powdery mildew: Control depends on reducing early-season inoculum and subsequent infection. Monitor and use the UC Davis risk assessment model to determine spray intervals and material selection.

13. Botrytis bunch rot: Bloom-time treatments preferred when necessary. Apply preharvest treatment(s) before rain if necessary. Achieving adequate spray coverage in dense canopies is difficult. See 11 and 12 under "Vineyard Management Notes," above.

14. Eutypa/Botryosphaeria dieback: The fungi that cause cankers can be found in most vineyards. If possible prune late (February–March) to reduce susceptibility of pruning wounds to some canker-producing fungi. Treat pruning wounds to prevent infection. See 4 under "Vineyard Management Notes," above.

15. Esca: The fungi that cause these diseases can be found in most vineyards. Spores are released during periods of high moisture and subsequent drying. Spores can enter vines through pruning wounds.

16. Pierce's disease: Incidence is low in centralcCoast with the exception of some areas in the Santa Cruz Mountains. Removing diseased vines to eliminate sources of bacteria that can be acquired by insect vectors may be effective, depending on vector type and site. Replant vines to maintain production.

17. Birds: Prevent crop loss by netting vines.

18. Rodents: Includes gophers, voles (meadow mice), rabbits, and ground squirrels. Set traps or bait regularly when vine damage occurs. Be sure to identify endangered species in your area prior to trapping or baiting. Exclude rabbits in newly planted vineyards with fencing or vine shelters.

19. Deer: Exclude deer year-round with fencing.

20. Weeds: Time application of most preemergence herbicides before winter rains and seed germination. In high-rainfall areas preemergence materials may be applied in early spring. Tank mixing with postemergence herbicides may be necessary. Weed size and growth stage will affect efficacy of postemergence herbicides. Mechanical weed control in the vine row is effective when weeds are small and soil moisture is optimal for the device used. Monitor weed species and populations to evaluate the success of weed control strategies.

Spider mites
Cutworm — 3
False chinch bug — 4
Thrips — 5
Branch and twig borer — 6
Pseudococcus mealybugs — 7
Vine mealybug — 8
Sharpshooters — 9
European fruit lecanium scale — 10
Phylloxera — 11
NEMATODES — 11
DISEASES
Powdery mildew — 12
Botrytis bunch rot — 13
Eutypa/Botryosphaeria dieback — 14
Esca — 15
Armillaria root rot — 16
Pierce's disease
VERTEBRATES
Birds — 17
Rodents — 18
Deer — 19
WEEDS
Preemergence herbicides — 20
In-row tillage
Postemergence herbicides

KEY:

— Timing of viticulture operations

-- Intermittent timing of viticulture operations

··· Pest active or symptoms present

··· Critical monitoring period

||| Preferred timing of control

3. CALENDAR OF EVENTS FOR VINEYARD AND PEST MANAGEMENT: SOUTH COAST

Larry J. Bettiga

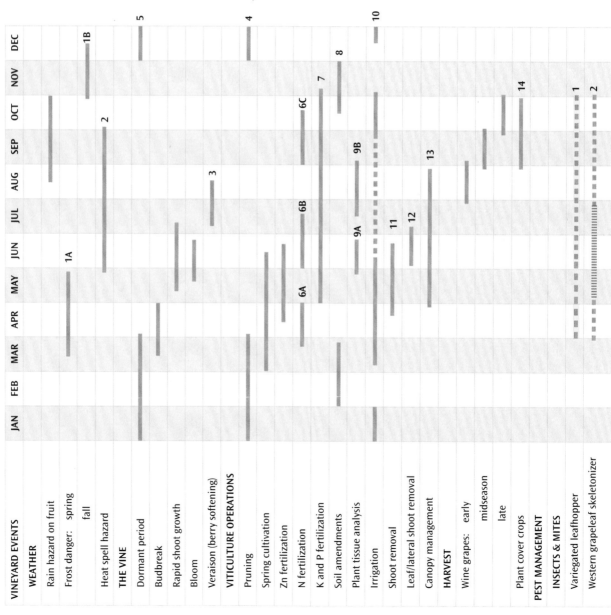

VINEYARD MANAGEMENT NOTES: SOUTH COAST

1. Frost danger: (A) Spring: Mow or disk ground cover before frost period (allows time for winter rains to re-wet freshly disked ground). (B) Fall: Late-season vigorous growth of young or recently converted vines results in poor wood maturity and cold injury to buds and wood.

2. Heat spell hazard: 2 or 3 days of high temperatures in bloom period can cause poor fruit set. Temperatures near or above 40.5°C (105°F) after set through ripening period can damage fruit depending on sunlight exposure.

3. Veraison (onset of ripening): Berries soften and sugar accumulation begins (8 to 10 Brix). Berries are no longer susceptible to new powdery mildew infection.

4. Pruning: Pre-pruning after leaf fall when followed by a final pruning near budbreak may reduce the incidence of pruning wound fungal infections.

5. Zinc fertilization: If needed, apply foliar sprays before or during bloom. For severe deficiencies, apply one or more foliar applications before bloom and another after bloom for shoot growth.

6. Nitrogen (N) fertilization: If needed, apply according to vine vigor. (A) Apply after heavy rains to avoid excessive leaching. (B) Do not apply high N rates before bloom to avoid shatter due to excessive tissue N. Early-summer applications are more efficient than those in early spring. (C) Fall, postharvest applications may be warranted in shallow soil and in sandy or low-vigor areas to increase vine-stored N. Do not apply postharvest N if excessive defoliation has occurred.

7. Potassium (K) and phosphorous (P) fertilization: If needed, apply K through the drip system for maintenance applications in summer, or per vine as a dry material in fall to correct a moderate or severe deficiency. Apply P in a similar manner, if needed.

8. Soil amendments: Spread compost in the fall or spring. Apply dry amendments in the fall prior to winter rains.

9. Plant tissue analysis: (A) For bloom-time petiole analysis, sample 75 to 100 petioles opposite the flower clusters to assess macro- and micronutrient status. Nitrate-N levels give a general view of N status. (B) Petioles collected after veraison from recently matured leaves more accurately estimate vine potassium status.

10. Irrigation: (A) Begin season by leaching root zone of excessive salt and filling root zone to field capacity. Irrigate during December and January if rainfall is inadequate. (B) Provide adequate moisture level during rapid shoot growth through bloom. (C) Reduce volume applied once adequate canopy develops; allow soils to dry down sufficiently to stop tip growth (June–July). Provide adequate moisture to prevent defoliation prior to harvest. (D) Apply irrigation postharvest to maintain leaf area until frost. Vines entering dormancy under dry conditions are more susceptible to cold damage and delayed spring growth. Irrigate dry soil in early dormancy.

11. Shoot removal: Remove unwanted shoots from vine base to head; also along cordons. Remove excess shoots from count buds to adjust crop level and reduce canopy congestion.

12. Leaf and/or lateral shoot removal: Cluster exposure may reduce Botrytis bunch rot and improve spray coverage. Grape quality will be influenced with increased exposure. Accomplish just after fruit set; late cluster exposure may cause sunburn.

13. Canopy management: Move trellis wires for positioned canopies. Hedge to maintain canopy shape, to shoot tip, or to facilitate cultivation and mechanization.

14. Plant cover crops: Plant after harvest if possible, but early enough to have seed germination before the onset of heavy winter rains. Select cover crops for erosion control and/or soil-building characteristics.

PEST MANAGEMENT NOTES: SOUTH COAST

Many south coast vineyards seldom require treatment for insect and mite pests, but all vineyards require control measures for disease management. The following pests and diseases may require control in specific years or specific areas of the region:

1. Variegated leafhopper: High populations of overwintering adults in some years warrant early-season treatments. Other years may not warrant any treatment or treatment only before harvest for ease of picking.

2. Western grapeleaf skeletonizer: Consider potential for reinfestation from neighboring vineyards and backyard grapevines. Monitor for presence of granulosis virus within the vineyard.

3. Cutworm, false chinch bug: Spot treatment may be needed.

4. Thrips: Wine grapes are rarely damaged sufficiently to warrant pesticide use. During prolonged cool spells in spring, high populations may cause stunting of shoots. However, when weather warms shortly after treatment, untreated vines do about as well as treated vines.

5. Branch and twig borer: Remove dead wood at pruning and shred. Burn brush or woodpiles before larvae hatch in March. Chemical control is often ineffective.

6. *Pseudococcus* mealybugs: Monitor spurs and canes at budbreak. If possible, prune to reduce contact of ripening clusters with woody parts of vine. Ant control alone may eliminate the need for a treatment directed toward *Pseudococcus* mealybugs. Reduce spread with sanitation practices.

7. Vine mealybug: Use pheromone traps to detect males from June through October. Treat prior to harvest to prevent canopy and cluster infestations at harvest. With severe late-season infestations, take measures that will reduce the spread during harvest activities. Reduce spread with sanitation practices at all times.

8. Glassy-winged sharpshooter (GWSS): Serious injury to grapevines is caused by Pierce's disease, which is vectored by GWSS. This insect has two generations per year. It overwinters as an adult, feeding on perennial host plants and vines. Best control of GWSS is achieved by area-wide reduction of insect populations and the use of systemic insecticides in affected vineyards.

9. Phylloxera: Use resistant rootstock for control.

10. Nematodes: Use resistant rootstock for control. Preplant fumigation may be necessary.

11. Powdery mildew: Control depends on reducing early-season inoculum and subsequent infection. Monitor and use the UC Davis risk assessment model to determine spray intervals and material selection.

12. Botrytis bunch rot: Bloom-time treatment(s) preferred when necessary. Apply preharvest treatment(s) before rain if necessary. Achieving adequate spray coverage in dense canopies is difficult. See 11 and 12 under "Vineyard Management Notes," above.

13. Eutypa/Botryosphaeria dieback: The fungi that cause cankers can be found in most vineyards. If possible prune late (February–March) to reduce susceptibility of pruning wounds to some canker-producing fungi. Treat pruning wounds to prevent infection. See 4 under "Vineyard Management Notes."

14. Esca: The fungi that cause these diseases can be found in most vineyards. Spores are released during periods of high moisture and subsequent drying. Spores can enter vines through pruning wounds.

15. Pierce's disease: Removing diseased vines to eliminate sources of bacteria that can be acquired by insect vectors may be effective, depending on vector type and site. Replant vines to maintain production.

16. Birds: Prevent crop loss by netting vines.

17. Rodents: Includes gophers, voles (meadow mice), rabbits, and ground squirrels. Set traps or bait regularly when vine damage occurs. Be sure to identify endangered species in your area prior to trapping or baiting. Exclude rabbits in newly planted vineyards with fencing or vine shelters.

18. Deer: Exclude deer year-round with fencing.

19. Weeds: Time application of most preemergence herbicides before winter rains and seed germination. Tank mixing with postemergence herbicides may be necessary. Weed size and growth stage will affect efficacy of postemergence herbicides. Mechanical weed control in the vine row is effective when weeds are small and soil moisture optimal for the device used. Monitor weed species and populations to evaluate the success of weed control strategies.

KEY:

Timing of viticulture operations

Intermittent timing of viticulture operations

Pest active or symptoms present

Critical monitoring period

Preferred timing of control

Cutworm

False chinch bug

Thrips

Branch and twig borer

Pseudococcus mealybugs

Vine mealybug

Glassy-winged sharpshooter

Phylloxera

NEMATODES

DISEASES

Powdery mildew

Botrytis bunch rot

Eutypa/Botryosphaeria dieback

Esca

Armillaria root rot

Pierce's disease

VERTEBRATES

Birds

Rodents

Deer

WEEDS

Preemergence herbicides

In-row tillage

Postemergence herbicides

4. CALENDAR OF EVENTS FOR VINEYARD AND PEST MANAGEMENT: NORTHERN SAN JOAQUIN AND SACRAMENTO VALLEYS

Paul S. Verdegaal and Chuck A. Ingels

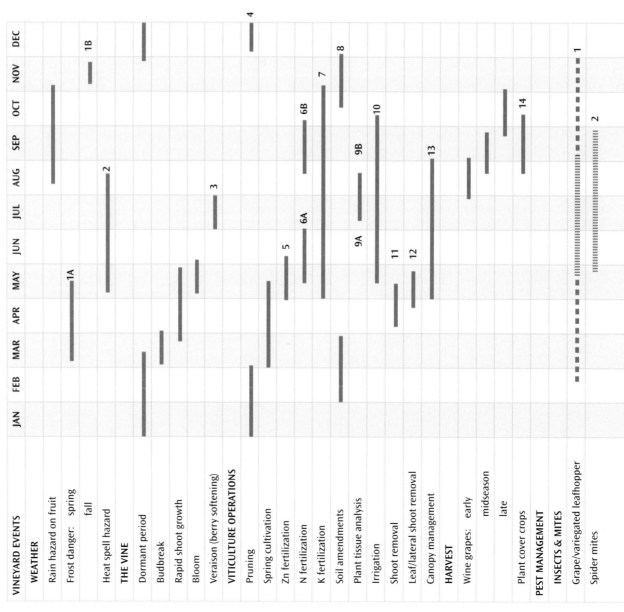

VINEYARD MANAGEMENT NOTES: NORTHERN SAN JOAQUIN AND SACRAMENTO VALLEYS

1. Frost danger: (A) Spring: Bare, firm, moist soil is warmer than weedy, recently disked, or dry surface. (B) Fall: Late-season vigorous growth of vines can result in poor wood maturity and possible winter cold injury to buds and wood.

2. Heat spell hazard: Berry burn or shoot collapse may result from rapid temperature changes before veraison. Grass cover and adequate soil moisture can alleviate this damage.

3. Veraison (onset of ripening): Berries soften and sugar accumulation begins (8 to 10 Brix). Berries are no longer susceptible to new powdery mildew infection.

4. Pruning: Pre-pruning after leaf fall when followed by a final pruning near budbreak may reduce the incidence of pruning wound fungal infections.

5. Zinc fertilization: If needed, apply foliar sprays before or during bloom. Zinc fertigation should occur 3 to 4 weeks prior to bloom.

6. Nitrogen (N) fertilization: If needed: (A) Spring and early-summer applications should be after bloom, unless compost is used or if pomace is applied in fall. (B) Postharvest application may be warranted for low-vigor vines to increase stored N. Adjust rates to vine vigor and monitor with tissue analysis. Multiple light applications with drip injection on coarse, rocky, or shallow soils improve uptake efficiency.

7. Potassium (K) fertilization: If needed, apply K through the drip system for maintenance applications in summer, or apply per vine as a dry material in fall to correct a moderate or severe deficiency.

8. Soil amendments: Spread compost in the fall or spring. Apply dry amendments in the fall prior to winter rains.

9. Plant tissue analysis: (A) For bloom-time petiole analysis, sample 75 to 100 petioles opposite the flower clusters to assess macro- and micronutrient status. Nitrate-N levels give a general view of N status. (B) Petioles collected after veraison from recently matured leaves more accurately estimate vine potassium status.

10. Irrigation: If seasonal rainfall is normal, begin irrigation in mid-May or later. Drip-irrigate until early fall or when rains begin and leaves senesce.

11. Shoot removal: Remove unwanted shoots on trunk and cordons. Removal of excess shoots and their flower clusters from the fruiting zone helps adjust crop level, opens canopy, and can reduce number of wounds at pruning.

12. Leaf and/or lateral shoot removal: Cluster exposure of some cultivars may reduce Botrytis bunch rot and reduce leafhopper nymph populations. Grape quality will be influenced with increased exposure.

13. Canopy management: Move trellis wires for positioned canopies. Hedge to maintain canopy shape, to shoot tip, or to facilitate cultivation and mechanization. Excessive or very early hedging can delay fruit ripening.

14. Plant cover crop: After harvest, soil is prepared and may be pre-irrigated before planting of annual winter cover crops.

PEST MANAGEMENT NOTES: NORTHERN SAN JOAQUIN AND SACRAMENTO VALLEYS

1. Grape and variegated leafhopper: Include *Anagrus* activity (red eggs) in monitoring program, which will influence treatment decisions on the number of nymphs per leaf and parasite activity. If population is made up primarily of the variegated leafhopper, control by *Anagrus* is less likely.

2. Spider mites: Early spring presents more problems with Willamette mites; in midsummer or later, Pacific mites are more likely. Identify and monitor mite and predator population distributions, then treat as necessary.

3. Omnivorous leafroller: Monitor until harvest to determine the need for treatment.

4. Grape mealybug: Monitor spurs and canes at budbreak. If possible, prune to reduce contact of ripening clusters with woody parts of vine. Reduce spread with sanitation practices.

5. Vine mealybug: Use pheromone traps to detect males from May through October. Treat prior to harvest to prevent canopy and cluster infestations at harvest. With severe late-season infestations, take measures that will reduce the spread during harvest activities. To reduce spread, use sanitation practices at all times.

6. Thrips: Usually a problem from budbreak until shoots are about 15 cm (6 in) long, especially in cool springs. Stunted shoots with bronzing and marginal burn indicate damaging thrips populations.

7. Branch and twig borer: Remove dead wood at pruning and shred. Burn brush or woodpiles before larvae hatch in March. Chemical control is often ineffective.

8. Glassy-winged sharpshooter: Begin monitoring before budbreak with yellow sticky traps around vineyard and within vineyard after budbreak.

9. Cutworm: A sporadic problem that can be very localized even within a vineyard. Species present will determine control strategy.

10. Phylloxera: Activity greatest in late spring to early summer, with some resurgence postharvest. Use resistant rootstocks for control. Use good viticulture practices that maintain vine vigor or to mitigate damage in own-rooted vines.

11. Nematodes: Resistant rootstocks are available. Avoid excessive stress of young vines and own-rooted vines by adequate water and nutrient management. Preplant fumigation may be necessary.

12. Powdery mildew: Control depends on reducing early-season inoculum and subsequent infection. Monitor and use the UC Davis risk assessment model to determine spray intervals and material selection.

13. Botrytis bunch rot: Bloom-time treatments are preferred when necessary. Apply preharvest treatment(s) before rain if necessary. Achieving adequate spray coverage in dense canopies is difficult. See 11 and 12 under "Vineyard Management Notes," above.

14. Phomopsis cane and leaf spot: Shoots are most susceptible from budbreak to 45 cm (18 in) long. Treatments must occur before rainfall. Treatment decision is based on cultivar and vineyard disease history.

15. Eutypa/Botryosphaeria dieback: The fungi that cause cankers can be found in most vineyards. If possible prune late (February–March) to reduce susceptibility of pruning wounds to some canker-producing fungi. Treat pruning wounds to prevent infection. See 4 under "Vineyard Management Notes," above.

16. Summer bunch (sour) rot: Irrigation and nutrient management help prevent compact clusters and rot. Mildew and insect larvae control are important to reduce berry injury and subsequent rot from a complex of opportunistic fungi.

17. Esca: The fungi that cause these diseases can be found in most vineyards. Spores are released during periods of high moisture and subsequent drying. Spores can enter vines through pruning wounds.

18. Pierce's disease: Removing diseased vines to eliminate sources of bacteria that can be acquired by insect vectors may be effective, depending on vector type and site. Replant vines to maintain production.

19. Birds: Timing and method of control depend on proper identification, location, population size, and activity. Scaring birds away is ineffective without threat of shooting and unless started early in season before ripening. Trapping can be effective but may require permit.

20. Rodents: Includes rabbits on newly planted vines or gophers and voles (meadow mice) on both young and older vines. Rabbits require exclusion, while baits or trapping can control other rodents. Be sure to identify endangered species in your area prior to trapping or baiting.

21. Weeds: Time application of most preemergence herbicides before winter rains and seed germination. Tank mixing with postemergence herbicides may be necessary. Weed size and growth stage will affect efficacy of postemergence herbicides. Mechanical weed control in the vine row is effective when weeds are small and soil moisture optimal for the device used. Monitor weed species and populations to evaluate the success of weed control strategies.

KEY:
— Timing of viticulture operations
- - - Pest active or symptoms present
||||| Critical monitoring period
||||| Preferred timing of control

Omnivorous leafroller
Grape mealybug
Vine mealybug
Thrips
Branch and twig borer
Glassy-winged sharpshooter
Cutworm
Phylloxera
NEMATODES
DISEASES
Powdery mildew
Botrytis bunch rot
Phomopsis cane and leaf spot
Eutypa/Botryosphaeria dieback
Summer bunch (sour) rot
Esca
Pierce's disease
VERTEBRATES
Birds
Rodents
WEEDS
Preemergence herbicides
In-row tillage
Postemergence herbicides

5 CALENDAR OF EVENTS FOR VINEYARD AND PEST MANAGEMENT: SOUTHERN SAN JOAQUIN VALLEY

Stephen J. Vasquez, William L. Peacock, and Jennifer M. Hashim

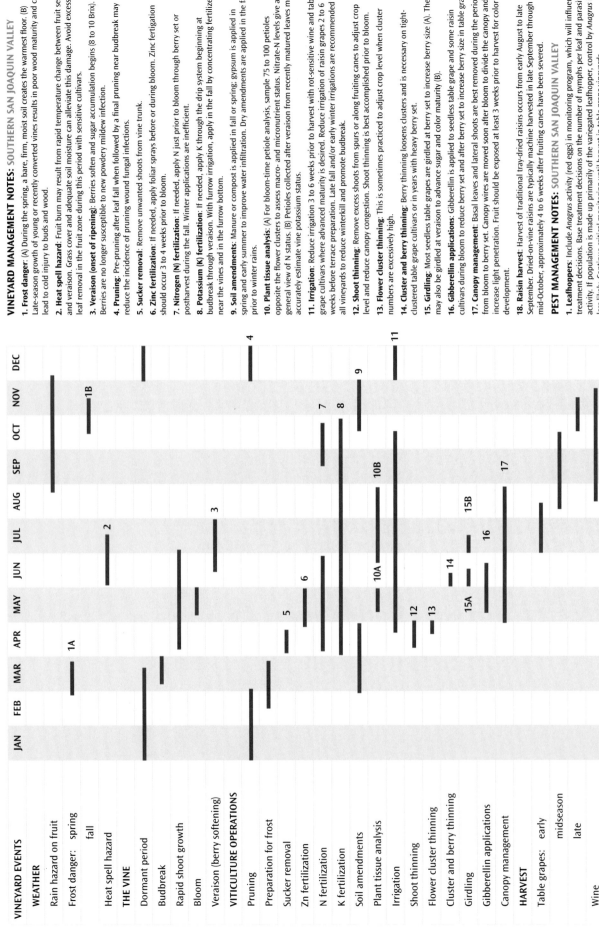

VINEYARD MANAGEMENT NOTES: SOUTHERN SAN JOAQUIN VALLEY

1. Frost danger: (A) During the spring, a bare, firm, moist soil creates the warmest floor. (B) Late-season growth of young or recently converted vines results in poor wood maturity and can lead to cold injury to buds and wood.

2. Heat spell hazard: Fruit burn may result from rapid temperature change between fruit set and veraison. Grass cover and adequate soil moisture can alleviate this damage. Avoid excessive leaf removal in the fruit zone during this period with sensitive cultivars.

3. Veraison (onset of ripening): Berries soften and sugar accumulation begins (8 to 10 Brix). Berries are no longer susceptible to new powdery mildew infection.

4. Pruning: Pre-pruning after leaf fall when followed by a final pruning near budbreak may reduce the incidence of pruning wound fungal infections.

5. Sucker removal: Remove unwanted shoots from vine trunk.

6. Zinc fertilization: If needed, apply foliar sprays before or during bloom. Zinc fertigation should occur 3 to 4 weeks prior to bloom.

7. Nitrogen (N) fertilization: If needed, apply N just prior to bloom through berry set or postharvest during the fall. Winter applications are inefficient.

8. Potassium (K) fertilization: If needed, apply K through the drip system beginning at budbreak through veraison. With furrow irrigation, apply in the fall by concentrating fertilizer near the vines and in the furrow bottom.

9. Soil amendments: Manure or compost is applied in fall or spring; gypsum is applied in spring and early summer to improve water infiltration. Dry amendments are applied in the fall prior to winter rains.

10. Plant tissue analysis: (A) For bloom-time petiole analysis, sample 75 to 100 petioles opposite the flower clusters to assess macro- and micronutrient status. Nitrate-N levels give a general view of N status. (B) Petioles collected after veraison from recently matured leaves more accurately estimate vine potassium status.

11. Irrigation: Reduce irrigation 3 to 6 weeks prior to harvest with rot-sensitive wine and table grape cultivars where advanced maturity is desired. Reduce irrigation of raisin grapes 2 to 6 weeks before terrace preparation. Late fall and/or early winter irrigations are recommended for all vineyards to reduce winterkill and promote budbreak.

12. Shoot thinning: Remove excess shoots from spurs or along fruiting canes to adjust crop level and reduce canopy congestion. Shoot thinning is best accomplished prior to bloom.

13. Flower cluster thinning: This is sometimes practiced to adjust crop level when cluster numbers are excessively high.

14. Cluster and berry thinning: Berry thinning loosens clusters and is necessary on tight-clustered table grape cultivars or in years with heavy berry set.

15. Girdling: Most seedless table grapes are girdled at berry set to increase berry size (A). They may also be girdled at veraison to advance sugar and color maturity (B).

16. Gibberellin applications: Gibberellin is applied to seedless table grape and some raisin cultivars during bloom to reduce berry set and after berry set to increase berry size in table grapes.

17. Canopy management: Basal leaves and lateral shoots are best removed during the period from bloom to berry set. Canopy wires are moved soon after bloom to divide the canopy and increase light penetration. Fruit should be exposed at least 3 weeks prior to harvest for color development.

18. Raisin harvest: Harvest of traditional tray-dried raisins occurs from early August to late September. Dried-on-vine raisins are typically machine harvested in late September through mid-October, approximately 4 to 6 weeks after fruiting canes have been severed.

PEST MANAGEMENT NOTES: SOUTHERN SAN JOAQUIN VALLEY

1. Leafhoppers: Include *Anagrus* activity (red eggs) in monitoring program, which will influence treatment decisions. Base treatment decisions on the number of nymphs per leaf and parasite activity. If population is made up primarily of the variegated leafhopper, control by *Anagrus* is less likely. Continue critical monitoring until harvest in table grape vineyards.

2. Omnivorous leafroller: Monitor fruit until harvest in table and wine grapes and postharvest fruit on trays in raisin vineyards.

3. Glassy-winged sharpshooter (GWSS): Serious injury to grapevines is caused by Pierce's disease, which is vectored by GWSS. GWSS has two generations per year in the San Joaquin Valley. It overwinters as an adult, feeding throughout the winter on plants and vines. Best control of GWSS is achieved by area-wide reduction of insect populations and the use of systemic insecticides in affected vineyards.

4. Spider mites: Base treatment decisions on mite populations, damage, and predaceous mite distribution. Cultural controls include reducing dust and avoiding severe water stress in vineyards.

5. Mealybugs: Vine mealybug is more damaging and difficult to control than other mealybugs. Pheromone traps for vine mealybug are available and are highly effective in determining whether an infestation is near or in the vineyard. Set traps by early April. Check traps for the presence of males every 2 weeks through October.

6. Western grapeleaf skeletonizer (WGLS): WGLS has three generations in the San Joaquin Valley. Consider potential for reinfestation from neighboring vineyards and wild grapevines. Monitor for presence of granulosis virus within the vineyard.

7. Grape leaffolder: Populations are not uniformly distributed in the vineyard, and spot treatments may be necessary to reduce sunburn damage to exposed fruit.

8. Thrips: Monitoring and treatment are critical for western flower thrips control during the bloom period in sensitive table grape cultivars such as Redglobe, Calmeria, and Thompson Seedless.

9. Phylloxera: Activity is greatest in late season, and heavier soils are more conducive to high populations. Resistant rootstocks are available. Good management practices are required to compensate for loss of root function.

10. Nematodes: Species and population determination is essential for management. Resistant rootstocks are available. Good management practices are required to compensate for root damage. Preplant fumigation may be necessary.

11. Powdery mildew: Control depends on reducing early-season inoculum and subsequent infection. Monitor and use the UC Davis risk assessment model to determine spray intervals and material selection. After berry set, table grape growers should apply products as dust or with concentrate sprayers to avoid spotting fruit. Table grape growers should continue control program until harvest to prevent stem mildew.

12. Botrytis bunch rot: Canopy management that ventilates the fruit zone is key to disease control. Preventative fungicides should be applied 1 week or less prior to significant rainfall in the fall. Table grape growers should apply products as dust or with concentrate sprayers to avoid spotting fruit.

13. Phomopsis cane and leaf spot: Shoots are most susceptible from budbreak to 45 cm (18 in) long. Treatments must occur before rainfall. Treatment decision based on cultivar and vineyard disease history.

14. Esca: The fungi that cause these diseases can be found in most vineyards. Spores are released during periods of high moisture and subsequent drying. Spores can enter vines through pruning wounds.

15. Summer bunch (sour) rot: Cultural practices that reduce cluster compactness can reduce rot. Mildew and insect larvae control are important to reduce berry injury and subsequent rot from a complex of opportunistic fungi.

16. Pierce's disease: Removing diseased vines to eliminate sources of bacteria that can be acquired by insect vectors may be effective, depending on vector type and site. Replant vines to maintain production.

17. Eutypa/Botryosphaeria dieback: Avoid making large pruning wounds during early-winter rains. Prune as late as possible and treat pruning wounds to prevent new infections during hazardous periods.

18. Birds: Late-winter period (January–March) refers to finch control. Summer period (June–September) refers to finch, sparrow, and starling control. Timing and method of control depend on proper identification, location, population size, and activity.

19. Rodents: Set traps or bait regularly when vine damage occurs. Be sure to identify endangered species in your area prior to trapping or baiting.

20. Weeds: Time application of most preemergence herbicides before winter rains and seed germination. Tank mixing with postemergence herbicides may be necessary. Weed size and growth stage affect the efficacy of postemergence herbicides. Mechanical weed control in the vine row is effective when weeds are small and soil moisture optimal for the device used. Monitor weed species and populations to evaluate the success of weed control strategies.

KEY:

—— Timing of viticulture operations

- - - Pest active or symptoms present

||||| Critical monitoring period

|||||| Preferred timing of control

Raisin: conventional
DOV
Plant cover crops

PEST MANAGEMENT

INSECTS & MITES
Leafhoppers
Omnivorous leafroller
Glassy-winged sharpshooter
Spider mites
Grape mealybug
Vine mealybug
Western grapeleaf skeletonizer
Grape leaffolder
Thrips
Phylloxera

NEMATODES

DISEASES
Powdery mildew
Botrytis bunch rot
Phomopsis cane and leaf spot
Esca
Summer bunch (sour) rot
Pierce's disease
Eutypa/Botryosphaeria dieback

VERTEBRATES
Birds
Rodents

WEEDS
Preemergence herbicides
In-row tillage
Postemergence herbicides

6. CALENDAR OF EVENTS FOR VINEYARD AND PEST MANAGEMENT: COACHELLA VALLEY

Carmen Gispert

VINEYARD MANAGEMENT NOTES: COACHELLA VALLEY

1. Veraison (onset of ripening): Berries soften and sugar accumulation begins (8 to 10 Brix). Berries are no longer susceptible to new powdery mildew infection.

2. Zinc fertilization: If needed, apply foliar sprays before or during bloom.

3. Nitrogen (N) fertilization: If needed, apply N just prior to bloom through berry set in the spring or at postharvest during the fall. Winter applications are inefficient.

4. Potassium (K) fertilization: If needed, apply K through the drip system for maintenance applications, or apply per vine as a dry material in fall to correct a moderate or severe deficiency.

5. Soil amendments: Spread compost in the fall or spring. Apply dry amendments in the fall prior to winter rains.

6. Irrigation: (A) Leach during dormancy to reduce salinity hazard. (B) Maintain green leaves during the postharvest period (through November).

7. Plant tissue analysis: (A) For bloom-time petiole analysis, sample 75 to 100 petioles opposite the flower clusters to assess macro- and micronutrient status. Nitrate-N levels give a general view of N status. (B) Petioles collected after veraison from recently matured leaves more accurately estimate vine potassium status.

8. Shoot thinning: Remove excess shoots from spurs or along fruiting canes to adjust crop level and reduce canopy congestion.

9. Flower cluster thinning: Sometimes practiced to adjust crop level when cluster numbers are excessively high.

10. Cluster and berry thinning: Berry thinning loosens clusters and is necessary for tight-clustered table grape cultivars or in years with heavy berry set.

11. Gibberellin applications: Gibberellin is applied to seedless table grape cultivars during bloom to reduce berry set and after berry set to increase berry size.

12. Girdling: Most seedless table grapes are girdled at berry set to increase berry size. They may also be girdled at veraison to advance sugar and color maturity.

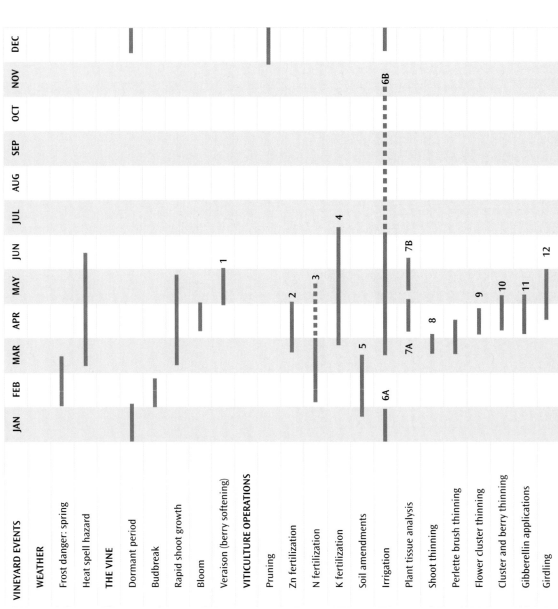

PEST MANAGEMENT NOTES: COACHELLA VALLEY

1. Variegated leafhopper: High populations of overwintering adults sometimes warrant early-season treatment. A second opportunity for preharvest control occurs in April. No treatment is required if overwintering adults are adequately controlled early in the season. A postharvest treatment may be needed to prevent premature defoliation.

2. Grape bud beetle: At budbreak, monitor beetles throughout the vineyard with a flashlight or UV light 1 hour after sundown and look thoroughly for feeding damage to opening buds during daytime. Control populations based on beetle counts or the presence of damaged buds.

3. Thrips: The most important time to protect the berries from thrips damage is during bloom, but late-June and July thrips populations can be so high that control on small grapevines is recommended since they can retard shoot growth.

4. Vine mealybug: Pheromone traps for vine mealybug are available and are highly effective to determine whether an infestation is near or in the vineyard. Set traps by early March. Check traps for the presence of males every 2 weeks through the growing season.

5. Glassy-winged sharpshooter (GWSS): Serious injury to grapevines is caused by Pierce's disease, which is vectored by GWSS. The insect has two generations per year and overwinters as an adult, feeding throughout the winter on plants and vines. Best control of GWSS is achieved by area-wide reduction of insect populations and the use of systemic insecticides in affected vineyards.

6. Nematodes: Resistant rootstocks are available. Good management practices are required to compensate for root damage. Preplant fumigation may be necessary.

7. Powdery mildew: Control depends on reducing early-season inoculum and subsequent infection. Monitor and use the UC Davis risk assessment model to determine spray intervals and material selection.

8. Botryosphaeria dieback: Prune out diseased wood. Avoid pruning during or near a rain event, and treat wounds with fungicide immediately after pruning.

9. Rabbits: Exclude rabbits from young vineyards with fencing.

10. Gophers: Set traps or bait regularly when vine damage occurs. Be sure to identify endangered species in your area prior to trapping or baiting.

11. Weeds: Time application of most preemergence herbicides before winter rains and seed germination. Tank mixing with postemergence herbicides may be necessary. Weed size and growth stage affect the efficacy of postemergence herbicides. Mechanical weed control in the vine row is effective when weeds are small and soil moisture optimal for the device used. Monitor weed species and populations to evaluate success of weed control strategies.

HARVEST

Table grapes

Raisin grapes

PEST MANAGEMENT

INSECTS & MITES

Variegated leafhopper — 1

Grape bud beetle — 2

Thrips — 3

Vine mealybug — 4

Glassy-winged sharpshooter — 5

NEMATODES — 6

DISEASES — 7

Powdery mildew

Botrytis bunch rot — 8

Botryosphaeria dieback

VERTEBRATES — 9

Rabbits — 10

Gophers

WEEDS — 11

In-row tillage

Postemergence herbicides

KEY:

— Timing of viticulture operations

- - - Intermittent timing of viticulture operations

▪ ▪ ▪ Pest active or symptoms present

Critical monitoring period

‖‖‖‖ Preferred timing of control

4 ABIOTIC DISORDERS AND INJURIES OF GRAPEVINES

Larry J. Bettiga, Rhonda J. Smith, William L. Peacock, Kurt J. Hembree, Edward A. Weber, and Paul S. Verdegaal

Grapes are susceptible to many diseases and pests, but environmental conditions, external factors, and vine abnormalities can also interfere with production or be confused with pest and disease problems. Weather can be responsible for many such instances; sometimes the cause of poor vine growth or fruit abnormalities is not known. This section describes some of the most common disorders and injuries of grapevines. They are loosely categorized according to general or assumed associations.

- **Growth problems.** Delayed growth, erratic budbreak, growth cracks, shoot deformities, and chimeras.

- **Water deficit–associated symptoms.** Poor vegetative growth and fruit development.

- **Weather-related disorders.** Winter cold damage, frost injury, drought-induced boron deficiency, hail injury, lightning injury, wind injury, shoot tip dieback, pigmentation on white grapes, heat damage to berries, and aerial roots.

- **Spray damage.** Residue spotting and emulsion injury.

- **Herbicide damage.** Sulfometuron, imazamox, pyrithiobac sodium, simazine, diuron, diuron plus simazine, paraquat, oxyfluorfen, flumioxazin, carfentrazone, norflurazon, glyphosate, glufosinate, dichlobenil, 2,4-D, trichlopyr, and dicamba.

- **Physiological problems.** Spring fever, freckle, early bunch stem necrosis, bunch stem necrosis, and berry shrivel.

GROWTH PROBLEMS

Delayed Growth

Symptoms of delayed growth include erratic budbreak and shoot elongation (fig. 4.1). There may be no budbreak on fruiting canes or none in the midcane section. Delayed growth is most prevalent in young vines. Factors that can lead to delayed growth include overcropping, late harvest date, excessive late-season growth, warm fall temperatures, and cold winter temperatures

Figure 4.1 Delayed growth in Thompson Seedless after a dry winter. Note poor budbreak and stunted shoots on the fruiting canes. *Photo*: L. P. Christensen.

leading to bud and conductive tissue damage. A dry soil profile during fall and winter increases susceptibility to delayed growth.

Deficit irrigation to stop vine growth by early fall can promote wood maturation and greatly reduce delayed growth the following spring. Avoid overcropping, especially on young vines. Post-harvest or early-winter irrigation may help minimize the problem in low-rainfall areas. The strongest, most vigorous vines of the vineyard usually show most severe delayed growth. As vines grow older, the propensity for the disorder greatly decreases. This condition is more prevalent in the San Joaquin Valley and Sacramento Valley, but it has also been observed in the central coast and in the Coachella Valley. Thompson Seedless, Crimson Seedless, Redglobe, Selma Pete, Fiesta, Alicante, Chardonnay, Merlot, Grenache, Cabernet Sauvignon, and Sauvignon blanc are particularly susceptible, but no cultivar is immune to delayed growth.

Delayed budbreak can be confused with vine symptoms of Pierce's disease, phylloxera and nematode damage, and grapevine fanleaf virus.

Growth Cracks

Growth cracks can appear on vigorously growing shoots in spring, especially after wet weather (fig. 4.2). As shoots mature, the cracks appear as oblong lesions. Relatively few in number and well spaced, they are most common near the shoot's base. Cracks vary in length and width. In general, they will not affect the vine and should not be confused with lesions produced by the fungus *Phomopsis viticola*. When establishing a vineyard, note that growth cracks on vigorous shoots trained up the stake are susceptible to infection by *Aspergillus niger,* which can result in cankers and girdling of shoots.

Growth cracks or splits may also form on berries during periods of rapid growth or ripening, particularly after rain or high humidity (fig. 4.3). As the fruit imbibes water,

cells may rupture, causing the berries to crack. Studies in the San Joaquin Valley have shown that deficit irrigation applied from early veraison through harvest significantly reduces cracking of Flame Seedless. There is some evidence indicating that during the ripening phase, berry cracking can increase when irrigation scheduling results in extreme fluctuations in soil moisture content. Cracks can occur along the side or on the stylar end of berries depending on the cultivar and the stage of berry development. In Pinot noir, pre-veraison (beginning of ripening) cracks are common. In this cultivar and others, fungi can infect split berries during ripening, reducing the harvestable crop. In table grapes, regardless of when the cracks occur, the fruit is not marketable and affected berries must be trimmed by hand. Cracking can be more widespread in certain years, suggesting that weather may affect berry growth and development or vine water balance.

Figure 4.2 Growth cracks on the base of a Thompson Seedless shoot following a wet period in the spring. *Photo*: L. P. Christensen.

Figure 4.3 Growth cracks on the ends of Exotic berries after an early-fall rain. *Photo*: L. P. Christensen.

Chimeras

Chimeras are changes in the appearance of vines as a result of mutation. Commonly referred to as bud mutations, or sports, chimeras rarely affect an entire vine unless it is propagated from the affected material. A chimera usually occurs on a single shoot originating from a mutated single bud, but it can increase on the vine if not pruned out. The most commonly expressed chimera is variegation, sometimes described as spilled milk (fig. 4.4). With this chimera, a mosaic pattern spreads into the new tissues of the shoot, with white areas in the leaf blades and clusters. Occasionally, an entire shoot, including the cluster, will lack chlorophyll. These affected shoots generally do not inhibit the vine's performance and are commonly pruned out in winter because of poor growth. Clusters can have white berries as well as berries that are white on one side and normal on another, which is especially common in the Pinot family, such as Pinot gris.

Growth referred to as bull vines, crab vines, or witches'-broom is another form of chimera that can affect individual vines, especially in older vineyards. It also starts from single mutated buds, but abnormal, vigorous, unfruitful growth can eventually crowd out normal shoots (fig. 4.5). In some cases, wood from these vines has been used for propagation, resulting in many vines being affected. Closely spaced nodes each have lateral shoots and small leaves. Crowded, numerous shoots will eventually dominate the affected portion of the vine. Little fruit is set, increasing the vigor of affected shoots. To maintain production, all abnormal growth must be removed with a pruning saw to encourage budbreak in latent buds or the growth of normal shoots that can be trained to replace fruiting positions.

Another type of chimera results in fasciated shoots and clusters. Affected shoots are enlarged and flattened, as if several shoots have been fused (fig. 4.6). Fasciated clusters are similarly flattened and straplike. Clusters and shoots may display unusual branching patterns. Fasciation occurs more frequently in certain cultivars and is especially common in Petite Sirah (Durif). Fasciated shoots are usually pruned out in winter and do not affect production. They should be avoided in the training of young vines.

WATER DEFICIT SYMPTOMS

Water deficits have many effects on grapevines. Symptoms of water stress depend on the stage of vine growth and on how fast the deficit develops. It should be pointed out that although severe water deficits can cause problems, carefully induced water deficits are an important management tool to control vegetative and fruit growth.

Figure 4.4 Genetic chimera in Barbera, showing a lack of chlorophyll as compared with surrounding normal shoots (A); variegation in Chardonnay (B). *Photos*: L. P. Christensen (A); L. J. Bettiga (B).

Figure 4.5 Vigorous growth of bull vine, or witches'-broom, chimera dominates the normal vegetation of this Thompson Seedless vine. *Photo*: H. L. Andris.

Vegetative Growth

Shoot growth is one indicator of a vine's water status (fig. 4.7). Well-watered vines or nonirrigated vines grown in soils with high water-holding capacity have actively growing shoot tips in early to midseason, which in many cultivars have a bright yellowish green to bronze green color (shoot tip color varies widely according to cultivar), normal internode extension, and long, succulent tendrils near the shoot tips. As water deficit occurs, shoot growth slows, internodes shorten, and the tip becomes a dull gray-green before growth completely stops. With severe water stress, shoot tips and tendrils dry and may die on the primary as well as lateral shoots.

The angle of the leaf blade to its petiole is also an indicator of vine water stress: the angle decreases as water deficit increases (fig. 4.8). Zinfandel is particularly responsive to water stress in this manner. In severely water-stressed vines, leaf blades almost touch the petiole to which they are attached.

Late in the season (July–September), the lower (older) leaves on water-stressed vines may yellow, develop necrotic areas at the margins, and abscise. This symptom may be seen in June in vines grown on shallow soils if the volume of applied water is inadequate. Leaf drop begins with the basal leaves and progresses toward the shoot tip. Partially defoliated vines give the canopy a tunneled appearance, which is not to be confused with the shading of interior leaves on excessively vigorous vines (fig. 4.9).

Moderate water stress in early to midsummer can also change overall foliage color, especially in Thompson Seedless. Leaves turn pale and light green to slightly yellow, resembling nitrogen deficiency symptoms. Closer inspection may reveal a lack of new shoot growth, dried shoot tips and tendrils, and more acute angles between leaf blades and petioles (fig. 4.10).

Grapevine leaves rarely wilt, especially on deep soils where available water is depleted in successive layers, allowing the vine to adjust gradually to the increasing deficit. Wilting may happen during sudden rises in temperature when all parts of the root zone of vines growing on shallow soils are depleted of water. In rare cases, it can occur under persistent high wind conditions on heavy clay soils with little available water.

Fruit Development

Before or during flowering, water deficits are very uncommon, except under low-rainfall conditions with no early-season irrigation. Severe stress can result in desiccation of portions of or the entire flower cluster. Fruit set may be reduced under excessive early-season water deficits.

From fruit set to veraison, berry size is reduced with moderate to severe deficits as a result of reduced cell division in the berries that cannot be rectified by favorable soil

Figure 4.6 Fasciated shoot chimera of Durif (Petite Sirah) with wide, flattened growth and fused, multiple growing points. *Photo*: L. P. Christensen.

Figure 4.7 Comparison of an actively growing shoot from an adequately irrigated vine (left) with a shoot that has recently ceased growth under moderate water deficit (right). The cultivar is Thompson Seedless. *Photo*: L. P. Christensen.

Figure 4.8 More-advanced water stress symptoms of a Thompson Seedless shoot, with a dead shoot tip, dried and abscised tendrils, and an acute angle of blade to petiole. *Photo*: L. P. Christensen.

Figure 4.9 Water-stressed Thompson Seedless vines with yellow, drying, and abscising basal leaves, resulting in a tunneled appearance of the leaf canopy. *Photo*: L. P. Christensen.

Figure 4.10 Severe water stress of Thompson Seedless shortly before bloom, resulting in desiccation of shoot tips, tendrils, and portions of the flower clusters. *Photo*: L. P. Christensen.

moisture at a later time (fig. 4.11). Water deficits during this stage of development increase the susceptibility of the fruit to sunburn during hot spells. Immature green berries are particularly sensitive if the temperature rises abruptly from cool to hot. Such changes are more frequent in the San Joaquin Valley from the end of May to the third week of June.

During ripening, mild water deficits 3 to 4 weeks before harvest can enhance color development and sometimes sugar accumulation. Severe water deficits increase sugar concentration by reducing berry weight through dehydration, but they may not increase overall sugar content per berry or per vine. At any time during ripening, severe water deficits may actually delay accumulation of sugar due to reduced photosynthesis or premature leaf drop. Sun-exposed fruit on stressed vines may wither and discolor.

Figure 4.11 Thompson Seedless cluster that has undergone periods of water stress during berry growth and ripening. Note the small berries as compared with the penny on the cluster shoulder, and the ambered and raisined berries. *Photo*: L. P. Christensen.

WEATHER-RELATED DISORDERS

Winter Cold Injury

Damage to vascular tissues of the permanent and fruiting wood of grapevines due to low temperatures during dormancy can cause delayed and erratic budbreak, stunted shoot growth, and even vine death or dieback in extreme cases (fig. 4.12). The damaged vascular tissues of the trunk and cordons appear dry and may have brown streaking. Fruiting canes may have brown or dark-colored interiors after cell contents have leaked across the different tissues then oxidized. Damage is most severe when freezing temperatures are preceded by warm days or when extreme winter temperatures fall below −9°C (16°F). Most susceptible are vines that are 1 to 3 years old, although damage can occur on mature vines at lower temperatures. This disorder has most commonly been observed in the inland areas of coastal valleys along the central coast. Chardonnay is very susceptible to this disorder. Rootstocks may influence vine damage, with 3309C, 110R, and Freedom often having more severe symptoms. If damage is not severe, vines begin to grow normally after the vascular cambium begins to replace injured vascular tissue. Depending on severity, it may take more than a year for a vine to recover. Spring symptoms of winter cold injury can be similar to drought-induced boron deficiency and delayed growth.

Frost Injury

Damage from spring frosts depends on the minimum temperature reached, its duration, and the stage of seasonal vine growth at the frost event. Mild frost injury following bud burst may manifest itself only in the death, or clearing, of a few leaf cells (fig. 4.13). Affected leaves have pale yellow or clear stippled areas between their veins (a stained glass effect). Eventually some leaf tissue may become necrotic, causing the blade to distort as it continues to expand. In severe frosts, most shoots are likely to be affected throughout their length (fig. 4.14). Leaves and clusters have a water-soaked appearance, then quickly turn brown and become necrotic. Removing damaged or dead shoots following a frost has not been shown to improve subsequent budbreak or crop recovery and therefore is not recommended.

Fall frosts are less common and may occur near the end of the growing season in inland areas of coastal valleys. Leaf damage can be severe enough to prevent further fruit maturation. Younger shoots, especially on new vines still being established, may have some dieback.

Drought-Induced Boron Deficiency

The symptoms of temporary early-season boron deficiency appear after budbreak (fig. 4.15). Budbreak is erratic, and shoots are stunted and distorted. Dwarfed shoots may grow in a zigzag manner, with numerous lateral shoots. The tip of the primary shoot may die. The

Figure 4.12 Vine stunting from winter cold injury (A). Severe symptoms occur in the low areas of the vineyard, where cold air drains (B). *Photos*: L. J. Bettiga.

Figure 4.13 Mild frost injury of Chardonnay, showing clear, pale yellow sections of leaf tissue, with some slight necrosis and puckering. *Photo*: L. J. Bettiga.

Figure 4.14 Frosted Grenache shoots with complete death of shoot bases, where early regrowth is apparent. *Photo*: H. L. Andris.

Figure 4.15 Drought-induced boron deficiency on a Thompson Seedless shoot. Note the short internodes and misshapen, crinkled leaves. *Photo*: L. P. Christensen.

lower leaves are misshapen and may be chlorotic. Leaf symptoms include fan-shaped, rounded, or missing lobes. Leaf blades are often crinkled with prominent veins. Most shoots begin to elongate normally by late spring, but cluster size may be reduced.

These symptoms appear sporadically and usually occur in years following very low rainfall in autumn to midwinter. The cause of symptoms is believed to be a late-season drought-induced boron deficiency that affects development of the shoots within dormant buds. Bud mite injury may cause similar symptoms.

Hail Injury

Hail is usually associated with injury or destruction of clusters, shoots, and emerging buds. Tender new shoots and flower clusters are particularly vulnerable. Initially, shoots and leaves may appear tattered, but eventually they may die back or show darkened pockmarks where hailstones hit (fig. 4.16). Small shoots are susceptible to complete removal by hail. Hailstorms occurring later in the spring are usually less destructive. Less common are fall hailstorms prior to harvest, which have been observed to cause leaf defoliation and bruising of ripening fruit.

Lightning Injury

Lightning may affect an individual vine or an entire row because the trellis wires conduct electricity. In nontrellised vineyards, a smaller, more circular area of vines is usually affected. Wood stakes are often split nearest the lightning strike; damage diminishes with distance from the strike (fig. 4.17). Mild symptoms of lightning injury are bronzing and marginal leaf burn. Internodes may turn completely brown, and as seen in a longitudinal section, the pith collapses and separates, especially on shoots touching trellis wires. More severely affected vines may completely collapse and the vine trunk may split.

Figure 4.16 Hail-damaged Thompson Seedless shoots with tattered leaves, dark pockmarks, and damaged shoot tips and flower clusters. *Photo*: H. L. Andris.

Wind Injury

Persistent winds are common to some coastal valleys and the desert regions. Winds may cause a significant reduction in vine growth as well as scarring and injury to shoots, leaves, and clusters. Scars result from plant parts rubbing together or against the trellis. In spring, severe winds can cause shoot breakage. Damage to the vascular connections between the shoot and its origin at the spur or fruiting cane can later result in shoot dieback due to reduced water and nutrient flow. Sandblasting of leaves and shoots can occur where the soil surface is unprotected by vegetation.

Shoot Tip Dieback

Shoot tip dieback is associated with young, rapidly growing shoots subjected to sudden, extremely hot weather (fig. 4.18). Brief windy conditions with very low humidity coupled with high temperature may have the same affect.

Colombard is particularly susceptible, but dieback can occur in many cultivars (fig. 4.19). Affected shoots can die from their tips down to several nodes. Not all shoots are affected; a random loss of shoots throughout a vineyard or on a vine is typical. Discolored pith can be seen inside affected shoots. Young, vigorous vines in the training stages are particularly vulnerable. New shoot growth will eventually develop from lateral buds below the damaged area.

Heat Damage to Berries

Heat damage, or sunburn, usually occurs between berry set and veraison. Berries directly exposed to the sun are the most susceptible, especially if maximum temperatures exceed 38°C (100°F) and the preceding weather is mild. Damage during the early stages of berry development can cause berries to brown completely and dry out. As berries become larger, the exposed surfaces may be darkened or scarred with sunken areas. In coastal regions, row orientation and vineyard aspect affect the severity of heat damage to clusters, especially in vineyards trellised to maximize cluster exposure. In

Figure 4.17 Lightning-damaged Thompson Seedless vines with severe vine burn at the strike zone, and less vine burn down the row. *Photo*: H. L. Andris.

Figure 4.18 Shoot tip dieback of Chenin blanc during a sudden hot spell in June. *Photo*: L. P. Christensen.

Figure 4.19 Longitudinal section of a Colombard shoot with tip dieback, showing collapse of sections of pith after sudden excessive heat. *Photo*: F. Swanson.

these regions, damage can occur from not long after berry set to anytime after veraison, even when maximum temperatures are less than 38°C. Vines under water stress or on low trellises and with bare, reflective soils are more susceptible. Cultivars highly susceptible include Thompson Seedless, Flame Seedless, Muscat of Alexandria, Redglobe, Calmeria, and many wine grape cultivars such as Chardonnay, Durif (Petite Sirah), and Syrah (figs. 4.20–4.21). Exposing the cluster zone by leaf removal just prior to a heat spell greatly increases the possibility of heat damage. Overexposure of table grapes prior to harvest can result in a buckskin (leathery-skinned) appearance of fruit and a raisin flavor. Overexposure of white wine grapes may result in ambering of the fruit.

Aerial Roots

Aerial roots occasionally develop at the base of green shoots or on spurs during spring, especially following wet weather, in excessive shade of vigorous canopies, or in humid conditions such as can be found near ornamental landscapes (fig. 4.22). They are usually short and corky in appearance and apparently have no function or deleterious effect. They are more prevalent on Perlette, Fantasy Seedless, and Thompson Seedless, but they also appear on wine grape cultivars such as Cabernet Sauvignon, Syrah, and Zinfandel. Plant growth regulators such as 4-CPA and 2,4-D can stimulate aerial roots.

Spray Damage

Residue Spotting

Residue spotting can occur on berries and leaves with the use of high-volume or diluted spray applications, although even concentrated sprays (especially wettable powders) can produce spotting (fig. 4.23). This cosmetic damage is a concern in marketing table grapes. Berries are susceptible once they reach 6 mm (0.25 in) in diameter. Because of the color contrast, black table grape cultivars are most susceptible to residue spotting, followed by red and then green cultivars. To minimize residue spotting, avoid wettable powders and apply materials as a concentrate or as low-volume sprays or dusts. Test a few rows and examine berry spotting before treating an entire vineyard. Excessive use of adjuvants, or specific adjuvants, may also cause the material to flow over the berry surface and collect at the lower end of the berry or leaf. As the water dries, the chemical residue remains, especially under hot, dry conditions.

Spray Oil and Emulsion Injury

The use of spray oils, or adding emulsifiers or adjuvants to spray mixes, can sometimes disrupt the waxy cuticle on

Figure 4.20 Heat damage to fruit of Muscat of Alexandria, resulting in complete drying of some exposed berries. *Photo*: L. P. Christensen.

Figure 4.21 "Ohanez spot" heat damage to Calmeria berries. The term refers to the characteristically dark, sunken areas on affected berries first described in the Ohanez (Almeria) cultivar. *Photo*: L. P. Christensen.

Figure 4.22 Aerial roots at the base of a Thompson Seedless shoot after wet spring weather. *Photo*: L. P. Christensen.

Figure 4.23 Spray residue spotting on Ruby Seedless berries from dilute application of wettable powder. *Photo*: L. P. Christensen.

developing berries. Growers refer to the waxy cuticle as the berry's bloom. Spray oil can remove or disrupt the bloom, causing the fruit to have a patchy, unappealing appearance. The damage is most commonly expressed as a dull or darkened discoloration of the skin or as russeted areas on the fruit surface (fig. 4.24). Tightly nested berries may develop ring-shaped areas of damage where they contact each other (fig. 4.25). In some cases, the affected areas may have a shined or glazed appearance. Severe injury may contribute to berry cracking. Damage to wine grapes is usually only cosmetic and does not affect yield, although darkened berries may be more susceptible to heat injury. Damaged table grapes may be unmarketable.

Herbicide Damage

Herbicide damage to grapevines occurs primarily as a result of foliar contact by spray drift, direct contact due to improper application techniques, contaminated sprayer tanks or plumbing, and root uptake of herbicide products. Herbicide damage symptoms vary and are influenced by several factors, including the type of herbicide, growth stage of the vines, soil type, and irrigation method. The timing of the onset of symptoms relative to the date that the herbicide came into contact with the vines also depends on the type of material used. In some cases, damage caused by weather-related conditions, nutrient deficiencies, and other disorders can be confused with herbicide-related injury. Common symptoms associated with herbicide-induced injury are described below, listed by mechanism of action.

Acetolactate Synthase Inhibitors

- **Sulfometuron.** Symptoms occur primarily in newly developing foliage as shortened internodes, deformed leaves with deep sinuses, and a tendency of leaf margins to curl upward (fig. 4.26). Mature leaves may show a purplish coloring. Clusters are compact and berries are small.

- **Imazamox.** Symptoms include shortened shoot and internode lengths and significantly reduced tendril growth (fig. 4.27). Leaves appear generally chlorotic, giving a yellowish appearance to the entire canopy. Upward cupping may appear on leaves (more distinctively on youngest leaves). Developing clusters are shortened in growth.

- **Pyrithiobac sodium.** Symptoms are similar to those of imazamox. Shoot and internode length are shortened by about 25% compared with vines injured by imazamox

Figure 4.24 Spray emulsion injury to Thompson Seedless berry, with russeted rings (middle and bottom) at berry contact points. *Photo*: H. L. Andris.

Figure 4.25 Spray oil injury to Chardonnay; note the ring scarring at the bottom of the berries and the disruption of the waxy cuticle, or bloom, on the berry surface. *Photo*: L. J. Bettiga.

Figure 4.26 Sulfometuron injury, with shortened internodes and deformed leaves with upward curling at the margins. *Photo*: L. J. Bettiga.

and 50% compared with untreated vines (fig. 4.28). Youngest leaves appear similar to those injured by glyphosate, with cupping and somewhat constricted veins. Leaves are chlorotic and leaf margins may be necrotic. Berry clusters appear compact.

Photosystem II Inhibitors

- **Simazine.** Young leaves do not show symptoms. Chlorosis first begins along the leaf margin of mature leaves. As the summer progresses, interveinal yellowing occurs in the leaf, while veins remain green (fig. 4.29). Advanced symptom is marginal necrosis that can affect the entire leaf.

- **Diuron.** Young leaves do not show symptoms. Veinal chlorosis, or sometimes blotchy chlorosis, occurs in the leaves with interveinal areas of blade remaining green (fig. 4.30). Advanced symptoms are yellowing of the entire leaf and necrosis. If excessive rates are used, there may be a rapid progression of massive chlorosis to tissue that becomes necrotic.

- **Diuron plus simazine.** Symptoms are primarily veinal chlorosis; interveinal areas are light green or chlorotic in mature leaves (fig. 4.31).

Photosystem I Inhibitors

- **Paraquat.** Scattered necrotic spots on leaves that may have light tan centers. Drift from a long distance or under very cool conditions often results in light yellow chlorotic spots that fade or bleed into green tissue (fig. 4.32). Bright, sunny days speed the injury progression. Young leaves may absorb herbicide, and some translocation can occur to basal leaves or shoots, which shows as marginal reddening or chlorosis and a scalding pattern on the leaf blade.

Protoporphyrinogen Oxidase Inhibitors

- **Oxyfluorfen.** Severe brown to purplish spotting of green tissue and stunted necrotic young shoots may occur from volatilization of the herbicide from the soil surface following rainfall or irrigation and under hot, dry conditions in early spring (fig. 4.33). Necrosis occurs along the leaf margins if the buds have swollen or leaves have begun to unfold when exposed to the herbicide.

- **Flumioxazin.** Exposed leaves, canes, and petioles have dark brown to purplish spotting with a slightly chlorotic margin, appearing in no distinctive pattern (fig. 4.34). Developing clusters and berries may completely darken if exposed directly.

Figure 4.27 Imazamox-injured Thompson Seedless vine, showing leaf chlorosis, marginal cupping upward, and shortened internodes and tendrils. *Photo*: K. J. Hembree.

Figure 4.28 Pyrithiobac sodium–injured Thompson Seedless shoot, with marginal necrosis and general leaf chlorosis. Note the shortened internodes and tendrils with compact flower clusters. *Photo*: K. J. Hembree.

Figure 4.29 Simazine injury, with interveinal chlorosis and necrosis. *Photo*: L. J. Bettiga.

Figure 4.30 Diuron injury, with veinal chlorosis. *Photo*: P. S. Verdegaal.

Figure 4.31 Diuron plus simazine injury, with predominance of veinal chlorosis and additional areas of interveinal chlorosis and necrosis. *Photo*: W. B. Fischer.

- **Carfentrazone.** Symptoms appear as yellowish spotting that appear in no distinct pattern, which progress into necrotic lesions with shoot and leaf abscision (fig. 4.35). Brownish water-soaked lesions may appear on developing berries that form a buck-skin-type corky lesion.

Carotenoid Biosynthesis Inhibitors

- **Norflurazon.** Bleaching or complete loss of color occurs in the veins of mature leaves (fig. 4.36). Advanced or more severe symptoms include tissue necrosis and death. Symptoms are more evident on very coarse or sandy soils that are irrigated with low-volume irrigation. Leaves may eventually drop and new buds may push.

Enolpyruvyl Shikimate-3-Phosphate Inhibitors

- **Glyphosate.** Symptoms vary, depending on the time of application. Exposure from spring to summer: New or maturing growth varies, with general leaf chlorosis from direct spraying to a chlorotic blotching from drift. The most common symptoms include leaf distortion (fig. 4.37), puckering, and glossy small leaves of new growth. Direct spraying of foliage can cause leaf blades to constrict into an arrowhead shape with necrosis and shoot dieback. In midsummer, prior to veraison, direct spraying of the canopy can affect color development of fruit later that summer. Exposure from late summer through dormancy: New growth

Figure 4.32 Scattered necrotic spots on leaves that may have light tan centers due to paraquat drift. Long-distance drift can result in chlorotic spots. *Photo*: C. L. Elmore.

Figure 4.33 Oxyfluorfen injury to developing shoots by volatilization off the soil surface. Note the curling and necrosis of the bottom leaves. *Photo*: L. J. Bettiga.

Figure 4.34 Flumioxazin injury to developing shoots from direct spray from a contaminated sprayer. Contacted tissues show brown to purplish spotting and leaf necrosis (A). More-limited exposure can result in necrotic spotting with no distinctive pattern (B). *Photos*: L. J. Bettiga (A); B. R. Smith (B).

Figure 4.35 Carfentrazone-injured Thompson Seedless shoot: leaf and shoot necrosis followed by secondary bud development of somewhat normal shoots. *Photo*: K. J. Hembree.

Figure 4.36 Norflurazon injury resulting in the bleaching or complete loss of color in the veins of mature Merlot leaves. *Photo*: L. J. Bettiga.

Figure 4.37 Glyphosate injury: interveinal chlorosis with some parallel vein construction (A); cupped and distorted leaves with surface puckering (B). *Photos*: L. J. Bettiga (A); K. J. Hembree (B).

with small, thin leaves that appear strapped. Newly developing shoots show slight chlorosis, parallel-constructed veins, distorted and cupped leaves, very severely shortened internodes, and aborted flowers. Symptoms may appear on a single cane or throughout entire vines. Symptoms may persist for 2 to 3 years with no additional exposure.

Glutamine Synthetase Inhibitors

- **Glufosinate.** Symptoms occur on any green tissue contacted. Rapid (2 to 5 days) necrotic spotting of leaves, stems, and fruit (fig. 4.38).

Cellulose Inhibitors

- **Dichlobenil.** Older leaves show chlorosis and necrosis of leaf tips and margins. The necrotic leaf tip is usually distinctive. The necrosis advances toward the leaf's center. High rates may cause the vine to defoliate, although regrowth normally occurs (fig. 4.39).

Synthetic Auxins

- **2,4-D.** Leaves are deformed, with deep sinuses and constricted veins that may be cupped. Leaves appear fanlike with slightly chlorotic or even bleached veins (fig. 4.40). Often confused with fanleaf virus, these herbicide symptoms are normally associated with a spray or drift patterns in a field. New growth is most sensitive, and shoot tips may have a twisted or corkscrew appearance. Internodes are often shortened, twisted, and bent. Flower clusters and fruit set are severely affected and fruit may abort.

Figure 4.38 Necrotic spotting of leaves caused by glufosinate injury. *Photo*: Courtesy Bayer Crop Science.

Figure 4.39 Dichlobenil-injured shoot, with marginal chlorosis and necrosis. *Photo*: W. B Fischer.

Figure 4.40 2,4-D-injured shoot with characteristic fan-shaped leaves. The parallel, straplike veins are clear in color and terminate as sharp points at leaf margins. Small, puckered interveinal spots have retained green chlorophyll. *Photo*: L. P. Christensen.

Figure 4.41 Trichlopyr-injured Thompson Seedless vines with severe stem epinasty (bending), cupped leaves with leaf blistering, and shortened tendril length. Note the few maturing grape clusters. *Photo*: K. J. Hembree.

Figure 4.42 Dicamba-injured grapevine in the spring after drift occurred in the previous fall. Leaf surface area is constricted along the leaf veins. Feathering of leaf margins occurs, with severe surface puckering or blistering. *Photo*: K. J. Hembree.

Figure 4.43 Spring fever in basal leaves of Thompson Seedless, showing chlorosis, curling, and browning of leaf margins. *Photo*: L. P. Christensen.

- **Trichlopyr.** Leaves are deformed, similar to 2,4-D damage, and may be twisted, with downward cupping. Shoot tips are killed, and tendrils may be extremely twisted. Stem swelling (particularly at the nodes), bending, and elongation occur (fig. 4.41). Tendrils and fruit clusters can become chlorotic and necrotic. Flowers or berries can abort, and entire clusters can desiccate.

- **Dicamba.** Younger leaves are deformed, similar to 2,4-D damage, and are cupped upward. The leaf veins may be so constricted that the leaf surface may be deeply wavy in appearance (fig. 4.42). Older leaves may appear rolled or folded inward. Internodes are often shortened, twisted, and bent. Flower clusters and fruit set are severely affected and fruit may abort.

Physiological Problems

Spring Fever

This disorder is also referred to as false potassium deficiency because the leaf symptoms resemble and are sometimes confused with potassium deficiency. Spring fever is caused by a temporary nitrogen metabolism disorder associated with high levels of ammonium and the polyamine putrescine in the leaves. With spring fever, leaf potassium will not be in the deficient range. Thus, laboratory analysis of leaf petioles can differentiate spring fever from true potassium deficiency. Symptoms occur in basal leaves and leaves in the fruit zone. Prevalent in certain cultivars (particularly Thompson Seedless, Flame Seedless, Chardonnay, and Syrah) and on young vines in their third and fourth growing seasons, it appears to coincide with alternating warm and cold weather patterns before bloom.

Lower leaf color fades and becomes chlorotic in spring, beginning at the leaf margins and progressing between the primary and secondary veins (fig. 4.43). In Syrah, there is little yellowing; instead, a reddish brown color predominates. Leaf margins may become slightly necrotic, resulting in the blades curling upward. In severe cases, marginal necrosis is significant and affected leaves can drop. The onset of symptomatic leaves decreases around bloom, however blades with existing symptoms will remain.

Fruit Pigmentation

Pigmentation, or freckle, is a disorder that occurs in some years in the San Joaquin Valley in which berries become spotted. The brownish discoloration occurs post-veraison only on the exposed side of the cluster and is not found on shaded or nonexposed fruit (fig. 4.44). It appears to occur in or just beneath the epidermal layers of the berry and does not extend into the pulp. No pathogen has been isolated from these spots, nor has pigmentation been associated with chemical application or cultural practices. Freckle occurs in many cultivars, but it is most obvious in white grapes. It does not appear to affect grape maturity, but it can seriously reduce the marketability of table grapes. There are no foliar symptoms associated with this disorder.

In some years, a pinkish to reddish brown pigmentation may develop on fruit of Thompson Seedless and Delight. This skin discoloration is more pronounced in cool summers. In experiments, the use of ethephon enhanced this pigmentation, thus precluding the use of this plant growth regulator on white table grapes (fig. 4.45).

Early Bunch Stem Necrosis

This disorder occurs prior to or during flowering and berry set. Sections of the rachis or the entire rachis become necrotic, resulting in drying and loss of many inflorescences (fig. 4.46). It is particularly pronounced on vigorous cultivars such as Princess, Fantasy Seedless, Flame Seedless, and Summer Royal. It can also occur in wine grape cultivars grown on soils that promote vigorous early-season vegetative growth. Girdling or shoot tipping in early bloom can reduce the incidence of the disorder. Withholding irrigation prior to berry set or using cover crops to deplete available soil water in the spring and early summer can also be effective.

Bunch Stem Necrosis (Waterberry or Redberry)

Clusters wither on the vine and berries dehydrate to raisins. Symptoms appear late in the season as fruit is ripening. They may start just after veraison or later in the ripening period; the earliest symptoms appear in the pedicles as a small spot of dark tissue that enlarges to affect the entire pedicel. Darkening followed by drying of the cluster stem may continue to expand into more general areas, particularly on the tips of clusters and the cluster laterals. The berries become flaccid and dehydrated and eventually may dry completely (fig. 4.47). Affected berries initially taste watery because the inflow of sugar, water, and other constituents is interrupted; as the berries dehydrate and sugars concentrate, they can acquire a sweeter taste. In red wine cultivars, color development is poor. Symptoms may begin on the tips or wings of clusters, but often the entire cluster is affected. This disorder is more prevalent in certain cultivars, years, and vineyard blocks, or areas within vineyards. There is no clear relationship between the disorder and crop load or irrigation practice. Higher nitrogen levels in affected vineyard locations and in affected tissues suggest that fertilizing with nitrogen should

Figure 4.44 Freckle spots with brownish discoloration on the sun-exposed side of a Thompson Seedless cluster. *Photo*: H. L. Andris.

Figure 4.45 Red pigmentation of table Thompson Seedless grapes following experimental treatment with ethephon, a nonrecommended practice. *Photo*: H. L. Andris.

Figure 4.46 Early bunch stem necrosis symptoms in Grenache: desiccation and loss of the entire flower cluster. *Photo*: L. J. Bettiga.

be closely monitored to minimize the disorder. Economic losses are greatest in table grapes. Wine grape quality may be affected if symptomatic clusters contain raisins and thus have associated dried fruit flavors.

Berry Shrivel

In this ripening disorder, berries become flaccid and may take on the appearance of a deflated ball. Unlike waterberry, the rachis and pedicels of clusters affected by berry shrivel remain green and appear healthy (fig. 4.48). Research has found that sugar accumulation during ripening is affected; thus it has been suggested this disorder be renamed sugar accumulation disorder. Investigations have determined that the disorder can affect whole vines in which symptomatic and asymptomatic clusters on the same vine have reduced soluble solids; however, in some sites, only symptomatic clusters are affected. Fruit from berry shrivel clusters have lower sugar, higher acid, and lower

berry weight, and they have a sour, watery taste. In red cultivars, color development is affected, resulting in light-colored berries. In white cultivars, affected clusters retain more green color and develop less yellow color, but this effect can be subtle. Affected clusters have been described as feeling velvety. Symptoms appear at any time after veraison, and the number of affected clusters on a vine may continue to increase until harvest. In a cluster with berry shrivel, most or all berries are affected. There is no obvious progression of symptoms within the cluster as in waterberry. Berry shrivel occurs in table grape cultivars such as Redglobe, Emperor, and Calmeria, as well as in wine grape cultivars such as Cabernet Sauvignon, Merlot, Syrah, Pinot noir, Sauvignon blanc, and Chardonnay.

Like waterberry, the incidence of berry shrivel varies by year, vineyard, and areas within vineyards. Also, there is no clear relationship

between the disorder and crop load or vine water status. Significant crop loss can occur because wineries require that all symptomatic clusters be dropped prior to harvest. Affected table grape fruit is not marketable. Affected berries are sometimes missed and are not trimmed during the packing operation. They become apparent after several weeks in cold storage, when they tend to brown and prematurely dehydrate. This can require that fruit be repacked, at considerable cost. Growers often pick fruit from problematic vineyards and let it sit at ambient temperature for a few hours before packing so that the shriveled fruit is more easily detected by the packers. Shrivel can be reduced in Redglobe, Emperor, and Calmeria by applying gibberellin 7 to 14 days after berry set. However, this creates the risk of gibberellin toxicity, which includes poor berry attachment, reduced fruitfulness, and delayed growth the following spring.

Figure 4.47 Late bunch stem necrosis, or waterberry, symptoms in Thompson Seedless, with shriveled and drying berries at the cluster tips and ends of laterals. *Photo*: L. P. Christensen.

Figure 4.48 Berry shrivel affected cluster (left) and a late bunch stem necrosis cluster (center) on the same Cabernet Sauvignon vine. Note the green rachis on the cluster affected with berry shrivel. *Photo*: R. J. Smith.

Part 2

Diagnostic
Techniques

Cabernet Sauvignon

5 DIAGNOSING VINEYARD PROBLEMS

Rhonda J. Smith and Jennifer M. Hashim

Diagnosing a problem in a vineyard is a process that involves the consideration of all factors associated with crop production and how they may interact. These include site characteristics, potential pests, nutrition, soil physical and chemical composition, water quality and management, disorders and injuries, and farm management practices. It is important to keep an open mind and ask questions when considering these factors.

An accurate diagnosis of a vineyard problem correctly associates damage or symptoms with a specific causal agent, conditions that exist in the vineyard, or certain farming practices. For problems caused by biotic factors, it is essential to understand insect and mite life cycles and disease epidemiology. For problems caused by abiotic factors such as low winter temperatures or soil conditions, knowing what questions to ask and what data to gather is critical. Laboratory analysis of samples collected from the site will be necessary to diagnose some problems. For example, the presence of specific fungal pathogens and grapevine viruses can be confirmed only by laboratory analysis; the same is true for determining soil chemistry and plant nutrient levels.

Although web-based and print resources contain photos and descriptions of common vineyard pests, identifying pests in the field can be challenging. In addition to the resources available through local University of California Cooperative Extension farm advisors, licensed pest control advisers are a resource for growers who need assistance identifying pest-related vine damage, as are certified crop advisers, who have expertise in agronomy and horticulture. The services of consulting viticulturists are often used to diagnose challenging vineyard problems and recommend practices that can improve vine performance.

Diagnosing vine problems involves a methodical approach that in challenging situations may rely on the process of elimination. Data are gathered, which may consist of production reports and farming practices as well as samples of plant material, soil, water, or pests that are sent to diagnostic laboratories. Lab results may be informative or not. Regardless, they will lead to decisions on the next steps to pursue. Occasionally, there are no known causes of vineyard problems, and thus the application of pesticides, fertilizers, or soil amendments to correct such problems cannot be justified.

Four general topics must be addressed when diagnosing a problem in the vineyard:

- determine whether the problem is biotic or abiotic
- determine the spatial incidence and severity of symptoms
- learn the site's performance history
- learn what farming practices are used

Depending on the situation and the observer's experience, it is likely that just one of these topics holds the key to an accurate diagnosis. Information gathered for one topic will be applicable to others.

Determine Whether the Problem is Biotic or Abiotic

This is an overarching topic that is answered in the process of collecting information on the other general areas of focus. It is important to keep abiotic causes on the table until there is a confirmed diagnosis otherwise. It is very common to assume that most vineyard problems are caused by pests, but that is often not the case. This publication describes vine growth problems; injuries and disorders related to weather, farming practices, and unknown causes; and specific pests of grapevines.

Pest problems

Diagnosing a vineyard pest problem requires knowing how to identify and monitor for insects, mites, and diseases as well as associated vine damage and symptoms. Nematode feeding damage can be identified by characteristic root growth; virus diseases may affect vine growth, yield, and fruit maturation. It is important to know the vine growth stages that

are associated with specific pest problems as well as weather and site conditions that tend to trigger damaging population levels of insects and mites or an increased incidence of fungal or bacterial disease.

If a pest is suspected, look in the affected area to determine whether it can be located above or belowground. The following three steps can help identify pest problems.

- Look for feeding damage caused by insects and mites and signs of vertebrate activity. If canker disease is suspected, use a knife to look for cankers in cordons or arms of head-trained vines. Look for signs of foliar fungal pathogens or symptoms of disease.

- On roots, look for phylloxera or signs of nematode damage. Significant vascular streaking or necrosis found in roots or belowground vine trunks may indicate fungal and bacterial pathogens.

- Look for irregular wood growth and necrosis just above, at, and below the graft union, which may be signs of virus or fungal disease. Samples will need to be collected to determine or verify a pest's presence. See "General Guidelines for Collecting Samples for Laboratory Analysis" later in this section.

Grapevine viruses may affect vine growth. Specific canopy and leaf blade symptoms are associated

with certain viruses. Some cause vine decline and eventually death, while others impair fruit ripening and create foliar symptoms similar to nutrient deficiencies. The association of vine growth symptoms with a virus can be confirmed if a laboratory detects a virus that is known to be the cause of the symptoms.

If the original problem cannot be associated with pests, then shift the focus to potential abiotic causes.

Determine the Spatial Incidence and Severity of Symptoms

Determining the location and incidence of the problem inside a vineyard will assist in the diagnosis. A very large area with vines that are nearly all symptomatic or showing signs of damage often presents a different set of potential causes than a localized area that contains scattered or contiguous symptomatic vines.

Remote sensing

Aerial imagery can be extremely useful in determining locations and patterns of vine growth that can lead to the identification of either a pest or disease or abnormal vine growth caused by poor soil conditions. Depending on the type of imagery utilized, canopy size can be determined, and changes in vine vigor can be tracked over time if image data are collected annually. This allows vineyard owners and managers to determine whether corrective measures have improved vine growth by reducing the size of the affected area.

A localized pattern of vines damaged by soilborne pests such as nematodes, phylloxera, or Armillaria root rot can be identified from aerial images, and the causal agent can often be verified by ground observations. Remote sensing can determine the extent of vine loss due to Pierce's disease associated with adjacent crops and noncrop vegetation that host the insect vector. Nematodes can reduce vine growth, and in large acreages this tool can help assess their impact on production.

Remote imagery can be used to locate areas of poor vine growth caused by soil conditions. Shallow, extremely rocky, or clayey soil will affect available soil moisture, which may explain vine size differences within or across vineyard blocks. Similarly, soil chemical properties that affect nutrient uptake will cause subtle to very obvious vine growth differences. All soil-related causes that affect vine size should be verified by using a backhoe or excavator to observe soil profiles or by soil sampling and chemical analysis. Aerial images can be valuable in identifying specific locations in which to make observations and collect samples.

Site history

Previous site use or crop performance can provide insights into pre-existing biotic or abiotic conditions that may be contributing to current problems. Vineyards planted in cleared woodlands may be likely candidates for Armillaria root rot. Vines planted in sites that were animal holding areas may have symptoms that can be related to soil compaction and zinc deficiency or excess sodium. Vineyards on ground that was subject to significant grading or erosion prior to planting may have considerable variability in effective rooting depth. Induced potassium deficiency is common in vineyards that followed long-established grass crops on some soil types. Soil types associated with low potassium,

especially in areas with moderate or high rainfall, may also have nutrient uptake and toxicity problems related to low pH. Vineyards that follow tree crops will most likely be affected by the same soil issues that impacted the previous crop such as poor drainage or extreme variability in soil texture.

Learn the Site's Performance History

Determine when symptoms or signs of the problem were first observed and whether the symptoms are chronic or acute. Observe the diameter of spurs or fruiting canes to gain insight as to whether the problem is long-term or has just recently occurred. Is budbreak, shoot growth, or fruit maturity delayed? Determine whether crop load and vine growth are in balance from current observations and cropping history. It is not uncommon for this type of information to be unavailable due to change in vineyard ownership or management.

Possible causes of poor vine growth

Winter injury and mechanical damage can stunt shoot growth. Poor carbohydrate storage resulting from heavy crop loads or delayed harvest the previous year can cause erratic budbreak and delayed shoot growth in spring. Soil chemical and physical factors can cause poor vine growth as can soilborne pests.

Winter injury. Unique weather conditions alone or in combination with specific farming practices can affect winter hardiness. An early fall freeze or extremely low winter temperatures can kill or damage buds and vascular tissues. Young vines are particularly susceptible to winter injury. Buds that have been

killed become dry and are easily identified by visual examination. Over-cropped vines or those farmed with late-season severe water deficits are more susceptible to winter injury, even with normal winter temperatures. When this occurs, budbreak may be reduced or shoot growth significantly delayed the following year. The latter reduces uniformity of crop maturity across the vineyard. Knowing the timing of temperature extremes in conjunction with cropping level, harvest date, and timing and volume of applied water can assist in the diagnosis of winter injury.

Delayed spring growth. Delayed or erratic budbreak and shoot elongation may be associated with poor carbohydrate storage in dormant tissues and is generally more prevalent in young vineyards. Overcropping and delayed harvest, especially in first and second cropping years of a vineyard, reduce carbohydrate reserves necessary to support early-spring shoot growth the following season. Delayed spring growth can easily be confused with disease; however, shoot growth of affected vines usually improves rapidly after a sufficient number of mature leaves are present. By early summer, vines that once had weak shoot growth are often indistinguishable from healthy vines.

Mechanical damage. Mechanical damage to the vine may cause canopy symptoms similar to those produced by partial girdling. Leaf blades may become chlorotic or turn reddish in white and red cultivars, respectively, beginning in early summer. Mechanical weed control practices within the vine row may cause damage by slicing or scraping vine trunks. In-row cultivators (various types) that articulate around vine trunks may abrade one side of the trunk if not adjusted or operated properly. Gas-powered hand-held devices that mow vegetation with a spinning metal "string" may cause trunk damage. This type of injury may not be immediately obvious but in subsequent years may cause reduced shoot growth.

Soil physical and chemical factors. If vines are under sufficient water stress prior to bloom, shoot growth may be restricted and fruit set will likely be reduced. Early-season water stress may occur in regions that commonly have insufficient winter rainfall to achieve optimal available water content in the soil profile prior to budbreak. Abnormally low rainfall years may produce the same effects in other regions.

Saturated soil conditions present during or shortly after budbreak may result in restricted shoot growth. Although shoot growth rate increases after the site has drained, total length may be reduced.

Soil sampling for chemical analysis is required if stunted shoot growth appears throughout the majority of the block and there is no association with soil water content, winter temperatures, or pests. Both excessive (toxic) and deficient levels of specific elements can negatively affect vine growth. Soil pH affects the relative availability of nearly all nutrients; a near neutral level (pH 7.0) is optimal, but a range of pH 5.8 to 7.8 is acceptable. High-rainfall regions may have extremely low soil pH (< pH 5.0), which increases the availability and plant uptake of manganese, aluminum, and nickel, leading to

stunted growth. Management practices can adversely affect soil pH over time; for example, the use of alkaline irrigation water will raise soil pH, while the use of acidifying fertilizers will lower soil pH.

Knowledge of the soil parent material or soil series may indicate that naturally occurring magnesium or boron is present. Serpentine soil, or soil with magnesium occupying greater than 60% of the exchange complex at a shallow depth, will severely stunt vine growth. Excessive magnesium and boron may be present in the groundwater and not the soil parent material, thus affecting quality of various groundwater sources and subsequently vine growth. These include the use of well water for irrigation, subsurface drainage from upland areas, and a high spring water table.

If leaf blades have symptoms of excessive salts or sodium or boron toxicity, samples of both soil and irrigation water should be collected for laboratory analysis. See "General Guidelines for Collecting Samples for Laboratory Analysis" later in this section.

Vertebrate damage. Feeding damage by vertebrate pests that gnaw the bark and cambium of trunks at or well above the soil level may partially girdle a vine, which results in reduced shoot growth. Such damage is often prevalent where weed growth surrounds the trunks of young vines. Growth is also affected when rodents feed on vine roots. Check for signs of vertebrate pests such as mounds, burrows, and tunnel systems. Rabbits feed on young vines emerging from protective cartons during the growing season and in winter.

Vine disease. Several diseases can cause reduced shoot growth; the pattern of the symptomatic vines in the vineyard, as well as leaf symptoms, can often assist in a diagnosis.

Learn What Farming Practices Are Used

Knowledge of timing, rates, and application intervals of pest control materials, fertilizer products, and soil amendments is required to determine what impact these may have on the problem. If available, study past lab reports of bloom or veraison tissue samples to determine whether nutrient levels are adequate, deficient, or excessive and to identify trends.

Vineyard practices may cause a vine growth problem or damage. Overcropping, poor irrigation scheduling, insufficient or excessive applied water, inadequate or excessive fertilizer applications, and other practices affect vine growth and production. Chemical damage to the vine can be caused by pesticides, adjuvants, and foliar fertilizers. Phytotoxicity may be due to excessive rates of material, tank mixtures of specific products, a misapplication of a material intended for a different use, equipment contamination with unintended products, and spray drift.

Damage may also be caused when certain materials are applied to the foliage just prior to or during temperature extremes or when vines are under temporary water stress. The onset of such damage tends to be very fast, which provides evidence that a single event—such as a spray application—caused the problem. Alternatively, damage symptoms may appear over a period of several days as the vine metabolizes the material.

Spray burn will occur if high temperatures follow a sulfur application or if the interval between sulfur and oil applications is too short. Labels for certain materials recommend against the addition of an adjuvant that has specific properties such as increasing the sprayed material's adhesion to the leaf surface or penetration into plant tissue. It is easy to overlook such a warning if a tank mixture contains two or more products, such as insecticides, fungicides, foliar fertilizers, and plant growth regulators.

If a misapplication of a spray material is suspected, look for a pattern of symptoms in the vineyard that corresponds to the application. Determine the sprayer's entry point into the block and, in large vineyards, where the reentry point is between tank refills. A group of contiguous rows in the vineyard may be affected by only a single spray tank load.

Damage caused by spray drift may occur from a nearby herbicide application made to a noncrop area for the management of natural vegetation, maintenance of a right-of-way, or eradication of noxious weeds. The source of drift may also be from an adjacent vineyard, other crop, or residential area. Occasionally, growers themselves can inadvertently damage their own vines by using spray equipment that was not properly cleaned after previous use. Tanks used to apply herbicides often contain residue that can damage vines.

Visually identifying the likely cause of phytotoxicity symptoms requires expertise. In addition, analyzing foliage samples for spray residue requires the services of a specialized laboratory. The lab will need to know what product most likely caused the damage. Analyzing plant tissue for residue or metabolites of an active ingredient can be costly. The county agricultural commissioner's office should be notified when the situation involves potential crop loss and material residue.

GENERAL GUIDELINES FOR COLLECTING SAMPLES FOR LABORATORY ANALYSIS

To determine or verify a diagnosis, portions of affected vines may need to be collected and submitted to commercial laboratories that have experience analyzing samples collected from vineyards. Plant pathology labs can isolate, identify, and report the presence of plant-pathogenic fungi, bacteria, and known grapevine viruses present in samples. Nematology labs can identify the plant-parasitic nematodes present in samples. Soil and plant nutrition labs will provide chemical analysis that may include suggested optimal ranges of elements and other components related to vineyard soil fertility and nutrient uptake.

Sampling Vines for Pests
Select vines that are on the margins of large impacted areas or just past the last affected vine within the row. Avoid collecting samples from severely damaged vines because they may be too compromised to support significant populations of the pest. This is true for any soil pest, including phylloxera and nematodes as well as fungal and bacterial pathogens. Samples collected for laboratory analysis must be taken to maximize the likelihood of detecting the pest.

Fungal pathogens may be isolated from all woody parts of the vine; however, targeting specific portions of the vine is advisable depending on what disease is suspected. For example, a cordon would be sampled if canker diseases are suspected, whereas belowground portions of the vine would be collected if soilborne fungal pathogens are suspected. For the latter, collect the lower portion of the trunk extending from just above the union to the base. Include roots that extend about 12.5 cm (5 in) from the trunk; include associated smaller-diameter suberized (woody) roots. It is rarely necessary to send an entire vine to a lab.

For nematode analysis, select vines from which to sample in the same manner as previously described. For diagnosing a vineyard problem in which nematode infestation is suspected, it is not necessary to take as many composite samples as recommended for preplant surveys or when obtaining baseline data in established vineyards. Instead, a single composite sample will suffice when collected from at least two subsamples associated with the same area of decline. If areas of concern are not contiguous, separate composite samples are required. Collect soil and associated 1-year-old feeder roots. Inform the lab if specific nematode types are suspected because different extraction methods can be used to maximize detection. Nematode populations tend to be at their lowest levels in summer.

Depending on the time of year, petioles, shoot tips, or woody tissue are preferred for determining whether or what grapevine viruses are present in affected vines. Most plant pathology labs provide diagnostic testing for groups of viruses and fungal pathogens commonly found in grapevines. Their websites describe sampling procedures and preferred handling and shipping methods to ensure that specimens are received in good condition. Alternatively, prior to collecting samples, contact the lab to learn exactly what parts of the vine to collect given the symptoms, suspected causes, and time of year.

Soil and Vine Nutrient Analysis

To determine whether soil chemistry is a contributing factor or a cause of reduced canopy size or vine vigor, it is usually necessary to collect several composite soil samples from within a single affected region of the vineyard. Ideally, a backhoe or excavator can be used to view the soil profile in an affected region so that soil samples may be collected from soil horizons or other obvious changes in the profile.

Soil must be sampled from different depths of the profile from five or more locations within a region of the vineyard with similar characteristics such as topography, surface soil color, and resident vegetation or relative vine growth. If the affected region includes more than one cultivar, collect composite samples by cultivar. Depending on size, collecting samples by block may be appropriate.

At each sampling site, remove the top 7.5 cm (3 in) of soil with a shovel, then using either a shovel, auger, or tube sampler, collect soil from under the emitter in the vine row to a depth of 23 cm (9 in), followed by intervals of 23 to 30.5 cm (9 to 12 in) deep through the effective root zone. If salinity is suspected, also collect samples from the center of the row middle. Do not combine samples collected from vine rows and row middles. For each sample site, place soil from each depth interval into a separate bucket. Repeat this process for other locations, adding soil to each bucket.

When all locations in a region have been sampled, mix the contents of each bucket, breaking up clods and discarding rocks before removing about 0.7 kg (1.5 lb) for a composite sample at that depth. Identify each composite sample with a descriptive label that includes the depth interval. Use soil collection tools and buckets that have not been contaminated with fertilizer products.

Compare vine nutrient levels in affected and unaffected vines. Collect petioles or blades (the latter is selected if a toxicity is suspected) that are about the same age based on shoot node position. A single pair of tissue samples collected from symptomatic and asymptomatic regions will suffice; however, do not sample across cultivars. About 75 to 100 petioles or up to 30 blades should be collected per sample.

6 REMOTE SENSING FOR VINEYARD PEST MANAGEMENT

Edward A. Weber, Larry J. Bettiga, Lee F. Johnson, and Mark Battany

Remote sensing is a valuable tool for vineyard managers to assess several aspects of their viticultural operations, including pest management programs. Remote sensing refers to the use of aircraft or satellites to provide pictures or digital images of vineyards. Synoptic images taken from above vineyards often provide insight into patterns in vine growth that are more difficult to discern from the ground. Subtle differences that may go unnoticed in the field may be seen as significant in a remotely sensed image.

REMOTE-SENSING OPTIONS

Color infrared photography from aircraft flying above the vineyard is a form of remote sensing that has been in use for decades. Color infrared film records reflectance in the green and red wavelengths of visible light, and in the near infrared (NIR) range. It does not react to heat or temperature differences in plants. Green plants absorb most of the red light that reaches them, but they reflect both green and NIR wavelengths. Green plants are the only objects with this combination of absorption and reflectance, thus they are the only objects that appear as a shade of red or magenta on the film. The shade depends on the cultivar, maturity, and health of the plant. The leaf's internal cell structure is responsible for reflectance of NIR radiation, so conditions that alter cell structure, such as water stress or disease may lower the NIR reflectance. The future use of color infrared film photography will likely become less common with the decline in availability from film manufacturers.

Digital imagery from cameras mounted on aircraft or satellites is a remote-sensing tool that has many additional uses beyond pest management. Digital imaging systems differ from conventional photography in that multispectral digital cameras measure energy reflected from the earth in several distinct spectral channels in the visible and NIR ranges. In contrast, traditional film photography generates a single image. The spectral information of digital images is recorded as a matrix of numbers, with each number indicating the brightness of each picture element, or pixel. The cameras typically record in blue, green, red, and NIR wavelength bands. Data collected from each channel can be compared, combined, or manipulated mathematically to generate useful images for vineyard managers.

Digital airborne imagery is typically georegistered to a ground coordinate system so that it can be readily combined with other site information using geographic information system (GIS) software to generate detailed maps and images for a variety of decision-making purposes. GIS can incorporate a wide array of information about vineyard blocks (cultivars, rootstocks, irrigation, fertilization, crop production, soils, slope, history, etc.) that when combined with aerial imagery can provide clues to understanding differences in vine performance that might not be obvious in the field. The derived map products can provide growers a broader perspective on vineyard performance than would be available from a simple photographic print.

Several types of spectral vegetation indices have been developed to maximize sensitivity to vegetation amount and condition. These indices integrate multiwavelength data at each pixel to a single value. Images can then be created based on the index values. One type of image often produced through digital imagery is based on the normalized difference vegetation index (NDVI). The NDVI closely relates to leaf area and provides a useful indicator of overall canopy development and vine vigor. It is derived from red and NIR wavelengths as follows:

$$NDVI = (NIR - red) \div (NIR + red)$$

Because green plants typically reflect more NIR (and less red) energy than soil, NDVIs are very useful in crops such as grapes where large amounts of soil show between the rows of plants.

Colors in NDVIs and other map products are assigned by the software user or image provider and may vary from image to image. For instance, a low-vigor vine may be colored red in one set of images and yellow in another. It is important to refer to the color key for each digital image to ensure its proper interpretation.

OBTAINING IMAGERY

Several commercial (and some public) sources of remotely sensed imagery are available for agricultural use. Most vendors offer an array of products and services, ranging from hard-copy prints and electronic files of vineyard maps and NDVIs to more full-service GIS consulting and creation of customized map products. Digital imagery providers generally apply data calibration to facilitate time-series (e.g., year-to-year or month-to-month) image comparisons. This may involve the use of a calibration lab, in-flight imaging of ground-based calibration targets, or in-flight monitoring of down-welling solar irradiance during image acquisition.

Aerial images can be taken anytime during the growing season, but they are most useful late in the season once vine canopies have fully developed and stress symptoms have become apparent. Images are usually taken only once during the season due to cost considerations. Images taken between veraison and harvest generally provide the most useful information. At this time, differences in vine development will be evident, and there will still be time to use the imagery for decisions related to harvest.

Aircraft imagery has generally been of higher spatial resolution than imagery from satellites, but high-resolution satellite images are becoming increasingly available and convenient to access. Images with 2 m (6.5 ft) resolution (pixel size) are of sufficient quality to provide valuable details on within-block vineyard performance, while 1 m (40 in) resolution provides a more detailed image.

The appropriate spatial resolution is related to the size of the grower's minimum management unit. Growers who use imagery to manage at the individual vine or row level, for instance, will have more stringent requirements than those who manage at sub-block or block level.

USING REMOTE IMAGERY

Two requirements of successful pest management are identification of where the problem is located in the vineyard and proper diagnosis of the causes. Remote-sensing technology can aid in both areas.

Aerial imagery is very useful for identifying variations in vine growth across vineyards, as well as identifying and mapping changes that take place from year to year. Differences in vine growth may appear in patterns that are regular or random. Regular patterns with straight lines or geometric shapes are usually related to differences in grape cultivar between vineyard blocks; the types of training or trellis systems used; vigor differences due to rootstocks, irrigation or fertilization practices; or other factors related to specific blocks. Patterns that are random or irregular are more likely to be caused by soil differences or related to disease or insect problems. Whether the patterns are regular or random, the causes of growth differences must be diagnosed using all available information about the blocks combined with on-the-ground inspections.

Problem areas with weak vine growth may first be identified in a remotely sensed image. This is especially true in large vineyards or in those with greater levels of mechanization, where field crews spend less time in each block. In addition to identifying areas with reduced canopy growth, images may show patterns of vine growth that provide clues as to the causes of poor vine performance. Year-to-year changes can be an important aid in diagnosing problems and can help separate pest problems from the effects of soil conditions. Remote sensing can also be used to monitor the effectiveness of subsequent remediation efforts.

Soil factors often contribute to significant differences in vine growth by influencing the vine root system and affecting water and nutrient uptake. Variations in soil texture, depth, drainage, and water-holding capacity can result in striking differences in vine size and color. Where vines have limited water availability due to shallow root zones or coarse-textured soils, vines are smaller and leaves may turn prematurely yellow (fig. 6.1). Areas of weak growth due to soil conditions are often apparent in color infrared (fig. 6.2) and NDVI (fig. 6.3) images. Management factors such as nonuniform irrigation delivery, fertilizer applications, and cultivation practices can also affect vine growth that may be evident in remotely sensed images, and information gleaned from them can be used to modify future practices.

Pests and diseases that affect vine growth and vigor can be detected through remote sensing. This includes soil pests such as phylloxera and nematodes that weaken vines by feeding on the roots, as well as diseases such as Armillaria root rot and Pierce's disease that can weaken and kill vines.

Vines weakened by phylloxera or nematodes are smaller than uninfested vines, and affected areas often increase in size over time. These differences can be seen in color infrared photos (figs. 6.4–6.5) and in NDVI images. Digital

Figure 6.1 This ground-level photo (from the roof of a car) was taken looking in the direction of the arrow in figure 6.2. The boundary between green and yellow vines is much less striking than in the aerial photo. *Photo*: W. E. Wildman.

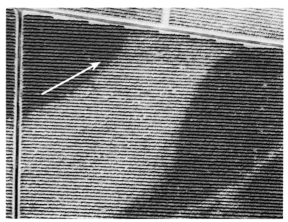

Figure 6.2 The sharp boundary in the color of vines is caused by a subsoil gravel layer that reduces the available water to the vines below the arrow. This effect, not always noticeable in midsummer, becomes obvious in late September or October. *Photo*: J. Caylor, U.S. Forest Service.

Vigor

High

Low

Figure 6.3 NDVI image of a vineyard adjacent to a river. The streaky appearance shows the effect of deposition of alluvium with a relatively high water-holding capacity. *Photo*: J. Hutton, Grayhawk Imaging.

data in NDVIs can be compared from year to year to create change images as shown in figure 6.6.

Pierce's disease kills grapevines and often occurs in patterns related to the habitat of its insect vectors. In northern California, Pierce's disease is often associated with riparian areas, with the greatest vine damage occurring adjacent to the riparian zone (fig. 6.7). This pattern is often most apparent in aerial images (fig. 6.8).

Armillaria root rot kills vines, which is apparent in remote imagery (fig. 6.9). It usually occurs in

relatively small areas that might appear anywhere in a block as a result of infected roots or woody debris remaining in the soil. These weakened areas may never support healthy vines, but they rarely increase in size to any great degree. However, in smaller plantings, such areas may make up a significant proportion of the total number of vines.

Vines weakened from nematode damage may have a similar appearance to drought-stressed vines in an NDVI image (fig. 6.10). If a weak area increases in size in subsequent years, one might

suspect a biological cause, such as phylloxera feeding on the roots, rather than a static difference in soil type. The differences between weak and healthy vines are very apparent in remote imagery, and patterns often emerge that are not apparent from ground level. The use of imagery can simplify diagnoses and help ensure proper treatment.

Remote sensing can identify and map areas of poor or variable vine growth and track their development over time, but it does not explain the causes of poor vine

Figure 6.4 This photo was taken 4 years after a phylloxera infestation was confirmed. In addition to the disease spreading outward from the original infestation, several new infestation centers of phylloxera have developed. *Photo*: W. E. Wildman.

Figure 6.5 After 8 years, most vines affected by phylloxera are still alive, yet are so reduced in size that no crop is produced. *Photo*: W. E. Wildman.

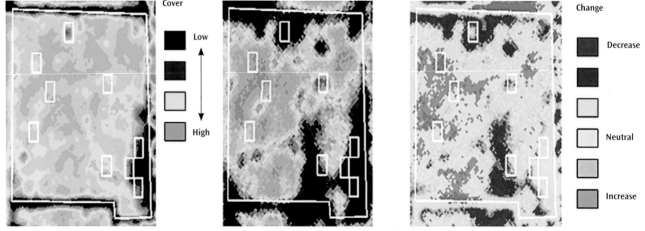

Figure 6.6 Phylloxera infestation. NDVI images showing vineyard cover in a 5 ha (12 ac) block in year 1 (left) and year 2 (middle). Relative change from year 1 to year 2, shown in the right image, indicates a decrease in cover in the yellow, red, and purple areas. *Photo*: L. F. Johnson.

performance. For this, the vineyard manager must interpret the information provided by the imagery and follow up with on-the-ground investigations.

ADDITIONAL USES

Remote sensing has many additional uses beyond pest management. Imagery can be used to track changes in vine performance over time after management actions such as increased fertilization, adjusted irrigation scheduling, or modified vineyard floor management practices. Imagery can also help identify representative areas within a vineyard that are appropriate for annual testing of petioles for nutritional appraisals.

Variability in vine growth and development occurs in every vineyard. Variability may arise from many factors, including changes in soil type or depth, differences in water availability, vine age, weeds and cover crops, cultural practices, crop load, rootstocks, pests, diseases, to name only a few. A goal for most vineyard managers is to minimize this variability or to manage it in such as way as to increase the overall uniformity of fruit quality. In order to reduce variability, it is necessary to characterize the nature of the variability, determine the sources responsible for it, and take corrective measures, if possible.

Many wineries use remote sensing to improve wine quality by differentially harvesting blocks based on NDVIs indicating vine vigor (fig. 6.11). Such NDVI images have also been correlated with soluble solids and phenolic levels in red wine grape cultivars. Images can provide winemakers with a

Figure 6.7 Ground-level photo of a vineyard near a riparian area impacted by Pierce's disease, with the greatest vine damage occurring adjacent to the riparian zone. *Photo*: R. J. Smith.

Figure 6.8 The pattern of Pierce's disease shown in this aerial photo is typical in grape-growing regions in which the blue-green sharpshooter is the principal vector of the bacterium that causes this disease. Vines closest to the riparian habitat of the sharpshooter leafhopper have died, while those farther from the stream are less affected. *Photo*: W. E. Wildman.

Figure 6.9 Armillaria root rot has killed vines in an area where an oak tree was standing prior to the vineyard being planted. In contrast to phylloxera, the spread of this disease is relatively slow and progresses outward in concentric rings. *Photo*: W. E. Wildman.

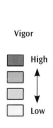

Figure 6.10 Nematode infestation. This NDVI image shows areas of depressed vine growth as yellow to brownish areas across the center of the image in all three main blocks. *Photo*: J. Hutton, Grayhawk Imaging.

better understanding of differences in vine vigor within blocks and across vineyards, allowing them to differentially sample and harvest sections of the vineyard that are similar to one another. By allowing different sections to ripen to the same extent prior to harvest, overall wine quality can be increased. Blocks that historically had produced average-quality wines when picked all at one time may generate wines of markedly higher quality when picked on the basis of uniform maturity.

Remote sensing is also being used in conjunction with GIS mapping and spatial analysis in the design of vineyard developments. A property's slope and aspect are two of the considerations used to determine block layout and row direction with the objective of maximizing uniformity of vine vigor within blocks. Soil structure, chemistry, and fertility data

can be generated from backhoe observation pits placed in locations relative to changes in natural vegetation for new developments or vine growth in redevelopments. These data are also used to determine block size as well as irrigation and drainage system design, planting density, and rootstock selection.

CONCLUSION

Remote sensing is a valuable tool for detection and monitoring of some pests and diseases in vineyards, as well as for identifying variability due to soil changes, irrigation practices, and other factors. The examples given here are just a few of the many conditions that can be recognized with relative ease by studying aerial images. Successful interpretation of the images and development of management plans require expertise in viticulture, soils, irrigation, and pest management.

REFERENCES

Johnson, L., D. Bosch, D. Williams, and B. Lobitz. 2001. Remote sensing of vineyard management zones: Implications for wine quality. Applied Engineering in Agriculture 17:557–560.

Johnson, L., B. Lobitz, R. Armstrong, R. Baldy, E. Weber, J. DeBenedictis, and D. Bosch. 1996. Airborne imaging aids vineyard canopy evaluation. California Agriculture 50(4): 14–18.

Lamb, D. W., M. M. Weedon, and R. G. V. Bramley. 2004. Using remote sensing to predict grape phenolics and colour at harvest in a Cabernet Sauvignon vineyard. Australian Journal of Grape Wine Research 10:46–54.

Nemani, R., L. Johnson, and M. White. 2006. Application of remote sensing and ecosystem modeling to vineyard management. In A. Srinivasan, ed., Handbook of precision agriculture: Principles and applications. Chap. 15. New York: Haworth Press.

Wildman, W. E., K. W. Bowers, and L. J. Bettiga. 1992. Aerial photography in vineyard pest, soil and water management. In D. L. Flaherty et al., eds., Grape pest management. Oakland: University of California Division of Agriculture and Natural Resources Publication 3343. 32–38.

Wildman, W. E., R. T. Nagaoka, and L. A. Lider. 1983. Monitoring spread of grape phylloxera by color infrared aerial photography and ground investigation. American Journal of Enology and Viticulture 34(2): 83–94.

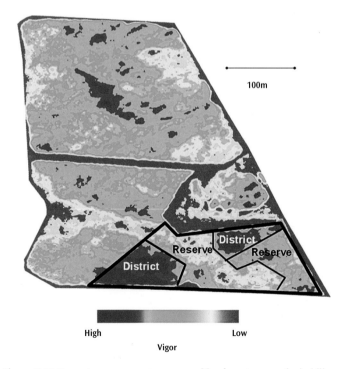

High   Low

Vigor

Figure 6.11 Harvest management zones resulting from topography in hilly 2.5 ha (6 ac) Chardonnay block as shown by NDVI imagery. Low- and moderate-vigor zones produced "reserve" quality wine, while the high-vigor zone produced lower "district" quality. *Photo*: Johnson et al. 2001.

7 LABORATORY TESTING FOR GRAPEVINE DISEASES

Deborah A. Golino, Stephen J. Vasquez, George M. Leavitt, and Kendra Baumgartner

Some grapevine diseases can be identified easily in the field by signs of the pathogen, which include microscopic and macroscopic microbial cells, tissues, and structures. For example, the appearance of the powdery mildew fungus on the surface of infected leaves and fruit is quite characteristic (fig. 7.1). Some diseases, such as crown gall (fig. 7.2), are characterized by their symptoms, which are defined as abnormal plant growth caused by damage from the pathogen. In contrast, the stunted shoots, scorched leaves, or other nondescript symptoms associated with other diseases make it difficult to narrow the list of possible causes. (See section 5, "Diagnosing Vineyard Problems"). In addition, a few diseases are identifiable only through controlled inoculations of healthy plants. Many grapevine viruses, for example, can be identified only by using a combination of lengthy biological tests and laboratory tests. To address the fact that many grapevine diseases are difficult to diagnose simply by observation of symptoms, it may be necessary in some cases to submit samples to a diagnostic laboratory for identification of the disease agent.

Laboratory technology for the detection of grapevine pathogens has undergone rapid development in the last decade. Reliable tests for numerous fungi, bacteria, and viruses have been developed in research labs. Many of these tests are currently offered by commercial and public laboratories, providing growers with the opportunity to submit samples from their vineyards for identification of grapevine diseases.

Several methods of disease testing are available from commercial plant pathology laboratories. These include direct culture of disease agents, serological tests such as ELISA, and nucleic acid sequence–based tests such as PCR. Other types of tests, such as indexing with biological indicators, are usually performed only at research institutions such as the University of California. (See "Management of Grape Virus Diseases" in section 24, "Grapevine Virus Diseases").

Figure 7.1 A diagnostic sign of the powdery mildew pathogen (*Erysiphe necator*) is the white, powdery appearance of the fungal tissue (hyphae) and spores that grow on the surfaces of fruit and leaves. *Photo*: L. J. Bettiga.

Figure 7.2 A diagnostic symptom of crown gall is the abnormal tumorlike gall that sometimes forms on the vine trunk and canes in response to infection by the pathogen *Agrobacterium vitis*. *Photo*: S. J. Vasquez.

CULTURING DISEASE AGENTS

Many of the pathogens that cause fungal and bacterial diseases can be identified in the laboratory when isolated from a diseased grapevine and grown on an agar media. This technique, known as culturing, typically involves placing samples from diseased tissue onto agar media to detect the presence of characteristic microscopic structures or colony growth. Certain types of media are specifically formulated for fungi, while others promote growth of only bacteria. Media formulas that encourage the growth of certain families of fungi or bacteria are known as selective media. For pathogens that are too small for observation with a light microscope or for those that appear similar to non-pathogenic species, culturing is an important first step to nucleic acid sequence–based tests such as the polymerase chain reaction (PCR). The use of selective media, in conjunction with microscopic observations (or other diagnostic testing) of the pathogens, helps laboratories identify and often confirm the causal agents of many diseases.

In grapes, culture methods are commonly used to diagnose many fungal diseases, such as the following: canker diseases (*Eutypa lata, Botryosphaeriaceae* spp.); Armillaria root rot (*Armillaria mellea*, fig. 7.3); Phytophthora root rot (*Phytophthora spp.*); and esca (*Phaeomoniella chlamydospora, Phaeoacremonium* spp.). Culture methods are also important for diagnosis of bacterial diseases such as crown gall (*Agrobacterium vitis*) and Pierce's disease (*Xylella fastidiosa*). This technique does not work for all grapevine diseases, though. For example, powdery mildew and all of the viruses are obligate parasites, which need living host material to survive and reproduce. There are also other fungi and bacteria that have not yet been successfully cultured.

In order to successfully culture an organism suspected of causing disease, it must be living in the sample provided to the lab. To ensure that the pathogens are viable, samples should include active lesions or interfaces between live and dead tissue (fig. 7.4). Collecting dead leaves, stems, or roots will be of no value toward culturing most pathogens.

Culturing is a slow, labor-intensive practice. Also, considerable expertise is needed to reliably identify organisms that grow on media. Check with your laboratory to see

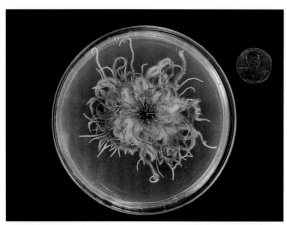

Figure 7.3 The pathogen that causes Armillaria root rot, *Armillaria mellea* (oak root fungus), is easily cultured from symptomatic root wood or mycelial fans of the pathogen on a selective medium that excludes many soilborne fungi that contaminate petri plates and obscure or prevent growth of the pathogen. *Photo*: S. T. Koike.

Figure 7.4 The dark brown, wedge-shaped canker in this cross-section of a live cordon is a suitable sample for diagnosis of infection by *Eutypa lata* or *Botryosphaeria* species. The tissue from which these organisms are cultured is the lighter-colored, healthy-looking wood at the margin of the canker, as this is most likely to be colonized by the pathogen. In contrast, the saprophytic fungi that follow the pathogen, as part of a normal succession of microbes, are likely to be cultured directly from the canker. *Photo*: L. J. Bettiga.

what types of culture services they provide. It may be necessary to consult several laboratories and a viticulturist to identify peculiar symptoms that may be caused by a pest, disease, or environmental condition.

SEROLOGICAL TESTS—ELISA

Serological methods of disease testing use antibody reactions with disease agents, usually viruses or bacteria. Antiserum is produced by first injecting an animal (typically a rabbit) with a purified preparation of a plant pathogen, such as a virus. The animal's immune system reacts to this foreign material by producing antibodies specific to the pathogen. The antibodies are then purified from blood serum, and the resulting antiserum is used in diagnostic tests. The most commonly used serological test is enzyme linked immunosorbent assay (ELISA).

Many laboratories offer ELISA tests for grapevine diseases caused by viruses and bacteria. These tests are rarely offered commercially for fungal pathogens, as most fungi produce visible structures in culture or on infected plant tissue that are taxonomically informative, making the use of ELISA tests unnecessary (fig. 7.5). ELISA tests are fairly simple to run and can provide results in just 1 or 2 days. For ELISA to be successful, antiserum for each disease agent must be available in the lab, and grapevine test samples must come from the appropriate tissue, must be collected at the proper time of year for the pathogen life cycle, and must be fresh.

One limitation to ELISA testing for grapevine viruses is that antisera do not exist for all of the viruses that infect grapes. Therefore, a vine could be infected with a particular virus, but if no

antiserum against that virus exists, ELISA will be unable to detect it. This is the situation with some of the leafroll viruses, where a negative result may not be meaningful if a leafroll is present in the plant for which no antiserum is available (see "Leafroll" in section 24, "Grapevine Virus Diseases")

Another issue with serological testing is the purity of the antiserum. In some cases, an antiserum may react against more than one pathogen or against other components of plant sap. This could lead to confusing results or potentially false positive results if the antiserum reacts to something other than the pathogen. A good lab uses proper internal controls in each test and advises clients when a particular ELISA test for a pathogen is prone to this problem.

MOLECULAR TESTS—PCR

Recently, molecular tests have been developed that directly target the genetic material (genome) of plant pathogens. They do not rely on antibody reactions, but rather look for nucleic acid sequences that are unique to a particular pathogen. One of the most sensitive molecular methods for pathogen detection currently available is polymerase chain reaction (PCR).

PCR involves the selective amplification (i.e., making many copies) of a small part of a pathogen's genome. If the pathogen is present in a sample, even in very low amounts, the amplification steps in PCR allow for its detection.

Figure 7.5 This chasmothecium (arrow) is a microscopic reproductive structure produced by *Erysiphe necator*. As a biotrophic pathogen, *E. necator* is not culturable, but the common occurrence of numerous chasmothecia and white hyphae on the surfaces of leaves and fruit makes its presence suitable for confirmation of powdery mildew. *Photo*: L. J. Bettiga.

It is this amplification that makes PCR such a sensitive test.

PCR can be used for the detection of pathogens in grape because each species of fungi, bacteria, or virus has its own unique genetic code. In the past decade, molecular scientists have identified genetic markers for many of these pathogens. Commercial PCR testing is currently available for 16 bacterial and viral pathogens of grapevines. Additionally, researchers are evaluating the feasibility of detection of some of the more common fungal pathogens, such as *Eutypa lata* and *Botrytis cinerea*, in symptomless tissue. As this is an active area of research, the list of pathogens detectable in plant tissue by PCR is sure to expand, giving growers a higher level of confidence in matching visual symptoms with causal organisms.

BIOLOGICAL INDEXING

Biological indexing (testing) is a valuable test for some pathogens, particularly viruses. Because these tests require greenhouses or field plantings, they are rarely offered by commercial labs and are most often used at research institutions. Although used most often to detect virus diseases, there are also biological indexing tests for bacteria, fungi, and herbicides.

Herbaceous indexing is performed in a greenhouse in the spring and involves rubbing an extract from the test vine onto leaves of sensitive indicator plants. If certain viruses were present in the test plant extract, the virus will multiply in the plant, and within several weeks, diagnostic disease symptoms will appear on the herbaceous indicator plant. For grapevine viruses, common indicators include *Chenopodium quinoa*, *C. amaranticolor*, *Nicotiana clevelandii*, and *Cucumis sativus*. Although this test is very sensitive for some viruses (particularly the nepoviruses, including grapevine fanleaf virus), it works only for the limited number of grapevine viruses that can reproduce on herbaceous hosts. In addition, although it indicates that virus is present, it does not differentiate between viruses, as will an ELISA test or a PCR test.

Woody or field indexing requires 2 years to complete. Indicator grapevine cultivars that are especially sensitive to virus diseases are grafted with buds from the vine being tested. If virus is present, it will move from the buds to the indicator, causing infection and eventually diagnostic disease symptoms. Once the buds heal, the indicators are planted in the field and observed for two seasons for the development of virus disease symptoms. Although indexing tests are labor intensive and time consuming, they are very useful if the symptomatic grapevines are valuable (e.g., an imported cultivar or a new cultivar released by a grape breeder) and a high level of confidence in the diagnosis is needed. Biological indexing is a very sensitive test because it provides an opportunity for the pathogen to multiply from very low population levels that can readily be detected by the symptoms it causes. Grapevine field indexing programs generally are performed using the indicators *Vitis rupestris* St. George, LN33, Kober 5BB, and Cabernet franc.

SAMPLE SELECTION AND HANDLING

Samples must be selected and collected properly to minimize the chances for false negative results. Sampling particular parts of the vine at certain times of the year can greatly increase the reliability of disease testing. For example, to test vines for grapevine fanleaf virus, shoot tips should be collected for testing in the spring. This virus is heat sensitive, and its concentration in vines becomes very low during summer, making detection less reliable. Diagnostic laboratories should be able to provide useful guidance about optimal sampling times. This publication has additional information about seasonal aspects of pathogen detection in individual disease descriptions.

Proper handling and shipping of samples is also important. In general, samples should be delivered to the testing lab as soon as possible. If the samples have been exposed to excessive heat or drying, or if they are stored for too long, it will not be possible to get reliable results. Be sure to consult with your lab for recommended delivery instructions.

RELIABILITY OF LABORATORY TESTING

No diagnostic test is perfect. All the methods described above have the potential to produce false positive or false negative results.

False positives occur when test results indicate that a disease is present but the vines were actually free of the disease. False positives usually occur as a result of contamination or mislabeling of samples. These errors could occur in the field when samples are collected or at the lab after the samples arrive. Contamination is of particular concern with PCR because of the sensitivity of the test. Just a few bacteria or fungal cells or virus particles carried over from one sample to another could lead to false positive results. With ELISA, false positives can also occur if an antiserum reacts against plant constituents in addition to the targeted pathogen.

False negative results are much more common than false positives. False negatives occur when test results indicate that no disease is present but the vines were actually diseased. Most false negatives occur because the sample from the diseased vine did not have the suspect organism in it, or the sample was mishandled and was not in good condition when it arrived at the lab. Given that pathogens are unevenly distributed in vineyards and within an individual vine, it is important to collect multiple tissue samples from the same symptomatic vine or from different vines. If the tissue sent to a lab is from a part of a diseased vine that does not contain the pathogen, the result will be a false negative. False negatives can also occur due to a variety of problems at the laboratory that compromise the testing procedure. Careful laboratories include controls in their tests in hopes of identifying these types of problems so that if the quality of the test is not good, the test can be repeated. The addition of a control gives the researcher or lab staff a known result that can be compared with samples submitted for pathogen identification.

INTERPRETATION OF RESULTS

In general, the larger the number of samples sent from a vineyard for testing, the higher the confidence level in the results. Keep in mind that many microorganisms that can cause disease are present in vineyards much of the time. Your sample may test positive for fungi, bacteria, or a virus that may be present but is not likely to cause the problem of concern. To cite a good example, when grapevine roots are sampled and cultured, many fungi are frequently found that may or may not be the cause of a disease; the fungi are common but disease only results when additional factors contribute. Culture results can provide a good lead in determining the cause of a problem, and possible solutions should not be the only tool used in diagnosis. Sometimes test results include reports on the presence of rare pathogens or pathogens that are rarely aggressive in grapevines. Often, secondary organisms may exist in greater numbers only after the primary organism has caused infection first (fig. 7.6).

Positive results from a laboratory can generally be counted on as being accurate. False positives are not common unless there were significant problems at the lab. Most labs run internal controls to check for these types of errors. However, if you suspect a problem because every one of your samples comes back positive, you might consider running them again. Including a healthy sample along with your diseased ones is usually a good idea.

Negative results, on the other hand, are of limited value. Because of the problems inherent in sampling, such as the uneven distribution of pathogens in the tissues of individual vines and changes in seasonal pathogen populations, false negative results are common (fig. 7.7). Keep in mind that a negative test result does not mean that the vine is free of the disease being tested for.

Test results for disease cannot be used to determine the general health of a grapevine. Rather, they can help determine whether a vine is infected with the particular pathogens being tested for. Because tests are not available for all known grape diseases, no vine can ultimately be declared disease-free. However, new technology is available today that makes the job of diagnosing vineyard diseases using laboratory tests far more reliable than it has ever been in the past.

Guidelines for sampling and disease testing for the most common diseases found in California vineyards are organized in table 7.1. It is important to note that symptoms may be similar for many diseases, which might necessitate multiple diagnostic tests to properly identify the cause of disease.

Table 7.1. Guidelines for sampling and disease testing.

Disease	Pathogen type	When to test	Tissue to sample	Diagnostic methods		
				Culturing	ELISA	PCR
Armillaria root rot	fungus	year-round	root crown and thick, woody roots	reliable	NA	reliable from pathogen culture
black foot disease	fungus	year-round	roots, root crown, base of trunk	reliable	NA	NA
Botryosphaeria dieback	fungus	spring through harvest	spurs, cordons, and trunk wood	reliable	NA	reliable from pathogen culture
Botrytis bunch rot	fungus	spring through harvest	fruit, shoots, and canes; scion/rootstock of new plants	reliable	NA	reliable from pathogen culture
crown gall	bacterium	year-round	trunk wood, buds, galls from canes or trunks, and roots	reliable	reliable from pathogen culture	reliable from pathogen culture and only fresh galls on plant tissue
downy mildew	fungus	spring	leaves and shoots	NA	NA	reliable from plant tissue
esca	fungus	year-round	canes, cordon, and trunk	reliable	NA	NA
Eutypa dieback	fungus	spring through harvest	spurs, cordons, and trunk wood	reliable	NA	reliable from pathogen culture
fanleaf (and other nepoviruses)	virus	spring is best; fall and winter are okay	active shoot tips in spring; shoots/canes for cambium scrapings in fall and winter	NA	reliable in spring	reliable in spring, less reliable in fall and winter
leafroll	virus	late summer, fall, and winter	petioles in late summer and fall; shoots/canes for cambium scrapings in fall and winter	NA	Not available for all GLRaVs; reliable in late summer and fall	Not available for all GLRaVs; reliable in late summer, fall, and winter
Petri disease/vine decline	fungus	year-round	roots, root crown, base of trunk	reliable	NA	NA
Phomopsis cane and leaf spot	fungus	spring and winter	canes and shoots	reliable	NA	NA
Phytophthora crown and root rot	fungus	year-round	fine roots, root crown, and soil adhering to roots	reliable	NA	NA
Pierce's disease	bacterium	late summer and fall	symptomatic leaves and adjacent stems	reliable	reliable from pathogen culture and plant tissue	reliable from pathogen culture and plant tissue
powdery mildew	fungus	spring through harvest	leaves, shoots, and fruit	NA	NA	reliable from pathogen scraped off plant tissue
rupestris stem pitting	virus	year-round	petioles, leaves, and cambial scrapings	NA	not generally available	reliable
Verticillium wilt	fungus	year-round	shoots	reliable	NA	NA
vitiviruses: GVA, GVB, and GVD	virus	spring, fall, and winter	petioles, leaves, or cambial scrapings	NA	available for GVA only; reliable in spring	available for GVA, GVB, and GVD

Figure 7.7 The nonuniform distribution of the Pierce's disease pathogen, *Xylella fastidiosa,* in symptomatic vines can confound laboratory diagnosis of this disease. The pathogen may be absent from a symptomatic leaf such as this, because symptoms form in advance of the infection. To maximize the chance of a positive diagnosis, collect sections of the adjacent stems, where the pathogen is more likely to be detected. Also, collect multiple stems adjacent to leaves showing a range of symptoms, from moderate to severe. *Photo*: J. K. Clark.

Figure 7.6 *Phytophthora cinnamomi* decomposes the cambium of the root crown, resulting in a dark brown layer of dead tissue beneath the bark, as shown on the thick root in the foreground. Culture attempts from the margin of a lesion often yield the saprophytic secondary fungi that follow *P. cinnamomi* infection, primarily because the pathogen is quickly replaced by these ubiquitous soilborne fungi. To guard against detection of secondary fungi instead of the primary pathogen, request that only the margins of lesions are plated and that cultures obtained from the roots, root crown, and soil are compared before a diagnosis is made. *Photo*: K. Baumgartner.

Part 3

Diseases

Bacterial Diseases
Fungal Diseases
Virus Diseases

Chardonnay

8 CROWN GALL

Stephen J. Vasquez and Jodi E. Creasap Gee

Crown gall in grape is caused by *Agrobacterium vitis* (formally *A. tumefaciens* biovar 3), a species of bacteria that lives systemically in grape. Crown gall is found throughout the grape-growing regions of the world and can cause severe damage when conditions are right. Presence of the pathogen in conjunction with injury to grapevine tissue, which could include mechanical or freeze damage, may result in the formation of galls. Once galls start developing, temperatures lower than 26.5°C (80°F) and high humidity encourage continued tumor growth that can girdle and kill grapevines. Crown gall incidence is relatively low in California vineyards, but the disease damage can be devastating when the pathogen is present and environmental conditions are favorable. This disease is identified more frequently in the cooler, wetter areas of California, but vines growing in California's hot, dry San Joaquin Valley are not immune to the disease. In December 2006, the San Joaquin Valley experienced more than 15 days of temperatures at or below freezing and only 3.25 cm (1.28 in) of precipitation, which resulted in a high incidence of crown gall in the spring of 2007. Vineyards with young vines, which tend to be more susceptible than older vines, or recently grafted vines were especially hard hit. San Joaquin Valley summers typically exceed 35°C (95°F), which helps dry the galls before vine death can occur. In this situation, few galls reappear within the current or following season unless optimal conditions are present.

The long-term effects of crown gall on California vineyards are difficult to assess or predict, especially in regions where disease severity appears to be relatively low. In vineyards where infection incidence is low, crown gall can become a major problem when new vines are planted or older vines are grafted to change cultivars. Gall formation leading to a dead or weakened plant can be costly to growers. Some research suggests that even mildly affected vines will not live as long or crop as well as healthy vines.

SYMPTOMS

Galls can be found as fleshy outgrowths on crowns, graft unions, and, to a lesser extent, on canes and larger subsurface roots. The galls are composed of soft, disorganized, white to light green cells that resemble natural callus formation found on healthy grafted vines or recent intentional girdling wounds used in table grape production for berry enlargement. As the galls age, they become rough, hard, and dark brown, with cracks on the exterior. Depending on environmental conditions, galls may remain active throughout the season, maintaining the whitish interior, or they may dry completely. Aerial galls usually dry out and slough off in regions with hot, dry summer weather because they lack a protective epidermis. On vines with recurring galls, new galls frequently develop near the site of old galls. Formation of galls on canes can be found in regions of California that experience periods of freezing temperatures and high humidity. Galls can range from 0.6 to 15 cm (0.25 to 6 in) in diameter or can appear in a contiguous arrangement along a trunk, cane, or graft union. Vineyards that display galls from year to year will show a decrease in vine vigor and likely an increase in vine deaths due to the girdling effects of the tumors.

DISEASE CYCLE

Agrobacterium vitis can live systemically in grape vascular tissue (fig. 8.1), which enables it to be spread through vegetative propagation. Initially identified as *A. tumefaciens* biovar 3, *A. vitis* is recognized as the primary species of *Agrobacterium* that infects grapes around the world. It can be isolated in pure culture by collecting sap in the spring and plating it on selective media. However, much like viruses, it is not uniformly distributed throughout a grapevine's vascular system, which can make collection for identification difficult. It can live in host tissue (roots, trunks, and canes) without producing galls as long as grapevine cells and tissues are free of wounds. Once a wound develops, either through freezing or mechanical damage, a chemotactic response triggers the initiation of plant cell transformation and subsequent gall formation. Phenolic compounds and other secondary metabolites that *A. vitis* recognizes are released from the wounded grapevine cells. The bacteria then transfer a portion of DNA

(T-DNA) to the plant cell, where the T-DNA is incorporated into the plant DNA. The genes on the T-DNA code for opines and plant growth regulators, all of which are necessary for gall formation. Opines are related to amino acids and are a carbon and nitrogen source for the bacteria, leading to rapid multiplication and conjugation (exchange of bacterial DNA) of the bacteria. T-DNA–coded plant growth regulator genes dramatically increase the levels of natural growth regulators found in grapevines. Elevated levels of auxins and cytokinins near the wound site enlarge host cell number and size, resulting in tumor development. Grapevine tissue in vineyard soils, especially roots from removed vines, may harbor the bacteria, providing inoculum for future infections. The pathogen is also transported to new sites when cuttings from infected vineyards are used to establish new blocks.

MANAGEMENT

Management of crown gall is difficult because *Vitis vinifera* cultivars tend to be highly susceptible to freeze injuries, and, hence, disease development (fig. 8.2). Mechanical damage should be avoided in established vineyards that have a history of high disease incidence. Cultivars that are cane pruned should have canes tied to wires without bending or cracking. Damaged cordons and trunks can be retrained, but this can be costly in areas prone to freeze damage. One solution for growers in freeze-susceptible areas (northern California counties) is to train more than one trunk per vine. Having multiple trunks can save time and money by not having to retrain a new trunk each year. Frost protection

strategies are strongly suggested for sites prone to freezing to minimize tissue damage and gall formation in such situations.

Growers should avoid new vineyard locations that consistently experience freezing temperatures. Lacking the corky periderm found on older vines, young vines are more susceptible to freeze damage. If freezing temperatures are frequently experienced at a new site, plants should be purchased from a nursery or clean stock program that propagates plants using shoot tip culture. Plant propagation also predisposes vines to wounds that can be infected by pathogens at the nursery and planting site (fig. 8.3). The practice of disbudding (the removal of buds below soil level) (fig. 8.4) and scion-rootstock grafting (fig. 8.5) produces wounds that can allow *A. vitis* entry to the xylem or begin the process of gall formation if already infected.

Establishing a new vineyard using plant material from a vineyard with a history of crown gall should be avoided. The systemic nature of *A. vitis* suggests that all plant material has the potential to be infected and potentially develop tumors under optimal disease conditions.

There are no chemical methods of control for crown gall. The biocontrol agent *A. radiobacter* K-84 is effective against crown gall caused by *A. tumefaciens* on other plants, but it does not work against *A. vitis* infecting grape. Consequently, cultural controls, including site selection, selection of cold-hardy material or rootstocks, and mounding soil around graft unions are critical in reducing disease development.

Figure 8.1 Crown gall disease cycle.

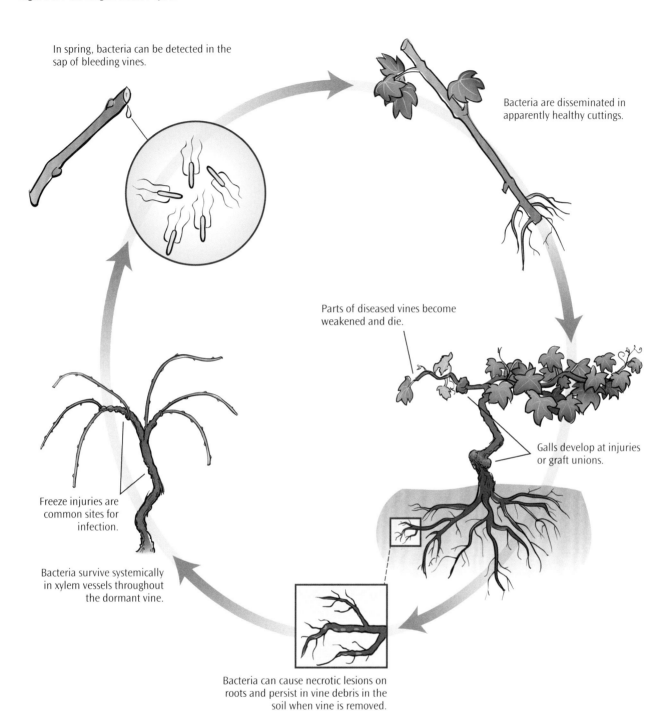

In spring, bacteria can be detected in the sap of bleeding vines.

Bacteria are disseminated in apparently healthy cuttings.

Parts of diseased vines become weakened and die.

Galls develop at injuries or graft unions.

Freeze injuries are common sites for infection.

Bacteria survive systemically in xylem vessels throughout the dormant vine.

Bacteria can cause necrotic lesions on roots and persist in vine debris in the soil when vine is removed.

Figure 8.3 Plant infected by crown gall in nursery. *Photo*: A. N. Kasimatis.

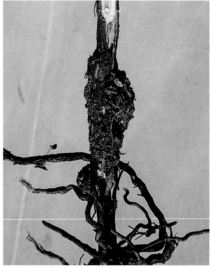

Figure 8.4 Gall development underground girdled this vine in the first year after planting, causing collapse of the vine canopy. *Photo*: L. J. Bettiga.

Figure 8.2 Freeze-damaged tissue can result in galls along the trunk and roots. *Photo*: S. J. Vasquez.

REFERENCES

Burr, T. J., and B. H. Katz. 1983. Isolation of *Agrobacterium tumefaciens* biovar 3 from grapevine galls and sap, and from vineyard soil. Phytopathology 73:163–165.

———. 1984. Grapevine cuttings as potential sites of survival and means of dissemination of *Agrobacterium tumefaciens*. Plant Disease 68:976–978.

Burr, T. J., and L. Otten. 1999. Crown gall of grape: Biology and disease management. Annual Review of Phytopathology 37:53–80.

Burr, T. J., C. Bazzi, S. Süle, and L. Otten. 1998. Crown gall of grape: Biology of *Agrobacterium vitis* and the development of disease control strategies. Plant Disease 82:1288–1297.

Burr, T. J., B. H. Katz, and A. L. Bishop. 1987. Populations of *Agrobacterium* in vineyard and nonvineyard soils and grape roots in vineyards and nurseries. Plant Disease 71:617–620.

Burr, T. J., C. L. Reid, C. E. Adams, and E. A. Momol. 1999. Characterization of *Agrobacterium vitis* strains isolated from feral *Vitis riparia*. Plant Disease 83:102–107.

Kawaguchi A., K. Inoue, and H. Nasu. 2007. Biological control of grapevine crown gall by nonpathogenic *Agrobacterium vitis* strain VAR03-1. Journal of General Plant Pathology 73:133–138.

Kerr, A., and C. G. Panagopoulos. 1977. Biotypes of *Agrobacterium radiobacter* var. *tumefaciens* and their biological control. Phytopathology 90:172–179.

Lehoczfy, J. 1971. Further evidence concerning the systemic spreading of *Agrobacterium tumefaciens* in the vascular system of grapevine. Vitis 10:215–221.

Figure 8.5 Damage caused by grafting can initiate gall formation. Gall growth at the graft union can reduce the success of grafts. *Photos*: S. J. Vasquez (A); L. J. Bettiga (B).

Bacterial Diseases

9 PIERCE'S DISEASE

Alexander H. Purcell, Bruce C. Kirkpatrick, Rodrigo Almeida, Lucia G. Varela, Rhonda J. Smith, Edward A. Weber, Jennifer M. Hashim, and Carmen Gispert

Pierce's disease (PD), a lethal disease of *Vitis vinifera* (European grapevine), is caused by the xylem-inhabiting bacterium *Xylella fastidiosa*. The pathogen is transmitted to grapevines by certain kinds of leafhoppers (family Cicadellidae) known as sharpshooters (subfamily Cicadellinae), as well as some other closely related insect vectors such as spittlebugs (family Cercopidae). Once introduced into grapevines, *X. fastidiosa* multiplies and spreads systemically through the xylem, causing blockages that may limit the vine's ability to transport water and nutrients. Vines that are symptomatic for more than one season (chronically infected) will usually die in just a few years.

Pierce's disease seems to be restricted in North America to regions with mild winters. It has been found in all southern states with commercial grape production, from Florida to California, and in Mexico and Central America. In the southeastern states, PD is the single most formidable obstacle to growing European grapes.

In California, PD occurs in some vineyards every year in localized areas known as hot spots. These hot spots occur where there is favorable habitat for the sharpshooter vectors, where *X. fastidiosa* resides in suitable host plants near vineyards, and where environmental conditions are favorable for the pathogen to persist in infested vines. Pierce's disease hot spots occur in coastal vineyards, in parts of the San Joaquin Valley, and in some southern California vineyards. Statewide, average annual vine loss most years is small; however, losses in individual hot spot vineyards can be devastating. In the southeastern United States, only PD-resistant cultivars with muscadine parentage can be grown.

Known originally as Anaheim disease, mysterious disease, and the California vine disease, PD has been present in California since at least the 1880s, when the first recognized epidemic destroyed more than 14,000 ha (35,000 ac) in the Los Angeles basin. The disease was first extensively studied by Newton B. Pierce and was later named for him. In the Central Valley, the disease was first noted in about 1917, and from 1933 to 1940, a major outbreak affected many Central Valley districts. Since then, PD has erupted on a serious scale in coastal grape-growing regions and in vineyards in the Central Valley and southern California.

In California, the incidence of PD has periodically increased over a much broader area. During these epidemics, PD may appear in vineyards with no previous history of the disease. Epidemics in the early 1970s and the mid 1990s led to extensive replanting of diseased vineyards. The causes of these major epidemics are unknown.

In the late 1990s, a newly introduced insect vector, the glassy-winged sharpshooter, caused a major epidemic in the Temecula Valley in southern California and raised concerns that this new vector might dramatically increase PD throughout California vineyards as the sharpshooter became established in new locations in the state. The Temecula epidemic demonstrated that the area-wide incidence of PD can change dramatically and unexpectedly with a change in a key factor in the disease's cycle, such as the introduction of a new vector.

Xylella fastidiosa causes many other diseases of economic importance. In California, these include alfalfa dwarf, almond leaf scorch, oleander leaf scorch, mulberry leaf scorch, leaf scorch disease, and sweet gum dieback. There are numerous strains of *X. fastidiosa* that differ in the plants they colonize. For example, strains that cause PD can also cause almond leaf scorch, but a genetically distinct group of strains that cause almond leaf scorch do not cause PD. Strains of *X. fastidiosa* that cause oleander leaf scorch do not infect grape, and vice versa. Strains from California that cause Pierce's disease do not infect citrus (orange, lemon, or grapefruit), but strains that cause citrus variegated chlorosis disease in South America cause mild PD symptoms in grapes. The introduction of these citrus strains into North America could increase PD where vineyards are near citrus groves and create a serious new threat to citrus production.

SYMPTOMS

Symptoms of new cases of PD first appear in the summer or fall and may include leaf scorch and discoloration (fig. 9.1; see fig. 9.3), atypical leaf blade abscission ("matchsticks," see fig. 9.4), cluster shrivel, and irregular maturation of canes (see fig. 9.5). The development of symptoms appears to coincide with xylem blockages caused by bacterial growth and plant reactions to infection. However, symptoms of PD are different from those of water deficit or drought.

In spring, foliar symptoms are typically a subtle yellowing between the veins (fig. 9.2). As berries mature, a more obvious marginal chlorosis of leaves or reddening gradually increases in severity to create a series of concentric zones of discolored and dead tissues by early autumn (fig. 9.3). Both white- and red-fruited *V. vinifera* cultivars have some degree of yellow chlorosis bordering the scorched portions of symptomatic leaves. In red-fruited cultivars, there is usually red discoloration along with chlorosis. Grape cultivars vary in the pattern of foliage discoloration and scorching as well as in the speed with which these symptoms appear. Relatively resistant cultivars, such as Sylvaner and Thompson Seedless, usually

Figure 9.1 Progression of foliar symptoms in a white cultivar (Chardonnay) leaf (A) with Pierce's disease. Scorching of leaves begins at outer leaf margins (B) and progresses inward beginning in late summer (C, D). *Photos:* J. K. Clark.

develop extensive yellowing of leaves, but the marginal drying of leaf tissue is irregular and may occur in patches rather than in concentric bands. Vines infected during previous growing seasons will develop scorching in older leaves first. Older leaves typically show the most severe scorching, while other leaves have less scorching and the youngest leaves may not have any symptoms. Usually only one or two canes show PD symptoms late in the first season of infection, unless multiple infections occur in the vine early in the growing season. However, in young vines, particularly in sensitive cultivars such as Pinot noir, Chardonnay, or Barbera, symptoms may appear over the entire vine in

a single year. In older vines and in cultivars such as Sylvaner, Riesling, Petite Sirah (Durif), or Ruby Cabernet, foliar symptoms usually extend only 25 to 50 cm (10 to 20 in) or less from the point of inoculation during the first season, even in vines infected early in April. Infections established after the middle of the growing season may develop only generalized yellowing or reddening in one leaf or a few leaves.

Often, scorched leaves dry down to the base of the blade and detach from the tip of the petiole. This is unlike normal leaf abscission, where the leaf blade and petiole stay together and the base of the petiole detaches from the cane. With PD, the petiole often remains attached to the cane and gradually dies back toward its base. This symptom is referred to as matchsticks because the petioles appear to be slowly "burning" back toward the cane (fig. 9.4).

Some or all of the clusters or portions of clusters on symptomatic canes may shrivel and dry prior to harvest. On vines with extensive PD symptoms, complete crop loss may result. Clusters on red grape cultivars may develop color prematurely prior to wilting and drying.

Canes lignify irregularly, producing green patches surrounded by mature brown tissue (fig. 9.5). This symptom of PD may be seen in late summer or early fall, and it may help to confirm a field diagnosis.

The spring growth of chronically infected vines is delayed or slower than normal. On canes or spurs that had foliar symptoms the preceding fall, new growth may be delayed up to 2 weeks and will be somewhat dwarfed or stunted.

Figure 9.2 The first leaves on shoots (A, arrow) with early-spring symptoms have interveinal chlorosis, but later leaves appear normal. Chronically affected vine with early-spring symptoms of delayed and stunted growth (B). Note how interveinal chlorosis of young leaves (C, middle and right); compare with a healthy vine leaf (left). *Photos*: J. K. Clark.

Figure 9.3 Autumn foliar symptoms of Pierce's disease in a red fruit cultivar, Cabernet Sauvignon. *Photo*: J. K. Clark.

Figure 9.4 Petioles of leaves remain attached to cane after leaf blades fall. *Photo*: J. K. Clark.

Figure 9.5 Irregular, patchy bark maturity is prominent on many cultivars (Pinot noir shown here). Fruit may raisin on infected vines. *Photo*: J. K. Clark.

Some canes or spurs may fail to bud out at all. The first four to eight leaves on stunted shoots may also have a faint yellow mottling between major leaf veins and may be distorted or asymmetrical. Young shoots are often stunted, with a zigzag growth pattern. Shoot wilting in the spring or early summer has been observed on rare occasions. If fall symptoms are confined to one arm or cordon, usually only that part of the vine will show symptoms the following spring.

Except when severely affected, most vines exhibiting stunted early growth will produce near-normal growth from late April through late summer, at which time leaf scorching reappears. The tips of canes on chronically affected vines die back, although this occurs later than the first scorching of leaves. The woody trunks and cordons are generally dry, especially on chronically infected vines, but there is no discoloration or brown streaking in the woody tissues. In cases where most of the vine has PD symptoms, especially if many arms or canes are dead, suckers may sprout from the base of the trunk or rootstock. The last part of the vine to die is often the crown near the soil line.

In general, PD has more severe effects in hot climates than in cooler ones. Symptoms appear sooner and vines die more quickly in California's Central Valley than in the coastal regions. Advanced PD symptoms appear as early as midsummer in Florida and southern Texas. The time of appearance, extent, and severity of symptoms depend to some degree on temperatures and available soil moisture. Sites with shallow or loose-textured soil, moisture stress, or very high temperatures can cause sudden collapse of vines or portions of vines.

Other Causes of Similar Symptoms

Other diseases, nutrient deficiencies, and injuries of grapevines can produce symptoms that can be confused with PD. Refer elsewhere in this manual for details of diagnostic symptoms of esca (section 17); root diseases caused by *Armillaria* (section 10) or *Phytophthora* (section 19); Eutypa dieback (section 15); and phylloxera (section 32). Salt injury or water stress may also lead to summer leaf scorch, but the incidence of symptomatic vines is quite different than it is for PD. Salt injury or water stress tends to occur uniformly across large areas, whereas the pattern for symptomatic PD vines is scattered yet localized. The appearance of matchsticks and the irregular lignification of the cane are associated only with PD. With experience, PD can be reliably diagnosed in the field based on summer and early-fall symptoms.

Spring symptoms of PD may be confused with a number of factors that can delay spring growth. Overcropping the previous season, winter injury, frost damage, and waterlogged soils can all lead to delayed spring growth, as can fungal root diseases. Zinc deficiency results in stunted shoots with zigzag growth and small, distorted leaves with interveinal mottling, similar to that of PD. A temporary spring boron deficiency causes delayed growth symptoms nearly identical to PD. Field diagnosis of PD based on spring symptoms can be difficult, especially if foliar symptoms were not noted in the previous summer or fall. Often, it is necessary to wait until later in the season to confirm PD based on foliar symptoms or laboratory testing.

Commercial laboratories can test plant samples for the presence of *X. fastidiosa*. The two most common tests are ELISA, which identifies proteins that are specific to *X. fastidiosa*, and the polymerase chain reaction (PCR), a DNA-based test that targets and amplifies genetic material unique to *X. fastidiosa*. ELISA is less sensitive than PCR, but it is generally reliable for detecting the bacterium in symptomatic grape leaves. Detection of *X. fastidiosa* in dormant cuttings by either method is not always reliable due to the low numbers and irregular distribution of the bacteria within dormant woody canes. Follow the testing laboratory's instructions for selecting, collecting, and shipping sample tissues.

In chronically diseased vines, *X. fastidiosa* is often not detectable in spring growth until mid-June, even from leaves that are stunted or have slight marginal browning (necrosis). Samples from such diseased vines will test negative early in the season until the bacterial population spreads from the permanent parts of the vine into the new growth. This may not occur until June or July in many regions.

Therefore, laboratory testing is best reserved for testing symptomatic vines in summer and fall.

DISEASE CYCLE

Pierce's disease is a complex disorder involving the biology of the causal pathogen, *X. fastidiosa*, its growth and development within grapevines and other host plants, variable transmission rates among different vectors, the reaction of grapevines and other plants to infection, the ecology of plant communities in and around vineyards, the population dynamics of its insect vectors, and environmental conditions that may influence the survival of the pathogen.

The bacterium naturally occurs only in plants and the alimentary tracts of insects that feed on xylem sap. In plants, it is restricted to xylem tissues. Bacteria attach to the inside of xylem vessels and have threadlike structures (pili) that enable them to move downward against the xylem stream. *X. fastidiosa* produces a chemical signal that affects gene expression in other nearby *X. fastidiosa*. This chemical signal may influence the formation of bacterial aggregates that can plug xylem vessels, and it is probably important in other aspects of the bacterium's behavior within plants and insect vectors; hence, it is of interest for developing novel control methods.

The PD strain of the pathogen can colonize many plant species, but the pathogen population size and its systemic movement within plants vary among plant hosts. As a consequence, plants vary greatly in their effectiveness as reservoirs of the pathogen. In most species, such as willow and mugwort, *X. fastidiosa* multiplies locally. It rarely

or never moves systemically within these plants and eventually dies out after 2 or 3 months. However, in some plants, such as elderberry and blackberry, *X. fastidiosa* moves systemically throughout the xylem system and can attain high populations. Both systemic and nonsystemic hosts can harbor sufficient populations of *X. fastidiosa* for insect vectors to acquire the bacterium by feeding. However, systemic hosts that harbor high populations and rapid pathogen movement are much better plants for insect acquisition than are nonsystemic hosts. Unlike in *V. vinifera* grapes, *X. fastidiosa* causes no symptoms or only very mild stunting in most plants, both systemic and nonsystemic hosts.

Sharpshooters acquire the bacterium while feeding on plants colonized by *X. fastidiosa*, whether the plant has symptoms or not. Once insects have acquired *X. fastidiosa* by feeding on an infected plant, they can transmit it to other plants immediately. Immature sharpshooters stop transmitting *X. fastidiosa* after molting because the lining of the mouth and sucking pump (foregut) are shed. However, they can rapidly reacquire the ability to transmit by feeding on infected plants. Adult vectors that have acquired *X. fastidiosa* remain infective indefinitely, because they do not molt. See section 45, "Sharpshooters," for more information on the biology of these vectors.

Grapevines are systemic hosts of *X. fastidiosa* and can support larger pathogen populations than do symptomless wild hosts. Once transmitted to grapevines by an infected vector, *X. fastidiosa* moves rapidly upward and slowly downward through the xylem, eventually spreading throughout the vine and into the roots. *X. fastidiosa* spreads faster in xylem of susceptible cultivars than in resistant ones, and it spreads faster in warm regions than in cool ones. Bacteria that reach the permanent parts of the vine (cordons, trunk, and roots) are more likely to survive through winter, leading to chronic infections. In spring, grapevine growth outpaces the multiplication and spread of *X. fastidiosa* from permanent tissues, so the current season's growth may be free of *X. fastidiosa* until as late as June or July in some regions.

Many vines that become infected with *X. fastidiosa* and show signs of PD recover from these infections and are disease-free the following season for reasons that are not understood. In northern California, summer and fall infections are much more likely to be eliminated than are spring infections, so preventing spring infections (April–May) is most critical to preventing systemic infections of vines. Grape cultivar strongly influences the rate of winter recovery. Highly susceptible cultivars such as Redglobe and Chardonnay seldom recover over the winter if they have clear symptoms of the disease. Less-susceptible cultivars such as Riesling, Chenin blanc, Thompson Seedless, Ruby Cabernet, and Cabernet Sauvignon consistently have higher rates of recovery. The severity of winter climate appears to be an important factor in recovery rate, with fewer recoveries in climates with mild winters or after mild winters in normally cold regions. Unusually mild winters in parts of Georgia and Texas have been correlated with subsequent large increases in losses to

PD. Experiments have shown that freezing potted vines can completely eliminate *X. fastidiosa*, but the means by which bacterial death occurs appears to be due to an unknown mechanism rather than by the direct effect of freezing alone. Occasionally, recovered vines may have spring symptoms of delayed and stunted growth, but they do not develop foliar scorching or fruit raisining later in the summer. Presumably, this is due to lowered carbohydrate reserves and residual xylem damage caused the previous growing season.

MANAGEMENT

To reduce the incidence of PD, the number of infective vectors entering the vineyard must be minimized. This may be achieved by modifying vector breeding habitats to make them unsuitable for supporting large populations of infective adult insects or by using insecticides to kill vectors before they can enter nearby vineyards. Insect management is discussed in section 45, "Sharpshooters."

In north coastal California vineyards adjacent to riparian vegetation where the blue-green sharpshooter is the major vector and the glassy-winged sharpshooter is not established, altering the composition of the riparian

plant community may reduce the incidence of PD (fig. 9.6). Removal of nonnative plants, such as Himalayan blackberry and periwinkle, which are the blue-green sharpshooter's principal breeding hosts, and replacement with native nonhost plants results in fewer blue-green sharpshooters during the spring months. Because riparian corridors are ecologically sensitive and regulated by federal, state, and local authorities, the unauthorized removal of vegetation is prohibited or restricted. Contact the nearest office of the California Department of Fish

Figure 9.6 (A) Pattern of missing vines caused by Pierce's disease along natural riverbank vegetation, a preferred habitat for the blue-green sharpshooter. (B) Aerial view of spread of Pierce's disease after severely diseased vines were removed. Color infrared photo shows spread downwind from former alfalfa hay fields. Note lower incidence of disease in Thompson Seedless cultivar. Heaviest concentrations of diseased vines are downwind (left) from former alfalfa fields, breeding grounds of sharpshooters. *Photos*: J. K. Clark (A); A. H. Purcell (B).

and Wildlife for current regulations and guidelines concerning any proposed modification within the riparian corridor. In addition to addressing concerns related to PD, any vegetation management plan must enhance and protect important natural resource values provided by the riparian habitat. Vegetation provides habitat for wildlife and fish, promotes stream bank stability, and protects water quality. A well-designed vegetation management plan will protect these resources and enhance plant diversity and structure, as well as reduce the population of the blue-green sharpshooter.

Where glassy-winged sharpshooter appears to be the main vector of *X. fastidiosa*, overwintering hosts such as citrus are important in disease incidence. Even though citrus has not been shown to be a host of *X. fastidiosa* strains that cause PD in California, the groves are a preferred source for food and shelter for infective adult sharpshooters from late fall through early spring. The glassy-winged sharpshooter feeds on dormant grapevines during warm winter days and has been shown to transmit *X. fastidiosa* to grapevines during January and February in the Central Valley. Thus, treatments to prevent the glassy-winged sharpshooter from entering vineyards should include the winter months if this insect is present in significant numbers in habitats near vineyards.

When glassy-winged sharpshooter is not present, removing diseased vines has not been shown to affect the subsequent incidence of PD in California vineyards. Instead, the spatial patterns of diseased vines reflect the spatial patterns of vectors entering vineyards from vector habitats such as riparian vegetation in coastal regions and pastures and hayfields in the Central Valley. This may be explained by the combination of very low rates of vector acquisition of bacteria from grapevines during the spring months and the low rate of disease persistence (chronic disease) for infections established after early summer. In the spring, bacterial populations are low or absent in the new growth of chronically infected vines. In the summer, these vines have bacterial populations that are high enough for vector acquisition; thus, other vines can become infected. When this occurs, however, it is too late in the season in most regions and cultivars for chronic infections to establish. Chronically infected vines present one year will not be an acquisition source of *X. fastidiosa* that will result in more diseased vines the following year. In this manner, vine-to-vine movement of the bacteria by vectors usually does not result in chronic disease. However, for highly susceptible cultivars, the early or midsummer vine-to-vine dispersal of *X. fastidiosa* by sharpshooters within the vineyard may be important. It is possible that these cultivars may become chronically infected during summer months or where mild winter climates lower rates of overwinter recovery.

In regions where glassy-winged sharpshooter is the main vector, removing diseased vines may reduce the subsequent incidence of PD. When this vector is present, it is believed that infected grapevines are often the main acquisition source of *X. fastidiosa*. These vines may contribute to vine-to-vine movement of the bacteria by glassy-winged sharpshooter and result in chronic disease. In these areas, prompt removal of diseased vines is recommended.

The importance of vines infected with *X. fastidiosa* as acquisition sources in the fall for vectors that will re-enter vineyards the following spring is not clear. In the Napa Valley, rates of natural infectivity of blue-green sharpshooters sampled during the early fall typically ranged from 5 to 15%, but rates of infection over 25% in some locations were not unusual. The infectivity rate did not differ significantly between sharpshooters collected in vineyards and those in adjacent riparian habitats, suggesting that both vineyards and riparian vegetation can serve as an acquisition source.

Replanting may be the only practical way to maintain a productive vineyard, and it is likely to be necessary on an annual basis in many PD hot spots to maintain economic crop production levels. Mark diseased vines in late summer or fall when PD symptoms are most recognizable. Vines with severe symptoms over most of the vine should be removed the same fall or following winter. In spring, remove any marked vines that show signs of delayed growth. Marked vines that grow normally or with only slight stunting may have recovered during the winter.

When establishing or replanting vineyards near a known or suspected hot spot, varietal tolerance to PD should be considered. Although no European grape cultivar is immune to PD, some comparatively resistant cultivars are likely to have fewer vines that develop PD, and infected vines of these cultivars decline more slowly. Sylvaner, Riesling, Chenin blanc, Thompson Seedless, and Ruby Cabernet are among the cultivars most resistant to PD. Petite Sirah (Durif), Sauvignon blanc, Cabernet Sauvignon, Merlot, Napa Gamay, and Trousseau gris (Gray Riesling) are moderately resistant. Sensitive grape cultivars are not as effectively protected by insecticidal control of vectors as are more-resistant ones. Mission, Barbera, Pinot noir, Redglobe, Fiesta, and Chardonnay are very sensitive and should not be planted near sharpshooter breeding grounds such as stream banks, ravines, and weedy irrigation ditches. While it is unlikely for nursery stock to be infected with *X. fastidiosa*, hot water treatment may be used as a precautionary measure by commercial nurseries. Hot water treatment of dormant cuttings kills *X. fastidiosa* after 3 hours at 45°C (113°F), 20 minutes at 50°C (122°F), or 10 minutes at 55°C (131°F).

Once vines develop chronic PD, there are few management options other than removal and replanting

Figure 9.7 Diseased vines, becoming increasingly stunted over multiple seasons, have fewer and shorter canes that produce dwarfed leaves and little usable fruit. *Photo*: J. K. Clark.

(fig. 9.7). Under experimental conditions, antibiotics have cured PD in young vines, but human health and environmental concerns render this approach infeasible for vineyards. Other experimental treatments, such as foliar sprays or direct injections of copper or zinc compounds, reduced some symptoms, but after 2 or 3 years, severe PD invariably reoccurred in treated vines.

Selective pruning of symptomatic canes or cordons does not increase the rate of winter recovery. Severe pruning, in which diseased vines are severed just above the graft union to eliminate infections, was tested as a method to speed redevelopment of vines and minimize the economic losses associated with PD. Vines retrained from a sucker the year following severe pruning were not only free of PD symptoms but seldom had detectable bacterial growth in the foliage the year after pruning. However, the second year after being severely pruned, high bacterial populations had redeveloped from the roots and most vines developed PD symptoms. The regeneration of some pruned vines into healthy vines did not compensate for the loss of crop caused by severe pruning. Severe pruning is not a viable control practice for PD in most vineyards.

REFERENCES

Almeida, R. P. P., and A. H. Purcell. 2003. Transmission of *Xylella fastidiosa* to grapevines by *Homalodisca coagulata* (Hemiptera: Cicadellidae). Journal of Economic Entomology 96(2): 264–271.

Baccari, C., and S. E. Lindow. 2011. Assessment of the process of movement of *Xylella fastidiosa* within susceptible and resistant grape cultivars. Phytopathology. 101(1): 77–84.

Baumgartner, K., and J. G. Warren. 2005. Persistence of *Xylella fastidiosa* in riparian hosts near Northern California vineyards. Plant Disease 89(10): 1097–1102.

Costa, H. S., E. Raetz, T. R. Pinckard, C. Gispert, R. Hernandez-Martinez, C. K. Dumenyo, and D. A. Cooksey. 2004. Plant hosts of *Xylella fastidiosa* in and near Southern California vineyards. Plant Disease 88(11): 1255–1261.

Park, Y-L., T. M. Perring, R. K. Krell, C. A. Farrar, and C. Gispert. 2006. Spatial distribution of Pierce's disease in the Coachella Valley: Implications for sampling. American Journal of Enology and Viticulture 57(2): 2202–2225.

Purcell, A. H. 1974. Spatial patterns of Pierce's disease in the Napa Valley. American Journal of Enology and Viticulture 25(3): 162–167.

———. 1975. Role of the blue-green sharpshooter, *Hordnia circellata*, in the epidemiology of Pierce's disease of grapevines. Environmental Entomology 4(5): 745–752.

Purcell, A. H., and S. R. Saunders. 1999. Fate of Pierce's disease strains of *Xylella fastidiosa* in common riparian plants in California. Plant Disease 83(9): 825–830.

Varela, L. G., R. J. Smith, and P. A. Phillips. 2001. Pierce's disease. Oakland: University of California Division of Agriculture and Natural Resources Publication 21600. ANR CS website, http://ucanr.org/sites/intvit/files/24470.pdf.

Wistrom, C., and A. H. Purcell. 2005. The fate of *Xylella fastidiosa* in vineyard weeds and other alternate hosts in California. Plant Disease 89(9): 994–999.

Fungal Diseases

10 ARMILLARIA ROOT ROT

Kendra Baumgartner and David M. Rizzo

First described on grapevines in California in the 1880s, Armillaria root rot occurs in all major grape-growing regions of the state. The causal fungus, *Armillaria mellea*, infects woody grapevine roots and the base of the trunk (the root collar), resulting in a slow decline and eventual death of the vine. Armillaria root rot commonly affects vineyards planted on sites that were previously occupied by infected wild or cultivated hosts. Despite its common name of oak root fungus, *A. mellea* has a broad host range, infecting over 500 species of woody plants. Native hosts include oaks and other common forest trees such as Douglas-fir, California bay laurel, and madrone. The fungus also infects many cultivated plants, including walnuts and other orchard trees, as well as many woody landscape plants. Armillaria root rot does not affect as many acres as do some other fungal diseases of grapevines, but where it does occur, it is extremely difficult to eradicate and reduces yields throughout the life of an infected vineyard and that of successive plantings.

SYMPTOMS

Symptoms vary according to the extent of root infection by the fungus. In most cases, symptoms progress gradually over the course of several years. Vines with moderate symptoms of infection have stunted shoots, fewer and smaller clusters, clusters that ripen poorly, and lower petiole nitrogen and potassium than healthy vines in the same vineyard. More-severe infection causes more-significant levels of all of these moderate symptoms, in addition to wilted leaves, premature defoliation, and berry desiccation (fig. 10.1). Vines with severe symptoms that do not succumb to Armillaria root rot before harvest usually die during the dormant season. Occasionally, severe symptoms develop suddenly between veraison and harvest, and the vine dies in a matter of weeks. Armillaria root rot affects vines in localized sections of the vineyard. These disease centers appear to expand radially over time and typically include a combination of dead, symptomatic, and healthy vines.

Figure 10.1 Vine in foreground shows severe symptoms of Armillaria root rot, including stunted shoots, chlorotic and wilted leaves, and very few clusters. *Photo*: K. Baumgartner.

To diagnose a suspected infection, clear the soil from the root collar at the base of the trunk to a depth of 15 to 30 cm (6 to 12 in) and remove the bark to look for thick, white to cream-colored mats of fungal tissue called mycelial fans (figs. 10.2–10.3). Examine the root collars of dead vines in a disease center first. Mycelial fans occur close to the soil surface and are easier to locate on root collars of dead vines than on symptomatic vines. The fungus may also form black rootlike structures called rhizomorphs that originate from mycelial fans and grow on the surface of and underneath root bark (fig. 10.4). Rhizomorphs can extend into surrounding soil from infected roots to colonize the roots of nearby vines. Because *Armillaria mellea* makes relatively short rhizomorphs, its capacity to spread from infected vines to adjacent vines in the form of rhizomorphs is very limited. This is in contrast to other *Armillaria* species (e.g., *A. gallica*) that create prolific networks of rhizomorphs and spread primarily in this form in forest ecosystems.

Armillaria mellea mushrooms sometimes form at or near the base of infected grapevines during the rainy season (fig. 10.5). They are reliable indicators of infection, but they do not always form. Like most mushrooms, *A. mellea* produces windblown spores. These are, however, not thought to be a significant cause of new infections in vineyards or among other susceptible crops.

DISEASE CYCLE

The fungus is established at a site prior to planting in its vegetative form (mycelium). The mycelium survives in infected woody roots left buried in the soil (residual roots) after a site is cleared; viable mycelium has been recovered from residual roots found buried in vineyard and orchard soils for 10 or more years. Newly planted grapevines become infected when their roots come into direct contact with infected residual roots and are subsequently colonized by *A. mellea*

mycelium. Infected vine roots then become a source of inoculum for neighboring vines and replants whose roots grow into direct contact with them.

Vine-to-vine growth of rhizomorphs of *A. mellea* has been thought to be responsible for the expansion of disease centers in vineyards. The fungus can spread from an infected to a healthy root via rhizomorphs, which are extremely rare in vineyards. Instead of reflecting a radial pattern of rhizomorph growth from vine to vine, the development of a disease center reflects a high density of residual roots at its core, surrounded by decreasing densities toward its margin. Vines planted on top of the highest densities of inoculum become infected first, and infections of adjacent vines (and subsequent symptom expression and mortality) follow because the latter occupy soil with lower inoculum densities. In this way, a single disease center appears to expand over time, but it is actually

Figure 10.2 Look beneath the root bark and below the soil line for white mycelial fans, the vegetative stage of *Armillaria mellea,* which are typically found at the root collar (shown here) and on woody roots deeper in the soil profile. *Photo*: K. Baumgartner.

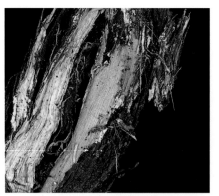

Figure 10.3 Close-up of mycelial fans of *Armillaria mellea*. Photo: L. J. Bettiga.

Figure 10.4 *Armillaria mellea* forms dark, rootlike filaments called rhizomorphs, which can extend out into the soil from an infected root to infect the roots of neighboring vines. A rhizomorph is shown here (arrow) growing across the surface of an infected root. *Photo*: K. Baumgartner.

a succession of primary infections (i.e., contacts between residual roots and vines) rather than vine-to-vine spread of rhizomorphs. The practical significance of this distinction is that the disease is better controlled by removing residual roots, both in the short-term and the long-term, than by trying to prevent rhizomorph spread.

Armillaria mellea colonizes a root by secreting enzymes that dissolve root bark. The fungus then attacks and kills a small section of cambial tissue before forming a mycelial fan. Once established, the mycelial fan continues to grow under the root bark, usually in the direction of the root collar. The fungus destroys the underlying root wood. Since it grows slowly, it may take up to a year for the fungus to completely kill a root.

Aboveground symptoms begin to appear when *A. mellea* colonizes the root collar and decays the underlying root wood. Infection at only the root tips rarely causes symptoms. However, once the fungus spreads from the end of a root up to the root collar, it girdles the base of the trunk. Eventually, so much vascular tissue is destroyed that water and mineral nutrients cannot move past the root collar, and the vine dies.

MANAGEMENT

The best way to control Armillaria root rot is to avoid planting on infected sites. Before clearing an orchard or vineyard, look for disease centers. Symptoms are most noticeable just before harvest in all susceptible crops. Unfortunately, the fungus is harder to detect on forest trees because aboveground symptoms are often not found. Nonetheless, the pathogen is relatively common in hardwood forests that cover the hillsides of the coastal mountains and Sierra Foothills (e.g., mixed oak woodland), and it also occurs in fragmented patches of hardwoods

situated within more vast areas of chaparral. Former riparian areas in the Central Valley are possibly the original sources of *A. mellea* in vineyards in this grape-growing region.

On sites infected with *A. mellea*, the most effective control is sanitation through preplant removal of residual roots. Whether or not the fungus is positively identified, good sanitation is, nevertheless, strongly recommended, especially on a forested site. The absence of symptoms and mycelial fans does not ensure that the site is free of the fungus, since infections below the root collar may escape detection. Deep-ripping the soil in several directions after clearing tree trunks and stumps will bring large roots to the surface, where they should be removed. Large roots, moist soil, and cool temperatures improve the ability of the fungus to survive in the soil in infected residual roots. The smaller the diameter of a residual root and the closer it is to the soil surface, where soil is warmer and drier, the lower the probability that the fungus will survive.

As mentioned earlier, a vine can tolerate infection at distal portions of the root system, but infection at the root collar can significantly limit transport of water and mineral nutrients. Therefore, cultural controls that make the root collar less hospitable to infection, namely by reducing frequent soil moisture, may decrease the rate of decline of infected vines. For example, drip emitters should be installed at least 30 to 40 cm (12 to 16 in) from the base of the trunk, so that root collars are less favorable sites for colonization by mycelial fans present on distal portions of the root system. Armillaria root rot is not typically found in vineyards

Figure 10.5 *Armillaria* mushrooms at the base of several vines in a row (A). Note that the canes barely reach the upper foliage wires. The mushrooms (B) are not a significant source of inoculum of the disease. *Photos*: K. Baumgartner.

with poor drainage and water-logged soils. In fact, reports of onset of symptoms in vineyards and orchards after changing from flood irrigation to drip irrigation suggest that occasional standing water is less of a problem for this disease than consistently moist soil. Furthermore, wood decomposition by *Armillaria* and other wood decay fungi is hampered by saturation, as these microbes are aerobic.

Permanent removal of soil from the root collar to the depth at which main roots originate—approximately 30 to 40 cm (12 to 16 in), a technique known as root collar excavation (fig. 10.6)—has been shown to cause mycelial fans to recede from the root collar and to improve yields when done in the early stages of root collar infection. This early stage of infection is characterized by the presence of a mycelial fan at the root collar and no visible decomposition of the underlying root wood, and it is typically associated with moderate stunting of shoots. This is in contrast to severely stunted vines, which are characterized by substantial decomposition beneath mycelial fans at the root collar

Figure 10.6 Root collar excavation causes mycelial fans to recede, protecting this important part of the root system from decay. *Photo*: K. Baumgartner.

and shoots that are less than 50% of the length of shoots on healthy vines. Assuming that the efficacy of root collar excavation comes from improved soil drying, planting vines on elevated berms as a preventive measure in replanted vineyards with a history of Armillaria root rot may also achieve similar soil conditions.

Chemical approaches for reducing the amounts of inoculum are limited to preplant soil fumigation, which is used on a spot basis or when establishing or replanting entire blocks. Refer to the UC IPM Grape Pest Management Guidelines, www.ipm.ucdavis.edu/PMG/, for fumigants available for control of Armillaria root rot on grape. Preplant soil fumigation is effective only if the fumigant reaches residual roots. Based on experimental evidence, it seems that inadequate penetration of the soil is more likely to reduce the efficacy of fumigants than is inadequate penetration of thick roots. Even for thick roots, the relatively low doses of fumigant that reach the center may not directly kill the mycelium but instead weaken *A. mellea* to subsequent attack by antagonistic soilborne microbes (e.g., *Trichoderma* spp.). Fine soil texture, high levels of soil moisture, and high levels of organic matter in the soil decrease the efficacy of soil fumigation; the efficacy of fumigants in such soils will be increased by proper sanitation. Use recommended application procedures and site preparation for the fumigant being considered. Soil fumigation often delays infection by *A. mellea* for a number of years and may reduce disease incidence, but it rarely eradicates the fungus.

Research is in progress to identify biological controls for Armillaria root rot. Several

microbial inoculants have been identified that contain strains of bacteria that inhibit the pathogen in culture, and a subset has been demonstrated to improve yields of infected vines in the field. The limited number of rootstocks that have been tested vary in their relative resistance to the pathogen, and trials are in progress to identify more-resistant rootstocks. As with other root pathogen systems, it is typically the integration of different approaches, rather than a single approach such as soil fumigation, that collectively bring about numerous incremental improvements in vine yield.

REFERENCES

Baumgartner, K. 2004. Root collar excavation for postinfection control of Armillaria root disease of grapevine. Plant Disease 88:1235–1240.

Baumgartner, K., and D. M. Rizzo. 2002. Spread of Armillaria root disease in a California vineyard. American Journal of Enology and Viticulture 53:197–203.

———. 2006. Relative resistance of grapevine rootstocks to Armillaria root disease. American Journal of Enology and Viticulture 57:408–414.

Baumgartner, K., and A. E. Warnock. 2006. A soil inoculant inhibits *Armillaria mellea* in vitro and improves productivity of grapevines with root disease. Plant Disease 90:439–444.

Baumgartner, K., M. P. A. Coetzee, and D. Hoffmeister. 2011. Secrets of the subterranean pathosystem of *Armillaria*. Molecular Plant Pathology 12:515–534.

Fungal Diseases

11 ASPERGILLUS VINE CANKER

William L. Peacock and Themis J. Michailides

Aspergillus vine canker is caused by *Aspergillus niger*, which is common in vineyard soils and may occur as an epiphyte on the surface of vines. Another species that causes the disease and was isolated less frequently was *A. carbonarius. A. niger* can also cause sour bunch rot later in the season. It attacks many fruits and some vegetables and can grow on dead plant and animal tissues. Its spores (conidia) are very common in the air in vineyards from veraison to harvest. Aspergillus vine canker is the result of pathogenic activity of either *A. niger* or *A. carbonarius.*

Aspergillus vine canker was first noted in the Coachella Valley in 1986 and seen again in the San Joaquin Valley in the fall of 1989 on exceptionally vigorous Redglobe vines that had been trained up the stake that year. In the Coachella case, disease was consistently found on the trunk in the area where the vine was girdled due to nonexpanding ties. The disease is rare and has been identified in only a handful of cases over the past 20 years. In infected vineyards, about 2 to 6% of the vines had the canker. Since 1989, Aspergillus vine canker has been observed in Tulare, Kern, and Fresno Counties on Redglobe, Crimson Seedless, Chardonnay, and Grenache vines. It occurs during the year the vines are trained up the stake and on vines that are exceptionally vigorous. Aspergillus vine canker has not resulted in serious setbacks in the establishment of vineyards or economic consequences to growers, but it can force the retraining of 2 to 6% of vines the following spring using a shoot originating from below the canker.

SYMPTOMS

The first symptoms appear in August, when red sap balls the size of a pinhead occur on the surface of shoots near the site of initial infection. Cutting into the shoot where sap balls are present reveals brown to rusty discolored tissues. The canker, defined as the localized diseased area of the vine whose tissues are eventually killed, is very obvious by the fall (fig. 11.1). In October and November, the canopy of vines that has been girdled by the canker prematurely displays fall colors, and infected vines are easily distinguished from healthy vines. A closer examination of diseased vines reveals a canker on the young trunk. The trunk is slightly larger

Figure 11.1 In fall, infected vines that have been girdled show premature fall colors. *Photo*: T. J. Michailides.

where the canker occurs, appears puffy, and may feel spongier than healthy tissue. Cutting into the canker exposes dead brown tissue. Black, powdery spores are abundant within the canker, and spores may be visible on the surface of the canker. Growers and field personnel should not confuse secondary black molds and saprophytic sooty molds with *A. niger*. Callous tissue is often associated with the canker as the vine attempts to repair the damage (fig. 11.2). Autoclaving samples of affected vines and removing the outer bark reveals various shapes of cankered areas (fig. 11.3).

Cankers can range from 10 to 30 cm (4 to 12 in) long and appear in anywhere from a small fraction of the shoot cross-sectional area to completely girdling the shoot. Shoots usually heal and grow normally if less than half of the cross-sectional area has been killed by the canker. Cankers do not continue to grow in subsequent years. Shoots completely girdled by the canker can be retrained the following spring.

DISEASE CYCLE

Aspergillus niger thrives in warm weather—28.5° to 34°C (83° to 93°F)—and most infections occur from late April to July. *A. carbonarius* also thrives in warm, dry climates. *A. niger* can infect vigorous shoots that are being trained up the stake to form the trunk and cordons of a new vine. The fungus becomes established in the vascular tissue of the shoot by entering through a wound; the moisture provided by the shoot's sap promotes and stimulates growth. In inoculation experiments, only wounded canes were infected by mycelial plugs or conidia of *A. niger*. Green canes developed larger cankers than did brown, lignified canes. About 60% of natural cankers were found at the crotch of the vine, and these infections occurred when the shoot was topped to form cordons (fig. 11.4). The remaining infections were usually found along the shoots, predominately at nodes but also at internodal sites. These infections entered through wounds caused by removing laterals or leaves or possibly through growth cracks that occur on very rapidly growing shoots. In addition, exuded sap following removal

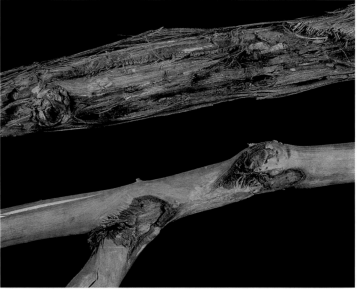

Figure 11.3 Removal of bark by autoclaving (lower vine) reveals the shapes of the cankers. *Photo*: T. J. Michailides.

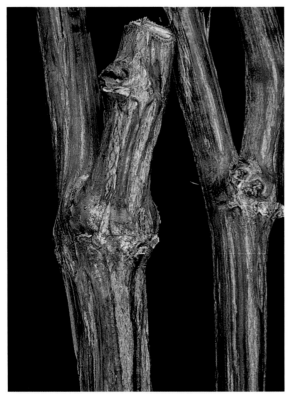

Figure 11.2 Discolored tissue and callous tissue are associated with Aspergillus vine cankers. *Photo*: T. J. Michailides.

of laterals or leaves and growth cracks seems to provide nutrients favoring the germination and growth of the pathogen. In laboratory experiments, media amended with 4% sap (g/vol) resulted in spore germination rates that were at least twice as fast as and conidia production more than 70 times greater than control cultures, suggesting that exuded sap (which is rich in various amino acids) facilitates infection.

MANAGEMENT

The application of fungicides to control Aspergillus vine canker is not practical because of the rarity of the disease. Grow guards may provide favorable environmental conditions for growth of *A. niger*. Therefore, care should be taken to make sure that sufficient ventilation is provided through holes on the guards; when no longer needed, the guards should be removed promptly. The best management approach when Aspergillus vine canker appears in a young vineyard being trained up the stake is to survey the vineyard in November when affected vines are easily distinguished from healthy ones by their display of fall leaf colors (such as leaf reddening in red cultivars). These vines can be cut back below the canker immediately or marked and re-evaluated the following spring. Cutting back in the fall ensures that all cankers have been removed. However, vines with a small canker may heal and develop into a normal healthy vine. Growers can opt to delay cutting back the vines until spring. In April, revisit vines identified as having a canker and determine whether shoot growth is normal. Vines with normal growth should be left alone and those with weak shoot growth cut back below the canker; these vines can be retrained.

REFERENCES

Michailides, T. J., W. Peacock, P. Christensen, and D. P. Morgan. 2007. Aspergillus vine canker of table grapes caused by *Aspergillus* Sect. *Nigri* in California. Phytopathologia Mediterranea 46:103-104.

Michailides, T. J., W. Peacock, P. Christensen, D. P. Morgan, and D. Felts. 2002. First report of Aspergillus vine canker of table grapes caused by *Aspergillus niger*. Plant Disease 86:75.

Figure 11.4 Cankers most commonly occur at the crotch or on the upper trunk of the vine. Note the growth of shoots below the canker (arrow). *Photo*: W. L. Peacock.

12 BLACK FOOT DISEASE

W. Douglas Gubler and Elsa L. Petit

First identified in California in the late 1990s, black foot disease is worsening in all major viticulture regions of California, except in the warmer areas of the San Joaquin Valley. The disease primarily affects young vines up to 8 years old. Black foot causes substantial economic losses due to replanting costs, even though generally small areas of vineyards are affected. Two species of the fungus *Cylindrocarpon* are known to cause the disease: *Cylindrocarpon liriodendri* and *C. destructans*. Both are weak pathogens that are more damaging in soils with high moisture or compaction. Juvenile plants seldom recover from the disease, and diseased plants must be removed.

SYMPTOMS

Above ground, leaves of infected vines appear to be scorched by water stress (fig. 12.1), and the entire vine becomes stunted and frequently dies (fig. 12.2). In cross-section, the xylem at the base of the trunk is necrotic and xylem vessels are plugged with occlusions and tyloses (fig. 12.3). Often there is a general blackening of the internal infected vascular tissue and on occasion a red streaking of the area just above the roots. This does not always occur, but it is thought to be associated with the disease in California and New Zealand. Roots of symptomatic grapevines show black, sunken, necrotic lesions (fig. 12.4). In many instances, black foot can be found in association with the condition known as J rooting (fig. 12.5). This condition is the result of poor planting of the vines in which roots are oriented upward.

Figure 12.1 Black foot disease causes leaf scorch that resembles water stress. *Photo*: E. L. Petit.

Figure 12.2 Reduced growth and leaf chlorosis on a young vine. *Photo*: E. L. Petit.

Figure 12.3 Black tissue at the base of the rootstock (A), and a cross-section of the rootstock showing plugging of the xylem by fungal tissue, gums and tyloses (B). Red coloration above lateral roots often is associated with black foot. *Photos*: L. J. Bettiga.

DISEASE CYCLE

It has been observed that black foot disease occurs primarily in sections of a vineyard that are poorly drained and where soil is compacted. In California, it is most widespread in the north coast, probably because the region has a cool climate.

The disease cycle of *Cylindrocarpon* species on grapevines is not completely known. Nevertheless, *Cylindrocarpon* species are ubiquitous soilborne pathogens that cause root rot on a wide range of hosts. By referring to other diseases that these species cause on other plants, it is assumed that they live in a dormant state in the soil and can attack susceptible plants under certain conditions. There is evidence that this disease also has a connection with nursery production, and occurrence of the pathogen in the nurseries and vineyards most likely plays an important role in the disease. The fungus infects its host through natural openings or wounds on the roots or through the crown of the rootstock. Over time, the fungus invades lignified tissues of the plant, causing root lesions and subsequent plugging of the xylem by fungal tissue, gums, and tyloses. The reduced mineral and water uptake causes plants to die back. When young plants are attacked, they die very rapidly, but as the vines age, infection results in a slower decline in which death may take more than 1 year to occur. Although death appears to be unavoidable if vines are infected when less than 10 years old, 25-year-old vines also were observed succumbing to the disease in the southern San Joaquin Valley. Sticky spores produced by the fungus are spread by water. The production of chlamydospores allows the pathogen to survive in the soil for extended periods of time.

MANAGEMENT

No specific fungicides have been developed against *Cylindrocarpon* species; therefore, host resistance, biological control, and cultural practices are the main means of suppressing the disease. Because the primary source of inoculum is the soil, it is important to find ways to protect the plant belowground. Control can be achieved by planting clean rootstock and by avoiding planting in heavy, poorly drained soils. Drainage in heavy soils can be accomplished by planting on berms and by moving drip irrigation emitters away from the vine.

All phylloxera-resistant rootstock cultivars show differential levels of susceptibility to black foot disease. AXR#1 is not susceptible to the disease.

Recent research has also shown that inoculation of roots with the mycorrhizal fungus *Glomus intraradices* resulted in excellent control of the disease in greenhouse testing.

REFERENCES

Petit, E., and W. D. Gubler. 2005. Characterization of *Cylindrocarpon* species, the cause of black foot disease of grapevine in California. Plant Disease 89:1051–1059.

———. 2006. Influence of *Glomus intraradices* on black foot disease caused by *Cylindrocarpon macrodidymum* on *Vitis rupestris* under controlled conditions. Plant Disease 90:1481–1484.

Scheck, H. J., S. J. Vasquez, and W. D. Gubler. 1998. Grape growers report losses to black foot and grapevine decline. California Agriculture 52:19–23.

Figure 12.4 Dry, cortical, sunken root lesion. *Photo*: E. L. Petit.

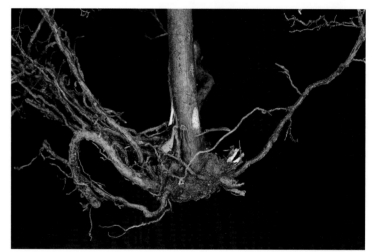

Figure 12.5 J-rooting is often associated with black foot disease. *Photo*: L. J. Bettiga.

13 BUNCH ROTS

Larry J. Bettiga and W. Douglas Gubler

Many species of microorganisms may infect grape berries, including fungi and bacteria. Several species of these fungi, including *Botrytis cinerea, Aspergillus niger, A. carbonarius, Cladosporium cladosporioides, C. herbarum, Penicillium* spp., *Rhizopus arrizhus, and Alternaria* spp., participate in bunch rot of grapes, though the latter four species are not true pathogens but rather secondary colonizers. *Botrytis cinerea* may directly penetrate and infect healthy berries, but the others require wounds or previously infected berries to infect the fruit. Economic losses result from the direct reduction in yield as the rotted fruit is culled and from the increased harvest costs associated with this practice. Table and raisin grape quality and storage potential, as well as wine quality, are all negatively affected by bunch rots. Losses can be extremely high in some years, especially in locations where conditions for *B. cinerea* are extremely favorable. Botrytis bunch rot is the principal fruit rot disease of grapes grown in the production areas of the coast and the northern San Joaquin Valley subject to the marine influence of the San Francisco Bay. In the warmer central and southern San Joaquin Valley, summer bunch rot or sour rot is the more common fruit disease. However, in coastal areas during warm summers it is not uncommon to see sour rot occurring, particularly on Zinfandel but on other cultivars as well.

BOTRYTIS BUNCH ROT

The most important fungal plant pathogen responsible for bunch rot of grape berries is *Botrytis cinerea* (Persoon). This fungus has a wide host range of both native and cultivated plants. On grape it can grow on any plant tissue that is succulent (young leaves and shoots or flower parts), stressed (damaged fruit), ripened fruit, or dead tissue (yellow leaves or senescent flower parts). The enzymes produced by the fungus can destroy the integrity of a grape berry within a few days. Botrytis bunch rot can severely affect tight-clustered, thin-skinned cultivars, especially under heavy canopies or during wet growing seasons. In the production of late-harvest wines, a late-season rot caused by *B. cinerea* is referred to as Noble rot and is highly desirable to produce a concentration of sugars and flavor components under the right environmental conditions for fruit processed into dessert wines.

SYMPTOMS

Foliage

In the spring, *Botrytis* can infect succulent shoots, flowers, or young leaves when prolonged warm, moist conditions caused by frequent rains occur. Patches of soft brown tissue develop, resulting in the death of the infected plant part. Small shoots can be killed by this type of infection, and it can reduce yields due to the loss of flower clusters. Older shoot stems may be girdled at the site of infection and wilt or break off (fig. 13.1). Infection of young expanded leaves can produce areas of brown necrotic tissue (fig. 13.2). In almost all cases, infection occurs in the axils of leaf or inflorescence junctions with the main shoot (figs. 13.3–13.4). The infection results from water pooling in these crotches and remaining for a long duration.

Fruit

Bunch rot often begins when blossoms become infected during rainfall. The pathogen invades the flower parts and becomes dormant until veraison. At veraison, individually infected berries in the cluster turn brown on white cultivars or reddish on red and black cultivars due to enzymes produced by the fungus and subsequent fungal invasion of the pulp (fig. 13.5). This stage is known as slip skin because fungal enzymes break down the cutin in the epidermis and it easily slips off the berry (fig. 13.6). If temperatures are moderate, moisture is high, and wind speed is low, epidermal cracks will form in which fungal growth produces mycelium and spores (fig. 13.7), resulting in the characteristic gray, velvety appearance of infected berries (fig. 13.8). The fungus can then spread

Figure 13.1 Rotting of young tissue characteristic of Botrytis shoot blight. *Photo*: J. K. Clark.

Figure 13.2 Spring *Botrytis* infection on leaf. *Photo*: L. J. Bettiga.

Figure 13.3 *Botrytis* lesion at node of young shoot in spring. *Photo*: J. Hall.

Figure 13.4 *Botrytis*-blighted flower cluster. *Photo*: W. J. Moller.

from berry to berry causing a nested appearance of infected berries. If conditions remain favorable, the disease can result in a high percentage of berries being rotted (fig. 13.9), and if disease is severe enough to reach the rachis, raisining of infected berries can occur (fig. 13.10).

Canes

Poorly matured canes can become infected late in the growing season and show a bleaching of the bark.

Figure 13.5 Infected berries turn a brown color on a white cultivar. *Photo*: L. J. Bettiga.

Figure 13.6 Breakdown of cutin in the epidermis (A) allows the pulp to be easily squeezed out (B). This is often referred to as the slip skin stage. *Photos*: L. J. Bettiga.

Figure 13.7 Clusters of *Botrytis* spores on long stalks (conidiophores) on a berry surface. *Photo*: L. J. Bettiga.

Figure 13.8 Single infected berry and epidermis split on Riesling cluster (A); sporulation on infected berry (B). *Photos*: L. J. Bettiga.

Figure 13.9 Destruction of the central part of a Chardonnay cluster caused by *Botrytis* (A). Desiccation and sporulation late in the growing season (B). *Photos*: L. J. Bettiga.

This whitening and the development of sclerotia can be seen during dormancy (fig. 13.11). Sclerotia are hard, black dormant structures about 3 mm (0.13 in) in diameter.

Disease Cycle

Overwintering

Botrytis survives winter by forming sclerotia either on the surface of or inside colonized plant tissue, including canes, rachises, and berries (fig. 13.12). The two most common sources of sclerotia in vineyards are grape mummy clusters from the previous season and canes that were infected in the fall of the year. After rains or irrigation in spring, the sclerotia germinate

Figure 13.10 Raising caused late in the season from *Botrytis* infection on Riesling. *Photo*: L. J. Bettiga.

Figure 13.11 Lesions and sclerotia on a cane from *Botrytis* infection. *Photo*: L. J. Bettiga.

Figure 13.12 Botrytis bunch rot disease cycle.

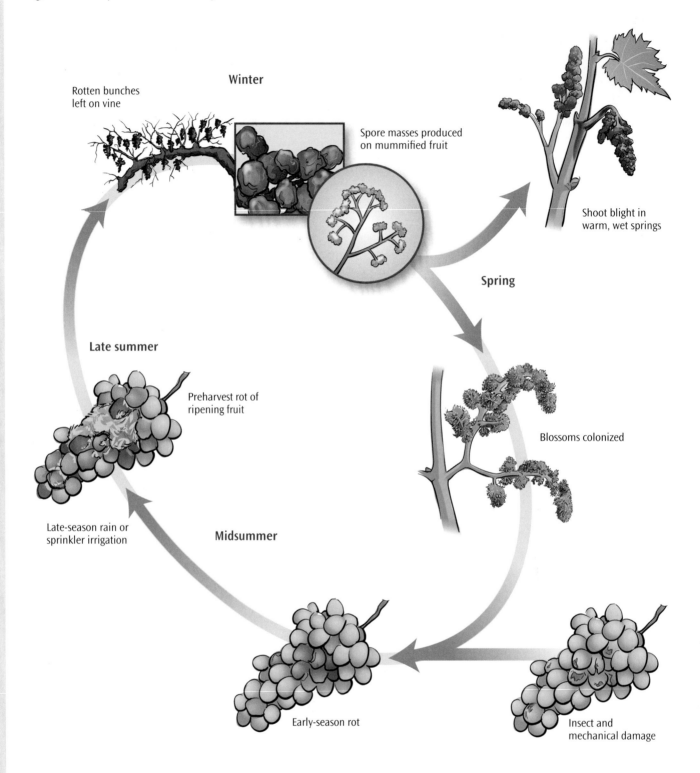

Winter

Rotten bunches
left on vine

Spore masses produced
on mummified fruit

Shoot blight in
warm, wet springs

Spring

Late summer

Preharvest rot of
ripening fruit

Blossoms colonized

Late-season rain or
sprinkler irrigation

Midsummer

Early-season rot

Insect and
mechanical damage

Figure 13.13 Overwintering *Botrytis* on mummies (A); spore production on mummies in early spring (B). *Photos*: J. K. Clark.

Figure 13.14 Strands of fungal tissue develop on berry surfaces. *Photo*: J. K. Clark.

and produce masses of spores (conidia) (fig. 13.13), which are spread by air currents, workers, or rain splashing. The production of spores by *B. cinerea* results in the characteristic gray, fluffy appearance of the fungus on infected tissue (fig. 13.14).

Growing Season

To germinate and grow, spores of *B. cinerea* require continuous free water and nutrients for certain durations of time given certain temperatures. For example, at temperatures of 18° to 24°C (64.5° to 75°F), only 2 hours of free water are needed for germination to occur, while at temperatures lower than 16°C (61°F) and higher than 27°C (80.5°F), more time is needed for germination to occur. The free water can be from dew, fog, irrigation, rain, or juice from damaged berries. Periods as short as 15 minutes with no available water are sufficient to stop germination. However, even with water present, germination also requires nutrients, which can come from many sources, even from the surface of a healthy grape berry. The main nutrient required is a simple sugar, such as fructose or glucose. After veraison, *Botrytis* germination and infection can begin in a cluster where the berries have been damaged. Insects, birds, or mechanical damage can cause juice to be released, providing the spores with the nutrients and free water they need for germination. In coastal areas, this can result in a high incidence of Botrytis bunch rot.

Ambient air temperatures also affect germination. Warmer temperatures usually hasten the drying of the berries and directly reduce germination. Under field conditions, both temperature and duration of free moisture enable the fungus to infect. At and above 32°C (90°F), the fungus does not grow, but it will grow slowly even at 1°C (34°F), which allows it to continue to infect stored table grapes (see section 20, "Postharvest Diseases of Table Grapes").

In early spring under moist conditions, the spores can infect the grape flowers, succulent young stems, or young leaves. During bloom, detached withering floral tissue (calyptras and stamens), aborted ovaries trapped within the developing cluster, and scar tissue on the receptacle (tip of the pedicel) left by the detachment of the calyptras can become infected and become a source of inoculum. These colonized tissues can give rise to spores when wet at any point later in the growing season.

Latent or quiescent berry infections can also occur when the style of the flower becomes infected during bloom. At veraison, as the sugar concentration increases the fungus resumes growth and spreads inside the berry. After veraison, sugar increases and the skins begin to soften; the berries themselves become more susceptible to infection. Rot can spread to adjoining berries in a cluster, or new infections can be initiated by airborne spores. Late-season infections are most severe when relative humidity exceeds 92%, free moisture is present on the fruit surface, and temperatures are in the 15° to 28°C (59° to 82.5°F) range. Research in controlled laboratory studies found a range in the proportion of berries infected when temperatures varied from 12° to 30°C (53.5° to 86°F) and the hours of leaf wetness varied from 4 to 20 hours. As little as 4 hours of surface moisture at optimal temperatures of 22°C (71.5°F) can lead to significant berry infection.

The fungus can penetrate grape berries through wounds; it can directly penetrate undamaged berries after veraison. The berry skin and epicuticular wax (known as bloom) are the main protection from infection by *Botrytis*. Any chemicals or cultural practices that alter these physical and chemical defenses will change the susceptibility of the berry to infection. For example, if fruit are grown in shady canopies with high relative humidity, the cuticle on the berries is generally significantly thinner and less wax is laid down, affording reduced protection from *Botrytis* infection. On the other hand, if fruit are exposed early, they develop a heavier cuticle and epicuticular wax layer and have more protection from infection.

In infected berries, cracks appear in the skin. The spores develop first in the cracks and then spread over the entire berry. The infection of other berries by the rapidly growing fungus and airborne spores contributes to the extremely rapid increase in disease observed after rains late in the season. Under optimal conditions, *Botrytis* can infect a berry, destroy it, and begin to produce spores in only 3 days. After infection, the berry may dry up if high temperatures and low relative humidities prevail. However, the fungus will still be alive and can continue to grow if favorable conditions for growth resume.

Feeding wounds caused by high populations of birds, the tortricid moths orange tortrix (*Argyrotaenia franciscana*) and omnivorous leafroller (*Platynota stultana)*, or other berry-feeding insects can significantly increase the levels of bunch rot caused by *Botrytis* and other secondary fungal and bacterial pathogens. Berry scarring caused by early powdery mildew infections of developing berries can result in cracking during later growth stages, leading to increased levels of bunch rot. Warm, dry weather at harvest can desiccate *Botrytis*-infected berries (fig. 13.15).

MANAGEMENT

Control of Botrytis bunch rot is best achieved through an integrated approach that considers the management options listed below. The manipulation of the fruit zone to reduce humidity and promote cluster drying when preharvest rains occur is a cornerstone of the program. The efficacy of a fungicide, when needed, depends on getting good coverage, and coverage is affected by the canopy density and the stage of growth of the fruit clusters. By employing cultural control methods and properly applying fungicides as needed, the disease can be managed.

Sanitation

Sanitation is an important foundation for all effective disease control. Clusters left on vines or on the vineyard floor from the previous season can be a source of inoculum the following spring. Removing clusters from vines at pruning and placing them into the row middles where they can be incorporated into the soil can reduce inoculum.

Canopy Management

Since *Botrytis* spores have rigid environmental requirements for germination and growth, control can be obtained by creating a canopy microclimate that is less conducive to disease development. The objective is to expose the grape clusters to increased wind speed and light so that they dry out more quickly after a wetting.

Canopy management can be directed to the canopy or to overall growth of the vine. Vineyard design decisions such as rootstock and scion selection, trellis type, training or pruning method, and plant spacing can affect canopy density. Row orientation can influence the fruit microclimatic parameters of wind speed, humidity, and temperature, which can alter the evaporative potential of the canopy and fruit. Careful planning to design a

Figure 13.15 Warm, dry weather at harvest can desiccate *Botrytis*-infected berries. *Photo*: L. J. Bettiga.

vineyard to the anticipated vigor of the site conditions will produce balanced canopies with moderate shoot vigor that optimizes leaf and cluster exposure that is appropriate for the site conditions. Vineyard design decisions generally have long-term effects on vine canopies that are not easily changed for the life of the vineyard. Other growing practices, such as irrigation and nutrition, can be altered annually; these practices can influence canopy density by increasing or decreasing the rate and amount of shoot and lateral growth. In general, the more dense the canopy (that is, the more layers of leaves surrounding the clusters), the more optimal conditions will be for development of Botrytis bunch rot. With careful management, it is often possible to reduce the density of the canopy, which in turn helps alleviate disease pressure.

Shoot thinning, shoot positioning, leaf removal, and hedging can increase air and light penetration to the clusters when canopies are too dense. Shoot thinning is a common practice for table and wine grape production. It can reduce density temporarily; the lateral shoot growth promoted by this practice can often increase canopy density by bloom to a level similar to a nonthinned vine. A light hedging is often used in vineyards in California to maintain an upright pattern of shoot growth that enhances air movement directly to the clusters. However, careful timing is needed to achieve satisfactory results. If hedging is used too early, lateral regrowth often makes the canopy denser than nonhedged vines, and

in some cases these hedged vines have more bunch rot at harvest. Also, severe hedging removes a very large portion of the most photosynthetically active leaf area on the vine. This can result in delays of fruit maturity up to 3 weeks, offsetting any advantages of the open canopy for *Botrytis* control.

Removal of leaves and laterals around the clusters creates a microclimate within the canopy that is less conducive to development of Botrytis bunch rot. In many cases, the level of disease control obtained can equal or exceed the control from fungicide applications. When conducted immediately after fruit set, this practice can also physically shake off some of the floral debris that can be infected with *Botrytis*, reducing this source of inoculum. Leaf removal should be done on the side of the canopy that receives morning sun (east or north side) to reduce fruit damage from sunburn. In warmer areas, do not remove excessive numbers of leaves. If leaves are removed in the period after fruit set to when berries are BB-size, the berries acclimate readily to the sunlight and develop a thick cuticle and epicuticular wax that help prevent sunburn as well as *Botrytis* infection.

The microclimatic conditions in the canopy that most affect development of *Botrytis* are those that affect the duration of free water on the berries. The evaporation rate of water is affected by the temperature, light, vapor pressure deficit, and wind speed of the ambient air. When leaves around the clusters are removed, the wind speed around the clusters

is increased, as are berry surface temperatures. These two factors contribute to drying the clusters after they have become wet.

In an unusually wet year, the benefits of microclimate modifications are reduced because of the impact of the macroclimate, and it may be necessary to increase applications of fungicides. If fungicides are required, however, proper canopy management will continue to be of benefit because more fungicide will be deposited on the more-exposed clusters.

Irrigation

Choosing the right type, timing, or level of irrigation can help control bunch rots. For example, overhead sprinkler irrigations near harvest can increase *Botrytis* levels. If this is the only type of irrigation available, vary the time of day or length of application to speed drying of the clusters. For example, in cool coastal valley vineyards, many growers irrigate at night to take advantage of the warmer, drier daytime conditions that aid drying. The length of time free moisture is on the clusters should not be greater than 15 hours, including the time it takes to dry the clusters completely.

Other types of irrigation should also be used judiciously. High levels of drip or furrow irrigation encourage dense canopy growth and provide moist conditions through increased relative humidity, which is favorable to sporulation. Growers should determine the optimal levels of irrigation at each vineyard site that will result in canopy development that produces desirable yields without excessive shoot or lateral growth.

Reduce Berry Damage

Reducing feeding wounds caused by birds, the tortricid moths orange tortrix (*Argyrotaenia franciscana*) and omnivorous leafroller (*Platynota stultana*), or other berry-feeding insects can significantly reduce Botrytis bunch rots in coastal areas and diseases caused by other secondary fungal and bacterial pathogens that are more common in the warmer interior valleys. Controlling powdery mildew also reduces berry scarring that can result in cracking during later growth stages, leading to increased levels of bunch rot. Careful monitoring and management of these injuries caused by insects and disease are key components in reducing bunch rot infections. Also, avoid any physical damage to the berries during canopy and cluster management operations.

Chemicals

Lime sulfur has long been used for dormant applications on grapevines. Research has shown that applying lime sulfur at 10 gal/ac (93.6 l/ha) in a high volume of water (at least 100 gal/ac, or 936 l/ha) during the dormant or delayed-dormant state reduces overwintering sclerotia of *Botrytis cinerea* by 70 to 75%. Lime sulfur kills the sclerotia and significantly reduces inoculum, generally making it a good cleanup product.

Several fungicide classes are available for in-season control of Botrytis bunch rot. Alternating fungicides that have different modes of action is essential to prevent pathogen populations from developing resistance. Fungicides with a single-site mode of action are more prone to selecting resistant

fungus biotypes. Resistance of *B. cinerea* to benzimidazole (benomyl) fungicide has been observed in California vineyards. Refer to the UC IPM Grape Pest Management Guidelines, www.ipm.ucdavis.edu/PMG/, for the most current information on registered fungicides for Botrytis bunch rot control.

Spray programs may consist of sprays at bloom or multiple applications at bloom, cluster pre-close, veraison, and preharvest. The frequency should depend on the history of Botrytis bunch rot in a particular vineyard, cultivar susceptibility, and the seasonal variation in environmental conditions that are conducive to infection.

Studies to determine the optimal timing of a single application have yielded variable results. A single application at bloom has rarely proved to be significantly more effective than a single application at any other time during the season, the exception being at vineyard sites where there was rain during bloom. At these sites, bloomtime fungicide applications were slightly more effective than at other times. Data collected over many years have shown a direct relationship between the number of fungicide applications and the level of Botrytis bunch rot control when conditions during bloom and after veraison are conducive for infection.

Timing sprays according to the plant's growth stage is usually not effective; a better method is to apply sprays only when environmental conditions conducive to the growth of the fungus have been forecasted. Fungicide applications before rain are more effective

in reducing *Botrytis* infections than those applied after rain. Information on the amount of berry infection resulting from the interaction of temperature and hours of free moisture has been incorporated into commercial software and weather stations, and these can be used to assist in timing applications of fungicides against *Botrytis*. Real-time or forecasted data can be used to run the *Botrytis* infection risk model. Generally, the fungicides currently available do not have very long "kick back" activity and must be applied prior to or as soon as possible after a medium- or high-risk event is forecasted.

To obtain optimal coverage with pesticides, spray adjuvants (most commonly surfactants) are often added to the tank mix. The purpose of these surfactants is to reduce the surface tension of the water droplets, allowing better dispersion over the plant's surface. The nonwettability of a plant part is due mainly to the layer of wax on its surface; some adjuvants actually alter the structure of plant waxes. Although specific situations may call for using spray adjuvants, one must consider that most chemicals already contain them in their formulation, and that adding more adjuvants can be justified only by data that positively demonstrate a significant increase in efficacy against *Botrytis* in grape.

Plant Resistance

Several factors are involved in a grape berry's resistance to infection by *B. cinerea*. Many red cultivars contain compounds that inhibit the fungus. Also, the berry skin provides a mechanical barrier to infection, as does the epicuticular wax on the surface of the berry. Wax formation is inhibited when berries grow in contact with other berries or when the environment is shady and relative humidity is high. These contact areas have been shown to be more susceptible to infection by *B. cinerea*. In general, tight, thin-skinned white grape berries are the most susceptible to Botrytis bunch rot. However, the thin-skinned red cultivar Zinfandel is also highly susceptible. Although it is unlikely that grape cultivars will ever be developed solely for resistance to *Botrytis*, a wide range of resistance is already available. See table 13.1 on the relative susceptibility of major grape cultivars in the western United States.

Research has shown that cluster architecture or tightness may be more important in affecting how much disease develops than the susceptibility of individual berries. Cabernet Sauvignon berries are as susceptible to infection as Zinfandel berries; it is the difference in cluster tightness that influences the microclimate within a Zinfandel cluster that increases *Botrytis* infection susceptibility.

Compact clusters often retain more *Botrytis*-infected senescent flower parts, and when wetted, the clusters dry more slowly, resulting in a more favorable microclimate for disease infection and spread. Excessively compact clusters also have more physical damage or cracking as berries expand against each other. Clonal evaluation research has shown that selections of Chardonnay and Pinot noir with looser clusters generally have lower levels of bunch rot.

SUMMER BUNCH ROT COMPLEX, SOUR ROT

Ripening berries are susceptible to invasion by many microorganisms that frequently enter through injuries such as insect or bird feeding sites, mechanical cracks, or lesions caused by powdery mildew or esca. These organisms can cause extensive damage because their resulting rot may progress well beyond the original injury. Dark-spored fungi including *Aspergillus niger, A. carbonarius, Alternaria tenuis, Cladosporium cladosporioides, C. herbarum, Rhizopus arrizhus,* and *Penicillium* species are common,

and one or more of them are usually involved in the summer bunch rot complex (fig. 13.16). However, it is the *Aspergillus* species that have been shown to be the first colonizers of wounded berries in the San Joaquin Valley. *Botrytis cinerea*, the same organism that causes Botrytis bunch rot, also frequently colonizes berries after they have been injured. The summer bunch rot complex is the more prevalent fruit rot in the warmer central and southern San Joaquin Valley, while *Botrytis* is the more common cause of bunch rots in the northern San Joaquin Valley and coastal production areas. Sour rot is a further development of the summer bunch rot complex, when yeasts and bacteria colonize the rot.

Symptoms

Rot associated with secondary invaders can be recognized by masses of black, brown, or green spores on the surface of the berries (fig. 13.17), leakage of berry juices, and the presence of vinegar flies (*Drosophila* spp.) and dried fruit beetles (*Carpophilus* spp.). A complex of many of the fungi mentioned above along with yeasts

Table 13.1. Relative susceptibility to bunch rot of major grape cultivars in the western United States

Very susceptible	Susceptible	Moderately resistant	Highly resistant
Carignane	Barbera	Autumn Royal	Cabernet Sauvignon
Chardonnay	Calmeria	Colombard	Merlot
Chenin blanc	Flame Seedless	Crimson Seedless	Muscat of Alexandria
Melon	Grenache	Emperor	Rubired
Petite Sirah	Pinot noir	Semillon	Ruby Cabernet
Ruby Seedless	Sauvignon blanc	Sylvaner	
White Riesling	Redglobe	Thompson Seedless	
Zinfandel	Ribier		

and bacteria causes sour rot (fig. 13.18). The pungent vinegar odor associated with sour rot comes from acetic acid produced by *Acetobacter*. The bacteria are carried to rotting clusters by vinegar flies or driedfruit beetles that are attracted to these clusters. By the time sour rot has developed, it is often difficult to determine the primary cause.

DISEASE CYCLE

Many of the fungi are opportunists, able to colonize only wounded berries, while others are able to initiate primary infections. Recent research has shown that both *A. niger* and *A. carbonarius* enter wounded berries and can lead to sour rot. *Aspergillus* infects only after veraison. Once the fungus enters the tissue, a rapid decay of the berry pulp occurs, and this is usually followed by insect visitations and colonization by other fungi and yeasts. These secondary invaders and sour rot organisms are present on most plant surfaces and on debris in the soil. They can be distributed by wind, rain, or insects and are able to begin the rot process almost as soon as the berries become wounded.

Susceptibility of grapes to secondary invasion increases as berries mature and develop sugar; berries with less than 8% sugar are relatively resistant, and their wounds often heal without rot development. In tight-clustered cultivars, berry-to-berry contact and growth pressure may cause cracks and promote berry leakage and rot. Insect damage, especially by the tortricid moths omnivorous leafroller and orange tortrix, along with bird feeding, also cause wounds that fungi can colonize.

MANAGEMENT

Chemical treatments are generally ineffective in preventing infection of wounds by most of the summer bunch rot complex organisms. Control strategies, therefore, must be related to the cause of the wounds. Often, controlling damage caused by birds, insects, and early-season powdery mildew infections can reduce the rot complex. Canopy management practices as discussed for Botrytis bunch rot management has also been shown to reduce the incidence of the summer bunch rot complex.

Figure 13.16 Rotting cluster with *Botrytis* and *Penicillium* present. *Photo*: J. K. Clark.

Figure 13.17 White and green spore masses produced by *Penicillium* and gray spores in upper left by *Botrytis*. *Photo*: J. K. Clark.

Figure 13.18 *Botrytis* and *Penicillium* bunch rot complex. *Photo*: J. K. Clark.

References

Barbe, G. D., and W. B. Hewitt. 1965. The principal fungus in the summer bunch rot of grapes. Phytopathology 55:815–816.

Bettiga, L. J., W. D. Gubler, J. J. Marois, and A. M. Bledsoe. 1989. Integrated control of Botrytis bunch rot of grape. California Agriculture 43(2): 9–11.

Broome, J. C., J. T. English, J. J. Marois, B. A. Latorre, and J. C. Aviles. 1995. Development of an infection model for Botrytis bunch rot of grapes based on wetness duration and temperature. Phytopathology 85:97–102.

Coley-Smith, J. R., K. Verhoeff, and W. R. Jarvis, eds. 1980. The biology of Botrytis. New York: Academic Press.

Duncan, R. A., J. J. Stapleton, and G. M. Leavitt. 1995. Population dynamics of epiphytic mycoflora and occurrence of bunch rots of wine grapes as influenced by leaf removal. Plant Pathology 44:956–965.

English, J. T., C. S. Thomas, J. J. Marois, and W. D. Gubler. 1989. Microclimates of grapevine canopies associated with leaf removal and control of Botrytis bunch rot. Phytopathology 79:395–401.

Gubler, W. D., J. J. Marois, A. M. Bledsoe, and L. J. Bettiga. 1987. Control of Botrytis bunch rot of grape with canopy management. Plant Disease 71:599–601.

Hewitt, W. B. 1974. Rots and bunch rots of grapes. California Agricultural Experiment Station Bulletin 868.

Marois, J. J., A. M. Bledsoe, R. M. Bostock, and W. D. Gubler. 1987. Effect of spray adjuvants on the development of *Botrytis cinerea* on grape berries. Phytopathology 77:1148–1152.

McClellan, W. D., and W. B. Hewitt. 1973. Time of infection and latency of *Botrytis cinerea* Pers. in *Vitis vinifera* L. Phytopathology 63:1151–1157.

Thomas, C. S., J. J. Marois, and J. T. English. 1988. The effects of wind speed, temperature, and relative humidity on development of aerial mycelium and conidia of *Botrytis cinerea* on grape. Phytopathology 77:260–265.

Vail, M. E., and J. J. Marois 1991. Grape cluster architecture and the susceptibility of berries to *Botrytis cinerea.* Phytopathology 81(2): 188–191.

Vail, M. E., J. A. Wolpert, W. D. Gubler, and M. R. Rademacher. 1998. Effect of cluster tightness on Botrytis bunch rot in six Chardonnay clones. Plant Disease 82(1): 107–109.

14 BOTRYOSPHAERIA DIEBACK

José R. Úrbez-Torres, W. Douglas Gubler, and George M. Leavitt

Botryosphaeriaceae Theiss. & P. Syd. 1918 is a species-rich family that includes plant endophytes, saprophytes, and parasites occurring worldwide under varied ecological niches on a vast number of annual and perennial hosts. Several Botryosphaeriaceae species are well-known pathogens causing cankers, dieback, leaf spots, fruit rot, and eventual death on many economically important woody perennial crops. However, their importance in grapevines has been largely overlooked. For many years, species of Botryosphaeriaceae were mainly considered to be saprophytes, secondary colonizers, or weak parasites of grapevines. In addition, field diagnosis of grapevine symptoms caused by Botryosphaeriaceae has also remained unnoticed because of their similarity to those caused by other grapevine trunk disease pathogens such as *Eutypa lata* and *Phomopsis viticola*, the causal agents of Eutypa dieback and Phomopsis cane and leaf spot, respectively. Although species of Botryosphaeriaceae have been reported to cause grapevine dieback since the mid-1960s, it has been only in the last decade that the significance of these fungi as grapevine pathogens has been recognized. Currently, 21 Botryosphaeriaceae species in the genera *Botryosphaeria*, *Diplodia*, *Dothiorella*, *Guignardia*, *Lasiodiplodia*, *Neofusicoccum*, *Phaeobotryosphaeria*, and *Spencermartinsia* have been isolated from grapevine dieback symptoms, including perennial cankers, dark streaking of the wood, light brown discoloration of the xylem, wood necrosis, graft failure, cane bleaching, bud mortality, and fruit rot in grape-growing regions of the Northern and Southern Hemispheres.

Botryosphaeria dieback of grapevines was first reported in vineyards of southern San Joaquin and Coachella Valleys in California in 1987. The disease was then associated with the botryosphaeriaceous fungus *Lasiodiplodia theobromae*. In the early 1990s, disease incidence in the southern California region of Coachella Valley was reported to be as great as 100% in vineyards 10 years old and older, with several cankers per vine. Since then, this disease has been known to be prevalent in the hot and dry areas of southern California, Arizona, and Mexico, where the disease has been recognized by growers as Bot canker. Although perennial cankers caused by Botryosphaeriaceae species are more prevalent in mature grapevines, they have also been observed in vineyards 5 years old and younger. Currently known to occur throughout all grape-growing areas in California, Botryosphaeriaceae species have been shown to be the most prevalent fungi isolated from cankers in the state. Furthermore, Botryosphaeria dieback has recently been confirmed to occur in vineyards in Arkansas,

Maryland, Missouri, New York, Oregon, Pennsylvania, Texas, and Virginia in the United States, as well as in grape-growing areas of Australia, Chile, New Zealand, Portugal, South Africa, and Spain. Further studies on the taxonomy of Botryosphaeriaceae along with the recent implementation of DNA-based diagnostic techniques have allowed the identification of Botryosphaeriaceae species other than *L. theobromae* to be involved in Botryosphaeria dieback, including *Botryosphaeria dothidea, Diplodia corticola, Diplodia mutila, Diplodia seriata, Dothiorella iberica, Dothiorella americana, Lasiodiplodia crassispora, Lasiodiplodia missouriana, Lasiodiplodia viticola, Neofusicoccum australe, Neofusicoccum luteum, Neofusicoccum mediterraneum, Neofusicoccum parvum, Neofusicoccum ribis, Neofusicoccum viticlavatum, Neofusicoccum vitifusiforme,* and *Spencermartinsia viticola.* Among

these, pathogenicity studies have revealed fungal species in the anamorphic genera *Lasiodiplodia* and *Neofusicoccum* to be the most virulent. Species in the genera *Botryosphaeria* and *Diplodia* are less virulent but are still able to infect grapevines and cause necrotic vascular symptoms. Species of *Dothiorella* and *Spencermartinsia* are the least virulent and may be considered weak pathogens on grapevines.

Botryosphaeria dieback decreases the life of a vineyard, reduces yields, and increases production costs when management practices are implemented to reduce disease impact. The importance of this disease has been reflected in a study in which the overall loss for the California wine industry due to perennial cankers caused by both Botryosphaeriaceae species and *Eutypa lata* was estimated to be over $260 million per year (Siebert 2001).

SYMPTOMS

Although wedged or pie-shaped perennial cankers in spurs, cordons, and trunks are the most characteristic symptom associated with Botryosphaeria dieback, other symptoms such as dark streaking of the wood, light brown discoloration of the xylem, and bud mortality can also be observed on Botryosphaeriaceae-infected vines. Perennial cankers caused by Botryosphaeriaceae species are indistinguishable from cankers caused by *E. lata,* and thus visual field diagnosis is difficult. However, grapevines affected by Botryosphaeria dieback fail to manifest the distinctive foliar symptoms caused by *E. lata* (small cupped and chlorotic leaves, short internodes, and stunted chlorotic spring growth) during the years following infection. Grapevines infected with Botryosphaeria dieback, on the other hand, show either a total absence of spring growth or normal and healthy development of shoots (fig. 14.1). Lack of spring growth in one or more spur positions and normal healthy growth in others can often be observed in the same cordon of the vine (fig. 14.2). Another distinguishing characteristic of infected grapevines is the formation of black, ostiolate, spheric, erumpent pycnidia (asexual fruiting bodies) on the surface of cankers 1 to 4 years after the death of the wood, instead of the typical stroma containing the perithecia (sexual fruiting bodies) of *E. lata* (fig. 14.3). Pycnidia of botryosphaeriaceous fungi such as *L. theobromae* and *D. seriata* can be seen on infected canes. Grapevine cankers caused by Botryosphaeriaceae species start developing primarily from pruning

Figure 14.1 A common symptom associated with Botryosphaeria dieback is the lack of development of new shoots from infected spurs. *Photo*: J. R. Úrbez-Torres.

Figure 14.2 Lack of spring growth in one or more spur positions and normal healthy growth in others can often be observed in the same cordon of the vine (A, B). *Photos*: J. R. Úrbez-Torres (A); G. M. Leavitt (B).

Figure 14.3 Botryosphaeriaceae species fruiting bodies can be found on the surface of flat or sunken cankered wood on spur positions, cordons, and trunk. *Photo*: G. M. Leavitt.

Figure 14.4 Old, infected pruning wounds, where fruiting bodies (pycnidia) of Botryosphaeriaceae species can be found, are the main source of inoculum for new infections (A, B). *Photos*: J. R. Úrbez-Torres (A); G. M. Leavitt (B).

wounds, which are the main points of infection. However, cankers can also develop from mechanical injuries or natural openings on the framework of the vine as well as from large cuts left after retraining vines (fig. 14.4). Cankers that begin in pruning wounds exhibit faster growth basipetaly from the point of infection. Vascular streaking and wedge-shaped cankers are the typical symptoms in the earliest stages of the disease (fig. 14.5). Cankers are perennial and also grow in a lateral direction in the wood of the vine until only a small wedge is left alive (fig. 14.6). Botryosphaeria dieback mainly affects

spurs, cordons, and trunks, causing eventual death of those parts or the entire grapevine when the fungus kills the remaining live wedge. Vascular symptoms are not commonly found below the graft union; however, recent studies have confirmed the isolation of *L. theobromae* and *N. parvum* from cankers in the rootstock that appear to start developing from cracks in the graft union area (fig. 14.7). Additionally, reports have associated both *L. theobromae* and *D. mutila* with root necrosis, but these symptoms have been rarely associated with Botryosphaeriaceae species in California grapevines.

DISEASE CYCLE

Botryosphaeriaceae species such as *B. dothidea*, *L. theobromae*, and *D. seriata* have been reported to occur in over 500 different hosts, including perennial fruit and nut trees, native plants and trees, vegetable crops, as well as ornamental plants. The wide host range of this family potentially provides an excellent source of further inoculum in the vineyard due to the numerous fruiting bodies produced on those hosts. Because the sexual stage of the different Botryosphaeriaceae species associated with cankers in California has rarely been found on grapevines, it is thought that

Figure 14.5 A wedge-shaped canker is the typical vascular symptom of Botryosphaeria canker. *Photo*: G. M. Leavitt.

Figure 14.6 Perennial cankers caused by Botryosphaeriaceae grow in a lateral direction in the spurs, cordons, and trunk for several years. Death of the vine parts occurs when the remaining alive tissue is killed by the growth of the canker. *Photo*: J. R. Úrbez-Torres.

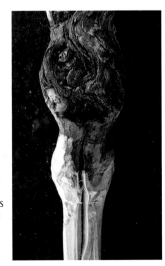

Figure 14.7 Species of Botryosphaeriaceae can infect grapevines through wounds or cracks in the graft union area and cause perennial cankers in the rootstock. *Photo*: J. R. Úrbez-Torres.

conidia may be the principal source of infection in California. Conidia (fig. 14.8) are released from pycnidia (figs. 14.9–14.10), then colonize pruning wounds. Botryosphaeriaceae species overwinter as pycnidia in diseased woody parts of the plant and in wood debris left in the vineyard after pruning. Recent findings have also shown the presence of Botryosphaeriaceae fruiting bodies on native plants and trees around vineyards and in riparian areas throughout California. In California, spore discharge of Botryosphaeriaceae species has been shown to occur from the first fall rain through the last spring rain, coinciding with September to April. However, most spores (over 60%) are released after rain events during December, January, and February, which coincides with the main dormant pruning season. Spore release is much lower in fall and early spring, and very few or no spores are present in late spring and summer in the vineyard. The correlation between rainfall and spore release has been observed to be very consistent throughout California. Spores of Botryosphaeriaceae were captured during and after rain events. Conidia exude from pycnidia and disseminate in splashing rain. In the hot, dry grapevine regions of southern California such as Coachella Valley characterized by the absence of rain during most of the year, spores of *L. theobromae* were shown to be released during and after overhead sprinkler irrigation.

Spores land on pruning wounds and germinate if environmental conditions (relative humidity and temperature) are appropriate for colonizing the wood, thus initiating infection. Conidia of botryosphaeriaceous species infecting grapevines are capable of germinating under a broad range of temperatures, including those considered to be extreme, which may explain the success of these species as grapevine pathogens. Conidia of *B. dothidea* and *N. parvum* are able to germinate at temperatures as low as 5°C (41°F), and these species are thus more prevalent in vineyards in colder climates such as northern California. The optimal temperature for *L. theobromae* was found to be 35° to 40°C (95° to 104°F). Moreover, *L. theobromae* conidia did not germinate well at temperatures below 20°C (68°F). *Lasiodiplodia theobromae* is rarely isolated from cold regions, and it is not only the most prevalent but occasionally the only fungus isolated from diseased vines in the warmest grapevine-growing regions of California, Mexico, and Australia. Thus, it is reasonable to speculate that geographical distribution of Botryosphaeriaceae species is strongly associated with climatic conditions, especially temperature.

Studies conducted in California have shown susceptibility of grapevine pruning wounds to infection by botryosphaeriaceous fungi to be highest immediately after

Figure 14.8 Characteristic conidia of *L. theobromae*. Conidia are exuded from pycnidia and disseminated by wind or in splashed droplets during rain or sprinkler irrigation. *Photo*: J. R. Úrbez-Torres.

Figure 14.9 Pycnidia of *L. theobromae* embedded in the bark of a cordon. *Photo*: J. R. Úrbez-Torres.

Figure 14.10 Top view of a *L. theobromae* pycnidium, showing the opening (ostiole) from where conidia are released. *Photo*: J. R. Úrbez-Torres.

pruning and to decrease significantly as the interval between pruning and infection increases. In California, susceptibility of pruning wounds is highest after pruning in December through January and lowest in late February to early March. Grapevine pruning wounds can be susceptible for up to 12 weeks after pruning in November and December; however, infection rates can decrease from 100% in the first week to as low as 5% 84 days after pruning. In addition, these studies have shown that the susceptibility of pruning wounds does not differ between 1- and 2-year-old wood. Grapevine cankers caused by species in the genera *Lasiodiplodia* or *Neofusicoccum* have been shown to develop rapidly, colonizing the wood up to three times faster than cankers caused by *E. lata*. Buds on cordons and spur positions are often killed due to the rapid growth of the pathogen; thus, there is no shoot development on infected spur positions while other parts of the vine show normal and healthy growth. In California, infections normally originate during winter and

may be observed during the first growing season, depending on the species involved. The characteristic wedge-shaped canker can generally be observed 2 years after infection. However, symptoms can appear earlier if the plants are under high stress or if young wood is infected. Additionally, Botryosphaeriaceae species are known to be able to infect grapevines during the propagation process in nurseries and have been frequently isolated from the graft union in young planting material.

MANAGEMENT

In California, both Botryosphaeriaceae spore release and pruning wound susceptibility are highest during rainfall from November to February. Consequently, pruning grapes in dry weather appears to be critical for reducing the maximum risk of infection. It also reduces airborne inoculum and enhances mechanisms that reduce the susceptibility of pruning wounds, such as the increase in the speed of pruning wound healing. Therefore, the most recommended cultural practice to reduce

the risk of infection by these fungi in California is pruning in late February to early March, or as close as possible to budbreak. This cultural management is feasible for growers with small vineyards. However, it allows a short window of time for pruning, which may not be feasible for growers with large vineyards. Late pruning in large vineyards can be accomplished by double pruning, which involves two pruning passes through the vineyard, the first using a mechanical pruner and the second by hand. Double pruning has been shown to be an effective strategy to reduce infections caused not only by *E. lata* but also by botryosphaeriaceous fungi under California weather conditions.

Alternative control techniques such as pruning wound protectants have also been evaluated. Although pruning wound protectants have been shown to reduce infection by Botryosphaeriaceae species, they do not completely prevent the disease. Significant research has been conducted to develop both chemical and biological products to be applied with a paste on pruning wounds. It is still not clear how long the pruning wounds can be protected by these treatments, and more than one application may be necessary throughout the dormant season. Therefore, pruning wound protection through spray programs has been developed to reduce costs and make the treatment of large-acreage vineyards possible in a shorter period of time. Spray applications can be rapidly made after pruning late in the season, providing an extra protection period if the risk of infection occurs. Consult the UC IPM Grape Pest Management Guidelines, www.ipm.ucdavis.edu/PMG/, for fungicides registered for wound protection against Botryosphaeriaceae infections. Although both chemical and biological control against Botryosphaeria dieback has been demonstrated, an extensive sanitation of the vineyard should be practiced to keep the inoculum level as low as possible. This is accomplished by pruning out all diseased wood, removing it from the vineyard, and destroying it by burning or burying. Because numerous fruiting bodies (pycnidia) can be found on pruning debris left in the vineyard, total destruction is essential in order to reduce the source of inoculum and avoid new infections. Additionally, in order to reduce the chance of Botryosphaeriaceae entering the plant, it is important to avoid unnecessary wounding of grapevines, as the larger the wound the greater the chance of infection.

As the cankers move through and kill portions of the plant, strong suckers often grow from the lower area of the trunk, allowing for retraining. Cutting the trunk at least 4 to 5 inches below the visible canker and retraining the vine from this shoot can achieve control. If the vines are own-rooted, the suckers that come from below the ground are best for retraining. Retraining of cordons is also effective to replace sections killed by the disease. If retraining is not possible, the vine should be removed. In the United States both *Vitis vinifera* and interspecific hybrid cultivars are susceptible to Botryosphaeria canker. To date, no Botryosphaeriaceae-resistant cultivars are available.

REFERENCES

Gramaje, D., and J. Armengol. 2011. Fungal trunk pathogens in the grapevine propagation process: Potential inoculum sources, detection, identification, and management strategies. Plant Disease 95:1040–1055.

Phillips, A. J. L. 2002. *Botryosphaeria* species associated with diseases of grapevines in Portugal. Phytopathologia Mediterranea 41:3–18.

Pitt, W. M., R. Huang, Y. Qiu, C. C. Steel, and S. Savocchia. 2012. Evaluation of fungicides for the management of Botryosphaeria canker of grapevines. Plant Disease 96:1303–1308.

Pitt, W. M., R. Huang, C. C. Steel, and S. Savochia. 2010. Identification, distribution, and current taxonomy of Botryosphaeriaceae species associated with grapevine decline in New South Wales and South Australia. Australian Journal of Grape and Wine Research 16:258–271.

Rolshausen, P. E., J. R. Úrbez-Torres, S. Rooney-Latham, A. Eskalen, R. J. Smith, and W. D. Gubler. 2010. Evaluation of pruning wound susceptibility and protection against fungi associated with grapevine trunk diseases in California. American Journal of Enology and Viticulture 61:113–19.

Siebert, J. B. 2001. *Eutypa:* The economic toll on vineyards. Wines & Vines (April): 50–56.

Úrbez-Torres, J. R. 2011. The status of Botryosphaeriaceae species infecting grapevines. Phytopathologia Mediterranea 50:S5–S45.

Úrbez-Torres, J. R., and W. D. Gubler. 2009. Pathogenicity of Botryosphaeriaceae species isolated from grapevine cankers in California. Plant Disease 93:584–592.

———. 2011. Susceptibility of grapevine pruning wounds to infection by *Lasiodiplodia theobromae* and *Neofusicoccum parvum*. Plant Pathology 60:261–270.

Úrbez-Torres, J. R., M. Battany, L. J. Bettiga, C. Gispert, G. McGourty, J. Roncoroni, R. J. Smith, P. Verdegaal, and W. D. Gubler. 2010. Botryosphaeriaceae spore trapping studies in California vineyards. Plant Disease 94:717–724.

Úrbez-Torres, J. R., E. Bruez, J. Hurtado, and W. D. Gubler. 2010. Effect of temperature on conidial germination of Botryosphaeriaceae species infecting grapevines. Plant Disease 94:1476–1484.

Úrbez-Torres, J. R., G. M. Leavitt, T. Voegel, and W. D. Gubler. 2006. Identification and distribution of *Botryosphaeria* species associated with grapevines cankers in California. Plant Disease 90:1490–1503.

15 EUTYPA DIEBACK

W. Douglas Gubler, Philippe Rolshausen, and Florent Trouillas

Eutypa dieback, one of the most common canker diseases of grapevines in California, is caused by the fungal pathogens *Eutypa lata* (Pers.:Fr.) Tul. & C. Tul. (= *E. armeniace* Hansf. & M.V. Carter) and *E. leptoplaca* Rappaz. *Eutypa lata* has been known to be a pathogen for many years, while *E. leptoplaca* was only recently shown to be a pathogen of grapevine in the north coast production area in California.

The first association between vine dieback symptoms and *E. lata* (long known as a pathogen of apricot trees) was made in 1957 in Australia, where the disease was called dying arm. University of California researchers subsequently confirmed the pathogenicity of *E. lata* on grapevines, and reports indicated a distribution of the disease in all grape-growing regions worldwide.

Eutypa dieback is progressive over many years. Economic losses may be minor in early years, but the most damaging effects are observed on older vines. Failure to control the disease leads to severe economic losses, primarily as a consequence of decreased yields and berry quality, increased vineyard management costs, and reduced longevity of the grapevines. Surveys in California in 1999 estimated the loss of net income to grape growers in California at $260 million per annum.

In California, the disease is ubiquitous but is most prevalent in the northern counties (San Joaquin, Napa, Sonoma, and Yolo). A lower incidence of *E. lata* was noted in the southern counties of the state, and the pathogen was not recovered from Riverside County in vineyards located in desert areas. In these areas, other fungal pathogens are the primary cause of canker diseases.

Vitis vinifera is susceptible to the disease, but variability in susceptibility was observed among cultivars. The most-susceptible cultivars include Cabernet Sauvignon, Grenache, Sauvignon blanc, Ugni blanc, Alicante Bouschet, Chardonnay, Chenin blanc, Gewürztraminer, Pinot noir, Pinot Meunier, Syrah, and Tannat, and the most-tolerant cultivars include Cabernet franc, Colombard, Gamay, Malbec, Riesling, Merlot, and Semillon. In the cooler grape-growing regions of New York, Washington, Michigan, and Ontario, several cultivars of *V. labrusca*, notably Concord, and a number of French-American hybrids are also known to be susceptible.

Eutypa lata has a broad host range and can infect over 80 plant species worldwide. In California, especially in higher-rainfall areas, ascospore inoculum can come from within vineyards and also from infected orchard trees or forest and riparian trees in the vicinity of vineyards. These pathogens require wind-driven rain to disperse the ascospores to 4- to 6-week-old pruning wounds, where infection takes place. Aside from grapes, important hosts of the disease in California include apricot, cherry, almond, pear, apple, crabapple, willow, big leaf maple, oleander, California buckeye, *Ceanothus*, blueberry, and kiwifruit.

SYMPTOMS

A characteristic diagnostic symptom of Eutypa dieback is the development of stunted spring foliage. The leaf and shoot symptoms of the disease are best seen in spring, when normal shoots are 25 to 38 cm (10 to 15 in) long, just ahead of rapid shoot growth. Affected vines, distributed at random throughout the vineyard, show individual weak, stunted shoots with shortened internodes (fig. 15.1). Symptomatic shoots contrast strikingly alongside healthy shoots. At first, leaves on affected shoots are small, chlorotic, and misshapen, and sometimes they appear cupped and marginally necrotic with small areas of dead interveinal tissue; later in the season, they take on a tattered, scorched appearance (fig. 15.2). Many of the flowers fall off; most berries that do establish on these shoots fail to mature. If the shoots are only mildly affected, the tattered leaves appear on just the first few nodes, and subsequent growth is normal.

Another recognizable symptom is the formation of pruning wound cankers (fig. 15.3). These dead areas occur in the water-conducting tissue and in the area of medium to large old pruning wounds, the outline of which often can only be found by removing the rough outer bark (fig. 15.4). Cankers are frequently located adjacent to the affected spurs showing foliar symptoms. In advanced cases, the wood around an unhealed wound assumes a ridged and flattened appearance so that the trunk or cordon may be twisted and malformed. Older cankers show a marginal zonation, indicating successive annual attempts of the vine to overgrow the necrotic area. Trunk cankers can be extensive in length, and a cross-section through the canker often reveals only a narrow strip of live wood. In its early stages, a canker in cross-section appears

Figure 15.1 One cordon of this Chenin blanc vine severely affected with Eutypa dieback exhibits typically weak, stunted shoots with shortened internodes. *Photo*: J. K. Clark.

Figure 15.2 Leaves affected by Eutypa dieback take on a tattered, scorched, and often misshapen appearance; axillary shoots die, and many flowers shell off. *Photo*: W. J. Moller.

Figure 15.3 Large pruning wound canker on trunk is exposed by removing bark. *Photo*: W. J. Moller.

Figure 15.4 Incipient Eutypa dieback canker adjacent to pruning wound is revealed by removing bark tissue with a knife. *Photo*: W. J. Moller.

as a wedge-shaped darkened area coming to a point in the center of the cordon or trunk (fig. 15.5). However, these wood cankers are not specific to Eutypa dieback, as Botryosphaeriaceae species (Botryosphaeria dieback) are known to cause the same symptom. It is common to find streaks or flecks of darkened tissue in the live wood below the canker. These flecks may or may not be caused by *E. lata*.

The disease appears first in one or two spurs and spreads in the following seasons to adjacent spurs, eventually killing the arm or cordon (fig. 15.6). Shoots developing from below the affected arm are healthy the first year but may show symptoms in subsequent seasons. Unless a major portion of the vine's structural framework is involved, the affected shoots eventually may be covered by normal overgrowth from the vine's healthy portion. It is common to find several spurs on one side of the vine dead, while the spurs on the other side appear healthy. When the cordons or the trunk of a vine have been killed or severely affected by Eutypa dieback, strong suckers can develop from the still-healthy lower portion of the trunk or the root system of own-rooted vines.

DISEASE CYCLE

Eutypa lata and *E. leptoplaca* infection invariably occurs through pruning wounds (fig. 15.7). Several growing seasons may elapse before visible cankers develop around an infected wound or before stunted shoot symptoms appear (fig. 15.8). Once an arm or portion of the vine has been killed, it takes several more years before perithecia (fruiting bodies bearing ascospores) are produced on the old infected host tissue (figs. 15.9–15.10), and then only under conditions of high moisture, that is, greater than 40 cm (16 in) per year. A blackened crust (stroma) appears as the perithecial layer matures (fig. 15.11). By using a sharp knife, one can cut tangentially through the blackened wood to confirm the perithecial cavities holding the ascospores (fig. 15.12).

Ascospores are discharged from perithecia during and soon after rainfall and are dispersed by wind. The asexual (*Libertella blepharis* A.L. Smith) (syn. *Cytosporina* Sacc. sp.) spores of *E. lata* do not play any known role in the disease cycle. Pruning wounds can remain susceptible for up to 6 weeks, but that time depends on the size of the wound, wood age, and the time of pruning. Pruning wound susceptibility is at its highest right after pruning in December. Wounds made in January and February are not as susceptible even on the day they are made. Wound susceptibility decreases faster with high degree-day accumulation, which occurs in spring. Wound healing occurs by deposition of polymerized phenolic compounds in the xylem vessels. Often, when wounds are made in February and March, natural establishment of a microbial population on the wound surface occurs. These natural epiphytes, including *Cladosporium herbarum* and *Fusarium lateritium*, grow over the surface of pruning wounds and can prevent infection by *E. lata* spores, thus serving as a natural biological control. Pruning wound susceptibility is also affected by grapevine cultivar.

Figure 15.5 Young canker appears in cross-section as a wedge-shaped dark area coming to a point in the center of the arm or trunk. *Photo*: W. J. Moller.

Figure 15.6 Affected arms and cordons become progressively weaker and usually die during winter. *Photo*: W. J. Moller.

Figure 15.7 Eutypa dieback disease cycle.

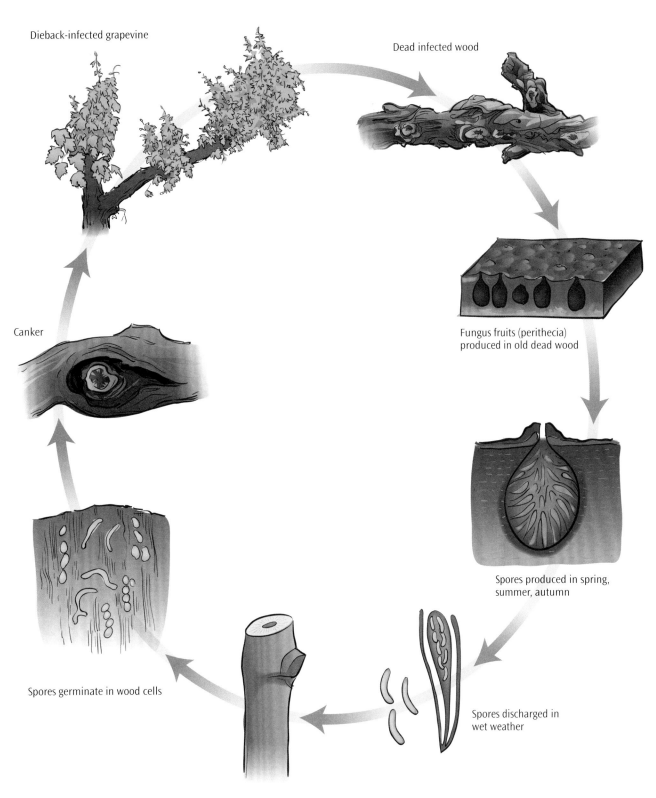

Dieback-infected grapevine

Dead infected wood

Fungus fruits (perithecia) produced in old dead wood

Spores produced in spring, summer, autumn

Spores discharged in wet weather

Fresh pruning wound

Spores germinate in wood cells

Canker

Figure 15.8 This large trunk infection on a 12-year-old Cabernet Sauvignon vine occurred when the vine was retrained several years earlier. Such severely affected vines die before the next season. *Photo*: J. K. Clark.

Figure 15.9 Mass of *E. lata* fruiting bodies, magnified, shows numerous small, pimplelike protrusions. *Photo*: J. K. Clark.

Figure 15.10 Magnified vertical section reveals a mass of *E. lata* perithecia embedded in old, diseased grape wood. *Photo*: J. K. Clark.

Figure 15.11 In California's wetter areas, perithecia (fruiting bodies) of Eutypa dieback form on diseased wood tissues. Small blackened areas on an exposed stub indicate their location. *Photo*: J. K. Clark.

Figure 15.12 A sharp blade was used to expose spore cavities. Each cavity contains thousands of *Eutypa* spores. *Photo*: J. K. Clark.

MANAGEMENT

In higher-rainfall areas of California, Eutypa dieback can be partially controlled by vineyard sanitation practices. Growers can reduce the risk of infection through reducing inoculum levels in their vineyards by removing infected wood in winter and burning it before rainfall occurs or as soon as regulations allow.

Eutypa dieback can also be partially controlled with vineyard management strategies. Pruning grapevines late in the spring can reduce the likelihood for wounds to become infected. At this time, rains are less likely to occur in California and ascospore release tends to be depleted by springtime in normal rainfall years. However, in years when winter rains are sparse, ascospore release can be delayed until April. Pruning wounds heal faster in the spring and remain susceptible to infection for a shorter period of time. Double pruning is a technique that removes canes 25 to 30 cm (10 to 12 in) above the previous year's spur positions. This can be accomplished using a tractor-mounted mechanical pruner early in the dormant season. A

second and final pruning takes place by hand in late February or March to select spurs when tissue is less susceptible to infection and inoculum is less prevalent. The second pruning takes relatively little time compared with a single hand-pruning operation because there is very little brush pulling required. This procedure works for Eutypa and other canker diseases because the fungus moves so slowly that it cannot invade the length of the 25 to 30 cm (10 to 12 in) prepruned canes prior to the final spur selection in spring.

Late spring is a good time to locate and remove diseased woody structural portions of vines before vigorous adjacent shoots mask characteristic stunted foliage or dead arms. The final saw cut must show completely healthy tissue and no evidence of the pie-shaped sector of dead wood extending downward from the canker site. Where the surgery has been neglected and the vine framework has become extensively infected, it may be impossible to cut back to healthy wood. In this case, if the vine is weakened to the point that strong suckers are emerging from

the lower trunk, the best alternative is to remove the dead trunk and rebuild the frame from one of these suckers or layer from a healthy adjacent vine. Bear in mind that partial trunk removal presents more opportunity for infection, due to the large wound. If possible, make such cuts in dry weather and use a reliable wound protectant. For vineyards planted on rootstock, if the trunk infection has moved beyond the graft union into the rootstock the vine should be removed and replaced.

Chemical wound protection results in good protection, assuming it is practiced each year. Research has shown that benzimidazole fungicides and boron gave excellent disease control in field trials. Fungicides can be applied as liquid formulations, but their efficacy on pruning wound surfaces decreases quickly because they decay over a couple of weeks and are washed off with rain. Optimal long-term protection is achieved after mixing fungicides with a paste, which provides improved physical protection of wounds and increases longevity of treatments in rainy conditions. Research has also shown that boron-based materials are effective wound protectants when mixed with a paste. However, if spur tips are treated with excessive rates of boron, budbreak will be reduced in the terminal bud position.

Biocontrol agents have been tested as an alternative method for control. However, unlike chemical applications, which have an immediate effect, maximum protection from biocontrol agents requires colonization of the surface of the wound. Thus, there is a window of susceptibility after treatment until the agent is established well enough to prevent development of *E. lata*. Evaluations have shown mixed success, but the best results were achieved when the agent was applied 2 to 3 weeks before infection occurred. Research continues, and evidence is mounting that protection of pruning wounds and disease prevention (Eutypa and Botryosphaeria dieback) are vital to the long-term health, vigor, and production capacity of a vineyard. Refer to the online UC IPM Grape Pest Management Guidelines, www. ipm.ucdavis.edu/PMG/, for registered materials to be used against these cankers.

REFERENCES

Carter, M. V., A. Bolay, and F. Rappaz. 1983. An annotated host list and bibliography of *Eutypa armeniacae*. Review of Plant Patholoby 62:251–258.

Moller, W. J., and A. N. Kasimatis. 1980. Protection of grapevine pruning wounds from Eutypa dieback. Plant Disease 64:278–280.

Munkvold, G. P., G. A. Duthie, and J. J. Marois. 1994. Reductions in yield and vegetative growth of grapevines due to Eutypa dieback. Phytopathology 84:186–192.

Ramos, D. E., W. J. Moller, and H. English. 1975. Production and dispersal of ascospores of *Eutypa armeniacae* in California. Phytopathology 65:1364–1371.

Rolshausen, P. E., L. C. Greve, J. M. Labavitch, N. E. Mahoney, R. J. Molyneux, and W. D. Gubler. 2008. Pathogenesis of *Eutypa lata* in grapevine: Identification of virulence factors and biochemical characterization of cordon dieback. Phytopathology 98:222–229.

Rolshausen, P. E., N. E. Mahoney, R. J. Molyneux, and W. D. Gubler. 2006. Reassessment of the species concept in *Eutypa lata*, the causal agent of Eutypa dieback of grapevine. Phytopathology 96:369–377.

Rolshausen, P. E., F. Trouillas, and W. D. Gubler. 2004. Identification of *Eutypa lata* by PCR-RFLP. Plant Disease 88:925–929.

———. 2005. Use of boron to control Eutypa dieback in California vineyards. Plant Disease 89:734–738.

Siebert, J. B. 2001. The economic toll on vineyard. Wines & Vines (April): 50–55.

Trouillas, F., and W. D. Gubler. 2004. Identification and characterization of *Eutypa leptoplaca*, a new pathogen of grapevine in northern California. Mycological Research 108:1195–1204.

Trouillas, F. P., J. R. Úrbez-Torres, and W. D. Gubler. 2010. Diversity of diatrypaceous fungi associated with grapevine canker diseases in California. Mycologia 102:319–336.

Weber, E. A., F. P. Trouillas, and W. D. Gubler. 2007. Double pruning of grapevines: A cultural practice to reduce infections by *Eutypa lata*. American Journal of Enology and Viticulture 58:61.

16 DOWNY MILDEW

W. Douglas Gubler, George M. Leavitt, and Larry J. Bettiga

Downy mildew of grapevine caused by *Plasmopara viticola* occurs in many California production regions. However, the almost total absence of favorable weather conditions for the disease limits its occurrence and associated losses. It was first found in 26-year-old Barbera and Grenache vineyards in the Sacramento Valley in 1990 and since has been found in foothill vineyards east of Sacramento, in Lodi, and in the Santa Cruz Mountains. In 1995 downy mildew was found in a nursery and in the table grape production area of Tulare County and more recently in grapevine nurseries in San Joaquin and Monterey Counties. Downy mildew is a very destructive plant disease. Fruit and foliage may be destroyed in just a few days once infection occurs. Downy mildew on grape reduces yield by causing rot in fruit clusters. In addition, wood viability for production of shoots and fruit can be detrimentally affected.

Plasmopara viticola (Berk. & Curt.) Berlese & de Toni is native to America and was introduced to Europe in the late 1870s. The pathogen requires free water for infection. It invades leaf and fruit tissue rapidly under wet conditions, causing rotting of the fruit and death of leaves and shoots. The downy mildews were previously classified as a fungus because of their resemblance to true fungi. However, because of fundamental differences (cell wall not composed of chitin, diploid nuclei) today's taxonomic system places *P. viticola* in the kingdom Straminopila.

SYMPTOMS

The pathogen can attack all green parts of the vine. Leaves and terminal ends of the shoots as well as young clusters are particularly susceptible to infection. Symptoms of downy mildew include yellow spots on the upper leaf surface soon after infection. These spots take on an oily appearance and are known as oil spots (fig. 16.1). Leaf lesions are often limited by leaf veins and are often angular in appearance (fig. 16.2). Heavily infected leaves often fall from the vine. Infected shoot tips take on a fasciated appearance, that is, they thicken, flatten, and curl (shepherd's crook, fig. 16.3), then become white with sporulation (fig. 16.4). Terminals eventually turn brown and die. Symptoms can also be seen on petioles, tendrils, and flower clusters, which when infected early in their development will turn brown and desiccate.

Figure 16.1 Oil spot symptom of downy mildew on the upper leaf surface (A) and the sporulating colony on the underside of the same leaf (B). *Photos*: L. J. Bettiga.

Figure 16.2 Necrotic tissue on upper leaf surface from downy mildew development on the underside. *Photo*: L. J. Bettiga.

Young berries are very susceptible and often are covered by a white velvety growth of the pathogen. As the fruit ripens, infected berries become dull or gray-green in appearance for white cultivars and a pinkish red for black cultivars. Berries infected after flowering can develop a purple color and shrivel as they dry (fig. 16.5). Berries become less susceptible as they age, but the rachis remains susceptible for a longer period. Rachis infections can lead to a symptom called brown rot. As the fungus moves through the rachis into the berries, it causes them to turn brown and rot. In this case there is no cottony growth on the surface of the berry.

DISEASE CYCLE

Grapevine downy mildew occurs in regions where it is warm and wet during the vegetative growth of the vine. The absence of rainfall in spring and summer limit the spread of the disease in California. *Plasmopara viticola* overwinters mainly as oospores in infected leaves on the ground. Oospores survive best in the surface layer of moist soil until at least the following spring. *Plasmopara viticola* can also survive as mycelium in buds and in persistent leaves on the grapevine. The overwintering spore (oospore) germinates in water in the spring as soon as temperatures reach 11°C (52°C). It produces sporangia, which release small spores

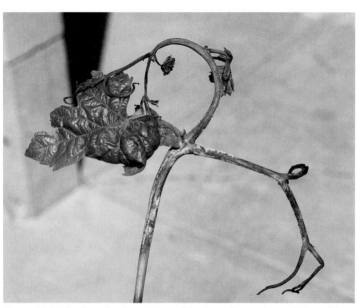

Figure 16.3 Infection of a shoot tip, resulting in curling and sporulation. This symptom is referred to as shepherds crook. *Photo*: L. J. Bettiga.

Figure 16.4 Close-up of a sporulating colony showing dense white growth. *Photo*: L. J. Bettiga.

Figure 16.5 Berries infected develop a pinkish red color and shrivel as they dry. *Photo*: W. D. Gubler.

called zoospores. Zoospores are capable of swimming and can be spread from the soil to the new foliage on the vine by wind and splashing rain. Zoospores infect green tissues through the stomates. The optimal temperature for disease development is 18° to 25°C (64.5° to 77°F). The disease can tolerate a minimum temperature of 12° to 14°C (53.5° to 57°F) and a maximum temperature of about 30°C (86°F). Once inside the plant, the fungus grows and spreads through tissues. At night during periods of high humidity and temperatures above 13°C (55.5°F), the fungus grows out through the stomates of infected tissues and produces microscopic, branched, pine tree–like structures (sporangiophores and sporangia) on the lower leaf surface. These structures make up the whitish downy growth on the lower leaf surface. The lemon-shaped sporangia are dispersed by the wind to cause secondary infections of leaves, shoot tips, and fruit by direct germination or by the release of zoospores.

Plasmopara viticola is an obligate parasite. As a biotroph (requires green grape tissue to reproduce), it has no saprophytic ability. Cultivars of *Vitis vinifera* are highly susceptible. *Vitis aestivalis* and *V. labrusca* are less susceptible, while *V. cordifolia*, *V. rupestris*, and *V. rotundifolia* are relatively resistant.

MANAGEMENT

When environmental conditions are favorable for disease development, cultural controls such as sanitation and irrigation management provide limited suppression. For vineyard sites with a history of downy mildew, infection management depends on the use of fungicides. Fungicides for use against downy mildew can be categorized as either preventive or curative. Preventive fungicides must be applied before an infection period begins. Control of downy mildew is best achieved in the spring, as disease can occur only during periods of rainfall or overhead irrigation. At about 25 cm (10 in) of shoot growth, apply preventive fungicides at 2-week intervals until bloom. If rainfall has ceased, no further applications are necessary. In California, it is believed that fall infections occur after harvest, allowing the perpetual presence of the pathogen in vineyards. Though no lasting injury to the vine occurs during this infection as it is after harvest, it does allow the pathogen to maintain a presence in the vineyard.

REFERENCES

Dubos, B. 2000. Cryptogamic diseases of vine. Bordeaux, France: Éditions Féret.

Hawksworth, D. L., P. M. Kirk, B. C. Sutton, and D. N. Pegler. 1995. Ainsworth & Bisby's dictionary of the fungi. 8th ed. Wallingford, UK: CAB International.

Pearson, R. C., and A. C. Goheen, eds. 1988. Compendium of grape diseases. St. Paul, MN: APS Press.

Spencer, D. M. 1981. The downy mildews. London, UK: Academic Press.

17 ESCA (BLACK MEASLES) AND PETRI DISEASE

W. Douglas Gubler, Suzanne Rooney Latham, Stephen J. Vasquez, and Akif Eskalen

Figure 17.1 Teleomorphs (A) of *Tognina minima* are found in cracks and crevices of decaying vascular tissue (B and C, arrows). *Photo* (C) shows teleomorphs. *Photos*: W. D. Gubler.

Esca is also known as black measles and apoplexy. Although this disease occurs in all grape production systems, grapes grown for fresh-market consumption suffer the greatest financial losses. Disease symptoms are most prevalent in vineyards in warmer, Mediterranean-type climates. However, the fungal pathogens have also been isolated from vineyards in cooler climates, where they typically cause a mild form of the disease. The disease occurs more frequently in years of higher-than-normal spring rainfall followed by consistently high temperatures. Vineyards older than 10 years are most commonly affected by esca. However, Petri disease (young esca, or vine decline) has become more common in young or newly established vineyards, primarily in the north coast region of California. Younger vineyards that have been planted with rootstocks resistant to phylloxera (*Daktulosphaira vitifoliae*) have experienced the most losses due to Petri disease, costing growers hundreds of thousands of dollars in replanting costs.

In older vineyards, the primary cost to growers is yield loss, which is difficult to estimate since the disease occurs sporadically within a vineyard and varies from season to season. Individual vines may express symptoms one year but not the next. Growers producing Thompson Seedless, Crimson Seedless, or other fresh-market cultivars suffer the most serious losses. Affected clusters are unmarketable due to their undesirable appearance and flavor. Affected berries also become more susceptible to infection and colonization by *Botrytis cinerea* and other fungi that cause bunch rot.

Esca is caused by several species of *Phaeoacremonium* and by *Phaeomoniella chlamydospora*. To date, nine species of *Phaeoacremonium* have been isolated from California vineyards, with the most prevalent being *Pm. aleophilum,* which colonizes and survives in the xylem tissue of grapevines. The vegetative fungal hyphae can produce copious amounts of asexual spores in the xylem and pith. Xylem infections can plug the vascular system and compromise the health of the grapevine. The teleomorph (sexual or perfect state) of *Pm. aleophilum* has been identified as *Togninia minima. Togninia minima* produces a unique perithecium that can be found on decaying vascular tissue in the cracks and crevices of trunks, cordons, and spurs (fig. 17.1). These perithecia enable the fungus to survive the winter and also serve as a reservoir of infectious spores that are released in winter and spring following periods of rainfall. *Phaeomoniella chlamydospora* is associated more closely with Petri disease. However, both fungi can be found in grape-vines of any age. The teleomorph of *Pa. chlamydospora* has not been identified; this fungus overwinters as pycnidia (asexual fruiting bodies), which contain spores. This black, flask-shaped structure also can be found on the exposed vascular tissue of grapevines.

Symptoms of esca were first documented in California vineyards in the late 1930s, at which time a causal organism was not identified. In the late 1950s, internal wood rot and vascular streaking at large pruning wound sites were suspected of contributing to esca. Species of fungi in the genera *Fomes*, *Cephalosporium*, and *Stereum* (*Phellinus*) were most frequently isolated from symptomatic wood, but no symptoms could be produced by these fungi. In the 1990s, interest in the causal organism of esca peaked with an increase in symptom expression in San Joaquin Valley table grape vineyards and the identification of similar fungi isolated from newly established grapevines in north coast vineyards. Extensive research subsequently identified the two genera of fungi *(Phaeoacremonium* and *Phaeomoniella)* ubiquitous in California's vineyards that were capable of causing typical esca symptoms in vascular tissue and in fruit and foliage.

Symptoms

One of the most noticeable symptoms of esca occurs on the fruit and inspired the common name black measles after the discovery of the disease in California. Superficial dark spots (fig. 17.2) develop on the berry epidermis and are particularly noticeable on white

Figure 17.2 The peculiar berry spotting of esca. The berry skin is peppered with small, round, dark spots. *Photos*: L. J. Bettiga (A); J. K. Clark (B).

Figure 17.3 Some berries have cracked and shriveled in a Chenin blanc cluster affected by esca. *Photo*: L. J. Bettiga.

Figure 17.4 Berries dry up or rot on vines severely affected. *Photo*: L. J. Bettiga.

cultivars. The skin is peppered with small, round-to-irregular, dark spots, each bordered by a brown-purple ring. These spots typically appear between fruit set and ripening and can affect individual berries or entire clusters. On severely affected grapevines or clusters that develop symptoms early in the season, the dark spots coalesce, causing berries to shrivel and entire clusters to dry on the vine (figs. 17.3–17.4). Berry symptoms can be quite irregular, occurring on only a portion of a cluster, the entire cluster on a single shoot, or all of the fruit on a single grapevine.

Leaf symptoms usually develop on canes with symptomatic fruit, but there are incidences when the fruit remains unaffected. One of the earliest symptoms of esca often seen is shoot tip dieback in early to midspring during the active growing period. The shoot tips first appear wilted before defoliating and dying back within a short time. Later in the season, affected leaves display small, chlorotic interveinal areas that enlarge over time and eventually dry out (figs. 17.5–17.7). Dark-colored cultivars display dark red margins that surround the dead interveinal areas, and as this symptom progresses, the entire leaf may take on a dramatic tiger stripe (fig. 17.8) pattern. Severely affected leaves drop, and the canes begin to die from the shoot tip toward the base. Foliar symptoms may appear at any time during the growing season but are most prevalent during July and August (fig. 17.9). Entire vines or portions of a vine may be affected. It has been shown that toxin production by these fungi when under water stress and

Figure 17.5 Early leaf symptoms appear as small, chlorotic interveinal areas. *Photo*: J. K. Clark.

Figure 17.6 Yellow margins surround the dead interveinal areas as esca progresses. *Photo*: J. K. Clark.

Figure 17.7 Severely affected leaf shows death of most of the leaf blade. *Photo*: J. K. Clark.

Figure 17.8 Tiger stripe pattern on Pinot noir. *Photo*: L. J. Bettiga.

subsequent translocation of the toxin to the foliage and berries are responsible for these symptoms.

Apoplexy is an acute form of esca that appears quickly and dramatically. Symptoms include the sudden scorching of foliage and drying of the fruit over the entire vine, leading to an overall dead appearance. Depending on when this occurs during the season, the vine could die, show mild fruit and/or foliar symptoms, or be completely healthy the following

Figure 17.9 Striking leaf symptoms are most prevalent in July and August. Entire vines or only portions may be affected. *Photo*: J. K. Clark.

season. If apoplexy appears in grapevines over consecutive seasons, the lack of foliage reduces carbohydrate storage, and the vines subsequently weaken and die. The phenomenon is commonly seen in the hot southern San Joaquin Valley in table grape vineyards beginning in late spring.

Internal wood symptoms are expressed as brown to black vascular streaking. This streaking may be discontinuous or may extend only for some distance. Upon cutting affected cordons or trunks, phenolic compounds ooze from the xylem vessels and begin to oxidize, turning dark brown to black. The wood is often very dry and may take on a silvery appearance. The wood of older infected grapevines may also become more susceptible to colonization by secondary wood-rotting fungi, further weakening the vine and decreasing its longevity.

Disease Cycle

The *Phaeoacremonium* group includes opportunistic fungal endophytes that reside in the water-conducting tissue of grapevines. A general description of the biology of *aleophilum* (teleomorph: *T. minima*) will be discussed since its teleomorph-anamorph relationship is the best documented among the species of *Phaeoacremonium*. *Togninia minima* resides in the xylem and pith (endophyte), where it freely produces spores that are transported throughout the grapevine in the sap. The fungus has the ability to move, germinate, and penetrate through the vascular parenchyma cell walls, causing tissue necrosis. The grapevine responds to the presence of *T. minima* within the xylem by producing gums and tyloses that help compartmentalize and restrict pathogen movement and growth. *Togninia minima* also can reside externally on the vine as perithecia in rotted vascular tissue of old pruning wounds.

Perithecia of *T. minima* begin developing during the hot, dry months of midsummer and mature by the end of the season. Perithecia are found in old, rotted vascular tissue, on pruning wounds, and on other injuries that expose rotted xylem. The perithecia are well protected and are typically embedded in deep cracks. The long necks of the perithecia are capable of sensing light and extending toward the crack openings. Inside each perithecium are sacs called asci, which contain the ascospores. Ascospores are released following hydration during periods of rainfall or sprinkler irrigation. Ascospores are discharged forcibly from their ascus via the ostiole (opening) of the perithecium neck. Ascospores forcibly discharged to a height of 10 cm (4 in) are carried by wind currents before landing on fresh susceptible pruning wounds. Some ascospores accumulate in a sticky droplet at the tip of the perithecial neck. This may be important in that it appears that the fungus might also be insect vectored. Although it is not known whether insects play a role in the spread of esca, spores were documented to be contaminants on termites and on at least one species of mite. Spore release occurs naturally during fall, winter, and spring rains, but it can also take place during irrigation events, especially via overhead sprinklers.

Esca remains a perplexing disease. Symptoms are usually discontinuous and may be expressed one year and not the next, though it is common for vines to show symptoms in many consecutive years. The reason for the irregular symptom expression over time is not yet fully understood. Research suggested that symptoms appear within the same year as new infections or the year following infection. It is fairly well documented that environmental conditions and/or physiological stressors dictate whether symptoms will be seen in a particular year.

Management

Currently, few strategies are being used to manage esca. Protection of pruning wounds likely helps prevent new infections. Pruning wounds have been shown to be susceptible to infection by *Phaeoacremonium* species and *Phaeomoniella chlamydospora* for up to 4 months. Pruning and making large cuts in grapevines should be avoided during periods of heavy rainfall when spores are likely being dispersed. Research on the efficacy of various wound protectants is currently being assessed. Double pruning or late pruning has been shown to reduce the incidence and severity of disease and is currently the recommended control strategy for this disease.

PETRI DISEASE (YOUNG ESCA, VINE DECLINE)

Petri disease, also known as young esca and vine decline, is caused primarily by the fungus *Phaeomoniella chlamydospora*. Petri disease affects young grapevines and usually results in stunted or weak plants after the rootstock becomes infected. Petri disease became well known in California after vineyards planted with AXR#1 rootstock were replaced with grapevines grafted onto rootstocks resistant to phylloxera and nematodes. In root-stock susceptibility experiments, AXR#1 showed virtually no vascular streaking when inoculated with *Pa. chlamydospora*. However, nearly all the rootstock cultivars currently used in California were shown to be quite susceptible. Although *Pa. chlamydospora* is considered the predominant pathogen causing Petri disease, species of *Phaeoacremonium*, including *Pm. aleophilum*, have also been found to be associated with vine decline. Although the pathogens are the same as those causing esca, the vine declines (Petri disease and vine decline) are usually associated with root infections and infections originating during the propagation process, whereas esca results from pruning wound infections of the scion wood.

SYMPTOMS

Symptoms of Petri disease include overall stunting, reduced foliage, and foliar symptoms similar to esca (fig. 17.10). The vine will struggle and show more severe symptoms each year, especially if

under stress conditions. Severely affected grapevines may die within a few years, but more commonly they just remain unthrifty. Root growth restriction (J rooting) is also very common and may in fact be a cause of vine decline on its own. J-rooted vines will generally start showing decline symptoms from 5 to 10 years after planting. However, J rooting can also be predisposition stress leading to increased severity symptoms of Petri disease and other vine declines. Black vascular streaking, especially in the rootstocks, is common and may occur in continuous streaks for several millimeters (fig. 17.11). A cross-section of the woody tissue displays gumming that turns dark when exposed to air. Cut wood often will also look extremely dry and turn a silvery purplish color.

DISEASE CYCLE

Phaeomoniella chlamydospora and *Phaeoacremonium aleophilum* can gain entry into the xylem of young plants at the nursery or in recently established vineyards through root infections. In South

Africa, infected mother plants have been shown to be a source of inoculum for cuttings. Furthermore, these pathogens have also been detected in some grape-growing areas including California during the propagation process in water samples (used for both hydration and during grafting) as well as in callusing media.

Phaeomoniella chlamydospora is also soilborne and can survive for many months in the soil as conidia, mycelium, and resting spores called chlamydospores. In laboratory studies, *Pa. chlamydospora* and *Phaeoacremonium* species have been shown to be able to penetrate uninjured young roots. In vineyards, *Pa. chlamydospora* also overwinters as pycnidia on young pruning wounds. Spores are released during rain events and can be water splashed to fresh wounds (e.g., disbudding wounds). Like *Pm. aleophilum*, *Pa. chlamydospora* colonizes xylem vessels and pith parenchyma cells, easily moving between the two. Fungal sporulation can readily be seen in the pith of infected grapevines. These fungi have also been found to survive as epiphytes living

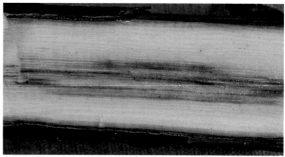

Figure 17.11 Longitudinal vascular streaking associated with Petri disease. *Photo*: L. J. Bettiga.

Figure 17.10 Weak growth and decline of a young vine (foreground). *Photo*: L. J. Bettiga.

on the surfaces of berries and bark of both symptomatic and asymptomatic grapevines.

Disease progress is greatly tempered by root health and vigor of the vine. In nearly all of the cases in California involving Petri disease or vine decline, some type of predisposing stress factor has been involved. Such factors include poor irrigation management, stress brought on by early cropping, and poor planting practices that result in J rooting. With increased stress and the use of susceptible rootstocks during the mid to late 1990s, disease incidence rose dramatically. Research has shown stress to be the primary factor in Petri disease. Greenhouse studies have shown that artificially inoculated grapevines have a much higher rate of mortality when subjected to water stress than those that were not water stressed.

MANAGEMENT

Management of Petri disease can be accomplished by choosing asymptomatic vines and planting them correctly. Once vines are planted, adequate vine and root development should be allowed to occur prior to placing a heavy fruit load on vines in the early production years. Rootstock performance will differ from site to site and among cultivars and can be negatively affected by poor planting practices followed by inadequate irrigation. Research also indicates that proper propagation practices also can reduce new infections. The use of clean propagation planting material and tools as well as reducing the number of wounds made during the propagation process can all reduce disease levels.

REFERENCES

Esca (Black Measles)

Bruno, G., and L. Sparapano. 2006. Effects of three esca associated fungi on *Vitis vinifera* L.: I. Characterization of secondary metabolites in culture media and host responses to the pathogens in calli. Physiology and Molecular Biology of Plants 69:209–223.

Eskalen, A., A. J. Feliciano, and W. D. Gubler. 2007. Susceptibility of grapevine pruning wounds and symptom development in response to infection by *Phaeoacremonium aleophilum* and *Phaeomoniella chlamydospora*. Plant Disease 91:1100–1104.

Eskalen, A., W. D. Gubler, and A. Khan. 2001. Rootstock susceptibility to *Phaeomoniella chlamydospora* and *Phaeoacremonium* spp. Phytopathologia Mediterranea 40: S433–438.

Rooney-Latham, S., A. Eskalen, and W. D. Gubler. 2005a. Ascospore release of T*ogninia minima*, cause of esca and grapevine decline in California. Plant Health Progress doi:10.1094/PHP-2005-0209-01-RS.

———. 2005b. Occurrence of *Togninia minima* perithecia in esca-affected vineyards in California. Plant Disease 89:867–871.

———. 2005c. Teleomorph formation of *Phaeoacremonium aleophilum*, cause of esca and grapevine decline in California. Plant Disease 89:177–184.

Tabacchi, R., A. Fkyerat, C. Poliart, and G. Dubin. 2000. Phytotoxins from fungi of esca of grapevine. Phytopathologia Mediterranea 39:156–161.

Petri Disease (Young Esca)

Feliciano, A. J., and W. D. Gubler. 2001. Histological investigations on infection of grape roots and shoots by *Phaeoacremonium* spp. Phytopathologia Mediterranea 40:387–393.

Ferreira, J. H. S., P. S. van Wyk, and F. J. Calitz. 1999. Slow dieback of grapevine in South Africa: Stress-related predisposition of young vines for infection by *Phaeoacremonium chlamydosporum*. South African Journal of Enology and Viticulture 20:43–46.

Retief, E., A. McLeod, and P. H. Fourie. 2006. Potential inoculum sources of *Phaeomoniella chlamydospora* in South African grapevine nurseries. European Journal of Plant Pathololgy 115:331–339.

Scheck, H. S., S. J. Vasquez, and W. D. Gubler. 1998. Grape growers report losses to black foot and grapevine decline. California Agriculture 52(4): 19–23.

18 PHOMOPSIS CANE AND LEAF SPOT

Stephen J. Vasquez, George M. Leavitt, and Paul S. Verdegaal

Phomopsis cane and leaf spot, caused by the fungus *Phomopsis viticola*, results in small yellow spots on grape leaves and black lesions on shoots, rachis, and canes. Yields can be reduced in cane-pruned cultivars (e.g., Thompson Seedless and Redglobe) used for raisin or table grape production when cane infections are severe. The fungus attacks all green tissues of the vine (fig. 18.1). Because its spores are splash dispersed, *P. viticola* is less common as a foliar pathogen in California than in grape-growing regions that are characterized by frequent rain during the growing season.

Phomopsis cane and leaf spot was first seen in California vineyards in 1935 near the American River in Sacramento County. It subsequently moved southward throughout the San Joaquin Valley growing regions for raisins and table grapes. For many years, Phomopsis cane and leaf spot was known as deadarm. UC researchers identified other fungi, namely *Eutypa lata* and the Botryosphaeriaceae species identified as causal agents of Botryosphaeria dieback, as the primary pathogens causing the characteristic deadarm symptoms: dead spurs and cordons, stunted shoots, shoot dieback, and wood cankers. However, recent studies in California and France have once again implicated *P. viticola* as a cause for deadarm. In some Mediterranean grape-growing regions, *P. viticola* is thus considered to be more of a trunk pathogen than a foliar pathogen.

In wet spring years, Phomopsis cane and leaf spot can be particularly severe as a foliar pathogen on the following cultivars: DOVine, Fiesta, Flame Seedless, Grenache, Redglobe, and Thompson Seedless grown in the Central Valley between Lodi and Bakersfield. Also susceptible to *P. viticola* are the minor cultivars Cardinal, Calmeria, Concord, Emperor, Flame Tokay, and White Malaga. The traditional wine grape cultivars (i.e., Cabernet Sauvignon, Chardonnay, Chenin blanc, Syrah, and Zinfandel) popular in the north and central coast are less susceptible to *P. viticola* but can experience disease during an abnormally wet spring. The incidence of *P. viticola* as a trunk pathogen is not well characterized to date, and the relationship of its wood canker symptom to the typical foliar symptoms of Phomopsis cane and leaf spot has not been examined.

The impact of Phomopsis in most years is minor due to the rare occurrence of cool, wet weather in spring. However, in years when cool, wet weather coincides with the start of the growing season, severe foliar infection can occur, and yield losses may result indirectly from shoot breakage near the base where numerous lesions coalesce or on the rachis, reducing the cluster counts and cluster weights per vine. Infected cane wood

Figure 18.1 Phomopsis cane and leaf spot disease cycle.

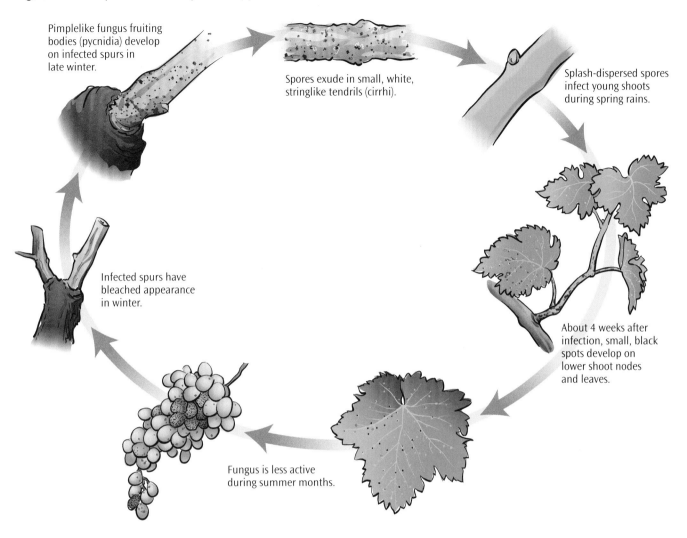

Pimplelike fungus fruiting bodies (pycnidia) develop on infected spurs in late winter.

Spores exude in small, white, stringlike tendrils (cirrhi).

Splash-dispersed spores infect young shoots during spring rains.

Infected spurs have bleached appearance in winter.

About 4 weeks after infection, small, black spots develop on lower shoot nodes and leaves.

Fungus is less active during summer months.

likely has a lower fruiting capacity than healthy cane wood, so infected canes may yield less fruit the following season. Mild symptoms on infected canes may be difficult to see during the dormant season, and pruning out all infected wood is time consuming and can increase pruning costs (fig. 18.2). Direct infection of fruit by spores rarely occurs but can reduce storage longevity of infected table grapes.

Symptoms

Leaves
The first symptoms occur as tiny, dark brown to black spots with yellow margins that appear on leaf blades and petioles (fig. 18.3). These spots first show 3 to 4 weeks following rainfall after budbreak. If large numbers of leaf spots develop and begin to coalesce, portions of the leaf will die. Basal leaves with heavy infection become distorted

and usually never develop to full size. When petioles are severely infected, the leaves turn yellow and abscise. Once spring rains cease, warmer dry weather encourages healthy leaves to develop on subsequent nodes, hiding the distorted or killed basal leaves.

Shoots
Small spots with black centers, similar to those found on the leaves, are the first evidence of shoot infection (fig. 18.4). This

Figure 18.2 Severely infected spurs or canes appear bleached in winter and should be removed where possible. *Photo*: J. K. Clark.

Figure 18.3 Leaf spots (usually on basal leaves) appear as tiny black spots with yellowish margins. *Photo*: G. M. Leavitt.

Figure 18.4 Primary infections show up as small spots with black centers on basal portions of shoots. *Photo*: J. K. Clark.

infection usually occurs on the basal portion of shoots. When these oblong spots become 6 mm (0.25 in) long, the epidermal layers of the shoots usually crack at the point of infection. Where the spots are in large numbers, they coalesce and may ultimately give a scabby appearance to infected parts of the shoots (fig. 18.5). Severely diseased shoots can be stunted, and some may die (fig. 18.6). When shoots are 30 to 60 cm (12 to 24 in) long, the leaves create an umbrella effect that reduces further infections from rain-splashed spores; however, shoot breakage can occur during strong winds or as fruit begins to mature. The fungus within the shoot lesions becomes inactive during summer but may resume growth in autumn and produce black pycnidia (round spore-producing structures). Spores developed within the pycnidia become infectious propagules during the following rainy season.

Clusters

Spots similar to those on the shoots and leaves also appear on the rachis. Occasionally, cluster stems are so badly infected that the clusters wither. These lesions also become inactive in summer, but early-fall rains, combined with cool weather, may reactivate the fungus, resulting in berry and bunch rotting. Fruit infections (fig. 18.7) rarely occur in California, and when they do occur they are generally not extensive. However, rain just before harvest can cause light brown spots on berries; the spots enlarge quickly and become dark brown. Pycnidia often occur in concentric rings on the skin of the berry, and yellow spore masses may exude from pycnidia under

wet conditions. Finally, the berries shrivel and become mummified.

Canes

During the dormant season, infected wood appears bleached (fig. 18.8). Severely infected canes or spurs exhibit an irregular dark brown to black discoloration intermixed with the whitish bleached areas on the bark. Tissue in the vicinity of the original lesions that were established when the tissue was green and at the nodes is also whitish with black speckling. These black specks are the pycnidia (fig. 18.9), which develop during the dormant season, break through the surface, and appear as minute, black, pimplelike pustules. They are the source of overwintering spores for the next season. Severely affected canes and spurs are more sensitive to low temperatures than are healthy ones. Low temperatures and the lack of functioning phloem and xylem weaken and kill diseased canes, spurs (fig. 18.10), and buds (fig. 18.11).

DISEASE CYCLE

Heavy, prolonged rains in late March and April, when the susceptible young green tissue is abundant, create ideal moisture and temperature conditions for severe spring infections. Infection generally occurs when there is spring rain in the period that begins shortly after budbreak and includes early shoot growth (see fig. 18.1), when the shoots are 30 to 38 cm (12 to 15 in) long. Spores released in large quantities from the overwintering pycnidia found on diseased spurs, canes, and bark are splashed by rain onto newly developing shoots. Infection occurs when free moisture remains on the

Figure 18.5 Phomopsis-infected Thompson Seedless shoots. *Photo*: L. P. Christensen.

Figure 18.6 Heavily infected shoots near the head of this Thompson Seedless vine are retarded or killed, resulting in a bare center that reduces available wood for the following season. *Photo*: J. K. Clark.

Figure 18.7 Spore-bearing bodies of *P. viticola* on infected berry. *Photo*: UC Davis Plant Pathology.

Figure 18.8 Dormant infected canes on Thompson Seedless. *Photo*: W. J. Moller.

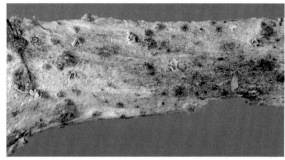

Figure 18.9 In early spring, swollen pycnidia of *Phomopsis viticola* are visible on infected tissue. During rainy periods, exuding spore masses can be easily detected with a hand lens. *Photo*: J. K. Clark.

Figure 18.10 Dormant infections on Tokay show longitudinal cracks on bleached spurs. *Photo*: J. K. Clark.

unprotected green tissue for 5 to 10 hours in optimal temperatures, from 16 to 20°C (61° to 68°F). Symptoms become visible within a few days on leaves and 2 weeks later on shoots. However, because the occurrence and frequency of spring rain fluctuate from year to year, infection incidence and disease severity vary on basal nodes.

MANAGEMENT

The use of an eradicant chemical (such as lime sulfur) during late dormancy helps reduce overwintering inoculum and new shoot infection if early spring rains occur. Sensitive cultivars should also be treated with a foliar fungicide during the early shoot growth stages. Contact fungicides protect young shoots satisfactorily if applied before cool, wet weather. Additional applications may be needed if wet weather continues. Sprays applied from budbreak to shoot length of 1.3 cm (0.5 in), and possibly again when shoots are 12.5 to 15 cm (5 to 6 in) long, provide good control. If an extended period of precipitation is expected, a fungicide with systemic activity should be applied prior to the rain event. Additional foliar applications may be necessary prior to any heavy spring rains, as post-rain applications will not control disease incidence. In severely affected vineyards, both dormant and spring treatments may be advisable in addition to selective heavy pruning of infected tissue.

REFERENCES

Erincik, O., L. V. Madden, D. C. Ferree, and M. A. Ellis. 2003. Temperature and wetness-duration requirements for grape leaf and cane infection by *Phomopsis viticola*. Plant Disease 87:832–840.

Pine, T. S. 1958. Etiology of the dead-arm. Phytopathology 48:192–197.

———. 1959. Development of the grape dead-arm disease. Phytopathology 49:738–743.

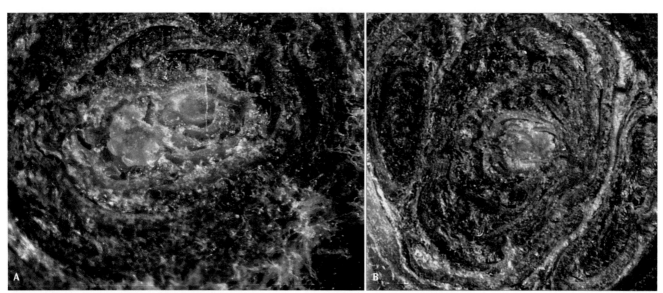

Figure 18.11 Cross-section of a normal (A) and a Phomopsis-infected necrotic bud (B). *Photos*: S. J. Vasquez.

19 PHYTOPHTHORA CROWN AND ROOT ROT

Larry J. Bettiga and Gregory T. Browne

Many perennial and annual crops worldwide suffer serious losses due to Phytophthora root and crown rot, but the disease is of relatively minor importance on grapevines in California. Several species of *Phytophthora* have been isolated from grapevines in the state, but only *P. cinnamomi* is pathogenic on grapes and only on certain rootstocks. Root and crown rot caused by *P. cinnamomi* has tended to occur in coastal valleys of California on fine-textured soils.

SYMPTOMS

Grapevines affected by Phytophthora crown and root rot may be stunted and foliage may be sparse and senesce prematurely as the disease progresses in the root system (fig. 19.1). In red-fruited varieties, foliage may turn red in the summer or fall in response to initial girdling of the crown. This can be an early indication of infection, and these vines often die in the winter or during the following year. Once vines are completely girdled by Phytophthora crown rot, they will die quickly.

Diagnosis of vines suspected to be infected with Phytophthora involves examining crown and root tissue at and below the soil surface. A knife can be used to cut into roots to examine crown tissue underneath the bark. Infected roots become dark brown to black throughout their outer and inner tissues as they die, but a few healthy feeder roots may remain on those affected (fig. 19.2). The tissue under the bark of infected crowns is killed and turns dark brown to black. Species of *Phytophthora* do not form visible mycelium in or under the host bark.

DISEASE CYCLE

Species of *Phytophthora* can survive in soil for many years, existing as a saprobe in the absence of a living host. In infected roots, the pathogens can produce chlamydospores and oospores, which are resilient resting spores that facilitate the pathogen's survival in the soil as the plant tissues degrade.

Rapid reproduction, localized spread, and root infection by *Phytophthora* species are favored by frequent, prolonged periods (i.e., more than 24 hours) of water-saturated soil (fig. 19.3). This can occur in poorly drained soils following heavy rain or improper irrigation. Saturated soil stimulates the production

Figure 19.1 Affected vines appear weak and stunted and usually develop premature fall colors. Beware of confusion with other root disorders, such as Petri disease and Armillaria root rot. *Photo*: J. K. Clark.

and release of zoospores, which can swim through the water-filled pores to infect new host roots. The motile zoospores are attracted by host root exudates. As the frequency and duration of periods of saturated soil conditions increase, so do the numbers of zoospores released and the likelihood of them reaching and infecting the host.

Long-distance spread of *Phytophthora* species can result from planting infected stock, transport of infested soil on farm equipment, and movement in surface water during flooding or runoff. Although rivers and canals have been demonstrated to carry species of *Phytophthora* in agricultural areas, *P. cinnamomi* has not been detected in these sources. Many ornamental plants are hosts of *P. cinnamomi,* and they can introduce the pathogen to vineyards that are located around home landscapes.

MANAGEMENT

Rootstock susceptibility and soil moisture conditions are probably the most important manageable factors influencing incidence of the disease on grapevines in California. The rootstocks Kober 5BB and Rupestris St. George have been observed to have greater susceptibility to *P. cinnamomi* than other grape rootstocks and should not be used on poorly drained soils.

Once introduced into an area, *Phytophthora* species can survive in the soil for many years. Although preplant soil fumigation can temporarily reduce the inoculum density, eradication of the pathogen from soil is not feasible. Therefore, care should be used to avoid planting infected grape nursery stock or planting susceptible ornamentals uphill from or adjacent to a vineyard. Because infested soil can spread Phytophthora, care should be used during vine replacement and cultivation operations not to spread the pathogen from diseased to healthy areas.

Careful soil water management can reduce the risk of infection. Irrigations should be managed to meet vine water needs while avoiding periods of saturated soil conditions greater than 24 hours, especially near the crown. Drip emitters should be positioned to avoid having water directly contact trunks or creating a wetted zone at the base of vines. Planting the vines on berms or raised beds may also provide improved drainage around the crowns. At some sites, steps should be taken to improve surface infiltration rates and subsurface soil water drainage, preferably before vineyard planting.

REFERENCES

Gubler, W. D., K. Baumgartner, G. T. Browne, A. Eskalen, S. Rooney Latham, E. Petit, and L. A. Bayramian. 2004. Root disease of grapevines in California and their control. Australasian Plant Pathology 33:157–165.

Marais, P. G. 1979. Fungi associated with root rot in vineyards in the Western Cape. Phytophylactica 11:65–68.

Zentmeyer, G. A. 1980. *Phytophthora cinnamomi* and the diseases it causes. Monograph 10. St. Paul, MN: APS Press.

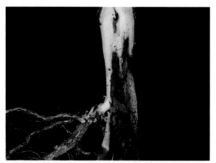

Figure 19.2 Infection from Phytophthora causes crowns and roots to become dark brown to black throughout their outer and inner tissues as they die. *Photo*: L. J. Bettiga.

Figure 19.3 Missing and weak vine growth due to Phytophthora infection caused by temporary saturated soils above a soil interface. *Photo*: L. J. Bettiga.

20 POSTHARVEST DISEASES OF TABLE GRAPES

W. Douglas Gubler, Jennifer M. Hashim, Joseph L. Smilanick, and George M. Leavitt

GRAY MOLD (BOTRYTIS CINEREA)

Botrytis cinerea (Persoon), the cause of gray mold, is the most important pathogen of stored table grapes. In fact, 32.5% of the USDA-inspected table grape shipments arriving from 1972 to 1984 in New York had detectable levels of *Botrytis*-infected berries. Of those shipments, 84% were from California. The only disorder more common than *Botrytis* infection was shatter, which affected 47% of the inspected shipments.

Botrytis cinerea, which also causes Botrytis bunch rot in the field, severely affects stored table grapes. The fungus can infect grapes in the field and then continue to grow in the berries during storage at temperatures as low as 0°C (32°F). The fungus produces abundant aerial growth that enables it to spread rapidly to adjacent berries, causing a condition known as nesting. Because of its ability to grow at such low temperatures and its broad host range, *Botrytis cinerea* is a severe postharvest pathogen of many crops, including flowers, strawberries, and lettuce.

The degree of susceptibility of stored grapes to *Botrytis* depends on the level of infection in the field before storage, the cultivar of grape, the condition of berries at harvest, and the effectiveness of fumigation and cold storage practices for control.

SYMPTOMS

Because of the low temperatures during storage, several weeks may pass before symptoms of the disease are visible. The first symptoms are water-soaked lesions. These progress in 1 to 4 days at 0°C (32°F) to the slip skin phase, in which enzymes produced by the fungus cause the cuticle and epidermal cells to easily slip away from the berry pulp with only slight pressure (fig. 20.1). Shortly after the slip skin phase, gray-brown lesions develop on the surface of the grapes (fig. 20.2); these, however, are difficult to see on red or black berries, and visible symptoms may not appear until the fungal mycelium begins to grow out of the berry.

The mycelium growing from an infected berry can begin to infect adjacent berries within 1 week, eventually resulting in the formation of nests of infected berries covered with gray-white fungal mycelium. In late stages of decay, the berries darken and begin to lose their juice, which may collect in bags of plastic-wrapped grapes or contaminate other clusters (fig. 20.3).

The rachis is also susceptible to *Botrytis*. Infected stems turn brown, and mycelium may be seen growing on them. Stem infections are

Figure 20.1 A slip skin lesion has been ruptured by very slight pressure. It is difficult to detect these lesions visually; if overlooked, they can be sources of decay in the packed fruit. *Photo*: J. K. Clark.

Figure 20.2 Advanced infection by *Botrytis cinerea* on Thompson Seedless berries as indicated by the conspicuous brown berry in contrast to the green unaffected berries. *Photo*: J. K. Clark.

significant because the infection causes desiccation of berries from the infection down and the fungus can move through the stems and pedicles to infect berries.

DISEASE CYCLE

Initial infection begins in the field before harvest, or spores can contaminate the external surface of berries. Asymptomatic berries may contaminate the rest of the box during storage. The fungus does not usually spread from box to box, but originates instead from infections within a box. The spread of fungal mycelium from berry to berry is referred to as contact infection. Contact infection is the primary means of postharvest spread of *Botrytis*. Conidia or spores of the fungus are not as important in the disease cycle in storage as they are in the field.

MANAGEMENT

Management of postharvest losses due to gray mold begins in the vineyard. Removal of old, desiccated bunches or berries from the vines during pruning, proper

timing of fungicide applications, and canopy management techniques (Gubler et al. 1987) that improve air movement within the canopy are effective methods to minimize gray mold incidence (see section 13, "Bunch Rots"). Botrytis fungicides applied prior to harvest have been shown to reduce gray mold incidence in storage. Harvest conditions and practices can also influence postharvest *Botrytis* development. Avoid harvest during rainy periods, particularly when the rain has penetrated into the vines and thoroughly wetted the clusters. These conditions cause gray mold to increase significantly, and harvest should resume only after the clusters are dry. Drying of clusters can be accelerated by simply blowing air through the canopy using a spray rig without water. Furthermore, it is essential that workers properly pack the box to its correct weight with well-trimmed bunches free of decayed and damaged berries. Given the wide variety of packaging combinations currently available for table grapes, the box and internal

packing materials should be chosen to maintain fruit quality and ease of transport but must not impede fumigation during storage.

Management of postharvest diseases of table grapes requires knowledge of the potential for disease to develop in a particular lot and methods to control it. While it may take weeks for *Botrytis* to cause visible symptoms at storage temperatures, it may take only 2 days at room temperature. The potential for decay of a particular lot can be determined by sampling a few random boxes of grapes at harvest and storing them at room temperature. Infections can then be detected within a week, and lots with a high decay potential should be avoided if a long storage life is needed.

Current commercial control of *Botrytis* in storage is achieved by promptly cooling and fumigating the fruit with sulfur dioxide (SO_2) gas. Traditional fumigation practices include gassing fruit with 5,000 ppm SO_2 initially, followed by additional fumigations at a 7- to 10-day interval with 2,500 to 5,000 ppm. After a fumigation cycle of

Figure 20.3 In this pack, inadequate sulfur dioxide fumigation has allowed the fungus to spread from the field-infected berry into adjacent unaffected berries by contact infection. *Photo*: S. Vasquez.

Figure 20.4 Hairline fractures (A) caused by *Aspergillus niger* result in non-Botrytis slip skin. Further development and sunken decayed areas (B) will break the berry epidermis and allow liquefied pulp to drip onto neighboring berries. *Photos*: S. Vasquez.

about 30 minutes, the remaining SO$_2$ in the room must be cleaned with a scrubbing system for safe re-entry.

From 1987 to 1991, research was conducted to modernize SO$_2$ fumigation practices in order to reduce residues on fruit (below the legal tolerance of 10 ppm), decrease environmental pollution, and increase worker safety. From this work, the total utilization system was developed. This system consists of an initial fumigation done in conjunction with forced-air cooling, which ensures good gas penetration, as well as additional fumigation in the storage room at weekly intervals. The quantity of SO$_2$ applied during fumigation depends on the number of boxes present, the material used in their construction, and the ability of SO$_2$ to penetrate the box and internal packing material. Total utilization integrates the concept that the amount of SO$_2$ gas needed to kill *Botrytis* spores and exposed mycelium depends on the concentration and the length of time that the fungus is exposed to the fumigant. A cumulative concentration, calculated as the product of the concentration and the time, called CT product, describes the SO$_2$ exposure needed to kill the decay organism. A CT of at least 100 ppm-hour is the minimum required to kill spores and mycelium of *Botrytis* at 0°C (32°F). To monitor the effectiveness of the fumigation program, dosimeter tubes are placed in boxes located in positions that have the least air flow or are the most difficult to fumigate. Following fumigation, the dosimeter tube should record a CT of at least 100 ppm-hour for

the fumigation to be regarded as effective.

Existing facilities using traditional fumigation should consider switching to the total utilization system. This change often uses half the amount of SO$_2$ gas, does not require venting the rooms to the atmosphere, and improves uniformity of SO$_2$ distribution. It can also increase the effectiveness of fumigation while minimizing the occurrence of chemical injury, or "bleaching," as a result of excessive SO$_2$ gas. More information on the total utilization system can be found in the *Sulfur Dioxide Fumigation of Table Grapes* (Luvisi 1992).

In addition to storage fumigation, slow-release sulfur dioxide generating pads are commonly placed in boxes of fruit intended for export or long-term retail handling where SO$_2$ fumigations cannot be conducted. The SO$_2$ generator pads contain sodium metabisulfide that becomes hydrated within the boxes and releases gas continuously at low rates. In California, the pad is used in combination with a perforated polyethylene box liner that retains the gas, reduces moisture loss, and augments *Botrytis* control without enhancing SO$_2$ bleaching.

OTHER ROTS

Several other fungi can cause decay in stored table grapes. The most significant after *Botrytis cinerea* is sour rot caused initially by *Aspergillus* species as they colonize cracks on the berry surface. *Aspergillus niger* and *A. carbonarius* are easily identified when sporulating by their black, sooty spores, which is often referred to as smut. Blue mold rot caused by *Penicillium*

species is also prevalent. The blue-green fungus destroys the entire berry, giving it a watery consistency. *Rhizopus* species can also cause postharvest losses of table grapes. Infection produces no readily visible symptoms; however, when light pressure is applied to an infected berry, the berry explodes, turning into a watery mass. The presence of *Rhizopus* or *Aspergillus* usually indicates a major failure in the cold storage management chain, as these pathogens will not grow at temperatures below 4°C (39°F). Brown spot caused by *Cladosporium cladosporioides* can also be a problem during storage of table grapes; this fungus is generally not a problem on grape berries. However, when berries become sunburned even slightly, *C. cladosporioides* can colonize the injured tissue, and in storage the colonized tissue will begin to break down. The resulting symptom is a brown spot on the grape berry surface. When these berries are removed from storage, the fungus begins to grow, producing green sporulation and growth on the rotted tissue.

Melting decay, or non-Botrytis slip skin (NBSS), of Redglobe grapes and to a lesser extent of Crimson Seedless grapes occurs in some seasons during cold storage. Symptoms include cracking and dissolution of the epidermis followed by the development of sunken, decayed areas (fig. 20.4). In extreme cases, nearly the entire berry is liquefied. Generally, the affected berries are randomly distributed over the cluster, but berry-to-berry spread does occur. The cause of NBSS is a *Hanseniospora* species yeast that colonizes the sugary and nutrient-rich epidermis of berries after they are covered by the oozing liquid resulting from sour rot infections. This layer of contamination dries in the field, but later in storage, under high humidity, one species of *Hanseniospora* that is resistant to SO$_2$ begins to ferment the wet sugary layer. The result is that the epidermal cell wall is dissolved and the yeast is able to begin rotting the berry pulp. Control of NBSS can be achieved by controlling sour rot in the vineyard or by not harvesting "dripped-on" clusters. Trimmed clusters will still exhibit NBSS symptoms and should be retained for sale in local or U.S. markets.

Although powdery mildew caused by *Erysiphe necator* does not develop or spread through storage, it can leave objectionable scarring on berries and decrease the storage potential of infected clusters if lesions occur on the fruit or rachis. Rachis infections cause an increase in water loss from the berries. Dried berries pull away from the pedicle and are more susceptible to bleaching during fumigation or may fall off the cluster. The rapid drying also reduces the marketability of the fruit. Rachis infection must be controlled in the field before harvest.

REFERENCES

Gubler, W. D., J. J. Marois, A. M. Bledsoe, and L. J. Bettiga. 1987. Control of Botrytis bunch rot of grape with canopy management. Plant Disease 71(7): 599–601.

Luvisi, D. L. 1992. Sulfur dioxide fumigation of table grapes. Oakland: University of California Agriculture and Natural Resources Publication 1932.

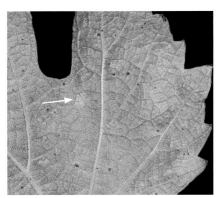

Fungal Diseases **21 POWDERY MILDEW**

Larry J. Bettiga, W. Douglas Gubler, and George M. Leavitt

Figure 21.1 Ascospore infection in spring can be monitored by examining the undersurface of basal leaves near the bark and looking for faint brown spots (arrow) caused by a developing colony. *Photo*: L. J. Bettiga.

Figure 21.2 Mildew colonies on a leaf's upper surface appear as small, white fuzzy patches (A) that can coalesce and cover the entire leaf (B). *Photos*: L. J. Bettiga.

Powdery mildew caused by the fungus *Erysiphe necator* Schweinitz (syn. *Uncinula necator*) is the most serious and widespread disease in California vineyards in terms of expenses incurred for control and losses in quality and yield. In some years, the disease can result in heavy yield losses, as well as a decrease in storage life and quality of table grapes due to rachis infections. In addition, reduced wine quality can occur if as little as 3% of the berries are infected. Severe mildew may also cause berries to crack, allowing rot organisms to enter, reducing the quality of table, raisin, and wine grapes.

The degree of susceptibility to mildew varies. Cabernet Sauvignon, Carignane, Chardonnay, Chenin blanc, and Ruby Seedless are severely affected, while Riesling, Semillon, Thompson Seedless, and Zinfandel are moderately susceptible. Colombard, Merlot, Petite Sirah, and Rubired are much less susceptible. However, in years when disease pressure is high, powdery mildew can cause severe losses on all cultivars.

The fungus also infects other members of the plant family Vitaceae, including all of the native North American grapes in the genus *Vitis*. These species are less severely affected than the *V. vinifera* cultivars commonly grown in California. Other related susceptible species are monk's hood vine (*Ampelopsis aconitifolia*), Virginia creeper (*Parthenocissus quinquefolia*), and Boston ivy (*P. tricuspidata*).

Symptoms

All succulent grapevine tissues are susceptible to mildew infection and show characteristic signs and symptoms. In most California production areas, especially on highly susceptible cultivars, initial powdery mildew symptoms have been observed to occur approximately 7 to 10 days after the first spring rain. Individual colonies appear on the underside of basal leaves (fig. 21.1). These colonies give rise to secondary inoculum (conidia), which spreads to other leaves and fruit in the canopy and subsequently to other vines. The fungus forms a white, weblike mat of hyphal strands (mycelium) over the infected tissue's surface (fig. 21.2). Short, rootlike branches (haustoria) grow from the mycelium into the outermost layer of plant cells to draw out nutrients. Chains of spores (conidia) borne on short stalks (conidiophores) arise from the mycelium, giving a dusty or powdery appearance (fig. 21.3).

In some vineyards, especially Carignane, young shoots entirely or partially covered with mildew (flag shoots) can be found shortly after budbreak (fig. 21.4). These flag shoots give rise to secondary inoculum (conidia). Conidia then are spread by wind and equipment and cause further disease increase. In powdery mildew's type of overwintering (bud perennation), infected shoots are expressed in the same leaf stage at which infection occurred the previous year.

Leaves

Mildew colonies on leaves are usually found either on the underside of exposed leaves or on both sides of well-shaded leaves. High light intensity or ultraviolet light is detrimental to the fungus, and it is more common to find colonies on the underside of the more-exposed leaves of canopies. The colonies can be detected at an early stage in

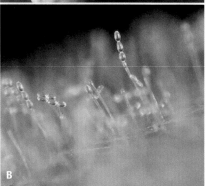

Figure 21.3 Mildew spores are formed on short stalks (A) and are borne in chains of three or four (B). *Photos*: J. K. Clark.

their development by faint yellow patches about 6 mm (0.25 in) in diameter on the upper leaf surface above the growing colony and by the associated webbing and spore chains that give the colonies their characteristic white to gray color on the underside of such leaves (fig. 21.5). When colonies are small, their detection is enhanced by the use of a hand lens (fig. 21.6). If severe infections develop when the leaves are young, yellowing, crinkling, distortion, and defoliation can result.

Shoots

Severe early-season shoot infections can stunt vine growth on susceptible cultivars. Mildew colonies on green shoots appear as grayish patches that turn to black (fig. 21.7) or reddish brown blotchy areas on the surface as the shoots mature into dormant canes (fig. 21.8).

Fruit

Early infection of berries can reduce size (fig. 21.9), produce scarring, and cause berries to split. Weblike scars on the surface of mature berries are a sign of previous mildew infections (fig. 21.10).

Late in the season (usually after mid-August in most production regions but by July in the central coast), small, spherical fruiting bodies (chasmothecia) may be formed amid the mycelial mats on leaves, fruit, and rachises; they contain a second type of spore (ascospore). As chasmothecia (previously called cleistothecia) form, they are first yellow, then amber, and then black as they mature in late summer and fall (fig. 21.11). Ascospores act as primary inoculum for grapevine powdery mildew in most of California's production regions.

DISEASE CYCLE

Overwintering

Powdery mildew cannot grow on dead or dormant grape tissue. *E. necator* can overwinter the dormant period on grapevines as chasmothecia or as bud perennation (mycelium, haustoria, or conidia in dormant buds). Ascospores from chasmothecia and conidia from bud perennation can provide the primary inoculum to start the initial infections after budbreak (fig. 21.12).

Bud perennation

Historically, this form of overwintering has been thought to be due to a piece of mycelium of the pathogen being trapped inside the bud at some point during the growing season. However, more recent research has shown that the mycelium in the bud results in infected leaf prophylls (rudimentary leaves) and trichomes (plant hairs) within the bud. Fungal haustoria are evident in many of these cells. This work has also shown the presence of both germinating and nongerminated conidia within the dormant bud. When budbreak occurs in the spring, the infected tissue will emerge from the bud, resulting in a flag shoot. This type of overwintering can be masked if spring temperatures are above 30°C (86°F) for extended periods of time. However, if temperatures are cool enough to allow fungal development on emerging shoots, the disease symptoms will still be readily evident. At temperatures in the range of 21° to 30°C (70° to 86°F), secondary infections will occur within 5 to 7 days as the infected part of the shoot emerges; disease infections on other plant parts will occur early. However, if

Figure 21.4 Bud perennation can result in the occurrence of flag shoots, which provide a source of inoculum for mildew infection in spring. *Photo*: J. K. Clark.

Figure 21.5 Faint yellow patches (A) on the upper leaf surface are an indication of mildew colony development; look at the underside (B) for the colony. *Photos*: L. J. Bettiga.

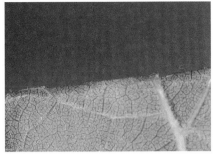

Figure 21.6 The viability of mildew colonies can be checked by rolling leaves and observing with a hand lens. Sporulating colonies will have spore stalks (conidiophores) that stand up within the colony. *Photo*: L. J. Bettiga.

Figure 21.7 Severe infection showing black scarring on the shoots. *Photo*: L. J. Bettiga.

Figure 21.8 Scarring on canes resulting from shoot infection. *Photo*: J. K. Clark.

Figure 21.9 Heavy mildew infection on Thompson Seedless shows berry stunting. *Photo*: J. K. Clark.

Figure 21.10 Weblike scars on Thompson Seedless. *Photo*: J. K. Clark.

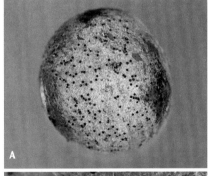

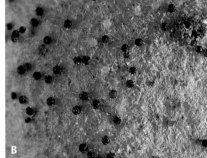

Figure 21.11 Development of chasmothecia in late summer (A). Chasmothecia (B) turn black when mature. *Photos*: L. J. Bettiga.

Figure 21.12 Powdery mildew disease cycle.

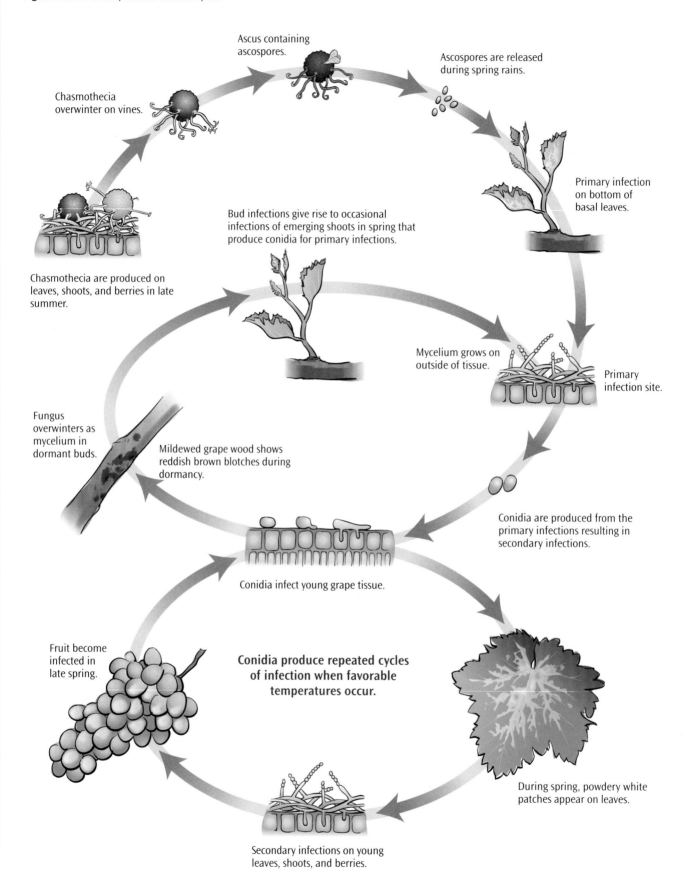

Ascus containing ascospores.

Chasmothecia overwinter on vines.

Ascospores are released during spring rains.

Chasmothecia are produced on leaves, shoots, and berries in late summer.

Bud infections give rise to occasional infections of emerging shoots in spring that produce conidia for primary infections.

Primary infection on bottom of basal leaves.

Mycelium grows on outside of tissue.

Primary infection site.

Fungus overwinters as mycelium in dormant buds.

Mildewed grape wood shows reddish brown blotches during dormancy.

Conidia are produced from the primary infections resulting in secondary infections.

Conidia infect young grape tissue.

Fruit become infected in late spring.

Conidia produce repeated cycles of infection when favorable temperatures occur.

During spring, powdery white patches appear on leaves.

Secondary infections on young leaves, shoots, and berries.

temperatures are below 21°C (70°F) or above 30°C (86°F), secondary infections will be delayed until late spring, when temperatures warm or cool to the optimal temperature range for the pathogen.

Chasmothecia

These sexually produced fruiting bodies are washed off leaves and shoots onto the bark of upper trunks and cordons during fall rains. Each chasmothecia contains multiple asci (spore sacs), with each ascus having eight ascospores (fig. 21.13). In the San Joaquin Valley, powdery mildew overwinters as both chasmothecia and as bud perennation. In the central San Joaquin Valley, chasmothecia are present at low densities, and their importance as a source of primary inoculum is not fully understood. Collections of chasmothecia in vineyards from Fresno and Madera Counties have been shown to produce viable ascospores, but only an average of one chasmothecium per gram of bark is common. In Tulare and Kern Counties and in all other areas, cordons contain numerous chasmothecia. In shoot-positioned canopies, 50% of chasmothecia produced on leaves fall and land on cordons, arms, and spurs, whereas in curtaining canopies only 25% of chasmothecia are caught on cordons, arms, and spurs. In areas where chasmothecia are not common, bud perennation provides the inoculum for primary infections in the spring.

The amount of overwintering mildew capable of starting disease is directly proportional to the amount of disease in the previous year.

Germination

Ascospores

Mature chasmothecia require free moisture for release and germination of ascospores. In the spring, ascospores are released during rains, heavy fogs, dew periods, and sprinkler irrigation. Ascospores are actively ejected to a height of about 24 mm (1 in) and are water splashed and windblown to newly emerging shoots and leaves. Ascospores are released at temperatures from 10° to 27°C (50° to 80.5°F), with the optimal temperature for spore release being 20° to 24°C (68° to 75°F). Increased efficiency of germination and infection occur at temperatures from 20° to 25°C (68° to 77°F). At optimal temperatures, ascospore germination and infection can occur in as few as 12 hours if the leaves remain wet. Germination and infection are negatively affected by temperatures above 25°C (77°F) and below 20°C (68°F). Individual colonies found on the lower surface of basal leaves are the first sign of the pathogen, and these give rise to the first symptom, the small, round, lightly chlorotic circles noticeable on the upper leaf surface directly above the developing colony. Visible powdery mildew colonies develop 7 to 10 days following a spring rainfall when temperatures are from 10° to 27°C (50° to 80.5°F).

Bud perennation

If mildew was severe in the previous season, reddish brown stainlike scarring from old infections will be apparent on canes. If scarring is located on or over the bud, the bud may contain overwintering haustoria and conidia. Growth of the fungus from infected buds takes on the appearance of extensive white, webby mycelium on part or all of one or more leaves and the shoot. This growth may occur on the second or third leaf that emerges, or the entire shoot might show a heavy infection. Secondary conidia are produced on this mycelium, and spores spread to other parts of the vine or to adjacent vines. In cool springs, shoots produced from such buds should be examined closely for onset of sporulation. The flag shoots often appear on the same vines from year to year. Bud perennation occurs when bud positions on the shoot become infected by the pathogen early in the season. As a bud develops, the outer scales become suberized, and the bud becomes less susceptible to disease infection. Research has shown that latent buds that become infected when shoots are in the three unfolded leaf stage can be expected to show disease the following year when shoots are in the same stage. This is true for infections at budbreak or six or nine unfolded leaves. Thus, growers who know when disease infection occurred in the previous year might begin to monitor at the same phenological stage in the current year. During hot springs, when temperatures are above 30°C (86°F), fungal growth and infection are delayed or do not occur.

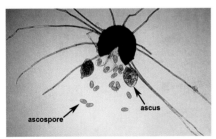

Figure 21.13 Chasmothecia showing asci and ascospores. *Photo*: W. D. Gubler.

Conidia

Mild weather favors powdery mildew. Conidia germinate at leaf surface temperatures from 6° to 32°C (43° to 90°F), the optimum being 25°C (77°F). Rapid germination and mycelial growth take place from 21° to 30°C (70° to 86°F). At optimal temperatures, the generation time (the time between spore germination and production of spores by the new colony) is only 5 days. Temperatures above 32°C (90°F) kill spores and mildew colonies if the duration is long enough (12 hours) and the fungus is exposed to direct ultraviolet light. *E. necator* is capable of developing at temperatures below those favorable for grape plant growth, but the pathogen is destroyed at high temperatures that do not harm the host plant.

The temperatures given in the previous discussion would be expected to occur at the leaf or fruit surface and may vary from 5° to 10°C (9° to 18°F) above or below the ambient air temperature, depending on the intensity of the radiation to which the leaves or fruit are exposed and the water status of the vines. The host plant buffers the lethal effect of air temperatures above 32°C (90°F). For instance, during short periods when air temperatures surpass 40°C (104°F), powdery mildew colonies exposed to sunlight and the full effects of high temperatures are killed rapidly (3 hours), but colonies on cluster stems protected by cool berries under foliage may survive. The fungus is destroyed completely when air temperatures exceeding 35°C (95°F) last for extended periods in the early part of the growing season, when direct sunlight penetrates all parts of the canopy.

Temperature plays a larger role than does moisture in disease development caused by conidia. The disease normally develops over a large range of relative humidities, with an optimum of 65%. However, free water, such as rain, dew, or irrigation water, can cause poor and abnormal germination of conidia or may wash them from the host tissue, especially when large volumes of water are used for eradication. However, the spores and mycelium are somewhat hydrophobic and are not easily wetted by water; under dense canopies, many may escape the effects of rain or wash water. Water lowers the temperature and increases the relative humidity under the canopy and may actually enhance the rate of development of surviving infections, as is evidenced by the occurrence of severe infections under drip or sprinkler irrigation.

Infection

Powdery mildew is spread by windborne spores. Nothing is known about the distance the spores can travel. However, observations show infections spread most rapidly in a downwind direction if conditions are favorable. Thus, vineyards downwind from a severely infected vineyard may receive more inoculum pressure and require a change in control practices. The spread of powdery mildew is assisted by the presence of extensive grape plantings, backyard grapevines, wild grapes, and other hosts. The spores land and produce new infections, and the cycle repeats itself many times during the growing season.

The damage sustained by a vineyard depends largely on the time of first infection. Early fruit infections cause stunted berries, scarring, berry cracking, reduced yield, lower color development (fig. 21.14), and off-flavors in wine. Powdery mildew also may affect the rate of photosynthesis by infected leaves, and, when vines are severely infected, it may impair their ability to produce adequate amounts of sugar.

The susceptibility of various plant parts to powdery mildew infection changes through the season. The fruit is susceptible to infection from the beginning of development until the sugar content reaches about 8%, which is why early-season control is vital. Established infections continue to produce spores until the berries contain 12 to 15% sugar. Old infections become inactive and the berries become immune after the sugar content exceeds 15%. Likewise, on leaves mildew develops best when leaves are just fully expanded and usually does not

Figure 21.14 Heavy mildew infection on Cabernet Sauvignon shows delay in coloration. *Photo*: J. K. Clark.

infect leaves more than 2 months old unless they have been growing under dense shade. Shoots, petioles, and cluster parts (fig. 21.15) are susceptible throughout the growing season. Because mildew requires a living host, dead or dormant tissues are not infected.

MANAGEMENT

Season-long control depends on reducing early-season inoculum and subsequent infection. Although control of powdery mildew is based on the use of fungicides in a preventative program, the integration of cultural practices that influence the microclimate within a vineyard can greatly influence disease control. Using a trellis or training system that adequately exposes the shoot growth followed by shoot thinning, leaf removal, and hedging when appropriate can produce a more-open canopy that can improve fungicide coverage and create a canopy microclimate less conducive to disease.

Fungicide treatment must generally begin promptly and be repeated at appropriate intervals. Timing of the first application depends on the fungicide used, vine growth stage, and potential

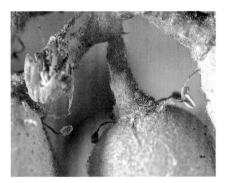

Figure 21.15 Cap stem infections. *Photo*: J. K. Clark.

for disease infection. Early-season control is essential in coastal, Delta, and southern San Joaquin Valley vineyards in most years. However, it is imperative that the effects of weather on disease development be observed. If rainfall after budbreak does not occur in a region, ascospore release may be greatly reduced, and early-season applications may not be needed. In this case, monitor vineyards using the UC powdery mildew risk index model and reduce production costs by eliminating unnecessary fungicide applications. Early-season control also may not be necessary if, after ascospore release, temperatures are cool—15.5° to 19.5°C (60° to 67°F) daytime, 7° to 15.5°C (45° to 60°F) nighttime. At these temperatures, the fungus can infect the vine, but disease does not generally increase simply due to cold temperatures. However, as soon as temperatures start approaching the optimum for the fungus, the pathogen can grow rapidly. Under these conditions, the first application should be oil, for eradication. The concept here is that growers can wait for the disease to be expressed, then use a highly effective eradicant such as one of the oils. At this time the canopy is small and coverage is generally not an issue. Good spray coverage is essential to successfully use this approach.

It has been shown that an application of dry flowable micronized sulfur or light summer oil at budbreak will reduce disease at onset (first visible symptoms of infection) by 95%. This control is due to the artificial release of ascospores by the liquid application: ascospores release onto the soil or into a film of sulfur or oil

and die. This same control was observed when DMI (demethylation inhibitor) fungicides were used. While oil and sulfur are less expensive for this application, it has been shown that an application of Rally (myclobutanil) after late pruning for Eutypa and Botryosphaeria dieback control also has this effect, making the application useful for multiple diseases. Frequency of treatment depends on fungicide choice and weather conditions. Monitor and use the UC Davis powdery mildew risk index model to determine when to start and the necessary spray intervals. Treatment may be discontinued for wine and raisin grapes when fruit reaches 12 Brix but should be continued up to harvest for table grapes.

UC Davis Powdery Mildew Risk Index Model

The UC Davis powdery mildew risk index model was developed and validated for use in California vineyards. It is comprised of components for ascospore and conidial stages. The model uses weather data (canopy temperature and leaf wetness) and the pathogen biology to accurately assess pathogen population increases and decreases during the growing season.

Ascospore Infection Forecasts

The ascospore model was designed to determine the risk of ascospore release and primary infection. It calculates the daily average temperature and measures the duration of leaf wetness. Treatment of ascospore infections is made when the model identifies temperature and surface conditions as high risk or when ascospores are released and germination occurs, namely, when chasmothecia are exposed to 10 mm (0.4 in) or more of moisture from rain, heavy dews, or sprinkler irrigation followed by 12 to 15 hours of leaf wetness when temperatures are from 10° to 27°C (50° to 80.5°F). Seven to 10 days after this initial infection, monitor vineyards for the presence of powdery mildew by collecting 10 to 15 basal leaves from 20 or so vines at random and examine the undersurface for powdery mildew colonies. Once ascospore infection has occurred, use the risk index (RI) to determine the potential of secondary infection by conidia.

Conidial Infections: Risk Index

Once initial or primary infection occurs, either from ascospore infection or bud perennation, the model switches to the RI. Pathogen population increase or secondary infection is based on the effect of temperature on the reproductive rate of the fungus. The key to using the RI is the careful monitoring of temperatures inside the vine canopy. Temperature monitoring equipment is available from a number of suppliers and can provide the information needed for accurate disease assessment. Most of these devices have the powdery mildew model software built in, so the model is easy to use. Some of these devices must be read in the field, while other systems will automatically download and compute the disease index on a mobile, laptop, or office computer. Systems have been designed to record multiple monitoring devices through a computer base station that can be accessed for regional information. The newer weather devices are web-based units that can be placed with ease at any point. Several companies and grower organizations have already established regional weather networks and can provide information to their members or for a fee.

Initiating the Risk Index

After the initial primary infection, an epidemic (widespread disease increase) will begin when there are 3 consecutive days with 6 or more continuous hours of temperatures from 21° to 30°C (70° to 86°F) as measured in the vine canopy.

1. Starting with the index at 0 on the first day, add 20 points for each day with 6 or more continuous hours of temperatures from 21° to 30°C (70° to 86°F).

2. Until the index reaches 60, if a day has fewer than 6 continuous hours of temperatures from 21° to 30°C (70° to 86°F), reset the index to 0 and continue. If using a unit that has the model software included, the fact that the index did not reach 60 points in 3 consecutive days automatically resets the index.

3. If the index reaches 60, an epidemic is under way. Begin using the spray-timing phase of the index.

Spray Timing

Each day, starting on the day after the index reached 60 points during the initiation phase, evaluate the temperatures and adjust the previous day's index according to the rules below. Keep a running tabulation throughout the season. In assigning points, note the following:

- If the index is already at 100, do not add points.

- If the index is already at 0, do not subtract points.

- Do not add more than 20 points per day.

- Do not subtract more than 10 points per day.

- If fewer than 6 continuous hours of temperatures occurred from 21° to 30°C (70° to 86°F), subtract 10 points.

- If 6 or more continuous hours of temperatures occurred from 21° to 30°C (70° to 86°F), add 20 points.

- If temperatures reached 35°C (95°F) for more than 15 minutes, subtract 10 points.

- If there are 6 or more continuous hours with temperatures from 21° to 30°C (70° to 86°F) **and** the temperature rises to or above 35°C (95°F) for at least 15 minutes, add 10 points. (This is the equivalent of combining points 2 and 3 above.)

Examples of temperature duration and ranges are shown in table 21.1. When using the RI, always monitor the vineyard for signs of the disease. The RI can be used to determine disease pressure and how frequently you need to spray to protect the vines. Spray intervals can be shortened or lengthened depending on disease pressure, as indicated in table 21.2.

Many scientists and growers have tried to use this model by simply keeping a thermometer in the vineyard. In every case, they have failed to compute the index accurately. It is therefore

Table 21.1. UC Davis powdery mildew risk index model

Day	Hours at 21° to 30°C (70° to 86°F)	Risk index (RI) points		Remarks
		Daily	**Cumulative**	
1	7	+20	20	
2	6	+20	40	
3	3	0	0	
4	8	+20	20	
5	7	+20	40	
6	6	+20	60	start of an epidemic
7	7	+20	80	high pressure
8	4	-10	70	high pressure
9	5	-10	60	high pressure
10	4	-10	50	moderate pressure
11	3	-10	40	moderate pressure
12	0	-10	30	low pressure
13	2	-10	20	low pressure
14	3	-10	10	low pressure
15	4	-10	0	low pressure
16	6	+20	20	low pressure
17	7	+20	40	moderate pressure
18	8	+20	60	high pressure
19	7	+20	80	high pressure
20	7	+20	100	high pressure
21	8	+20	100	high pressure
22	10, max temp. 36.7°C (98°F)	+10	100	high pressure
23	7	+20	100	high pressure

Note: After an epidemic has started, the RI is calculated by adding 20 index points for each day that has at least 6 continuous hours at temperatures from 21° to 30°C (70° to 86°F). If there are fewer than 6 hours or if the maximum temperature in the canopy that day is greater than 35°C (95°F) for at least 15 minutes, 10 points are subtracted from the index. The disease index never goes higher than 100 or lower than 0 and is measured in increments of 10 or 20. An index of 0 to 30 indicates nonexistent to low disease pressure, 40 to 50 indicates moderate disease pressure, and 60 to 100 indicates high disease pressure.

Table 21.2. Spray intervals based on disease pressure using the UC Davis powdery mildew risk index model

Index	Disease pressure	Pathogen status	Suggested spray schedule			
			Biologicals* and SARs[†]	Sulfur	Demethylation inhibitors (DMI)*[1]	Strobilurins and quinolines*
0–30	low	present	7- to 14-day interval	14- to 21-day interval	21-day interval or label interval	21-day interval or label interval
40–50	moderate	reproduces every 15 days	7-day interval	10- to 17-day interval	21-day interval	21-day interval
60 or above	high	reproduces every 5 days	use not recommended	7-day interval	10- to 14-day interval	14-day interval

Notes:

*Refer to the UC Grape Pest Management Guidelines for examples of currently registered products.

[†]SARs = Systemic acquired resistance products.

recommended that to successfully use the index you need to purchase or have access to an appropriate weather station that allows you to access the data easily. Weather stations range in price from $250 to $5,000. In every case and regardless of unit cost, growers have recouped the cost of the unit within the first year by saving on spray applications.

Resistance Management

Fungicides can be separated into chemical classes based on shared attributes such as basic structure, mode of action, type of fungi controlled, and resistance risk. Several classes of fungicides with different modes of action are available for powdery mildew management. Alternating fungicides with different modes of action is essential to prevent pathogen populations from developing resistance. The Fungicide Resistance Action Committee (FRAC, http://www.frac.info/) has assigned FRAC code numbers to fungicide classes according to their modes of actions. Fungicides with a different group

number are suitable to alternate in a resistance management program. In California, powdery mildew has developed a high level of resistance to the triazole fungicides in the demethylation inhibitor (DMI) fungicide class. Do not apply more than two sequential sprays of any fungicide before alternating with a fungicide that has a different mode of action. Fungicides with single-site modes of action (classes: DMI, strobilurins, quinolines) are more susceptible to the selection of resistant fungus biotypes. Once resistance to a fungicide has developed, reduced sensitivity to other fungicides within the same chemical class or between classes with the same mode of action will decrease fungicide efficacy. For the most current information on registered fungicides and FRAC code numbers to assist in selecting options for fungicide resistance management, refer to the UC IPM Grape Pest Management Guidelines (www.ipm.ucdavis.edu/PMG/) or "Efficacy and Timing of Fungicides, Bactericides and Biologicals for Deciduous Tree Fruit,

Nut, Strawberry and Vine Crops" at the UC IPM website (www.ipm.ucdavis.edu/).

Synthetic Fungicides

Demethylation inhibitors (FRAC Code 3)

Demethylation inhibitors (DMI), also known as sterol inhibitors (SI), sterol biosynthesis inhibitors(SBI), and ergosterol biosynthesis inhibitors (EBI), are locally systemic and have similar single-site modes of action by interfering with sterol formation in cell wall synthesis, causing the fungus to die. This group of fungicides contains several chemical classes that have similar modes of action. Triazole, imidazole, and pyrimidine are chemical classes that are represented by DMI fungicides that have been used for mildew control in vineyards. The first DMI to be used in California was a triazole compound, triadimefon (Bayleton), which was introduced in 1982. Resistance to triadimefon was suspected to be present in California vineyards in 1985 and was documented in

1986. Subsequently, other DMI fungicides have been registered for use on grapes. Research in California vineyards has shown that triadimefon-resistant mildew isolates have reduced sensitivity to other DMI fungicides, but that these other products can still be used effectively if applied correctly. If one is using the risk index for spray timing, then resistance is already considered, with the exception of product used.

Strobilurins (FRAC Code 11)

Also referred to as quinone outside inhibitors (QoI), these compounds are based on the chemical structure of naturally occurring fungicides extracted from wood-rotting mushrooms that have been chemically altered to make them both stable and biologically active. These are single-site mode of action materials that control mildew by interfering with electron transport in the cytochrome bc_1 complex. These materials are locally systemic. Fungicides in this group have activity against powdery mildew, *Phomopsis*, *Botrytis*, and downy mildew with varying levels of activity among the fungicides in regard to each disease. Resistance to these compounds has been reported, and it is suspected that reduced sensitivity occurs in California vineyards.

Quinolines (FRAC Code 13)

This chemical class has one active compound, quinoxyfen (Quintec). The fungicide prevents mildew from infecting grape tissue by preventing spores from developing appressoria (infection pegs) during germ tube development. It does not have any postinfection or curative activity. This material has a single-site mode of action, and

like the DMI and strobilurins fungicides it has a high risk for the selection of resistant isolates. After application, it is adsorbed by the cuticle of green tissues and locally redistributed by vapor action.

Benzophenone (FRAC Code 8)

This chemical class currently has one active product, metrafenone (Vivando). The fungicide prevents mildew from infecting grape tissue by preventing spores from developing appressoria (infection pegs) during germ tube development. It can also limit fungal mycelial growth and spore production. It does not have curative activity. This material has a single-site mode of action and has a proposed mode of action as an actin disruptor. After application, it is adsorbed by the waxy cuticle of green tissues and locally redistributed by vapor action.

Fungicide mixtures

Fungicide formulations are available for powdery mildew control that are mixtures of more than one active ingredient. Mixing fungicides with different modes of action can delay the development of resistance and can improve disease control by broadening the spectrum of activity. Since these products have multiple FRAC code numbers, it is important to recognize that for effective resistance management, rotational products with completely different FRAC codes need to be selected in developing fungicide programs for mildew control.

Natural Compounds, Oils, and Inorganic Salts

Many fungicides control mildew by direct contact. Light horticultural oils, fatty acids, and many different formulations of potassium or sodium carbonates can control

powdery mildew if used correctly in an integrated program. The drawback common to all of these materials is their relatively short residual activity and their need for direct contact with the fungus in order to achieve control. Another drawback is that these products must be applied frequently during high disease pressure to be economically viable. They do not compete with the pathogen successfully when the pathogen is reproducing every 5 days. Resistance management or the insertion of soft chemistry into any integrated pest management program makes these products valuable.

Light summer oils are excellent eradicants. Although complete eradication is not possible, this treatment does reduce inoculum and thereby reduces disease. An application of some other fungicide should follow within 5 to 7 days. Research has shown that mineral oils will reduce the viability of overwintering chasmothecia when sprayed as a dormant or 100% budbreak application, reducing the primary inoculum. Mineral- and plant-based oils vary in their potential for phytotoxicity. Oils act as penetrants and will move other chemicals on the surface of the canopy into the plant tissues. Oil treatments applied less than 14 days after a sulfur application can result in leaf burn.

Biologicals

Biological fungicides (fungal and bacterial products) can also be used to control powdery mildew. They have been shown to protect against disease if applied prior to the onset of disease, but they should be used only when disease pressure is low.

Systemic Acquired Resistance

Systemic acquired resistance (SAR) materials induce the grapevine to produce antifungal metabolites that increase the vine's resistance to mildew infection. These products may be used in an integrated spray program but may not give adequate disease control under high-pressure conditions.

Sulfur

Sulfur continues to be an effective and economical material, and in most years regular applications of sulfur dust provide adequate control. But to be effective, sulfur must be present before the fungus develops. Sulfur comes in dust and wettable formulations and is typically applied at 7- to 10-day intervals for dust and up to an 18-day interval for dry flowable sulfurs. Begin dusting 7 to 14 days after budbreak and repeat every 14 days under low to medium disease pressure. Or, if shoot growth is rapid, start applications when shoots are 7.5 cm (3 in) long, repeat when shoots are 15 cm (6 in) long, and continue every 10 days until fruit begins to ripen (in wine and raisin grape vineyards) or until summer temperatures exceed optimal temperatures for powdery mildew growth and infection. If dusting every other vine row, increase the sulfur dose and shorten the time interval to 7 days. The UC Davis powdery mildew risk index model described above can be used effectively to time sulfur applications based on disease pressure. Wine and raisin grape growers may be able to stop sulfuring when ripening begins because the berries become less susceptible after they reach an 8% sugar content. However, to make sure all berries have reached this point, continue sulfuring until the average sugar test is 12 to 13%.

Table grape growers should continue dusting as long as the temperature remains favorable for infection, to prevent infection of rachis and cap stems. In the San Joaquin Valley, sulfur applications in grapes are often discontinued during hot weather after early July, but they are resumed in late August when temperatures cool. Because sulfur washes off vines easily, reapply it immediately after rain or sprinkler irrigation. Temperatures favorable to mildew growth often follow rainstorms.

Sulfur prevents infection by mildew spores. It is not known whether the spores must be in direct contact with the sulfur particles to achieve control or whether a vapor phase of sulfur is toxic to the pathogen. In either case, good coverage is the key to effective control. There is no experimental evidence suggesting that dusting sulfur will eradicate existing mildew colonies.

Sulfur can cause severe burns on vines if applied when air temperatures are near 38°C (100°F), especially in spring and early summer, so exercise care during hot weather. Phytotoxicity often occurs when a sudden rise in temperatures, such as from 32° to 39°C (89.5° to 102°F), occurs shortly after sulfur application. Phytotoxicity may be lessened by reducing the amount of sulfur used per application or by applying dust in the early evening to allow slow oxidation during the night. Sulfur dust has been associated with off-site drift and can aggravate spider mite outbreaks by suppressing beneficial predatory mites and thrips in vineyards; the use of wettable sulfur can help prevent problems with drift and mite outbreaks, and can help preserve worker health and safety.

The severity of mildew problems varies greatly among grape cultivars and local climate types. Depending on the production area, different numbers of sulfur applications are required to achieve adequate control. Local conditions must be taken into account when outlining a mildew control program for each season.

Eradication

In years when conditions are particularly favorable for mildew, adequate control may not be achieved. Infections can become established if an application is missed or the fungicide selection, spray intervals, or coverage were not adequate. Since powdery mildew mycelium lives primarily on the surface of infected green tissues, the organism is susceptible to fungicides that have eradicant properties. Traditionally under these conditions, wettable sulfur, plus a suitable wetting agent and water, was used to wash off conidia and kill existing colonies. The eradication effect is probably from the combination of water and wetting agent; the wettable sulfur merely replaced the sulfur washed off during the application. Today, oils are considered to be the best eradicants as they kill *E. necator* on contact. Effective eradication of mildew depends on the spray water penetrating and covering the vine canopy and clusters. Penetration is generally more effective when shoots are short and decreases as the canopy develops and becomes denser. In severe cases, several eradication spray applications may be needed for adequate coverage and control once the canopy is fully developed (especially for very dense canopies). Opening the canopy by leaf removal or hedging, when appropriate, may improve spray coverage and improve disease control. It has been observed that if mildew eradication has been used as described above, a treatment of a fungicide with preventative activity should be used at the highest dose at 6 days after eradication. The reason for this is that eradication does not kill existing lesions, and they begin to sporulate about 5 to 6 days later.

The second application helps kill the pathogen in the lesion and prevent further infections.

Some synthetic fungicides with a high risk of resistance have eradicant properties. Their use when there are high levels of established infections should be avoided to prevent the development of resistance.

Mineral oils have also been shown to be effective in eradication programs. Similar to the wettable sulfur washes, control depends on adequate coverage of the infective tissues.

REFERENCES

Bulit, J. U., and R. Lafon. 1978. Powdery mildew of the vine. In D. M. Spencer, ed., The powdery mildews. New York: Academic Press. 525–548.

Delp, C. J. 1954. Effect of temperature and relative humidity on the grape powdery mildew fungus. Phytopathology 44:615–626.

Gubler, W. D., M. R. Rademacher, S. J. Vasquez, and C. S. Thomas. 1999. Control of powdery mildew using the UC Davis powdery mildew risk index. APSnet Feature, http://www.apsnet.org/online/feature/pmildew/.

Gubler, W. D., H. L. Ypema, D. G. Ouimette, and L. J. Bettiga. 1994. Resistance of *Uncinula necator* to DMI fungicides in California vines. In S. Heany,

D. Slawson, D. W. Hollomon, M. Smith, and D. W. Parry, eds., Fungicide resistance. Proceedings of the Fungicide Resistance Symposium, University of Reading, England, March 28–30, 1994. BCPC Monograph No. 60. Farnham, Surrey, UK: British Crop Protection Council. 19–25.

———. 1996. Occurrence of resistance in *Uncinula necator* to triadimefon, myclobutanil, and fenarimol in California grapevines. Plant Disease 80:902–909.

Miller, T. C., and W. D. Gubler. 2004. Sensitivity of California isolates of *Uncinula necator* to trifloxystrobin and spiroxamine, and update on triadimefon sensitivity. Plant Disease 88:1205–1212.

Pearson, R. C., and D. M. Gadoury. 1987. Cleistothecia, the source of primary inoculum for grape powdery mildew in New York. Phytopathology 77:1509–1514.

Rumbolz, J., and W. D. Gubler 2005. Susceptibility of grapevine buds to infection by powdery mildew *Erysiphe necator*. Plant Pathology 54:535–548.

Sall, M. A. 1980. Epidemiology of grape powdery mildew: A model. Phytopathology 70:338–342.

Sall, M. A., and J. Wyrinski. 1982. Perennation of powdery mildew in buds of grapevines. Plant Disease 66:678–679.

22 RAISIN MOLDS AND ROTS

Stephen J. Vasquez and Matthew W. Fidelibus

Raisin molds and rots may arise from infections initiated before or during harvest or while drying. The likelihood of infection depends on the grapevine cultivar, cultural practices, vineyard design, and environmental conditions. For example, thin-skinned berries and cultivars with tight clusters are particularly susceptible to damage and therefore are especially prone to rots. Rough handling of fruit by hands, knives, or machines during harvest, as well as insect damage, causes wounds where bunch rot organisms may establish themselves. Excessively close row or vine spacing and overly dense canopies also facilitate bunch rots by creating a favorable microclimate for disease. Vineyards whose rows are oriented north to south, or those having poorly prepared terraces, have suboptimal drying conditions that favor rot development, especially following rain. Rain and cool temperatures during the drying period (August–October) promote fruit infection and increased disease severity (fig. 22.1).

Although the amount of rainfall received during fruit drying is an important factor in mold development, overall weather conditions, such as clouds and high humidity following a storm, also influence the amount of damage. For example, the southerly tropical storms received in California during the raisin harvests of 1976, 1978, 1982, 2002, and 2011 resulted in heavy losses. Rains in excess of 2.5 cm (1 in) were followed by a week or more of poor drying weather. More typically, northerly storms drop 0.6 cm (0.25 in) or less and are followed by wind, sunlight, and drier air. New raisin production systems such as dried on vine (DOV) and continuous tray (CT) have eliminated some traditional practices that contribute to rot, but they have also created new challenges of their own.

CAUSAL ORGANISMS AND CONTAMINATION PROBLEMS

Raisin molds may be caused by a wide range of primary and secondary fungal organisms normally found in the vineyard. They include species of *Alternaria, Aspergillus, Botrytis, Chaetomium, Cladosporium, Helminthosporium, Hormiscium, Hormodendrum, Penicillium,*

Figure 22.1 Partially dried grapes with mold infection following rain. *Photo*: L. P. Christensen.

Rhizopus, and *Stemphylium.* Sour rot may occur if cracks or wounds in the berry skin are colonized by *Acetobacter* bacteria, which convert sugars to acetic acid. Some bunch rot fungi may produce mycotoxins, secondary metabolites made by fungi that cause a pathological condition in humans or animals after ingestion of a food product. Mycotoxins have been closely monitored for years in grain products and have recently been identified as potential contaminants of other foods, including grapes and grape products. In fact, many countries now monitor mycotoxin levels in raisins. A mycotoxin of particular concern in raisins is ochratoxin A (OTA). Three fungi commonly found in California vineyards, *Penicillium verrucosum, Aspergillus ochraceus,* and *A. cabonarius,* are capable of producing OTA. Although OTA has been detected in grapes and grape products, levels detected in raisins at the retail level are quite low. Even so, it is desirable to implement best management practices that minimize common vineyard pests and diseases that can lead to fungal rots. Such practices will limit the potential development of OTA. Commercial processing, which includes testing for mold by USDA inspectors upon arrival to the processor, further eliminates the presence of contaminates in the final product purchased by consumers.

DISEASE CYCLE

Throughout their growth and development, grape clusters are exposed to a variety of fungi commonly found in vineyards. Wetting of berries by precipitation or irrigation facilitates the migration of sugars and amino acids from the berry onto its surface. Spores of fungi such as *Alternaria, Botrytis, Aspergillus, Cladosporium,* and *Rhizopus* can quickly germinate and grow in this medium. The fungi may then penetrate the skin and colonize the interior of a berry, causing it to rot. Free moisture for 24 to 36 hours and temperatures of 16° to 24°C (61° to 75°F) are ideal for such mold development. Smashed or broken berries and fruit already infected with bunch rot are especially vulnerable to fungal infections. Fungi may also grow on the paper trays used for drying, causing the berries or raisins to stick to the tray.

The USDA Processed Products Inspection Branch classifies molds and rots as either nodular or putrid. Nodular mold is mostly on the berry's surface and can be removed by washing. Putrid mold infects the berry's interior, causing permanent damage. Both are detected by visual inspection after boiling the raisins in water for 30 minutes.

PREVENTION AND CONTROL

As the berries approach maturity, they become more susceptible to infection by *Acetobacter* species bacteria and an array of fungi that contribute to the development of the summer bunch rot complex (sour rot). Because summer rot results from the infections of many different organisms, the use of fungicides to prevent or control it is not always effective. Fungicides applied before cluster closure and prior to ripening may be useful if summer bunch rot has been a problem in the past. Management of summer bunch rot is mainly based on preventing or reducing injury to the berries as they mature.

Insecticide applications can reduce mold infections by preventing injury to the berries from insect feeding. Larvae of insects such as omnivorous leafroller and raisin moth feed on maturing fruit and will cause wounds that are susceptible to secondary fungal infections (see part 4, "Insect and Mite Pests," and part 5, "Stored Raisin Products Pests").

A good, season-long management strategy for powdery mildew control (see section 21, "Powdery Mildew") is an important approach to reducing rot at harvest. Powdery mildew infections cause cracks and lesions that lead to secondary infections by fungi and sour rot bacteria. Fungicide applications made prior to harvest help reduce the damage caused by rot-causing fungi. Preharvest applications are especially useful when significant precipitation is forecast and fruit is to be harvested shortly after a rain event. Post-rain treatments are not very effective. Fungicides should be used only according to label instructions.

Additional cultural practices that help reduce summer bunch rot include proper irrigation, fertilization, and canopy management practices. Vines should be pruned to achieve vine balance between vegetative growth and cluster number. Thompson Seedless vineyards with a history of tight clusters can be treated with gibberellic acid (GA) at bloom to thin and loosen clusters. GA is labeled for use only on Thompson Seedless and Zante Currant (Black Corinth) cultivars.

TRADITIONAL TRAY-DRIED PRODUCTION

Cultural practices and time of harvest can decrease the risk of raisin molds and rots. Bunch rot can be minimized with fungicide treatments, insect control, bloom-thinning gibberellin treatment, and irrigation and canopy management practices. If grapes are harvested late in the season, trays should be placed on a firm, smooth, steep-sloped terrace to reduce water retention after a rain. A poorly made terrace (fig. 22.2) will allow puddles to form and hasten fruit rot. Clusters should be placed evenly in a single layer on the tray to enhance drying. Also, minimizing crushed or broken berries and eliminating clusters with rot can reduce damage and contamination.

Time of harvest is often a compromise between attaining high grape sugar, high raisin yield and quality, and avoiding rain. Historical rainfall records from the Fresno area show that the risk of rainfall increases sharply in early October. Most growers prefer to complete harvest by September 15. September 20 is widely considered to be the latest date when raisin grapes should be harvested for natural sun drying and the last date insurers will allow coverage for a crop.

The type of tray material used can also affect mold infestation. Wet-strength trays are most widely used by growers because they have better properties for handling after a rain. Polyethylene-coated trays have been shown to perform better than non-wet-strength trays, which tend to pull apart and tear after wetting, particularly when trays are slipped, turned, or rolled after a significant rain event (fig. 22.3).

Polyethylene-coated trays are coated on the side that faces the soil to provide a moisture barrier from wet soil after a rain. Harvest can begin immediately after a rain instead of waiting for the soil to dry because the polyethylene reduces the adhesive properties of standard paper. Grapes harvested onto polyethylene paper laid on properly terraced soil can often be saved and finish-dried if needed.

Figure 22.2 Water pockets in poorly terraced raisin tray during rain. *Photo*: L. P. Christensen.

Figure 22.3 Mold infection on underside of drying fruit on paper tray (A); severe mold infection on underside after turning of tray (B); and biscuit roll showing mold growth on the outside (C). *Photos*: L. P. Christensen (A, B); S. J. Vasquez (C).

CONTINUOUS TRAY PRODUCTION

Cultural practices for continuous tray (CT) production are identical to traditional raisin production until harvest. When grape soluble solids reach 19 to 21 Brix, fruiting canes are severed. The fruit remains on the severed canes for 7 to 10 days to allow the rachises to dry, facilitating the harvest of individual berries. The berries are then mechanically harvested onto a continuous tray the length of the row. Fruit is laid on the tray as single berries, no more than two layers thick. As single berries, the fruit tends to dry much faster than berries on whole clusters harvested onto individual trays. September 25 is the last day for fruit to be harvested onto a CT for it to be insured, but only if the canes have been severed 10 days earlier. This date ensures proper drying and allows for pickup in late September or early October with little chance of damage.

Berries can be damaged during CT raisin production, which leads to juicing and possibly mold development. When fruit is harvested prematurely after cane severance, pedicels (cap stems) may not dry adequately and can tear from berries during harvest. As the fruit is shaken off the vine, falls onto belts or into buckets, and finally lands on paper, grape juice exudes from the broken berries, promoting fungal and bacterial infections (fig. 22.4). Cool weather and precipitation during drying can compound the problem.

During the 2006 season, some growers were forced to cut sections of the continuous tray paper and roll them for protection from rain events. Fruit that did not dry adequately in the field was dried using on-farm dryers or sent to commercial dehydrators in order to minimize mold damage.

DRIED-ON-VINE (DOV) PRODUCTION

Most dried-on-vine (DOV) vineyards are planted with early-ripening grapevine cultivars, many of which are very vigorous. Even when supported by more expansive trellis systems, the canopies in DOV vineyards can become excessively congested and difficult to manage. If not properly pruned and irrigated, canopies can develop that are 4 or 5 leaf layers thick, which can produce a humid microclimate. These large, dense, humid canopies are conducive to powdery mildew growth, which can lead to secondary infections by sour rot and mold-causing fungi. Proper selection of cultivar and rootstock

Figure 22.4 Continuous tray raisins harvested late displaying mold and bacterial growth. *Photo*: S. J. Vasquez.

plus good irrigation management are crucial to limiting raisin mold and rots. Vigorous rootstocks such as Freedom require careful water and fertilizer management for vigor control. The cultivar Fiesta is noted as being more susceptible to powdery mildew than are other raisin cultivars.

Rain may be less detrimental to DOV raisins than to tray-dried raisins. Although the raisins may absorb moisture, their natural hanging position does not allow much free moisture to settle on the raisins. Winds following a precipitation event help remove free moisture and continue the drying process. DOV raisins dry more slowly than tray-dried raisins and naturally have higher moistures. Therefore, they will probably benefit from supplemental drying after a rain event to minimize mold growth (fig. 22.5).

Figure 22.5 DOV raisins hanging after a rain event, displaying mold growth. *Photo*: S. J. Vasquez.

HANDLING INDIVIDUAL OR CONTINUOUS TRAY RAISINS FOLLOWING A RAIN

If rain occurs, follow these practices to minimize damage caused by mold and insects:

- Slip trays 2.5 to 5 cm (1 to 2 in) to break the seal between the paper and the soil to reduce wicking of moisture. Polyethylene-coated trays with the plastic side down will prevent moisture from wicking, making slipping trays unnecessary.

- Turn the trays as soon as possible to expose bottom fruit to sunlight and air movement.

- Discard fruit stuck to the bottom of trays. Do not try to save or mix sticky fruit with other fruit. Use new trays as needed, or reverse old trays at turning by putting the soil side next to the raisins (but only if soil is not sticking to underside of tray), leaving stuck fruit on the outside.

- Eliminate moldy or rotten fruit from the tray before rolling. This is the first opportunity to manually reduce mold infestation.

- As soon as possible, remove rolled fruit from the field. Moisture should be tested to determine if half or full boxes or bins will be needed. Raisins tested at greater than 18 to 20% moisture should be placed in half bins. When moisture is greater than 20%, sweat boxes should be used. Begin on-farm drying or get high-moisture fruit commercially dried as needed. Raisins found to be greater than 22% moisture should be sent to a commercial dehydrator.

- Bins identified with spoilage should be removed from the stacks and discarded.

- Run fruit across a shaker, if possible, to reduce insect infestation and to provide another chance to pick out mold. Do not run fruit with an excessive amount of uncured berries over a shaker.

- Deliver the raisins as soon as possible to the packer so they can be inspected and tested for mold (fig. 22.6) by the USDA and fumigated for long-term storage.

Procedures for reconditioning mold-contaminated raisins have been greatly improved in recent years. However, reconditioning should be considered as a last resort, since it is expensive and reduces raisin quality and storability.

REFERENCES

Christensen, L. P. 2000. Harvesting and handling. In L. P. Christensen, ed., Raisin production manual. Oakland: University of California Agriculture and Natural Resources Publication. 193–206.

MacDonald, S., P. Wilson, K. Barnes, A. Damant, R. Massey, E. Mortby, and M. J. Shepherd. 1999. Ochratoxin A in dried vine fruit: Method development and survey. Food Additives and Contaminates 16:253–260.

Figure 22.6 Natural-conditioned raisins are boiled to detect the presence of mold. Putrid mold is whitish; nodular mold is greenish black. Black split mold in the wrinkles is visible after rehydration. *Photo:* J. K. Clark.

Fungal Diseases

23 VERTICILLIUM WILT

Larry J. Bettiga

Verticillium wilt causes significant losses in many annual and perennial crops in California, but it is a minor disease of grapes. Caused by the fungus *Verticillium dahliae*, it was first detected in grapes in 1973. Disease incidence as high as 15% in certain young vineyards was reported at that time, but generally, incidence is low (1 to 2%) and may be seasonal. It has been generally found in new vineyards planted on sites previously planted in Verticillium wilt–susceptible crops such as tomatoes, melons, or other susceptible vegetables.

SYMPTOMS

Leaves begin to wilt and collapse as early-summer temperatures increase (figs. 23.1–23.2), followed by vascular brown discoloration, streaking of wood, and death of some shoots (figs. 23.3–23.4). Frequently vines are only partially affected, and strong new growth often appears in unaffected portions. Wilted leaves normally remain attached, and fruit clusters at the base of affected canes dry up (fig. 23.5). Vines that are not killed may recover completely by the following year.

Figure 23.1 Wilt and collapse occur with Verticillium infection (A), characterized by a dark streaking in the xylem tissue (B). *Photos*: L. J. Bettiga.

Figure 23.2 Water-conducting tissues of severely affected canes may be blackened by the fungus. *Photo*: W. J. Moller.

DISEASE CYCLE

The fungus survives in the soil and on other plant hosts, such as weeds, vegetables, and cotton; these plants can build up a reservoir of dark, microscopic resting structures (sclerotia). In other woody hosts, root infection is favored by cool spring weather and high soil moisture. Infection occurs through the grape roots, and the fungus migrates up the vascular tissue. Wilt symptoms appear when warmer weather exerts water stress on infected plants whose vascular tissue is plugged with gums, tyloses, and mycelium. Berries on affected shoots dry up early in the season. Exposure to prolonged hot summer temperatures eradicates the fungus from the tops of certain tree crops; this probably also occurs with grapevines and would explain the recovery of badly affected plants.

MANAGEMENT

Verticillium wilt has not occurred frequently enough in California vineyards to warrant control measures. Avoiding planting other susceptible crops for several years before planting grapes is a suggested precaution against losses.

Figure 23.3 Leaves lose turgor and show signs of scald because of invasion of xylem tissues by *Verticillium*. *Photo*: A. C. Goheen.

Figure 23.4 Verticillium-affected canes exhibit vascular streaking. *Photo*: W. J. Moller.

Figure 23.5 Dried-up berries on affected shoots. *Photo*: W. J. Moller.

24 GRAPEVINE VIRUS DISEASES

Deborah A. Golino, Adib Rowhani, and Jerry K. Uyemoto

Grapevines harbor more than 63 virus and virus-like agents that cause a range of diseases from the severely damaging ones (some of which kill grapevines) to others considered mild, with little or no apparent economic impact. Unfortunately, several damaging diseases caused by viruses and virus-like agents are widespread in California vineyards.

New vineyard blocks planted from virus-infected cuttings or budwood develop disease from the moment they are transplanted and suffer chronic losses for the entire existence of the block. In a diseased planting, cumulative losses are substantial because the crop may be smaller and of poorer quality with each harvest. To avoid losses from virus diseases, it is necessary to avoid using infected stock in propagation.

The intensity of virus symptoms depends on the cultivar of grape (scion and rootstock), cultural practices, and the weather during the growing season. Although some disease symptoms are diagnostic, the absence of symptoms is not a reliable indication that a plant is virus-free. Many grapevine viruses are latent (not showing symptoms nor causing disease) under certain circumstances. Using propagating wood that carries these latent viruses may lead to serious diseases or even vine death in a highly susceptible cultivar of rootstock or scion.

In many cases, the virus associated with a specific disease has been characterized, and a great deal of information is known about its biology and its genetic structure. However, some grapevine diseases are believed to be caused by viruses that are described as virus-like because the pathogen that causes them is still unidentified. The primary test for these diseases to be called virus-like is whether they are transmissible by grafting. This class of pathogens is known as graft-transmissible agents (GTAs). Many of these diseases are latent or semilatent in European grapes *(Vitis vinifera)* and most American *Vitis* species.

Virus diseases became an acute problem for California grape growers during the 1990s. Vineyards in California had largely been propagated on their own roots (where phylloxera was not present or would not survive) or were fruiting scions grafted onto the rootstocks AXR#1 or Rupestris St. George. In the 1990s, several factors drove growers to plant a number of rootstocks that had previously been uncommon in California. These factors included the susceptibility of the rootstock AXR#1 to phylloxera in north coast vineyards, the eventual establishment of phylloxera in central coast vineyards planted largely on their own roots in the 1970s and 1980s, and the maturation of the California table grape industry in the Central Valley. Although most table grape vineyards are in regions where phylloxera is not a problem, replanting issues, particularly increasing nematode populations, led growers to an increasing use of grafted plants. Coincident with the transition to new rootstock cultivars, an upsurge in the incidence of virus diseases in young grapevines occurred. For example, some viruses and virus strains producing mild symptoms or latent infections in own-rooted grapevines or on AXR#1 caused severe symptoms when grafted onto previously unused rootstocks. This happened because diseases such as leafroll, corky bark, and others developed predominately mild symptoms in own-rooted plants. Research showed that rootstocks AXR#1 and Rupestris St. George were highly tolerant of grape viruses, so diseased scions grafted on them produced well in spite of virus infection. Thus, the common practice of gathering scion materials from existing vineyards and grafting them onto healthy rootstocks served to exacerbate replant failures. The symptoms included bud failure, severe stunting, internode shortening, leaf discoloration, leaf rolling, and disorders of the graft union (graft incompatibility). Field buds failed, or diseased transplants grew poorly and often displayed swollen unions. A number of the grapevine leafroll viruses and vitiviruses have been implicated in this latent virus problem. In addition, some new virus diseases have been discovered as a result.

Diseases associated with necrosis, pitting, and grooving of bark tissue and the stems of affected vines are classified as the rugose wood complex of grapevines. Even though viruses alone or in combination are associated with rugose wood, the descriptions

in this section speak to specific viruses or GTAs rather than a complex. Overall, the diseases caused by single pathogens (including rupestris stem pitting, corky bark, and Kober stem grooving) are difficult to differentiate when diagnosis is based solely on symptomatology. Symptoms consist of low plant vigor, delays in budbreak and leaf drop, and a woody cylinder marked by pits and grooves. Also, graft union abnormalities of tissue necrosis, excessive callus formation, and a rough appearance are observed. Field indexing or laboratory tests, or both, are required to accurately differentiate the disease agents (see "Management of Grape Virus Diseases" at the end of this section).

The disease descriptions in this section are largely focused on the symptoms produced by a single-virus infection. In field situations, it is rather commonplace to find grapevines infected with more than one virus or GTA. Infection with one virus does not seem to protect against infection by other grapevine viruses. Unfortunately, the effects of a mixed infection may be more serious than those of a single virus. Mixed-virus infections are most often responsible for the failure and removal of young vineyards.

FANLEAF DEGENERATION

The terms grapevine fanleaf degeneration, infectious degeneration, and fanleaf describe the disease caused by grapevine fanleaf virus (GFLV). Grapevine fanleaf degeneration disease is a major viticultural problem in California, causing serious reductions in yields due to poor berry set. Many of the state's most

important viticultural regions were contaminated with the virus and its nematode vector in the early days of the grape-growing industry. This disease occurs in most countries around the world where grapes are grown. Apparently, the virus that causes the disease was spread over long distances with propagating wood as grapevines were established in the New World.

SYMPTOMS

Grapevine fanleaf disease can cause symptoms on leaves, shoots, and fruits. Affected vines may be smaller than healthy ones, particularly if the nematode vector is present. The canes and foliage appear clustered because of stunting. Internodes may be irregularly spaced on canes. Canes may develop secondary shoots (breaking of bud dormancy) or split; they may also become fasciated (fig. 24.1), and tendrils occasionally develop into lateral shoots.

Three types of leaf symptoms are commonly associated with infected vines:

- **Fanleaf deformation:** Leaves are asymmetric with an open petiolar sinus. The main veins are drawn close together and teeth along the margin of the leaf blade are elongated, giving the leaf the appearance of a fan (fig. 24.2).

- **Yellow mosaic:** Leaf blades develop a bright yellow color over the entire leaf or in irregular patches across the leaf blade. The intense yellow appears in early cool spring and fades rapidly with rising temperatures (figs. 24.3–24.5).

Figure 24.1 Double nodes and flattened fasciations caused by grapevine fanleaf virus. *Photo*: M. A. Walker.

Figure 24.2 Infected leaf, on right for each pair, shows a characteristic open petiolar sinus and elongated teeth along the margin of the leaf blade, giving a fanlike appearance, as shown in Colombard (A) and Cabernet Sauvignon (B). *Photos*: J. K. Clark (A); L. J. Bettiga (B).

- **Vein banding:** Bright yellow bands may develop along the major veins starting in early or midsummer (fig. 24.6). This is the most common symptom seen in California.

These three symptom types were originally described as separate diseases. However, as the virus that causes the disease was characterized with modern techniques, it became clear that all three were associated with the same virus. The predominance of the fanleaf deformation and yellow mosaic symptoms is cultivar dependent. Vein banding was originally attributed to a particular strain of GFLV. In reality, however, symptoms were due to dual infections by GFLV and the grapevine yellow speckle viroid; if the viroid is not present, the vein banding symptom will not be seen. Since this viroid is common in grapes, vein banding symptoms are widespread in GFLV-infected vines in California. Careful observation of infected vines will reveal a mixture of all three leaf symptom types, although one may predominate.

Fanleaf virus can greatly reduce fruit set, up to 80% in some cultivars. Affected clusters contain large and small berries. The small berries, or shot berries, are seedless. Severe economic losses may result from reduced fruit production (figs. 24.7–24.8). Disease severity varies with cultivar, rootstock, and environmental conditions. Dramatic differences in severity from one year to another are common.

Figure 24.3 Yellow mosaic symptoms of fanleaf virus on Cabernet Sauvignon leaves appear here as large, bright yellow patches. Also, teeth on the leaf margins are elongated, and leaf sinuses are larger than usual. *Photo*: S. T. Sim.

Figure 24.4 Yellow mosaic symptoms showing across a block of Chardonnay. *Photo*: L. J. Bettiga.

Figure 24.5 Not to be confused with fanleaf yellow mosaic, the yellow leaves on the right cordon of this vine are a common type of chimera that affects chlorophyll development. Chimeras are stable mutations that occur randomly. The leaves will eventually turn green later in the season and reappear the next spring, always on the same cordon and never spreading to the other side. *Photo*: S. T. Sim.

Figure 24.6 Vein banding symptoms on a Merlot leaf infected with grapevine fanleaf virus. *Photo*: M. A. Walker.

CAUSAL AGENT

Grapevine fanleaf virus (GFLV), the causal agent of fanleaf disease, is perhaps the best-characterized virus of grapevines. It is a mechanically transmissible nepovirus, a group of viruses characterized by nematode transmission, an isometric particle, and a bipartite genome. GFLV is transmitted by the nematode *Xiphinema index* (see section 83, "Nematodes").

Detection of this virus can be accomplished by transmission to herbaceous indicators, by grafting to the woody indicator Rupestris St. George in a 2-year field test, by ELISA tests, or by RT-PCR tests. Spring is the ideal time to test for GFLV. The virus is heat sensitive, so laboratory tests conducted in the summer may not be accurate. Unlike some other grapevine viruses, GFLV populations around the world are homogeneous serologically, so the same ELISA test kits work for all known strains of the virus.

DISEASE CYCLE

Fanleaf disease is easily spread into new sites via diseased planting stocks (fig. 24.9). Secondary spread depends on the presence of *X. index*, the only natural vector of GFLV. The nematode acquires a charge of virus during feeding on diseased grape roots and passes it into healthy grape roots. On its own, the nematode moves rather slowly through the soil profile, less than about 1 m (40 in) per year. However, in a favorable environment it is likely quite sedentary. Even so, patterns of secondary spread appear linear down the row or, depending on row spacing, elliptical in outline. The spread patterns are due to healthy plant roots expanding and commingling with diseased roots and offering resident viruliferous nematodes a smorgasbord of roots to forage on. Once GFLV is transmitted to a new plant, the virus moves systemically and spreads internally through the whole root system in approximately 2 years, extending virus inoculum well beyond the initial place of infection. Symptomatic grapevines may occur in patches across a vineyard, which would suggest (when uniform patches of diseased grapevines occur in sites with no previous disease history) that diseased planting stocks are likely suspects for its introduction, and the presence of *X. index* accounts for the broadening patchy spots.

Therefore, in addition to infected stocks, the vector nematode plays an important role in GFLV epidemiology. When old, diseased plants are pulled, root remnants and the vector population remain behind. Depending on the size, larger root pieces are slow to decay, and as they do they support a residual inoculative vector population, often for longer than 10 years. Under these circumstances, healthy grape transplants soon become infected when their roots expand through the soil profile and come into contact with nematode vectors.

MANAGEMENT

The key to control of GFLV is to plant only healthy stocks (see "Management of Grape Virus Diseases," below). Employing disease control measures after an infestation becomes established is, at best, difficult and expensive. Healthy replants in infested vineyards rapidly succumb to new infections. To date, the only control strategy for an infested site involves removing all exposed roots and allowing 10 years of fallow so that missed root pieces can decompose, while reducing or eliminating vector populations.

Soil fumigation with nematicides (see the UC IPM Grape Pest Management Guidelines, www.ipm.ucdavis.edu/PMG/, for current recommendations) has been used to kill nematode vectors, shortening the replanting interval. Fumigation rarely kills nematodes and vine roots completely, so control may be ineffective without a fallow interval, although temporary benefits may result from reducing the population of *X. index*. Fumigation is most successful in sites where the soil type and structure permit deep penetration by the fumigants. Where heavy clay or a standing water table in the upper soil horizon prevents penetration of the fumigant, results are disappointing.

Grapevine breeders are actively engaged in efforts to produce rootstocks with resistance to fanleaf degeneration and *X. index*. The rootstock O39-16, a hybrid between *V. vinifera* and *V. rotundifolia*, has demonstrated some field tolerance to both *X. index* and fanleaf degeneration. Because O39-16 has *V. vinifera* parentage, it has a possible link to phylloxera susceptibility and is recommended only for sites known to be infested with nematode-virus complex.

LEAFROLL

Leafroll disease exists in every major viticulture region in the world. Symptoms are commonplace in California, with a high level of disease incidence being observed in acreages replanted in the post-phylloxera era that had previously been planted on rootstock AXR#1. Although certified rootstocks

Figure 24.7 Fruit symptoms of fanleaf are manifested in Zinfandel vines in early summer by the presence of numerous small, shot berries. *Photo*: J. K. Clark.

Figure 24.8 At fruit maturity, clusters on affected vines are straggly, with large and small berries. Healthy Cabernet Sauvignon is at left. *Photo*: J. K. Clark.

Figure 24.9 Grapevine fanleaf degeneration disease cycle.

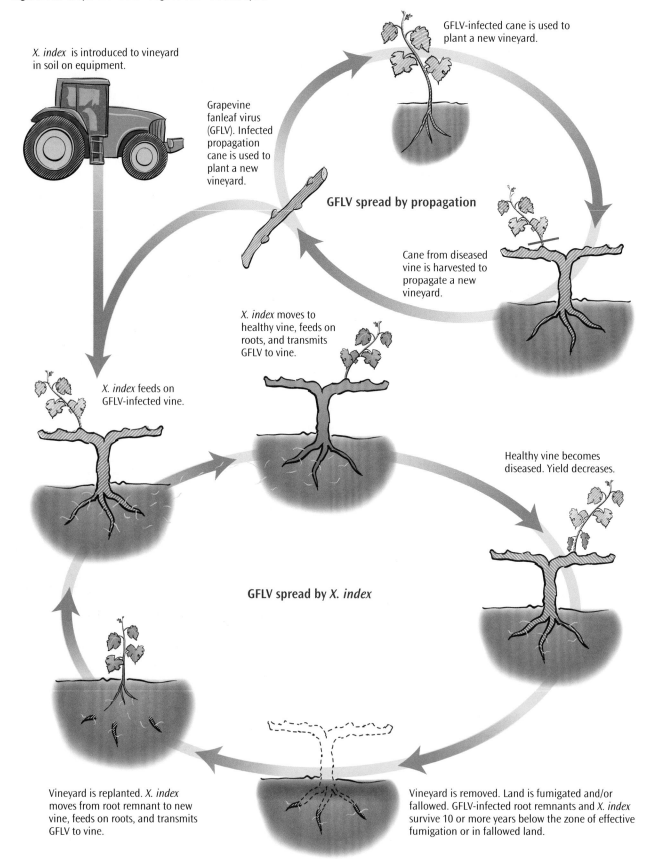

X. index is introduced to vineyard in soil on equipment.

GFLV-infected cane is used to plant a new vineyard.

Grapevine fanleaf virus (GFLV). Infected propagation cane is used to plant a new vineyard.

GFLV spread by propagation

Cane from diseased vine is harvested to propagate a new vineyard.

X. index moves to healthy vine, feeds on roots, and transmits GFLV to vine.

X. index feeds on GFLV-infected vine.

Healthy vine becomes diseased. Yield decreases.

GFLV spread by X. index

Vineyard is replanted. X. index moves from root remnant to new vine, feeds on roots, and transmits GFLV to vine.

Vineyard is removed. Land is fumigated and/or fallowed. GFLV-infected root remnants and X. index survive 10 or more years below the zone of effective fumigation or in fallowed land.

were used in replanting, the practice of harvesting uncertified scion canes from phylloxera-riddled vineyards to preserve cultivars and clones and propagating them as replants was, perhaps, the single most contributing factor to the present situation.

Loss from leafroll in a single year is usually not catastrophic, but it can be significant as reduced yield and quality continue year after year over the life of a vineyard. When the perennial nature of the disease and its worldwide distribution are considered, it is undoubtedly one of the principal contributors to production loss in grapes. For example, some studies show that yields of affected vines are reduced by 20% and fruit maturity is delayed by 3 weeks to 1 month. Often, fruit color is poor and sugar levels are low. The loss from reduced yield is obvious; loss from delayed maturity and poor fruit quality are more subtle, depending on projected uses of the grapes, such as for table fruit, raisins, or wine making; the advent of fall rains; and the length of the growing season.

SYMPTOMS

Leaf and fruit symptoms can be used to diagnose leafroll disease in many cultivars of *V. vinifera*. Symptoms are not reliable as an indicator of leafroll disease in most North American *Vitis* species and hybrids, including most rootstock cultivars. The lack of symptoms in any type of grapevine does not guarantee freedom from infection by the viruses that are the causal agents of leafroll disease.

Symptoms on infected grapevines are indistinct during dormancy and in the early portion of the growing season. Infected grapevines may be smaller than healthy ones, and budbreak and shoot growth may be delayed in early spring. Leaf symptoms become visually apparent by early summer and generally intensify into midsummer and fall (figs. 24.10–24.11). Physical stresses to the vine may increase symptom severity, and similar symptoms are caused by other abiotic and biotic injuries (figs. 24.12–24.13).

Visual symptoms develop in both leaves and fruit clusters of most *V. vinifera* cultivars as the crop matures. The most distinct leaf symptoms appear between harvest and leaf fall. On affected vines, the margins of the leaf blades roll downward, starting with the basal leaf on the cane. Areas between the major veins turn yellow or red, depending on whether the cultivar produces white or red fruit (figs. 24.14–24.15). In some cultivars, the area adjacent to the major veins remains green until late fall.

The most important effect of leafroll disease is a reduction in the yield and quality of berries from infected vines (fig. 24.16). Yield losses of 10 to 20% are fairly typical. Because leafroll viruses damage the phloem of infected vines, sugar accumulation is delayed and anthocyanin production is reduced. Fruit from infected vines will be low in sugar, poorly colored, and late in ripening (fig. 24.17). In some cultivars, fruit maturity is delayed so that fruit on the affected vine may be pale or even whitish at harvest when fruit on healthy vines is ripe.

Figure 24.10 Cabernet franc has yellow leaves in autumn. Red leaves often indicate leafroll virus infection. *Photo*: S. T. Sim.

Figure 24.11 Leafroll-infected Cabernet Sauvignon vines are red (right and front) in contrast with healthy Cabernet Sauvignon vines, which have yellow leaves in late fall (back). *Photo*: S. T. Sim.

Figure 24.12 Stem girdling damage caused by the three-cornered alfalfa hopper (*Spissistilus festinus*) is sometimes confused with leafroll (A); hopper and girdle injury on shoot stem (B). *Photos*: J. K. Clark (A); L. J. Bettiga (B).

CAUSAL AGENT

There are currently five recognized viruses or groups of viruses associated with grapevine leafroll disease. Taxonomically, the grapevine leafroll associated viruses (GLRaVs) are classified in the virus family Closteroviridae, which is characterized by large, flexuous, rod-shaped particles ranging from 1,250 to 2,200 nm long. The five viruses are known as GLRaV-1, -2, -3, -4, and -7. GLRaV-4 contains many strains, referred to as GLRaV-4 strains 5, 6, 9, Car, De, and Pr. Phylogenetically, GLRaV-1, -3, and -4 are in the genus *Ampelovirus*, whose members are vectored by mealybugs. Experimentally, one or more mealybug species are known vectors of GLRaVs-1, and -3, -4, and -4 strains -5 and -9. GLRaV-2 is in the genus *Closterovirus*; there is no evidence of GLRaV-2 transmission by a vector, but other viruses in this genus are vectored by aphids. GLRaV-7 has recently been tentatively assigned to the genus *Velarivirus*. The proposed group GLRaV-8 is no longer believed by experts to exist.

Leafroll viruses may be diagnosed using ELISA and RT-PCR tests. In California, biological indexes for leafroll are done on the woody indicator Cabernet franc and involve grafting chip-buds from accessions under test onto potted plants. The grafted indicators are later transplanted in the field and observed for two growing seasons. If the candidate grapevine is infected with leafroll virus, diagnostic leaf symptoms develop after an incubation of 1 to 2 years. Although it is a time-consuming assay, the nine GLRaVs are readily detected on Cabernet franc. The lone exception is the Redglobe (RG) strain of GLRaV-2, which is symptomless in Cabernet franc but incites stem lesions on certain rootstocks (see "Rootstock Stem Lesion Disease," below). In comparison, GLRaV-2 does not cause rootstock stem lesions. Finally, because several leafroll disease samples have tested negative using laboratory-based assays, it is very likely that new leafroll viruses await discovery.

Figure 24.13 Potassium deficiency symptoms on Cabernet franc show dark brown discoloration, not red as in leafroll. The black or red color can be distinguished by holding a leaf up to the sky and looking through the leaf blade. Also, leaf margins are flat, not rolled downward. *Photo*: B. Ferguson.

Figure 24.14 Leafroll symptoms in white-fruited cultivars like Sauvignon blanc, shown here, are generalized chlorosis and downward rolling of the leaf margins in late fall. *Photo*: D. A. Golino.

DISEASE CYCLE

One major factor contributing to the widespread occurrence of leafroll disease in California vineyards is the use of infected scion wood (see "Management of Grape Virus Diseases," below). Most rootstocks are produced from certified stocks. Secondary spread in vineyards with infected plants depends on the presence and feeding activity of mealybug and soft scale insect vectors. Thus far, five species of mealybugs found in California—obscure, long-tailed, citrus, grape, and vine—are proven vectors of GLRaV-3, a common virus detected frequently in California. Several mealybug species can also vector GLRaV-1, -5, and –9. In recent years, growers and pest control advisers have observed an apparent increase in incidence of leafroll disease in vineyards across the state. The increased sensitivity of popular rootstock-scion combinations in combination with the increasing distribution of leafroll viruses and mealybug vectors may explain this increase.

MANAGEMENT

The most effective control of leafroll or any other virus disease is to use healthy planting stocks or healthy propagating materials when field-budding vineyard sites. Also, care must be given to planting stocks free of the mealybugs that vector GLRaV. Leafroll disease alone rarely kills grapevines, but it does subtly impact grape yield and quality. For that reason, diseased plants are rarely removed from otherwise productive vineyards. However, given that the vines can be a reservoir in

Figure 24.15 Common leafroll disease symptoms on red-fruited cultivars are burgundy red areas between green main leaf veins accompanied by downward rolling of the leaf margins, most distinct in late fall, as seen on this Pinot noir vine. *Photo*: L. J. Bettiga.

Figure 24.16 Yield can be reduced markedly; diseased bunch of Emperor table grape is on right. *Photo*: J. K. Clark.

Figure 24.17 At harvest, fruit maturity is delayed so that fruit on an affected Cabernet Sauvignon vine is still immature (as shown by the hand-held bunch), while fruit on a healthy vine is ripe. *Photo*: J. K. Clark.

vineyards for secondary spread of the virus by mealybugs, it is advisable to practice good hygiene and remove the diseased grapevines, especially if disease incidence is low. Research is being conducted to determine whether the use of insecticides to control secondary virus spread is practical and effective (see "Management of Grape Virus Diseases," below).

ROOTSTOCK STEM LESION DISEASE

This recently recognized disease was first encountered in field trials of table grapes in early 1990. In those trials, grafted plants of the table grape cultivar Redglobe failed dramatically on certain rootstock cultivars. Symptoms akin to graft incompatibility were observed. However, when Redglobe was re-indexed onto the panel of standard grape disease indicators in accordance with the California grapevine clean stock program, the graft-inoculated indicators were normal. Subsequent investigations led to the discovery and characterization of a new strain variant of GLRaV-2, designated RG, the putative agent of rootstock stem lesion disease.

SYMPTOMS

The severity of grapevine rootstock stem lesion disease varies with rootstock cultivar. Acutely sensitive hybrid rootstocks develop stem lesions and often die. The sensitive rootstocks are 3309C, 1616C, Kober 5BB, Teleki 5C, and 1103P. Own-rooted plants of *V. vinifera* and the hybrid rootstocks Ramsey, Harmony, Freedom, O39-16, and 101-14 were found to be symptomless carriers of GLRaV-2RG.

When virus-infected scion buds were bench-grafted onto sensitive rootstocks, impacted plants developed weak shoot growth, solid red and red mottled leaves (fig. 24.18), and scion overgrowth at the scion-rootstock juncture (fig. 24.19). Grafted plants succumbed in one to three growing seasons.

CAUSAL AGENT

Although the Redglobe virus associated with rootstock stem lesion disease is officially designated as GLRaV-2RG, the serological relationship of this virus to common GLRV-2 is distant, which means that ELISA tests for GLRaV-2 will not reliably detect GLRaV-2RG. ELISA tests for GLRaV-2RG are not currently available, but there is an RT-PCR assay for GLRaV-2RG detection.

Also, GLRaV-2RG cannot be detected by a 2-year woody index on Cabernet franc. However, graft

Figure 24.18 Red leaf symptoms of rootstock stem lesion disease, caused by GLRaV-2RG, are visible on Cabernet Sauvignon grafted to 3309C rootstock. *Photo:* J. K. Uyemoto.

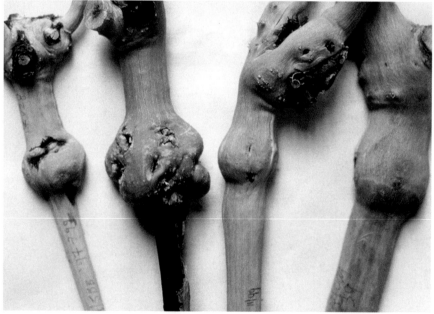

Figure 24.19 Woody cylinders with the bark peeled away showing the graft union of bench grafts of the table grape cultivar Redglobe that carried GLRaV-2RG on four different rootstocks. Necrotic fissures and enlarged graft unions are visible in the two rootstocks on the left: Kober 5BB (far left) and 3309C. The two rootstocks on the right (Freedom and 101-14 Mgt., far right) show smooth wood grain and normal unions. *Photo:* J. K. Uyemoto.

inoculations onto Cabernet Sauvignon on 3309C rootstock develop red leaves after 1 year and stem lesion symptoms after 2 years. The disease is often so severe that many of the infected test plants die during the first winter.

GLRaV-2RG has been detected in 20% of a collection of wine grape cultivars displaying red leaf symptoms and in grape cultivars imported from Europe as well as in all sources of the cultivar Redglobe, which was widely distributed around the world.

Disease Cycle

No vector is known for GLRaV-2RG. Spread of the virus is believed to be limited to the use of infected propagation stock. Because GLRaV-2RG has been discovered in several field selections of wine grapes, as well as Redglobe table grape, in California, extra caution should be taken when using noncertified scions or rootstocks. Since its discovery, the entire foundation vineyard at Foundation Plant Services (see "Management of Grape Virus Diseases," below) was screened by RT-PCR assay, and two more cultivars were found to be infected with GLRaV-2RG. The infected grapevines were removed from the foundation block; both were proprietary selections that had never been distributed, so the virus is very rare in certified stock.

Management

The primary control of rootstock stem lesion disease is prevention. Plant only healthy scions and rootstock that have been selected for freedom from this disease. See "Management of Grape Virus Diseases," below.

CORKY BARK

Corky bark disease occurs in a latent state in many *V. vinifera* cultivars, showing symptoms only after infected buds are grafted onto virus-susceptible phylloxera-resistant rootstocks. When this happens, the plant may initially appear normal, but gradually graft union disorders may develop, including pitting, grooving, lesions, or necrosis of rootstock or scion. Vine death may result; sometimes the scion dies, leaving only the rootstock, which proliferates after the scion is gone.

Symptoms

In commercial vineyards, corky bark symptoms vary in severity from very mild effects to the death of vines. The severity is strongly influenced by rootstock selection. In severe cases, vigor will be reduced so much that it can be detected even during dormancy. Shoot growth is delayed in the early spring. Early in the summer, foliage becomes discolored, turning red or bronze-yellow. Often, leaves do not drop normally but may remain attached to the vine after frost. Fruit maturity is delayed and yields are much reduced.

Many rootstock cultivars show no symptoms of infection. Other rootstocks develop deep pits and grooves in the stem (fig. 24.20), especially near the graft union. These symptoms are observed when the bark is peeled away. Pits and grooves may also be observed in scions. Stem symptoms may show in both scion and rootstock or in only one of the two.

Causal Agent

Corky bark disease is associated with a vitivirus, grapevine virus B (GVB). The vitiviruses are a group of single-stranded RNA viruses. GVB can be transmitted to healthy grapevines by the longtailed mealybug, *Pseudococcus longispinus*. The biological indicator for corky bark disease is the grapevine rootstock hybrid LN33, a cross of Couderc 1613 x *V. vinifera* cv. Thompson

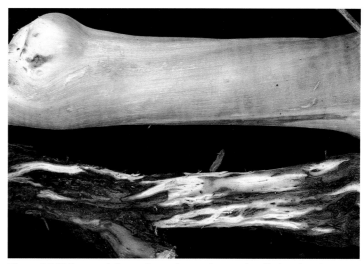

Figure 24.20 Severe pitting and grooving on the woody cylinder of an 8-year-old vine of the rootstock 1103P (below) are symptoms of corky bark disease. Healthy 1103P is above and shows smooth wood grain and larger trunk diameter. *Photo*: S. T. Sim.

Seedless. In the second year after grafting with GVB-infected wood, LN33 develops grooves and pits on the woody cylinder, bark splitting, and the swelling of canes and proliferation of spongy callus tissues (hence the name corky bark) (fig. 24.21). Europeans differentiate a separate disease, called LN33 stem grooving, if pitting and grooving symptoms develop without the bark splitting; at this time, a separate causal agent has not been found for LN33 stem grooving disease. Both are called corky bark disease by California virologists.

DISEASE CYCLE

In California, corky bark disease is most often spread by the use of noncertified scion wood for field grafting of rootstocks. GVB has been reported to spread in the field in several places in the world including Israel, Italy, and South Africa. At this time, no evidence of field spread in California has been found.

When GVB is present with GLRV-2, the disease caused can be much more severe than if either virus were present in a single infection.

MANAGEMENT

The primary control of corky bark disease is prevention. Plant only healthy scions and rootstock that have been selected for freedom from this disease. See "Management of Grape Virus Diseases," below.

MINOR VIRUS AND VIRUS-LIKE DISEASES

RUPESTRIS STEM PITTING

Grapevine rupestris stem pitting-associated virus (GRSPaV) causes rupestris stem pitting disease of grapevines. This disease is normally of little consequence, although some reports suggest it causes reduced vigor or decline in vines grafted onto rootstocks with *Vitis rupestris* parentage. GRSPaV is widely distributed in the world's vineyards and is allowed in most grapevine certification programs. The California Department of Food and Agriculture (CDFA) Grapevine Registration and Certification (R&C) Program allows the virus to be present in certified stock, but efforts are under way to eliminate

it as soon as possible from the program. Efforts to eliminate the virus from planting stock have been impeded by the unexplained spread of the virus in field-planting of grapevines. There is some evidence that this virus is transmitted by seed and pollen.

Specific leaf or wood symptoms do not show on most scion or rootstock cultivars. In Rupestris St. George and a few other rootstocks of *V. rupestris* parentage, the woody cylinder (stem) of the rootstock is covered with small pits that are visible with bark removal (fig. 24.22). If a healthy Rupestris St. George rooting is inoculated by a chip-bud graft from an affected selection, pits most often develop below the graft insert downward into the root zone, not above the bud (fig. 24.23). Occasionally, pits and grooves expand and may encompass the whole wood cylinder.

NEPOVIRUS DISEASES

The diseases in this virus group are caused by at least 16 different yet related viruses. They all are transmitted by dagger nematodes and

Figure 24.21 LN33 showing grooves and pits on the rootstock cylinder (A) and reddish yellow leaf symptoms caused by grapevine vitivirus B (B). *Photos:* Golino Lab.

have a polyhedral shape when purified and examined with an electron microscope (fig. 24.24). This is the source of the name nepovirus: "ne" for nematode and "po" for polyhedral. GFLV (see above) is the only one of this group of viruses that is common in vineyards in California. Two other nepoviruses may be of occasional concern in California vineyards.

Tomato ringspot virus (ToRSV) causes grapevine yellow vein disease. The virus is transmitted by several species of nematodes, including *X. americanum, X. californicum,* and *X. rivesi.* Although this virus is common in vineyards in the eastern United States and in California fruit trees, it has rarely been seen in California vineyards. Symptoms of yellow vein resemble those described for fanleaf, and they can be easily confused.

Arabis mosaic virus (ArMV) is widespread in grapevines in Europe. Although this virus is not found in California vineyards, it has recently been reported as common in Missouri, and some infection has also been reported in Canada. Care should be taken to avoid introduction of grape nursery stock from regions of the United States where ArMV is present. Vines from other countries must pass through federal quarantine screening for this and other virus diseases. Infected grapevines show symptoms similar to those of fanleaf, and ArMV can be present in a mixed infection with GFLV. Several nematode species can transmit ArMV to grapevines, the most common being *X. diversicaudatu.*

GRAPEVINE FLECK

Grapevine fleck virus (GFkV) is a graft-transmissible virus that causes obvious symptoms of disease only in *Vitis rupestris.* Other *Vitis* species can be infected but remain asymptomatic. In infected *V. rupestris,* symptoms include localized clearings (flecks) in the veinlets of young leaves (fig. 24.25). In older leaves, the symptoms diffuse into a mosaic pattern, and the leaves wrinkle and curl upward. Symptoms persist during mild weather and disappear with the onset of hot temperatures. Leaves with intense symptoms are wrinkled, twisted, and may curl upward. Severe forms of the disease also induce varying degrees of stunting, reduced rooting ability, and reduced graft take. Very little information is available about the economic importance of fleck virus. GFkV has worldwide distribution and is permitted in some European grape certification schemes. Fleck is not permitted in the California Department of Food and Agriculture (CDFA) Grapevine Registration and Certification (R&C) Program (see the section "Management of Grape Virus Diseases, below). GFkV is one of a group of viruses known as the fleck complex, which includes grapevine fleck, asteroid mosaic, grapevine Redglobe viruses, rupestris vein feathering, and other viruses that are latent (no obvious disease symptoms) or semilatent in *Vitis vinifera* and most American *Vitis* species and rootstock hybrids.

Figure 24.22 If the bark is peeled from affected vines, the wood frequently shows pits and grooves as well as overgrowth, especially near the graft union, as shown here on a Chardonnay scion on AXR#1 rootstock. *Photo:* A. C. Goheen.

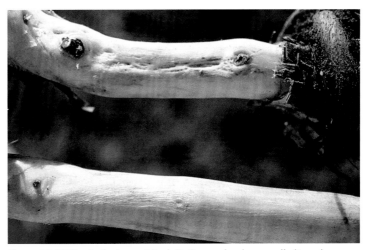

Figure 24.23 The indicator rootstock St. George develops small pits and grooves on the wood cylinder when inoculated with grapevine rupestris stem pitting associated virus (diseased trunk top, healthy trunk bottom). *Photo:* Golino Lab.

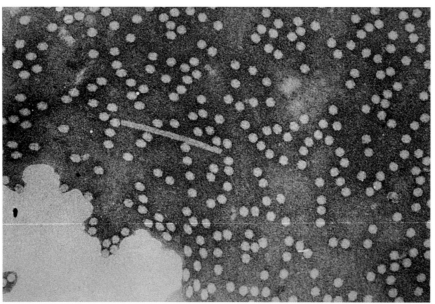

Figure 24.24 The white spots in this photo, taken using an electron microscope, show the polyhedral shape of the virus particles of a nepovirus. These particles are about 30 nm in diameter and are of the nepovirus tobacco ringspot virus. *Photo*: J. K. Uyemoto.

Figure 24.25 Grapevine fleck disease symptoms in St. George are subtle chlorotic areas (flecks) around the small veins of the leaves and are most visible in the cool weather of spring. *Photo*: S. T. Sim.

GRAFT-TRANSMISSIBLE DISEASES

In addition to the virus diseases and viruses described above, grapevines are infected by a number of virus-like graft-transmissible agents that have been studied to varying degrees but never demonstrated to be common or severe. They include enations, vein necrosis, vein mosaic, summer mottle, and bushy stunt. The causal agents have not been characterized and are called graft-transmissible agents (GTAs). Recently, two DNA viruses have been discovered and have tentatively been named grapevine vein clearing virus and grapevine red blotch associated virus.

MANAGEMENT OF GRAPE VIRUS DISEASES

The most important step in controlling grapevine virus diseases is for growers to guard against planting virus-infected stocks. Rootstocks, scion buds, and grafted plants can carry viruses. If one component is infected, the virus will move across the union into the healthy portion of grafted plants. Once a vine is infected, it will stay infected. There are no practical methods to eliminate a virus from an individual vine or a vineyard in the field. If a particular vineyard has rare and valuable grape cultivars or clones, those plants can be submitted to a facility like Foundation Plant Services at the University of California at Davis (see below). There, it is possible to perform microshoot tip culture to eliminate the virus from the selection and eventually release a virus-free form of the vine.

The most reliable way for a grower to avoid planting

virus-infected stock is to ensure that planting material is obtained from California-certified stock. Procedures for planting, growing, distributing, and certifying grape nursery stock in the California Grapevine Registration and Certification (R&C) Program are covered by the California State Agricultural Code. The Nursery Services branch of the CDFA monitors nursery stock production and ensures that program standards are being met. Nursery participation in the Grapevine R&C Program in California is on a voluntary basis. Thus, everyone does not participate in the program, and planting stocks or dormant canes from nonparticipating nurseries cannot be sold as certified. In addition, not all stock sold by participating nurseries is certified. Growers should insist on certified stocks, which should be accompanied by official tags issued by CDFA.

Commercial nurseries that produce certified grapevines and participate in the California Grapevine R&C Program obtain their clean stock from Foundation Plant Services (FPS) at the University of California, Davis. UC Davis has a foundation vineyard for major grape cultivars and clones. Before being planted in the foundation vineyard, all entrees are tested across biological indicators by ELISA and RT-PCR. The foundation vineyard is monitored by visual inspections in spring and fall, and a portion of it is retested every year by ELISA and RT-PCR for viruses known to spread naturally. This provides the highest level of confidence about the virus status of the selections. New laboratory technology is increasingly available to conduct diagnosis assays in a meaningful, reliable, and rapid manner.

Sometimes it is not possible to obtain virus-free selections of an important grape cultivar or valuable clone. To produce virus-free plants from infected vines, it is necessary to eliminate the virus from them. In the past, heat treatment techniques were used for virus elimination. Today, most laboratories use shoot-tip tissue culture techniques to free a candidate selection of virus. No matter what approach is used, careful testing of the candidates after treatment is necessary, because no technique is 100% successful. Therapy of an infected selection and retesting can take 5 or more years and requires a long-term commitment. This work can be done at FPS or at private laboratories.

The most common way in which viruses are spread in California is through field budding operations. Scion wood is sourced from commercial vineyards for a number of reasons: winemakers believe the field selection has superior quality, the selection has history with the grower, the selection is scarce at nurseries, or the cost is lower. Although practical considerations may require the use of wood from commercial vineyards for propagation, it is highly recommended that growers do everything possible to avoid spreading virus with the wood. Growers should visit the vineyards repeatedly in the cropping season and make a conscious effort to identify high-yielding grapevines from which to harvest dormant canes for propagations. Growers should avoid robust plants displaying leaves with fall color or other symptoms known to be caused by virus, and they should select vines with green leaves throughout summer and early fall. The lack of

symptoms in the source vineyard cannot be relied on as a guarantee that there is no virus; many of the major grapevine viruses are latent (show no symptoms) during some or all of the season. Particularly if wood is collected during the dormant season, it is unlikely that the source vines will show distinct symptoms of virus infection. Selected grapevines should also be pretested for virus by a competent diagnostic laboratory.

References

Al Rwahnih, M., S. Daubert, D. Golino, and A. Rowhani. 2009. Deep sequencing analysis of RNAs from a grapevine showing Syrah decline symptoms reveals a multiple virus infection that includes a novel virus. Virology 387:395–401.

Al Rwahnih, M., A. Dave, M. Anderson, J. K. Uyemoto, and M. R. Sudarshana. 2012. Association of a circular DNA virus in grapevines affected by red blotch disease in California. Proceedings of the 17th Congress of ICVG, Davis, CA. 104–105.

Alkowni, R., A. Rowhani, S. Daubert, and D. Golino. 2004. Partial characterization of a new ampelovirus associated with grapevine leafroll disease. Journal of Plant Pathology 86:123–133.

Atalla, S. S., M. I. Gomez, M. F. Fuchs, and T. E. Martinson. 2011. Economic impact of grapevine leafroll disease on *Vitis vinifera* cv. Cabernet franc in Finger Lakes vineyards of New York. Working paper, Dyson School of Applied Economics and Management, Cornell University, Ithaca, New York.

Bitterlin, M. W., and D. Gonsalves. 1988. Serological groupings of *Tomato ringspot virus* isolates: Implications for diagnosis and cross-protection. Phytopathology 78:278–285.

Boscia, D., E. Aslouj, V. Elicio, V. Savino, M. A. Castellano, et al. 1992. Production, characterization and use of monoclonal antibodies to grapevine virus A. Archives of Virology 127:185–194.

Boscia, D., M. Digiaro, M. Safi, R. Garau, Z. Zhou, et al. 2001. Production of monoclonal antibodies to grapevine virus D and contribution to the study of its aetiological role in grapevine diseases. Vitis 40:69–74.

Bovey, R., W. Gartel, W. B. Hewitt, G. P. Martelli, and A. Vuittenez. 1980. Virus and virus-like diseases of grapevines, color atalas of symptoms. Paris: La Maison Rustique.

Brunt, A. A., K. Crabtree, M. J. Dallwitz, A. J. Gibbs, and L. Watson. 1996. Viruses of plants, description and lists from the VIDE Database. Wallingford: CAB International.

Candresse, T., R. W. Hammond, and A. Hadidi. 1998. Detection and identification of plant viruses and viroids using polymerase chain reaction (PCR). In A. Hadidi, R. K. Khetarpal, and H. Koganezawa, eds., Plant virus disease control. St. Paul: APS Press. 399–416.

Clark, M. F., and M. Bar-Joseph. 1984. Enzyme immunosorbent assays in plant virology. Methods in Virology 7:51–85.

Converse R., and R. R. Martin. 1990. Enzyme-linked immunosorbent assay (ELISA). In R. Hampton, E. Ball, and S. DeBoer, eds., Serological methods for detection and identification of viral and bacterial plant pathogens. St. Paul: APS Press. 179–196.

Crowther, J. R. 2001. The ELISA guidebook. Totowa, NJ: Humana.

Das, S., and D. J. Raski. 1969. Effect of grapevine fanleaf virus on the reproduction and the survival of its nematode vector, *Xiphinema index* Thorne & Allen. Journal of Nematology 1:107–110.

Demangeat, G., R. Voisin, J. C. Minot, N. Bosselut, M. Fuchs, and D. Esmenjaud. 2005. Survival of *Xiphinema index* in vineyard soil and retention of *Grapevine fanleaf virus* over extended time in the absence of host plants. Phytopathology 95:1151–1156.

Dovas, C. I., and N. I Kitis. 2003. A spot multiplex nested RT-PCR for the simultaneous and generic detection of viruses involved in the aetiology of grapevine leafroll and rugose wood of grapevine. Journal of Virological Methods 109:217–226.

Feil, H., B. B. Westerdahl, R. J. Smith, and P. Verdegaal. 1997. Effects of seasonal and site factors on *Xiphinema index* in two California vineyards. Journal of Nematology 29:491–500.

Goheen, A. C. 1970. Grape leafroll. In N. W. Frazier, ed., Virus diseases of small fruits and grapevines. Berkeley: University of California Division of Agricultural Sciences Publication 4056. 209–217.

Golino, D. A., and V. Savino. In press. Certification and international regulation of planting material. In W. F. Wilcox, W. G. Gubler, and J. K. Uyemoto, eds., Compendium of grape diseases. St. Paul: APS Press.

Golino, D. A., S. Sim, R. Gill, and A. Rowhani. 2002. Grapevine leafroll disease can be spread by California mealybugs. California Agriculture 56:196–201.

Golino, D. A., J. K. Uyemoto, and A. C. Goheen. 1992. Grape virus diseases. In D. L. Flaherty, et al., eds., Grape pest management, 2nd ed. Oakland: University of California Division of Agriculture and Natural Resources Publication 3343. 101–110.

Hu, J. S., D. Gonsalves, D. Boscia, and S. Namba. 1990. Use of monoclonal antibodies to characterize grapevine leafroll associated closteroviruses. Phytopathology 80:920–925

Hull, R. 1993. Nucleic acid hybridization procedure. In R. E. F. Mathews, ed., Diagnosis of plant virus diseases. Boca Raton, FL: CRC Press. 253–271.

Klaassen, V. A., S. T. Sim, G. S. Dangl, F. Osman, M. Al Rwahnih, A. Rowhani, and D. A. Golino. 2011. *Vitis californica* and *Vitis californica* × *Vitis vinifera* hybrids are hosts for *Grapevine leafroll-associated virus-2* and *-3* and *Grapevine virus A* and *B*. Plant Disease 95:657–665.

Krake, L. R., N. S. Scott, M. A. Rezaian, and R. H. Taylor. 1999. Graft-transmitted diseases of grapevines. Collingwood, Victoria, Australia: CSIRO.

Ling, K., H. Zhu, N. Petrovic, and D. Gonsalves. 2001. Comparative effectiveness of ELISA and RT-PCR for detecting grapevine leafroll-associated closterovirus-3 in field samples. American Journal of Enology and Viticulture 52:21–27.

Mackay, I. M., K. E. Arden, and A. Nitsche. 2002. Survey and summary, Real-time PCR in virology. Nucleic Acid Research 30:1292–1305.

Martelli, G. P. 1992. Grapevine viruses and certification in the EEC countries: State of the art. Mediterranean Agronomic Institute of Bari Quaderno 3.

———. 1993. Graft-transmissible diseases of grapevines: Handbook for detection and diagnosis. Rome: FAO. 7–114.

———. 2003. Grapevine virology highlight. 14th Meeting of the International Council for the Study of Viruses and Virus-Like Diseases of the Grapevine (ICVG). Locorotondo: University of Bari. 3–10.

Martelli, G. P., and B. Walter. 1998. Virus certification of grapevines. In A. Hadidi, R. K. Khetarpal, and H. Koganezawa, eds., Plant virus disease control. St. Paul: APS Press. 261–276.

Martelli, G. P., N. Abou Ghanem-Sabanadzovic, A. A. Agranovsky, M. Al Rwahnih, et al. 2012. Taxonomic revision of the family Closteroviridae with special reference to the grapevine leafroll-associated members of the genus *Ampelovirus* and the putative species unassigned to the family. Journal of Plant Pathology 94:7–19.

Martelli, G. P., A. A. Agranovsky, M. Bar-Joseph, D. Boscia, T. Candresse, et al. 2002. The family *Closteroviridae* revisited. Archives of Virology 147:2039–2043.

Martin, R. R. 1988. Advanced diagnostic tools as an aid to controlling plant virus diseases. In A. Hadidi, R. K. Khetarpal, and H. Koganezawa, eds., Plant virus disease control. St. Paul: APS Press. 381–391.

Martin, R. R., D. James, and C. A. Levesque. 2000. Impacts of molecular diagnostic technologies on plant disease management. Annual Review of Phytopathology 38:207–239.

Osman, F., C. Leutenegger, D. Golino, and A. Rowhani. 2008a. Comparison of low-density arrays, RT-PCR and real-time TaqMan® RT-PCR in detection of grapevine viruses. Journal of Virological Methods 149(2): 292–299.

———. 2008b. Real-time RT-PCR assays for the detection of *Grapevine leafroll associated viruses 1–5* and *9*. Journal of Virological Methods 141:22–29.

Pearson, R. C., and A. C. Goheen. 1988. Compendium of grape diseases. St. Paul: APS Press.

Pudencio, S. 1985. Comparative effects of corky bark and rupestris stem-pitting diseases on selected germplasm lines of grapes. MS thesis. University of California Davis Department of Plant Pathology.

Raski, D. J., A. C. Goheen, L. A. Lider, and C. P. Meredith. 1983. Strategies against grapevine fanleaf virus and its nematode vector. Plant Disease 67:335–339.

Rowhani, A. 1992. Use of F(ab')2 antibody fragment in ELISA for detection of grapevine viruses. American Journal of Enology and Viticulture 43:38–40.

Rowhani, A., and B. W. Falk. 1995. Enzyme-linked immunosorbent assay (ELISA) methods to certify pathogen (virus)-free plants. In O. L. Gamborg and G. C. Phillips, eds., Plant cell, tissue and organ culture. New York: Springer. 267–280.

Rowhani, A., J. K. Uyemoto, and D. A. Golino. 1997. A comparison between serological and biological assays in detecting grapevine leafroll associated viruses. Plant Disease 81:799–801.

Saldarelli, P., A. Rowhani, G. Routh, A. Minafra, and M. Digiaro. 1998. Use of degenerate primers in a RT-PCR assay for the identification and analysis of some filamentous viruses, with special reference to clostero- and vitiviruses of the grapevine. European Journal of Plant Pathology 104:945–950.

Schieber, O., A. Seddas, C. Belin, and B. Walter. 1997. Monoclonal antibodies for detection, serological characterization and immunopurification of grapevine fleck virus. European Journal of Plant Pathology 103:767–774.

Tsai, C. W., A. Rowhani, D. A. Golino, K. M. Daane, and R. P. P. Almeida. 2010. Mealybug transmission of grapevine leafroll viruses: An analysis of virus–vector specificity. Phytopathology 100:830–834.

Uyemoto, J. K., A. Rowhani, D. Luvisi, and C. R. Krag. 2001. New closterovirus in Redglobe grape causes decline of grafted plants. California Agriculture 55:28–31.

Weber, E., and D. A. Golino. Understanding the disease: Rupestris stem pitting. 1994. Practical Winery and Vineyard. 15(4): 28–31.

Weber, E., D. A. Golino, and A. Rowhani. 2002. Laboratory testing for grapevine virus diseases. Practical Winery and Vineyard. 23(2): 13–26.

Zhang, Y., K. Singh, R. Kaur, and W. Qiu, 2011. Association of a novel DNA virus with the grapevine vein-clearing and vine decline syndrome. Phytopathology 101:1081–1090.

Part 4

Insect and Mite Pests

Orthoptera
Dermaptera
Isoptera
Hemiptera
Thysanoptera
Coleoptera
Hymenoptera
Lepidoptera
Diptera
Acari
Aranea
Other Invertebrate Pests

Malvasia bianca

25 GRASSHOPPERS

(Devastating, Green Valley, Valley, and Vagrant)

Walter J. Bentley

Of the four species of grasshoppers (Orthoptera: Acrididae) known to be found in California vineyards, the devastating grasshopper (*Melanoplus devastator* Scudder) is particularly harmful (fig. 25.1). As its common name implies, this species is the most destructive grasshopper in California agriculture. It regularly breeds in the grassy foothills of both the Sierra Nevada and Coastal Range mountains. It then migrates into the Sacramento and San Joaquin Valleys, where outbreaks have been known to occur periodically since 1722. Agriculture's advance into the foothills has greatly reduced the breeding ground of grasshoppers, and only small and localized migrations now occur. As in the case of most migratory grasshoppers, the devastating grasshopper moves from these breeding grounds in great numbers when conditions for survival are favorable. Migrating grasshoppers feed on everything in their path: grasslands, grain, forage, vegetables, vines, trees, shrubs, and flowers.

The valley grasshopper (*Oedaleonotus enigma* (Scudder)) is also distributed in the Sacramento and San Joaquin Valleys, being most often found on the floor of the valleys. As with the devastating grasshopper, widespread cultivation has greatly reduced the occurrence of this species.

Two species in the genus *Schistocerca* also attack grapes. These are the green valley grasshopper (*Schistocerca alutacea shoshone* (Thomas)), usually found from Bakersfield northward, and the vagrant grasshopper (*Schistocerca nitens nitens* (Thunberg)), found from Fresno southward.

A commonly found longhorned grasshopper, *Scudderia furcata* Brunner von Wattenwyl, is found feeding on grape leaves, but it does not destroy grape clusters as do the above mentioned species (see section 26, "Katydids").

DESCRIPTION

In its immature stage, the devastating grasshopper varies from straw colored to brownish black, with dark stripes along the sides of the head and thorax. The adult averages just under 2.5 cm (1 in) long, is

ACTUAL SIZE: GRASSHOPPERS

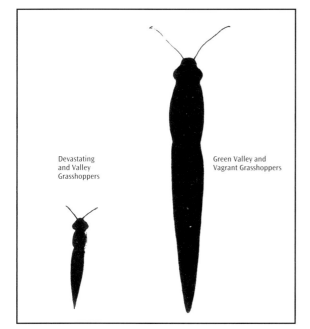

Devastating and Valley Grasshoppers

Green Valley and Vagrant Grasshoppers

Figure 25.1 Devastating grasshopper adult. *Photo*: J. K. Clark.

amber to brownish, and has dark markings on the thorax and a row of dark spots on the front wings. The femur (largest part of the leg) of the hind leg is blue at the base and shades gradually to amber at the tip. The tibia is red to gray.

The valley grasshopper is a small grasshopper with varying shades of brown predominating. The chevron markings on the femur are not solid, but broken. The hind tibia is bluish. Long- and short-winged forms of this species are often found. Interestingly, this species oviposits in hard, compact soil. This behavior renders the eggs somewhat waterproof.

The green valley grasshopper is recognized by its leaf-green color and red hind legs. It also possesses a yellow stripe along the middle of the head and thorax. It is one of the largest grasshoppers, the females being about 6.5 cm (2.5 in) long and the males about 4 cm (1.5 in) long.

The vagrant grasshopper is about the same size as the green valley grasshopper, but it is distinguished by its brown body, brown legs, and a tan stripe along the midline of the head and thorax. The front wings are tan with brown mottling.

INJURY

After winter hibernation in the adult stage, green valley and vagrant grasshoppers become active in spring, entering vineyards in great numbers and defoliating young shoots. Devastating grasshoppers damage shoots in mid to late summer when grasslands dry. Winged adults fly into vineyards to feed on green foliage. Damage from the valley grasshopper occurs earlier, from May to June.

SEASONAL DEVELOPMENT

Devastating and valley grasshoppers lay eggs in soil during the fall, after the first rains. They have only one generation per year and overwinter as eggs. All adults die in the fall and early winter. Overwintered eggs hatch in May, June, and July. In spring, nymphs begin their feeding in rangeland areas. They feed on natural vegetation and develop into adults in June and July. As the rangeland dries, movement occurs into vineyards. Migration back to rangeland occurs in the fall.

Weather conditions during fall and spring greatly affect grasshopper survival. Mild, late falls can extend the egg-laying period. Winter weather has little effect on egg survival. Most overwintering eggs will hatch the following spring. Cool temperatures and wet weather early in spring favor plant development and delay hatch. Wet weather is detrimental to newly emerged grasshoppers. Under such conditions, fungi and bacteria play an active part in grasshopper mortality. If a prolonged period of dry, warm weather occurs during the spring, a uniform hatch results with very little disease potential.

Both green valley and vagrant grasshoppers lay eggs in May. As habitat dries, movement into vineyards can occur after the grasshoppers lay eggs. The female lays egg masses in a hole she bores by inserting her abdomen into the ground. The eggs are embedded in a frothy material that hardens to a spongelike structure called a pod. Within a few weeks, eggs hatch into young, wingless grasshoppers that tunnel to the surface and begin feeding on plant foliage. They grow slowly through June and July, reaching the winged adult stage in late summer. They pass winter as adults. Both species have one generation per year.

NATURAL CONTROL

Diseases are the primary natural control. Early warm weather followed by moisture promotes diseases when young hoppers are present. Voles may attack egg cases in the soil.

MONITORING GUIDELINES

Monitor adjacent rangeland for nymphs in April and May. As the adult stage is reached, movement to vineyards will occur.

MANAGEMENT GUIDELINES

Plowing areas where eggs are deposited can greatly reduce emergence. This is not always possible, particularly if grasshopper habitat is not under the control of the vineyard owner. Adults are difficult to manage because of their movement into vineyards from untreated areas. If hoppers are in the vineyard, fast-acting contact sprays can be used to reduce their number. In recent years, grasshoppers have not moved more than a few yards into vineyards, and border sprays have been of value.

26 KATYDIDS

Lucia G. Varela

Katydids may occasionally become a damaging pest in vineyards after veraison if populations are very high; their feeding on berries opens up wounds that allow for the entry and development of bunch rot organisms. Katydids (family Tettigoniidae) are large, leaf-mimicking insects with slender legs and very long, threadlike antennae (often exceeding the length of the body). Although many katydids look like grasshoppers, from which their long antennae distinguish them, they are more closely related to crickets. Three species of katydids may be present in California vineyards: forktailed bush (*Scudderia furcata* Brunner von Wattenwyl) (fig. 26.1), broadwinged (*Microcentrum rhombifolium* Sassure) (fig. 26.2), and Mediterranean (*Phaneroptera nana* Fiebre). The former two species are native to North America; the latter species is a native of the Mediterranean and has been reported in coastal California since 1941.

Description

The forktailed bush katydid is about 4 cm (1.5 in) long from head to wingtip, the male being slightly smaller at 3 cm (1.2 in) long. The forewings are not much broader at the middle than near the end, and the hind wings are 5 mm (0.2 in) longer than the front wings. The antennal sockets are not separated as in the broadwinged katydid. The male of the forktailed bush katydid has a dorsal genitalia plate protruding as a conspicuous, forked, upturned process. The female ovipositor is bladelike, curved upward, and dark red. She inserts the eggs lengthwise into the edges of the leaves of evergreen shrubs and trees. Eggs are white, elongate, oval, and laterally flattened (kidney shaped) and about 3 mm (0.12 in) long. The nymph's body is cylindrical, arched, and green, with orange spots and blue patches (fig. 26.3) on the front part of the thorax.

The broadwinged katydid male is 5 cm (2 in) long and smaller than the female, which is 6.5 cm (2.5 in) from head to tip of wings. Their forewings are curved more sharply along the top than on the bottom, making them broader at the middle than at either end. The distance between the antennal sockets is 1 to 2 times the width of the basal antennal segment. The female ovipositor is short and upturned. Females cement the tan-to-gray, flat eggs on the surfaces of twigs or canes, in single or double overlapping rows. The nymph is green with tiny black flecks. The front of the nymph's head is smoothly rounded, with the sockets of the antennae separated. The body is compressed, with a convex crested back.

Figure 26.1 Forktailed bush katydid adult. *Photo*: J. K. Clark.

The Mediterranean katydid female is 3.2 cm (1.25 in) long, with the male slightly smaller. The forewings are not much broader at the middle than near the end, and the hind wings are 8 mm (0.3 in) longer than the front wings. The antennal sockets are not separated as in the broadwinged katydid. The body and legs of the Mediterranean katydid are marked with small, dark red dots in the adult and nymphal stages. The female ovipositor is similar to that of

Figure 26.2 Broadwinged katydid adult. *Photo*: J. K. Clark.

Figure 26.3 Forktailed bush katydid nymph. *Photo*: J. K. Clark.

Figure 26.4 Mediterranean katydid nymph. *Photo*: J K. Clark.

forktailed bush katydid but smaller. Females insert their eggs singly and lengthwise into the outer bark crevices of grapevines and into the leaves of evergreen shrubs and trees. Eggs are white and kidney shaped. The nymph's body is cylindrical, strongly arched, and green with red speckles (fig. 26.4).

INJURY

Katydids may occasionally cause damage when high populations feed on berries after veraison. The prime concern of a katydid infestation is the development of grape cluster rots caused by fungi and bacteria gaining entry into feeding wounds on the berries. Young nymphs feed on leaves, leaving holes in the center; as the nymphs become fourth and fifth instars and adults, they may feed on the berries as they soften. High populations of this pest occur in cycles, and they may cause damage one year but not the next.

SEASONAL DEVELOPMENT

All three species have one generation per year in the northern part of the state, but a second generation may develop in the warmer southern counties. They overwinter in the egg stage. Nymphs begin to emerge in mid-April to mid-May, depending on the region and species, and it takes approximately 6 weeks for all the nymphs to emerge from the eggs. Young nymphs begin to be seen feeding on the upper side of the leaf in May. They feed on a small section of the leaf before moving on to another feeding site. Adult katydids appear in midsummer. The male song is heard at dusk and in the evening as a series of "zeek," "zip," or "tick" sounds a few seconds apart. Females respond after a fraction of a second with ticking, which attracts the males toward them. Species can be distinguished by their songs. Females lay eggs in late summer and fall.

MONITORING GUIDELINES

Monitoring guidelines have not been developed for katydids in vineyards. If a vineyard has a history of rot at harvest, monitor for katydids the following season. If you see extensive feeding damage on the leaves, search for nymphs because other leaf feeders can cause similar damage. Feeding is characterized by large holes chewed from the leaf interior and not from the edge. Look for nymphs sitting on top of the leaves starting in May and feeding damage on the berries after veraison.

MANAGEMENT GUIDELINES

If treatment is warranted, the most susceptible stages are the young nymphs. Treat early in the season from late May to mid-June, after all the eggs have hatched and the nymphs are in second or third stage.

27 EUROPEAN EARWIG

Larry J. Bettiga and Rhonda J. Smith

European earwig (*Forficula auricularia* L.) (Dermaptera: Forficulidae) feeds on a wide range of live and dead organic matter. It is often found in vineyards and may cause some damage to emerging shoots and young foliage. It is a generalist predator of eggs and active stages of insects and plays a role in biological control of pests such as orange tortrix and omnivorous leafroller by feeding on egg masses as it forages over the grape canopy during the night. An introduced species, it was first discovered in Berkeley in 1923. Since then, it has become widespread in California and is most destructive in the cooler, coastal regions on many kinds of plants, including fruits, vegetables, and ornamentals.

DESCRIPTION

The adult has a dark, chestnut-brown body with pale yellow legs and is about 1.3 cm (0.5 in) long with a pair of forcelike appendages on its posterior (fig. 27.1). Males have curved forceps, while females have long, straight forceps. Adults have a pair of short wings and can fly, but they usually move about by running. The pearly white, oval eggs are laid in masses just below the soil surface. The young nymphs are similar in appearance to adults but are smaller, wingless, and tend to be lighter colored.

INJURY

Earwigs feeding on green tissue immediately after budbreak and on young foliage in early spring can damage grapevines (fig. 27.2). Damage is more noticeable and occasionally serious during cold springs when shoot growth is delayed. Signs of feeding may be present on swollen buds, but the damage is usually superficial. As shoots elongate, feeding occurs on the first leaves to emerge, causing basal leaves to have ragged margins. Damage is generally confined to the basal leaves.

Figure 27.1 European earwig adult. *Photo*: L. J. Bettiga.

ACTUAL SIZE: EUROPEAN EARWIG

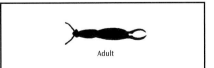

Adult

Figure 27.2 Earwig feeding on a shoot tip in early spring. *Photo*: L. J. Bettiga.

SEASONAL DEVELOPMENT

Earwigs overwinter as adults. Eggs are laid from December through February. Both nymphs and adults are nocturnal and feed at night. During the day they seek out dark, cool, moist places to hide and may be found under mulch or under rocks and in crevices. In vineyards, earwigs are often found under the loose bark of vines or protective trunk wraps, especially during wet springs.

NATURAL CONTROL

No information is available.

MONITORING GUIDELINES

Earwigs are usually not a problem in the vineyard unless populations become large. Peel off the loose bark on the trunks of vines that have feeding damage in the spring to find immature earwigs. Be alert because the insects move very quickly when disturbed. Economic damage has not been correlated to population density. Vines generally outgrow the injury since the damage is usually confined to basal leaves.

MANAGEMENT GUIDELINES

There are no recommended controls for earwigs on grapes.

28 TERMITES

Michael K. Rust and Philip A. Phillips

Numerous species of drywood and subterranean termites (Isoptera: Kalotermitidae, Termitidae, and Rhinotermitidae) attack grapevines, especially in southern California. Drywood termites are usually found aboveground infesting dead heartwood of vines, which serves as a nest for the colony. Colonies of subterranean termites must maintain contact with the soil where the nest is located. Both types feed on the vine's dead wood; only rarely have termites been observed feeding on living tissues or killing vines.

The western drywood termite (*Incisitermes minor* (Hagen)), and the western subterranean termite (*Reticulitermes hesperus* Banks) (fig. 28.1), are commonly found in vineyards throughout California. In the southern deserts, several species of subterranean termite (*Amitermes* and *Heterotermes aureus* (Snyder)) have been collected in vines. The desert dampwood termite (*Paraneotermes simplicicornis* (Banks)) has been frequently collected infesting the large wooden trellis posts used to support wires. Even though this species has not been collected from grapevines, it has been observed girdling and killing young jojoba and citrus plants.

DESCRIPTION

Termites are social insects belonging to colonies consisting of various castes.

Alates
Winged reproductives that swarm are called alates. Drywood termites are about 13 mm (0.5 in) long, including wings, and subterranean termites are about 10 mm (0.4 in) long. The body color of the western drywood termite (about 8 mm, or 0.3 inch, long) is diagnostic, with a blackish abdomen and reddish head and thorax. The body of the *Reticulitermes* and some *Amitermes* is black and about 5 mm (0.2 in) long. A few desert species are light brown. Wings are generally hyaline (clear). The abdomen at the junction of the thorax of termites is not slender as it is in ants.

Primary Queens and Kings
After swarming, the alates break off their wings, and the pair searches out a site to establish a new colony. They will serve as the primary reproductive caste of the colony.

Supplementary Reproductives
Wingless forms that never swarm and leave the colony, supplementary reproductives are generally a lighter color than the alates. These forms are frequently found in mature and older colonies.

Figure 28.1 Castes of the western subterranean termite (*Reticulitermes hesperus*): (A) winged alate, (B) dealated primary reproductive (future king or queen), (C) soldier, and (D) worker nymph. *Illustration*: M. Rust.

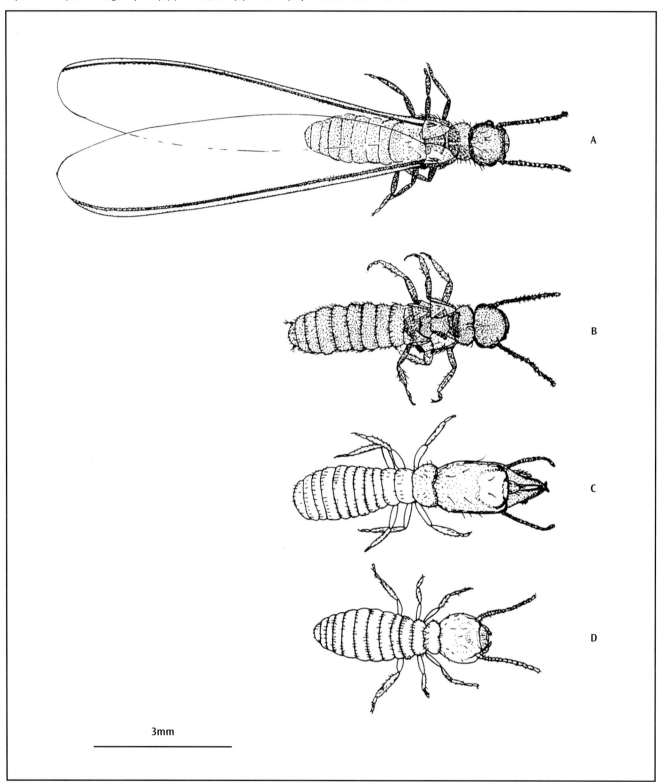

A

B

C

D

3mm

Worker Nymphs

These are a white, eyeless caste, 3 to 5 mm (0.13 to 0.20 in) long, that feed on wood, construct galleries, and care for the young, soldiers, and reproductives. They are the most abundant caste in the colony. Some will ultimately develop into soldiers and alates.

Soldiers

These are an eyeless caste 5 to 9 mm (0.20 to 0.35 in) long, with an enlarged head and mandibles. Soldiers protect the colony from predators, including ants. In addition to powerful mandibles, some species use chemicals stored in the soldier's head capsule to repel ants.

INJURY

When attacking the vine, termites feed on the heartwood (dead tissue) and usually avoid the living sapwood. They can live for years in the heartwood and only slightly penetrate the outer sapwood. Usually the entire core of the heartwood is honeycombed.

In some districts, 100% of the vines are infested in vineyards 40 years or older, possibly because their productive sapwood has become thinner and surface injuries and heavy saw cuts have exposed more of the acceptable heartwood to possible attack. The impact of termite foraging in vineyards has never been assessed.

In newly developed vineyards in southern desert regions, surface foraging by *Heterotermes aureus* has been observed in which young vines were killed. Heavy irrigation practices in desert areas appears, however, to deter continued attack of established vines. Clearing of native woods, cacti, and other cellulose debris before planting may be advisable in preparing new vineyards.

SEASONAL DEVELOPMENT

Winged alates swarm to establish new colonies. Drywood termites swarm on warm, sunny days, usually between 32° and 38°C (89.5° and 100°F). The subterranean termite, *R. hesperus*, swarms on sunny days following heavy rains in spring or fall, whereas many desert subterranean termites swarm during summer rains. Alates are generally poor fliers and glide downwind, where they alight and drop their wings. Drywood termites search out cracks and crevices in wood to excavate a chamber, whereas subterranean termites bury themselves in the moist soil. Initially, the colony develops slowly, and 3 to 4 years may be required before the colony produces its first swarm of alates. With increasing age, the colony produces supplementary reproductives, and the size of the colony grows rapidly.

NATURAL CONTROL

Even though ants are generally believed to be predatory on termites, no effective natural control of termites is known.

MONITORING GUIDELINES

No monitoring guidelines have been developed for termites. However, inspection of vines and stakes during the times when swarming occurs should reveal their presence.

MANAGEMENT GUIDELINES

Control is a matter of prevention. In newly established vineyards, remove all cellulose products and nonliving wood debris to help eliminate food sources. Take care to avoid scarring vines with cultivating tools. Saw cuts 30 cm (12 in) or higher above the ground are rarely a point of entry for termites unless the heartwood is softened by wood rot fungi or reduced by branch or twig borers. Some surface-foraging termites, such as *Heterotermes*, can gain access to the vines at these points.

Initiate a vine replacement program in older vineyards. Severely weakened vines may be replaced by layers from adjacent healthy vines.

Treat wooden stakes and posts having soil contact with a wood preservative to protect them from woodrotting fungi and termites.

ACTUAL SIZE: WESTERN SUBTERRANEAN TERMITE

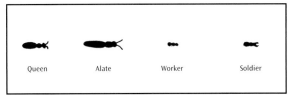

Queen   Alate   Worker   Soldier

Hemiptera
Aphids,
Leafhoppers,
Mealybugs, Scales,
True Bugs,
Whiteflies

29 APHIDS

Lucia G. Varela

It is not uncommon to find a few aphids (Hemiptera: Aphididae) on grapes in spring. Most are probably transients and are usually found on tips of shoots and clusters. Heavy infestations of aphids occurred in flower clusters of Emperor grapes in Tulare County in the 1950s, 1971, and 1987. Vineyards near citrus groves had the most problems. The aphid infestations were identified as spirea aphid (*Aphis spiraecola* Patch), a pest of citrus; green peach aphid (*Myzus persicae* (Sulzer)); and cotton aphid (*Aphis gossypii* Glover), which is also found on citrus and pomegranates. In spring 1980, heavily reproducing colonies of spirea aphid were found infesting vineyards in Soledad, Monterey County. Vine shoots, clusters, and especially tendrils were infested.

DESCRIPTION

Cotton aphid on citrus is always dark gray or dull black, but on other hosts it may be black, gray, green, or yellow. Spirea aphid is small and apple green (fig. 29.1). On citrus, when the wing pads begin to appear the thorax changes color, first becoming pale pink and finally dark brown or almost black when the wings are fully developed. The abdomen, however, usually remains green. Green peach aphid is one of the most common aphids in North America. The immature forms are yellow, pinkish, or pale green; the mature wingless forms are pale or bright green, with a characteristic large, dusky blotch on the dorsum of the abdomen.

INJURY

If heavy infestations in the clusters are allowed to go untreated, the berry set may be affected, resulting in very loose clusters with small berries.

SEASONAL DEVELOPMENT

No information on grapes is available.

NATURAL CONTROL

Aphid colonies may be tended by ants. Aphids have a number of predators, including several species of ladybird beetles, syrphid flies, and green lacewings. They are also attacked by parasitic wasps.

MONITORING GUIDELINES

No monitoring guidelines have been developed.

MANAGEMENT GUIDELINES

None have been developed.

Figure 29.1 Spirea aphid nymphs. *Photo*: J. K. Clark.

ACTUAL SIZE: APHID

Adult

Hemiptera
*Aphids,
Leafhoppers,
Mealybugs, Scales,
True Bugs,
Whiteflies*

30 BROWN MARMORATED STINK BUG

Larry J. Bettiga, Lucia G. Varela, and Walter J. Bentley

Brown marmorated stink bug (BMSB) (*Halyomorpha halys* (Stål))
(Hemiptera: Pentatomidae) is an invasive insect native to East Asia that
has been introduced into North America. The first official North American
detection of this pest occurred in Pennsylvania in 2001, but it is possible
that it had been introduced as early as 1996. As of 2011 this insect has
been identified in 33 states, including California. Large populations are
now established in several eastern states, where they have become significant agricultural and nuisance pests. BMSB can feed on a wide range
of plant hosts. It can be a significant pest of tree fruits, including apples,
pears, peaches, and cherries; small fruits, including grapes; fruiting vegetables, including corn, tomatoes, peppers, and legumes; and field crops,
including field corn and soybeans.

DESCRIPTION

The adult is 14 to 17 mm (0.55 to 0.67 in) long (fig. 30.1). The upper body
is a mottled brown with small, round, copper or bluish depressions on
the head and thorax. It can be distinguished from other stink bugs of
similar color and size by the following characteristics: the antennae have
two distinct white bands; the margin of the thorax (shoulder) is smooth;
and the exposed abdominal edges have alternating dark and light banding. The legs are brown with faint white mottling or banding.

    The light green, barrel-shaped eggs are 1.6 by 1.3 mm (0.065 by 0.050
in) and are laid singly in clusters of 20 to 30 on the underside of leaves.
BMSB has five nymphal instars, ranging from 2.5 mm (0.1 in) long for the
first stage to 12 mm (0.45 in) for the fifth stage. The abdomen of the first
instar is orange striped with black; after hatching, this stage will remain
aggregated near the egg mass (fig. 30.2). All instars have deep red eyes
and spines located before each eye and several on the lateral margins of
the thorax. The second to fifth instars are rust with broad brown markings and yellow dots; they develop wing pads as they molt into successive
stages. The nymphs have distinct pale bands on the antennae and legs.
They also have contrasting light and dark markings on the outer edge of
the abdomen.

INJURY

BMSB feeds on leaves, seeds, and fruit of host
plants. The damage from its feeding on fruit is
caused by the internal collapse of tissue and
necrosis due to the insect's probing with piercing and sucking mouthparts. Grape has been
reported to be a host of BMSB, but it is likely a

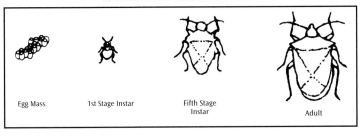

ACTUAL SIZE: BROWN MARMORATED STINK BUG

Egg Mass   1st Stage Instar   Fifth Stage Instar   Adult

Figure 30.1 Adult brown marmorated stink bug (top) and a fifth-instar nymph. *Photo:* S. Ausmus, USDA APHIS.

Figure 30.2 Egg mass and newly hatched first-instar nymphs of the brown marmorated stink bug. *Photo:* G. Bernon, USDA APHIS.

less-preferred host. In wine grapes, as with other stink bugs, there is concern that insects crushed in harvesting or processing operations can release chemicals that could be detected in the finished wine.

BMSB has become a major nuisance pest in urban areas due to the large aggregations of adults that can invade buildings in fall looking for overwintering sites. When disturbed, the insects produce a characteristic odor that adds to their nuisance potential.

SEASONAL DEVELOPMENT

In the currently infested areas of the U.S. mid-Atlantic states, BMSB appears to have one to two generations per year. In the warmer areas of its native habitat in Asia, it is reported to have up to six generations per year. BMSB overwinters as an adult in a state of facultative diapause. In spring, adults become active and feed for approximately 2 weeks before becoming reproductively mature, mating, and laying eggs. An adult female can lay up to 400 eggs throughout her lifetime. The eggs hatch into nymphs that go through five molts. In the mid-Atlantic states, adults have been observed to begin moving to overwintering sites in September and October.

NATURAL CONTROL

Little, if any, information is available on the natural control of BMSB in the United States by endemic predator and parasite species. *Trissolucus halymorphae* Yang (Hymenoptera: Scelionidae) is an egg parasitoid that is the principal natural enemy of BMSB in China, where parasitism rates of 50% have been reported. This and other natural enemies have been collected in Asia and are currently under evaluation in

quarantine for their potential as biological control agents for release in the United States.

MONITORING GUIDELINES

BMSB can be monitored visually by timed visual counts, attractant-baited traps, beating tray samples, and blacklight traps. Pyramid-shaped, black, ground-level traps are more attractive to BMSB than are yellow traps. An aggregation pheromone lure is also available. Effective monitoring method guidelines need to be developed for this pest in vineyards.

MANAGEMENT GUIDELINES

Management of BMSB seeks to prevent large populations from becoming established to reduce feeding damage and the chance of fruit contamination in wine and juice vineyards prior to harvest. It is currently unclear how damaging this pest can be in California vineyards. Consult the UC IPM Grape Pest Management Guidelines, www.ipm.ucdavis.edu/PMG/, for updates on management practices for this pest.

REFERENCES

Hamilton, G. C. 2009. Brown marmorated stink bug. American Entomologist 55(1): 19–20.

Hoebeke, E. R., and M. E. Carter. 2003. *Halyomorpha halys* (Stål) (Heteroptera: Pentatomidae): A polyphagous plant pest from Asia newly detected in North America. Proceedings of the Entomological Society of Washington 105: 225–237.

Northern IPM Center. 2011. Brown Marmorated Stink Bug Information website, http://www.northeastipm. org/working-groups/ bmsb-working-group/.

Hemiptera
*Aphids,
Leafhoppers,
Mealybugs, Scales,
True Bugs,
Whiteflies*

31 FALSE CHINCH BUG

David R. Haviland, Walter J. Bentley, and Edward A. Weber

False chinch bug (*Nysius raphanus* Howard) (Hemiptera: Lygaeidae) is an occasional pest that may breed in countless numbers in weeds within and adjacent to vineyards in early spring. When weed hosts dry, migration to green plants occurs. A vineyard situated in their path may suffer serious injury, usually in the prebloom period. When forced to leave drying hosts, the wingless immature stage predominates. Consequently, migrating insects do not fly, but walk. Winged adults may also be present, but instead of flying they march along with the wingless immatures. False chinch bugs are rarely a problem during the summer, but they can become problematic again in the fall. Migrations generally occur in the late evening or early morning. During the heat of the day, they may be found under plant debris and soil clods.

DESCRIPTION

Adults are about 3 mm (0.12 in) long and are light or dark gray (fig. 31.1). Be careful not to confuse them with small lygus bugs or big-eyed bugs; the latter have wider and flatter heads. The nymphs are gray with reddish brown abdomens (fig. 31.2). They have piercing-sucking mouthparts.

INJURY

When mass migrations of false chinch bugs invade a vineyard, they swarm up trunks of vines to leaves, where they immediately begin to suck juices. Within a few hours, leaves on a healthy, vigorous vine may wilt and eventually turn brown as though burned. Heavy infestations of nymphs and adults can completely kill new growth on established vines. Heavy feeding on young vines, especially those still being trained, can result in complete vine death. Some scientists hypothesize that a toxin is involved due to how quickly the leaves collapse and dry. Under most circumstances, heavy damage is usually isolated to vines near field edges, especially those on the edge from which the migration is originating.

SEASONAL DEVELOPMENT

Eggs are laid at random on rubble in the soil or in cracks in the ground. All stages may hibernate, but most pass the winter as immatures. There are about six generations each year. Population pressure, which exhausts their food supply in the fall, may produce fall migrations.

Overwintering false chinch bug adults are strongly attracted to London rocket as well as other plants in the mustard family such as shepherd's purse, mustard, wild radish, and pepperweed. They gather in large numbers on stands of these weeds in late February and early March. There,

Figure 31.1 False chinch bug adult. *Photo*: J. K. Clark.

ACTUAL SIZE: FALSE CHINCH BUG

Adult

Figure 31.2 False chinch bug nymphs on grape leaves. *Photo*: J. K. Clark.

they produce nymphal populations that will attack grapevines when the weeds dry up or are turned under after the vines leaf out. The most serious and destructive migrations occur in May and June, but there are occasional migrations in September and October.

NATURAL CONTROL

Little, if any, information is available on the natural control of false chinch bug.

MONITORING GUIDELINES

During the spring, monitor for false chinch bugs on weed hosts such as London rocket, wild mustard, wild radish, and shepherd's purse. This can be done visually with or without a sweep net on larger weeds, or by uprooting plants to expose bugs hiding near the soil surface.

Monitor both inside and outside the vineyard. In-field monitoring is important to determine resident populations of this pest, whereas monitoring weedy ditch banks and pastures near the vineyard can give an indication of the potential for mass false chinch bug migrations.

If large numbers of false chinch bug are found on weed hosts (especially if those weed hosts are drying down), inspect vines for damage. Look for false chinch bugs on the vines and a wilted, scorched appearance to the leaves. On young vines, look inside the cartons used to protect the trunks; false chinch bugs often hide inside these cartons and feed on the vine. Do this in the evening when the insects are more active.

MANAGEMENT GUIDELINES

Control is best achieved by disking the weeds in and near vineyards to prevent the buildup of bugs. If false chinch bugs have been a problem in past years, stands of London rocket and other host weeds should be disked or otherwise reduced about 3 weeks before grapevines leaf out. If disking has not been achieved by this time and large populations are found on the weeds, apply insecticides. Disking without first applying insecticides after the vines have leafed out will likely cause this pest to move off the weeds and onto the vines.

If an insecticide is used, apply it in the early morning or late evening, when the majority of the population is exposed and moving. If nymphs are found moving onto vines, apply an insecticide at once to both vines and weed sources. If the vineyard is young and still has cartons over the trunks, consider killing the bugs before they start moving to the vines; the efficacy of insecticides on bugs once they are hidden in the cartons is greatly reduced.

Since false cinch bugs migrate mainly in one direction, wilted vines along one edge of the vineyard can clearly indicate from which direction they are entering. In many cases, treatments on border rows on the one side of the field are sufficient to protect the entire vineyard. Alternatively, a water barrier may prevent movement to the crop.

Hemiptera
*Aphids,
Leafhoppers,
Mealybugs, Scales,
True Bugs,
Whiteflies*

32 GRAPE PHYLLOXERA

M. Andrew Walker, Jeffery Granett, Larry J. Bettiga, William L. Peacock, and Edward A. Weber

Grape phylloxera, *Daktulosphaira vitifoliae* (Fitch) (Hemiptera: Phylloxeridae), is an aphid-like insect that feeds on roots of European grapes (*Vitis vinifera* L.), resulting in stunted vine growth, decreased yield, and under some conditions, vine death.

Grape phylloxera is indigenous to North America, residing on native *Vitis* species found throughout the eastern, central, and southwestern United States, Mexico, and northern South America. The biology of this species varies by host and climatic region, with populations occurring primarily inside leaf galls and, in low numbers, on roots. When European grape cultivars are grown in the United States, phylloxera is restricted to root feeding on small, young feeder roots as well as larger, mature storage roots. On most native American grape species, phylloxera resides primarily inside leaf galls, with much lower populations on feeder roots and no populations on storage roots. Infestations on hybrid grapes may reflect susceptibility levels of one or both parental species.

Phylloxera populations were accidentally shipped on grape plants from the eastern United States to France in the mid-nineteenth century, and they subsequently ravaged European grape vineyards by feeding on mature storage roots. The pest is thought to have been introduced into viticultural regions of California about the same time through cuttings or rootings brought from both Europe and the eastern United States. Phylloxera populations were distributed around the world on exported vines, and this continues to be the primary means of spread.

Phylloxera is currently found throughout California's grape-growing areas north of the Los Angeles basin. The north coast region is uniformly infested, and root damage is lethal to susceptible vines. Significant infestations and damage also occur in the central coast region. Populations exist in the Sierra foothills and the Shasta and Lassen areas but have not spread uniformly because the viticultural areas there are not contiguous. In regions that are cooler than the coastal valleys, there are fewer generations of the pest per year, and hence populations are smaller and damage progresses more slowly. The hot Central Valley of California is widely infested, though damage is uneven and vines are not usually killed; they can be severely weakened on clay loam or finer-textured soils. The high midsummer temperatures may kill phylloxera within 30 cm (12 in) of the soil surface, thus limiting population growth.

In California, limited populations of phylloxera have been found on roots of wild *Vitis californica* adjacent to infested vineyards and in leaf galls on wild *V. girdiana* types around Death Valley.

DESCRIPTION

Phylloxera adults on roots and in leaf galls are female and reproduce asexually (without males). Commonly, adults are wingless, oval to pear shaped, from 0.7 to 1 mm (0.028 to 0.040 in) long and 0.4 to 0.6 mm (0.016 to 0.023 in) wide (fig. 32.1). They are barely visible to the naked eye but are easily seen with a 10× hand lens. Color varies from bright yellow when they are young and on an optimal root host to yellowish green, olive green, or light brown or orange when they are older or on a weakened root. Upon death they turn brown or black.

Newly deposited eggs are lemon-yellow ovals about twice as long as wide, approximately 0.50 by 0.25 mm (0.02 by 0.01 in). Within a short time of being laid, the outer surface of the eggs darken to yellow-gray. As the embryo develops, a pair of red eyespots and the dark

Figure 32.1 Close-up of phylloxera colony shows adult female, eggs, and nymphs. *Photo:* J. K. Clark.

ACTUAL SIZE: GRAPE PHYLLOXERA

Egg   Adult

line of the strawlike sucking mouth can be seen within the egg shell.

Nymphs (immatures) appear similar to the adults but are smaller. The newly hatched nymphs are called crawlers because they can move freely. Once the nymphs settle to feed, they rarely move, generally remaining in the same place as they alternately grow and molt to become egg-laying adults. Nymphs molt four times to become adults, each step being referred to as an instar.

INJURY

As they feed, phylloxera inject saliva, causing the host roots to swell. When they feed on small primary rootlets, yellow-white hooklike swellings appear at the growing rootlet tips or may form as clubs that curve around the insects (fig. 32.2). These galls are referred to as nodosities. In most cases the galling stops rootlet growth, and fungal necrosis kills the infested portions. Nodosities alone do not result in observable aboveground symptoms of vine damage.

Phylloxera feeding on larger, mature storage roots also causes swellings (called tuberosities), which may also decay. In California, aboveground phylloxera damage symptoms are associated with necrotic tuberosities (figs. 32.3– 32.5). Aboveground symptoms are reduced shoot length and foliage growth, shortened internodes, poor fruit production, appearance of water stress and nutrient deficiency, and vine death.

A number of soilborne fungal species have been found in roots wounded by phylloxera, including various *Fusarium* and *Pythium* species and young vine decline disease

organisms. These fungi are usually opportunistic on grapes; they cannot penetrate the roots without a wound being present, and once inside they spread slowly. Infections tend to remain in the area around the feeding site in the phloem parenchyma cells and do not penetrate the xylem. Infections spread radially around the root, girdling it, rather than moving laterally in the phloem or xylem. Girdled roots are killed, and vine damage symptoms are associated with this root death.

Severity of vine damage may differ because of rootstock cultivar, vine age and vigor, soil type and temperature, drainage, and the microbial ecology of the vineyard soil. Vigorous vines tolerate phylloxera and fungal attack better than do weak vines. Infested vines live longer in fertile, deep, well-drained soil than in shallow soil or soil with poor drainage; in the San Joaquin Valley, infested vines can continue to be productive with good farming practice. Soils with enough clay content to allow cracks to occur when dry will support severely damaging populations, while soils with a high percentage of sand do not. Some fungal species and strains are more damaging to vine roots than others; virulent fungal populations will result in much more rapid vineyard decline than those that are less virulent. Water stress does not alter root susceptibility to fungal virulence at root wounds.

Damage initially appears in a vineyard as a few contiguous, weakened vines at one or more locations. With time, the number of vines affected and the area increases, generally in all directions from the initial damage points. The vines at the center of the affected areas are the most severely weakened or are dead, while those at the damage periphery are stunted. As the size of the affected areas enlarges, satellite damage sites form, frequently downwind from the original locations. The number of vines affected increases at a variable rate, sometimes doubling or more per year. Populations of phylloxera decline as roots become severely weakened and almost disappear by the time the vines die. However, after the vineyards are removed, phylloxera can persist on deeply located root pieces for at least 6 years, serving as inoculum for the succeeding vineyard.

Phylloxera-associated vine injury may appear similar to symptoms caused by other debilitating organisms, such as nematodes and oak root fungus, that can also weaken vines and decrease crop production. Also, soil problems (shallow, sandy, salt-affected, poor water infiltration) can result in islands of weak vines in the vineyard that can be mistaken for phylloxera damage.

High populations of nodosity phylloxera have been found on resistant rootstocks at some sites. These phylloxera are genetically distinct and occasionally have difficulty forming tuberosities even on roots with *V. vinifera* parentage.

Vine damage observed at such sites may be due to other site-related conditions and not to the phylloxera.

Leaf galls were rarely seen in viticultural regions of California (fig 32.6), but they are now common in Yolo and Solano County rootstock nursery plantings. These leaf-galling phylloxera strains are genetically unique and may have been introduced from outside of the state. Frequent heavy irrigation of rootstock blocks may increase the occurrence of galls where these strains exist.

In viticultural regions where leaf galls regularly occur on non–*V. vinifera* cultivars (eastern,

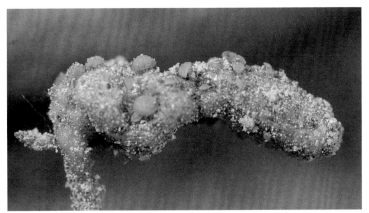

Figure 32.2 Typical clubbing of a primary root tip by phylloxera colony. *Photo*: J. K. Clark.

Figure 32.4 Heavily phylloxerated mature root. *Photo*: J. K. Clark.

Figure 32.3 Phylloxera colony on a mature storage root. *Photo*: J. K. Clark.

Figure 32.5 Comparison of healthy (lower) and phylloxerated (upper) mature storage roots. *Photo*: J. K. Clark.

central, and southwestern United States, as well as Europe and parts of Australia and South America), some leaf loss and stunting of cane growth are seen, but vines are not killed. In these regions, phylloxera leaf galls are also found on native *Vitis* species (in the Americas) and feral rootstocks.

SEASONAL DEVELOPMENT

The life cycle in California (fig. 32.7) is governed by season. Phylloxera overwinter on roots as first-instar nymphs called hibernants. In response to rising temperatures in spring, overwintering nymphs begin to feed, mature, and lay eggs. On a good root host, nymphs mature in less than 1 month, with

Figure 32.6 Phylloxera leaf galls on 3309C rootstock. *Photos*: L. J. Bettiga.

higher soil temperatures prompting more rapid maturation and greater egg production. Multiple generations occur through the summer and autumn. On a healthy, susceptible root, a single phylloxera may lay as many as 300 eggs in its month-long life as an adult. In a warm climate there may be five or more overlapping generations per year. Some phylloxera crawlers leave their feeding site and move along roots through soil cracks and on the soil surface to infest other portions of the roots or roots of other vines. Crawlers emerge from the soil from spring through autumn. Upon emergence crawlers may be blown by wind to distant vines, though desiccation may decrease success of such spread. By September some first instars begin to hibernate, and by November all are hibernating. Hibernants become tan or gray-brown and do not feed while dormant. However, in areas where soil temperatures do not go far below 15.5°C (60°F), feeding and reproducing forms may be found all winter and are most noticeable on immature roots. In summer and autumn, winged female adults (alates) appear, often arising from severely damaged roots. Each possesses two pairs of delicate, scantily veined, clear, membranous wings and an orange body with a grayish black head and thorax. Immatures destined to become the alates can be differentiated by the presence of a pair of black wing pads on the thorax. After emerging from the soil, the alates do not feed again but are capable of laying a few eggs that can develop into either males or females. These sexual forms appear similar to crawlers but do not possess functional mouthparts

and cannot feed. In California, sexual stages do not appear to be viable and apparently do not contribute to maintenance, dispersion, or diversity of California populations. In places where leaf galls are common, it is believed that the progeny of the sexual generation overwinter and initiate spring leaf galling.

Temperature, rainfall patterns, and soil types influence phylloxera infestations. Phylloxera do not develop where the temperature of their surrounding soil is above 32°C (90°F) or below about 16°C (60°F). Seasonal temperatures on the low side of this range allow fewer generations to develop per year than do temperatures on the high side of the range. The phylloxera population in the soil is directly proportional to the number of generations per year. Spring and summer rains influence root populations and, where they occur, leaf infestations. High rainfall apparently washes phylloxera off leaves before they can establish galls. However, it is believed that very low humidity also inhibits leaf galling by desiccating first instars responsible for forming the galls. Rootlets tend to be formed after irrigation or rainfall, and this allows feeding sites to form on them. Extended winter flooding of vineyards is known to kill soilborne phylloxera populations. Phylloxera populations often thrive in heavy clay soils but tend to be minimized in sandy soils. The mechanisms for these differences are unknown.

MONITORING GUIDELINES

Finding new phylloxera infestations in a vineyard is difficult because of the insects' uneven distribution and the labor involved with discerning a belowground presence. Search efficiency can be improved by initially focusing on sections of the vineyard with aboveground symptoms. Phylloxera should be suspected when a concentric area of vines in the vineyard begin to decline rapidly. Inspect the roots in these areas to determine the presence of phylloxera, or use emergence traps. When evaluating a large acreage in a vineyard, aerial images made in mid to late summer can be revealing (figs. 32.8–32.9). Infrared images from an altitude of 1 to 2 km (0.6 to 1.2 mi) are frequently used. Ground-truthing to determine whether phylloxera are in the locale of the stunted plants is necessary when using such images. In early stages of damage, phylloxera populations are easy to find on the roots near the vine trunk within 20 cm (8 in) of the soil surface. Nodosities are easy to spot by eye but a 10× hand lens is needed to identify the phylloxera. Where populations are high, portions of the roots may appear yellow from the number of insects present. Heavily damaged roots often appear blackened. The bark of these roots can be easily removed, and the root becomes dry and spongy with a charred appearance.

The best place to dig for infested roots is at the interface between the wet zone directly beneath a drip emitter and the drier areas on the periphery of the drip zone. With flood-irrigated vines, search for infested roots at the base of the trunk. A recent irrigation makes digging easier, but time should be allowed for drainage so the soil is not muddy. Root damage can be seen any time of

Figure 32.7 Life cycle of phylloxera in California.

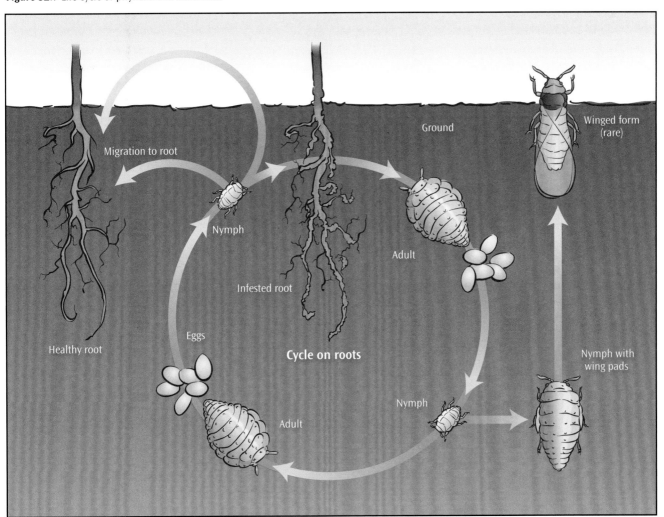

year, but live phylloxera are most easily viewed in the spring and late summer. Feeding phylloxera need active roots in order to live. Digging next to dead vines at the center of a heavily damaged vineyard spot is likely to be unsuccessful, while efforts on the healthy or mildly stunted plants surrounding the dead spot are more likely to uncover the insect. Damage symptoms spread more slowly in a vineyard than do phylloxera populations. By the time a severely damaged phylloxera site is found in a vineyard, phylloxera populations are likely to be found throughout the vineyard block.

Phylloxera populations are distributed very unevenly on root systems as well as over a vineyard block. Multiple vines and roots may need to be inspected to determine the extent of an infestation. In addition, traps situated on the vineyard berm can be used to monitor emerging crawlers and alates. These traps are inverted plastic bowls with a sticky gum-coated

tape strip (such as Tanglefoot) on the inside. Emergence trapping requires a dissecting microscope to count the catch.

MANAGEMENT GUIDELINES

Spread of Phylloxera
In many parts of California, phylloxera has been present for years. Once present, phylloxera can subsist on deeply buried roots from previous plantings. Populations can also live on nodosities of strongly resistant rootstocks, and the living vines show no symptoms. In addition, populations may be maintained in adjacent productive vineyards on escaped *V. vinifera* or wild *V. californica* vines. Removal of infested vines from a vineyard block does not eliminate phylloxera from the site.

In some locations phylloxera are not yet present. Phylloxera can be introduced on infested rootings or grafted vines. In addition, new strains of phylloxera can be introduced into a vineyard that already has other strains. Such spread can

be prevented by using noninfested planting material and not holding vines in infested areas before planting. Phylloxera can also be spread on machinery, vine stakes, boxes, shoes, and other objects that are moved from infested vineyards to clean ones. Newly hatched nymphs can live out of the soil for several days on such items. In addition, cultivating equipment can cut off infested roots close to the ground surface and spread phylloxera within and between vineyards. Cultivating and mechanical harvesting equipment should be thoroughly steam cleaned before being moved from an infested vineyard to another site.

Cultivation, ripping, row plowing, and mechanical harvesting can spread phylloxera from vineyard hot spots to vines throughout the vineyard. It is best to use noncultivation floor management when hot spots of phylloxera have been identified.

Some dispersal cannot be prevented. Wind dispersal of

Figure 32.8 Aerial view of Cabernet Sauvignon vineyard shows phylloxera damage (arrow). *Photo*: J. K. Clark.

Figure 32.9 Ground-level photo of same spot on aerial photo. *Photo*: J. K. Clark.

phylloxera crawlers is suggested by the apparent spread of damaged vineyard areas in a downwind direction. Although phylloxera has been trapped out of the wind stream in California, the insects' viability and their ability to start new infestations has not been proven. Irrigation or floodwater also can move phylloxera. Crawlers can live more than a week submerged in water, and eggs hatch readily in water. Spring rain runoff in hillside vineyards can wash phylloxera to uninfested vines.

Experience has shown that phylloxera eventually reach every vineyard in an infested district, despite concerted preventative efforts. The farther phylloxera have to move to reach a clean vineyard, the longer it will take. The delay between the initial infestation and occurrence of vineyard damage also limits the effectiveness of quarantine efforts and the ability to determine the source of a new infestation.

Once a vineyard or vineyard region is infested, resistant rootstocks must be used. However, in some regions, such as in the San Joaquin Valley, infested own-rooted vineyards can remain productive. It is important to avoid stressing vines, which requires good irrigation and nutrition practices, avoiding overcropping, and maintaining a healthy canopy by controlling other pests and diseases.

Treating Infested Nursery Stock

Phylloxera on nursery stock can be killed with a hot water dip. The roots should be washed free of soil and then use a 5-minute immersion in each of three water tanks: preheating at 30°C (86°F); hot

water at 52.8°C (127°F); and cooling at 23°C (73.4°F). The water bath should be large enough to maintain temperatures while roots are immersed. It may be better to preheat roots by immersing them in an initial warm water bath at 43°C (110°F) for 5 minutes, then placing them in a water bath of 52° to 54°C (125° to 130°F) for 3 to 5 minutes. After treatment, the roots should be plunged quickly into cold (ambient temperature) water. They should then be packaged to prevent drying. Similar treatments are also used to control mealybugs and nematodes.

Natural Control

No effective natural enemies or diseases are known for root phylloxera. Vineyard management procedures including use of organic composts may slow vine decline, though phylloxera populations will remain high. There are few examples of vine recovery from phylloxera damage, but efforts to improve root health and vigor by discontinuing disking and irrigating more broadly and frequently have occasionally retarded decline. Month-long flooding of vineyards in winter kills phylloxera. Planting vineyards in sandy soil may also decrease the severity of populations and hence damage. Most important, planting resistant rootstocks prevents phylloxera damage (see below).

Managing Infested Sites

Although a number of insecticides are registered for phylloxera control, their use may lessen but not eliminate the problem. Soil treatments are problematic because chemical penetration is poor in the clay soils that phylloxera prefers,

though treatments of phylloxera in lighter soils may be more effective. Most foliar insecticides do not have downwardly mobile systemic activity for killing root infestations.

Since the economic injury level for root-feeding phylloxera is not known, it is not clear when to begin treatments. Because damage symptoms are seen late in an infestation cycle, considerable root damage may occur before insecticides are applied, requiring years of treatments. Because the reproductive potential of phylloxera is so high, populations rebound rapidly after insecticide use, making repeat treatments necessary.

Soilborne secondary fungal pathogens play a role in phylloxera damage, and soil amendments have been considered for changing microbial ecology to prevent or minimize damage. Phylloxera populations may be unaffected by such treatments. To date, soil amendments have not been scientifically demonstrated to be efficacious. Because these amendments are not sold as pesticides, regulatory scrutiny is insufficient to eliminate ineffective products.

Special Considerations for the San Joaquin Valley

Well-irrigated vines growing in the heat of the San Joaquin Valley tolerate phylloxera much better than do vines in coastal and foothill areas that are dry farmed or receive only supplemental irrigation. When well managed, infested grapevines in the San Joaquin Valley can be productive over a normal life span. With poor care, however, phylloxera can weaken vines, shortening a vineyard's economic life considerably. Irrigation and fertilization practices must be designed to compensate for a loss of roots from phylloxera feeding. Infested vines should not be over-cropped because they do not have the normal capacity to recover.

Phylloxera-Resistant Rootstocks

Where phylloxera is damaging, resistant rootstocks must be used. Phylloxera-resistant rootstocks are American *Vitis* species and hybrids that were selected for their inability to support phylloxera populations on mature roots. This resistance is not immunity. Most rootstocks support small infestations on primary roots (as nodosities) but prevent the insect from developing on and damaging mature roots (tuberosities). There are hundreds of resistant rootstock cultivars. Most of these were hybridized and selected in France, Hungary, and Italy over a century ago. In addition to preventing phylloxera damage, they address problems with particular soil conditions and viticultural practices. These additional features include resistance to nematodes and adaptation to lime in soils, drought, and soil types ranging from rocky to alluvial clays.

Rootstocks were bred or selected from American *Vitis* within the native range of grape phylloxera, where these species evolved to resist phylloxera tuberosity formation. Rootstocks can be either cloned selections of a single such *Vitis* species (e.g., *V. rupestris*, *V. riparia*) or a hybrid between various American species, depending on the viticultural properties desired. These rootstocks have been durably resistant, some since the 1870s, when the initial ones were first selected. Experience has shown that rootstocks with

V. vinifera in the parentage lack a durable resistance. One of the critical needs for European soils is strong lime tolerance, and *V. vinifera* possesses some of the best lime tolerance among the *Vitis* species. For this reason it has been used in several rootstocks suitable for very chalky lime soils, where few other rootstock alternatives exist. If the lesser of two evils on these soils is phylloxera, using *V. vinifera* hybrids may be justified. In Europe, the two most popular such hybrids are Fercal and 41B (both *V. vinifera* × *V. berlandieri*). Neither of these should be considered for California. The rootstock AXR#1 (also called Ganzin 1, a *V. vinifera* × *V. rupestris* hybrid) was bred for its lime tolerance and good viticultural properties. However, it failed due to insufficient phylloxera resistance in Europe in the 1910s, in South Africa in the 1920s, and in California during the 1980s, in each circumstance after about 20 years of intensive use. Its California failure in the 1980s caused approximately a billion dollars of damage and replanting of a large percentage of the coastal valley vineyards. AXR#1 and other *V. vinifera*–containing hybrids should not be used as phylloxera-resistant rootstocks.

Vineyards are most successful when declining vines are replaced with pure American rootstocks in whole blocks. However, with the California AXR#1 situation, some growers attempted to convert the existing vines over to a new resistant root system by in-arch or approach-grafting them with newly planted rootstocks. These attempts had limited success. Interplanting new vines on resistant rootstock

between the existing vines was also attempted and was generally more successful. However, interplanting success was often limited because of root and light competition and unwillingness of growers to severely cut back the AXR#1 vines to provide space and light for the developing interplanted vines.

Rootstocks can be grouped by their *Vitis* species parentage, sharing common traits such as lime tolerance, drought adaptation, vigor induction, and horticultural characters of the mother vine (such as rooting ability, internode length, and presence of laterals). The following parentage-based listing of rootstocks have in most cases sufficient phylloxera resistance for commercial use in California.

Single-Species Selections

Vitis rupestris Scheele

Rupestris St. George, also called St. George or Rupestris du Lot, was the standard phylloxera-resistant rootstock in the nonirrigated soils of the coastal valleys through much of the twentieth century. Although it supports relatively large phylloxera populations on nodosities, it is tuberosity-free, and phylloxera-related decline of vineyards has not been observed. Its deep root system provides adaptation to drought, but it is not well adapted to dry, shallow hillside locations. Rupestris St. George is very susceptible to nematodes, oak root fungus, and Phytophthora root rot. This rootstock is relatively insensitive to a broad range of viruses that cause graft-induced incompatibility. Rupestris St. George vines are very shrubby and produce abundant laterals and short shoots, but it is easy to root, bud, and graft. On deep fertile soils when there are late-spring rains, the vigor induced by this rootstock can lead to poor set and straggly clusters. *Vitis rupestris* is now very rare over its native range. It is found in gravelly streambeds, where its deep, plunging roots prevent it from being uprooted during periods of high stream flow.

Vitis riparia Michaux

Riparia Gloire, also called Riparia Gloire de Montpellier, is seldom used in California, although its low vigor makes it suited for high-density plantings on vigor-promoting soils. Scions grafted on it are susceptible to lime-induced chlorosis, and it is very sensitive to drought. It has moderate resistance to root-knot nematodes and is easily rooted and grafted. *Vitis riparia* is found throughout the eastern United States in alluvial soils. It has a very shallow root system, which accounts for its ability to promote low vigor and sensitivity to drought.

Selections of *V. riparia* × *V. rupestris*

Couderc 3309 (3309C) has long been recommended for use on high-vigor Valley floor sites to help control excess vegetative vigor. 3309C is not drought tolerant and produces weak vines on shallow or dry soils. It is susceptible to nematodes. 3309C is easy to root, bud, and graft, and is a shrubby mother vine, although to a lesser extent than Rupestris St. George. 3309C use has declined due in part to its relatively high sensitivity to viruses that induce graft incompatibility.

101-14 Mgt has longer shoots with fewer laterals than its relative 3309C and is also easy to root, bud, and graft. 101-14 Mgt induces moderate vigor in scions grafted

to it (greater than 3309C) and has performed well on fertile Valley soils. It is not lime tolerant, nor is it adapted to drought. 101-14 Mgt mother vines lose their leaves very early in the autumn, much like *V. riparia*. This tendency seems to carry over to grafted plants on low-vigor sites and may limit 101-14 Mgt's use with late-harvest winemaking. This rootstock is currently very popular in California, and its moderate vigor and good nematode resistance make it adaptable to many sites. It may support noticeable phylloxera populations on nodosities, but it has been tuberosity-free.

The rootstock Schwarzmann is not widely used in California, but it has good ectoparasitic nematode resistance. It has moderate resistance to root-knot nematodes. It is slightly more lime tolerant than 101-14 Mgt.

Selections of *V. berlandieri* Planch. × *V. riparia*

Teleki 5C was one of the primary replacement rootstocks following the collapse of AXR#1 in California. It has good lime tolerance from its *V. berlandieri* parent and moderate vigor from its *V. riparia* parent. In California, it was initially misidentified and distributed as SO4 (Selection Oppenheim #4). These two rootstocks are very similar in appearance and viticultural attributes. Both have moderate resistance to root-knot and dagger nematodes. Interest in 5C in some coastal production areas has been declining due to its lack of adaptation to drought and generally poor response to deficit irrigation. Scions on both 5C and SO4 overgrow the rootstock, producing a wider scion than rootstock trunk,

suggesting incompatibility. However, no impact on vine longevity due to this overgrowth has been observed. Both 5C and SO4 are excellent mother vines, with long internodes and canes and few laterals. They root well but graft and bud less well than *V. riparia* × *V. rupestris* rootstocks.

Kober 5BB has good resistance to some root-knot nematodes and, like all members of this group, is well adapted to lime soils. However, it induces more vigor in scions than does its relatives. 5BB may induce too much vigor on deep fertile soils with high vine densities and irrigation. It is highly sensitive to viruses that induce graft incompatibility and is prone to Phytophthora root rot on poorly drained soils. 5BB propagates like 5C.

420A Mgt is a relatively low-vigor rootstock with good lime tolerance but is susceptible to nematodes. Its low vigor makes it a good choice for use with high vine densities on moderate- to high-vigor sites. It is difficult to propagate and roots less well than average, resulting in relatively poor bench graft success. 420A mother vines are among the most vigorous, yet they induce relatively low vigor as grafted plants. The mother vines retain their leaves until very late in the autumn, and vineyards grafted on 420A remain active late in the season.

Selections of *V. berlandieri* × *V. rupestris*

Richter 110 (110R) is susceptible to nematodes and is relatively drought tolerant. Despite often being slow to develop, it can induce too much vigor for deep, fertile Valley floor sites. On the central coast soils, it generally has been a moderate- to low-vigor rootstock. This rootstock was one of the primary choices after the collapse of AXR#1; however, its use has declined partially because of its sensitivity to viruses that induce graft incompatibility.

Paulsen 1103 (1103P) was produced to tolerate lime soils and dry summers. It induces relatively high vigor in scions and is susceptible to nematodes. 1103P mother vines are unusual among members of this group because they produce long canes with few laterals. 1103P roots, buds, and grafts well. It is well suited to dry-farmed Valley floor sites or dry hillsides with irrigation. On fertile sites it may induce too much vigor but is well suited to low-vigor sites.

140 Ruggeri (140Ru) was developed as a rootstock capable of growing on very weak limestone-based soils in dry climates and therefore is capable of inducing high vigor on deep soils with good water-holding capacity. Although 140Ru is not often used in California, it might be considered for shallow limestone soils in areas with limited rainfall and irrigation. It is susceptible to root-knot and dagger nematodes but has good phylloxera resistance. It also has strong salt tolerance. Its mother vines are similar to 110R and are brushy with frequent laterals.

Other hybrid selections

The Ramsey (incorrectly called Salt Creek in the past) rootstock, based on *V. champinii*, induces very high vigor and is best suited for sandy, infertile soils in hot climates where large canopies are needed.

It has also performed well on deep, sandy soils on the central coast. It has been used extensively in Australia for its drought and salinity tolerance. Ramsey has moderate phylloxera resistance but is generally not grown on soils that are conducive to phylloxera damage. It has very good resistance to nematodes. Ramsey mother vines are relatively shrubby and propagate with more difficulty than do most rootstocks. Dog Ridge, a closely related rootstock, is rarely used because of its poor propagation and excessive vigor.

Harmony and Freedom are also *V. champinii*-based rootstocks. They are nematode resistant with better viticultural attributes than Ramsey or Dog Ridge. They are primarily used in the lower San Joaquin Valley, where they are less vigorous than Dog Ridge or Ramsey, propagate more easily, and are more adaptable. They have an unusual parentage as hybrids of open-pollinated seedlings derived from 1613C (25% *V. vinifera*) and Dog Ridge. Both of these rootstocks induce high vigor in scions and should not be used in fertile soils where canopy growth needs to be restricted. Both have very good nematode resistance, but aggressive root-knot nematode strains have evolved and are capable of damaging them. Their phylloxera resistance is inadequate on soils that are conducive to phylloxera damage (the result of their *V. vinifera* parentage). Freedom is particularly sensitive to virus-induced incompatibility, and only certified

plant material should be grafted with it. These rootstocks root, graft, and bud relatively easily.

O39-16 is a hybrid between *V. vinifera* and *V. rotundifolia* (Michaux) (the muscadine grape of the southern United States). It is the only rootstock recommended for fanleaf degeneration sites, where it induces tolerance to this virus infection and resists the nematode vector. Although O39-16 appears to be resistant to phylloxera, its *V. vinifera* parentage prompts caution regarding the durability of its resistance. It is a vigorous rootstock, but this trait can be controlled by deficit irrigation and cover crops. O39-16 is susceptible to root-knot nematodes. This rootstock is relatively difficult to propagate, and well-matured wood must be used. The sibling rootstock, O43-43, is not phylloxera resistant and is no longer available from nurseries.

PLANTING NEW VINEYARDS

When choosing rootstocks, growers should take note of local rootstock trials while considering site specifications. Vineyard site differences have a large impact on rootstock behavior. Growers should get detailed information about soil depth, structure, and texture; water sources and availability; soilborne pests; and the previous crop history to make the best decisions as to which rootstocks are best adapted to their site.

Unfortunately, vineyard soils are rarely left fallow for more than 6 months, as vines are usually pulled in the autumn and replanted the following spring. Most vineyard land is too valuable to plant with an alternative crop, which means that crop rotation is also not an option. Rootstocks should be rotated to different parentage groups to avoid the selection of more aggressive strains of pests such as phylloxera and nematodes. Large-scale use of a given rootstock should also be avoided to prevent pest outbreaks associated with a monoculture.

Fumigation is used much less widely now than in the past. This practice is very effective at eliminating soil pests in the upper 60 cm (2 ft) of soil and helps in the rapid establishment of new vineyards. However, it often does not kill deeply buried roots, which are capable of hosting phylloxera and nematodes for many years. Thus, strong resistance to phylloxera and nematodes is even more important as vineyard land is replanted. The use of herbicides to kill vines is effective at killing the trunk portion, but it does not kill the deeply buried roots and thus has limited impact on controlling soilborne pests.

Grafting scion cultivars onto rootstocks occurs at nurseries or by budding after the rootstock is planted in the field. Leaves of grape rootstock cultivars are typically used for identification, although the leaf differences among some rootstock cultivars can be subtle. However, rootstock leaves are seen only prior to grafting or if rootstock suckers develop from underground. DNA extracted from tissue under the bark can also be used to identify rootstocks, but the test requires advanced laboratory equipment and is expensive. To ensure that the correct rootstock is being planted, it is important to buy certified nursery stock from reputable nurseries. The use of certified stock is also the best protection against the introduction of grape virus diseases.

It is essential that vines be properly planted with graft unions at least 10 cm (4 in) above the vineyard floor, otherwise scion rooting may occur. Scion roots can quickly become dominant, and vineyards that were originally planted on resistant rootstocks can fail from phylloxera damage after just a few years. Low graft unions are more likely to occur when rootstock rootings are planted and subsequently field budded because the rootstocks may be planted too deeply, limiting space for the bud, or because budders feel that their success rates will be higher with the warmth and humidity from the ground. Soil movement and buildup around the vines can also lead to scion rooting. A properly planted and managed rootstock-based vineyard should remain productive at least for 2 to 3 decades.

REFERENCES

Christensen, L. P. Rootstock selection. 2003. In L. P. Christensen et al. eds., Wine grape varieties in California. Oakland: University of California Division of Agriculture and Natural Resources, Publication 3419.

Davidson, W. M., and R. L. Nougaret. 1921. The grape phylloxera in California. USDA Bulletin 903:1–128.

Granett, J., A. C. Goheen, and L. A. Lider. 1987. Grape phylloxera in California. California Agriculture 41(1): 10–12.

Granett, J., A. C. Goheen, L. A. Lider, and J. J. White. 1987. Evaluation of grape rootstocks for resistance to type A and type B grape phylloxera. American Journal of Enology and Viticulture 38:298–300.

Granett, J., P. Timper, and L. A. Lider. 1985. Grape phylloxera (*Daktulosphaira vitifoliae*) (Homoptera: Phylloxeridae) biotypes in California. Journal of Economic Entomology 78:1463–1467.

Granett J., A. Walker, J. De Benedictis, G. Fong, H. Lin, and E. Weber. 1996. California grape phylloxera more variable than expected. California Agriculture 50(4): 9–13.

Granett, J. A., A. W. Walker, L. Kocsis, and A. D. Omer. 2001. Biology and management of grape phylloxera. Annual Review of Entomology 46:387–412.

Lider, L. A. 1958. Phylloxera-resistant grape rootstocks for the coastal valleys of California. Hilgardia 27:287–318.

Wildman, W. E., R. T. Nagaota, and L. A. Lider. 1983. Monitoring spread of grape phylloxera by color infrared aerial photography and ground investigation. American Journal of Enology and Viticulture 34:83–93.

Hemiptera
*Aphids,
Leafhoppers,
Mealybugs, Scales,
True Bugs,
Whiteflies*

33 WESTERN GRAPE LEAFHOPPER

Kent M. Daane, Jay A. Rosenheim, Rhonda J. Smith, and Richard L. Coviello

Western grape leafhopper (*Erythroneura elegantula* Osborn) (Hemiptera: Cicadellidae) was historically the key pest of grapes north of the Tehachapi Mountains, infesting vineyards in the Central Valley, Sierra Nevada foothills, and coastal regions. In California, this pest is commonly known as grape leafhopper, and this name will be used when referring to this insect in this publication. Where it is prominent, every vineyard can be infested with grape leafhopper. However, actual pest damage varies according to location of the vineyard, cultivar, plant vigor, market use of the crop (e.g., raisins, wine grapes, or table grapes), and season. While grape leafhopper is capable of defoliating vines by midsummer, defoliation typically does not happen because of site conditions, management practices, and biological controls. Less than a quarter of California's wine and raisin vineyards currently require treatment, while table grape vineyards are more sensitive to leafhopper damage because of the potential aesthetic injury to the grape cluster.

Grape leafhopper was first reported in California in 1864. Before the 1940s, severe damage occurred in some years, followed by periods of lower population densities and damage. Since that time, a series of synthetic insecticides have been used to control grape leafhoppers, including chlorinated hydrocarbons, organophosphates, and carbamates. Now, neonicotinoids and insect growth regulators (IGRs) are more commonly used and have resulted in greatly reduced leafhopper densities and damage. For these reasons, the most immediate concerns are accurate sampling, selecting the most appropriate insecticides that conserve natural enemies, and establishing insecticide resistance management programs to maintain the effectiveness of the current materials for as long as possible. Also, a closely related species, the variegated grape leafhopper (*Erythroneura variabilis* Beamer) replaced the grape leafhopper in importance in the 1980s in southern California and the Central Valley (see section 35, "Variegated Grape Leafhopper"). The Virginia creeper leafhopper (*Erythroneura ziczac* Walsh) is also present in California and is similar in appearance to the grape leafhopper (see section 36, "Virginia Creeper Leafhopper"). Although they have many similarities in control strategies, we will discuss these pest species separately.

DESCRIPTION

The adult leafhopper is about 3 mm (0.12 in) long and pale yellow with reddish and dark brown markings (fig. 33.1). The color patterns on the wings and head are more colorful on adults found in the fall and winter than on adults in summer and spring.

Adult females deposit eggs in mature grape leaves. Eggs are laid singly just under the leaf epidermal tissue and can be inserted on either the upper or lower leaf surface, although the lower is preferred. Each egg is minute, about 0.8 mm (0.032 in) long. The freshly deposited egg is colorless (transparent) and appears as a kidney bean–shaped blister. Their size and color make these eggs difficult to find without a hand lens and some experience working with locating this stage. When eggs are parasitized, they can be brown or reddish (see "Natural Control," below). Occasionally, eggs turn dark

brown or black and do not hatch; these are thought to be infertile or diseased.

The first-instar leafhopper emerges by pushing its head through the egg cuticle and leaf tissue, creating a slit through which it exits. The first instar is almost transparent and colorless, except for its prominent eyes. There are five nymph stages, with each resembling the previous except for increases in size, a deepening white to pale yellow color, and progressive development of wing pads. Nymph length ranges from about 0.8 mm (0.032 in) to 2.5 mm (0.1 in) for the first to fifth stages, respectively (fig. 33.2). Although nymphs molt five times, only the cast-off skins of the fifth molt stick to leaves. Newly molted adults have white wings for 2 to 3 days until the characteristic pale yellow coloring and reddish and dark brown markings begin to develop. These new adults do not fly for a day or two.

INJURY

Both nymphs and adults feed on leaves by using piercing mouthparts to puncture leaf cells and suck out the contents. Each feeding puncture and injured leaf cell leaves a white spot. As injury increases, photosynthetic activity declines, and heavily damaged leaves eventually lose their green color, dry up, and fall off the vine (fig. 33.3). Some leafhopper feeding damage is tolerable. For example, defoliation studies, in which leaves were removed by hand, suggest that vines can tolerate up to 20% leaf loss without reducing the crop load or vine health, provided leaves are not removed until about a month after fruit set. Nevertheless, this can be a regional or site-specific guideline, as even limited defoliation can open the vine canopy and expose fruit clusters to sun damage, especially in relatively weak vines with little foliage.

Figure 33.1 Grape leafhopper adult (A), and egg (with first instar emerging) (B). *Photos*: F. E. Skinner.

Grape leafhoppers can also cause damage when their liquid excrement drops onto the grape clusters, which serves as a substrate for fruit spotting molds in table grapes. This aesthetic damage to table grapes can occur at relatively low leafhopper population densities, where crop load or vine health is not in jeopardy. Adult leafhoppers can also become a nuisance pest during management operations by flying into the eyes, ears, and noses of fieldworkers. In fact, the aesthetic damage to table grapes and the pestiferous nature of adults to field crews are often the primary reasons for an insecticide application prior to harvest.

SEASONAL DEVELOPMENT

As adults, grape leafhoppers overwinter in a state of reproductive diapause. On warm winter days the adults are active, feeding on weeds or other succulent vegetation in or near vineyards. In cold weather they find shelter under leaves, dead grass, weeds, and bark; in brush and straw piles; in debris along ditches; and in alfalfa and old cotton fields.

Grape leafhoppers remain in reproductive diapause until a day length of about 11.6 hours is reached (typically mid-March), at which time their reproductive organs begin to mature. Production of eggs (ovigenesis) in females continues as they feed on weeds and other suitable plants. However, the ovaries do not mature until the female has fed on grape foliage, so an extended delay in egg development can occur if grape budbreak is delayed. Adults may mate before feeding on grapes, but females will not lay eggs on other plants.

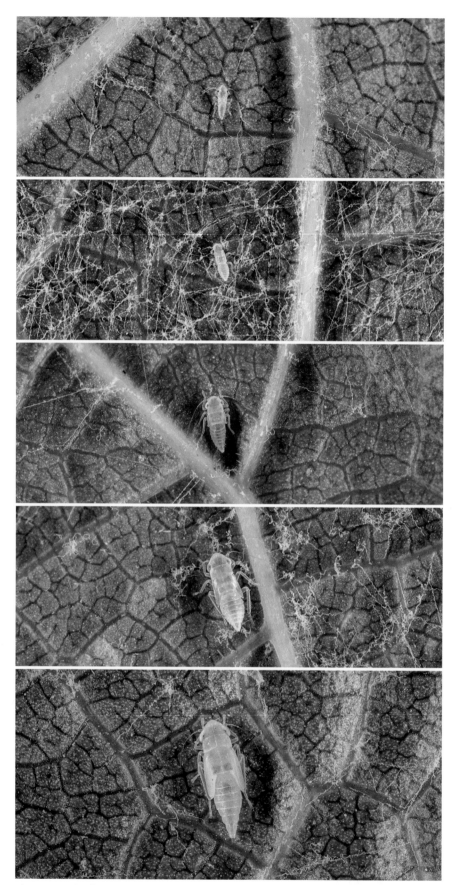

Figure 33.2 The five nymphal stages of the grape leafhopper. Note developing wing pads on the last three stages. Stage 1 is about 0.8 mm (0.03 in) long; stage 5 is 2.5 mm (0.1 in) long. *Photos*: L. J. Bettiga.

Figure 33.3 Grape leafhopper nymphs and adults feed on the leaf mesophyll, using piercing-sucking mouthparts to remove plant fluid, killing leaf cells and resulting in the white dotted pattern in (A). When left untreated, populations with hundreds or thousands of leafhoppers feeding on each vine leave the leaves brown and dry, eventually causing defoliation (B). Adults of both grape and variegated leafhoppers can also hamper field crews by flying into their eyes, noses, and ears (C). For table grapes, leafhopper excrement can be a substrate for molds, which cause cosmetic damage, especially on light-colored cultivars (D). *Photos*: J. K. Clark (A); H. L. Andris (B); H. L. Andris (C); J. K. Clark (D).

From March to April, adults migrate from winter shelters into the vineyard to feed on grape leaves. In cold weather, however, they still seek protection in the ground cover or under the vines, feeding on leaves during warm parts of the day and moving to sheltered areas in the evening or on cold or wet days.

Overwintering females lay eggs for up to 6 weeks starting about mid-April. The subsequent development of leafhopper offspring and the number of leafhopper generations largely depend on temperature. For example, eggs of the first brood may take 20 days to hatch, while eggs in the second (or third when present) brood may hatch in fewer than 7 days. After egg hatch, peak densities (i.e., the highest average count per leaf) of grape leafhopper nymphs occur approximately 222 degree-days Celsius (DDC) above 10.3°C, or 400 degree-days Fahrenheit (DDF) above 50.5°F. Each subsequent nymphal generation peak occurs approximately every 833 DDC (1,500 DDF). Therefore, development from egg to adulthood can range from 4 (warm regions) to 10 (cool regions) weeks.

Figure 33.4 provides a photographic diagram of the seasonal presence of grape leafhopper life stages (egg, nymph, and adult). The number of broods depends on the region and vineyard condition. Three full and a partial fourth generation occur in the San Joaquin Valley; two full generations are more typical in the cooler coastal regions. Figure 33.5 provides a more common linear representation of grape leafhopper nymphs per leaf, with the leafhopper density and number of broods representing a coastal population.

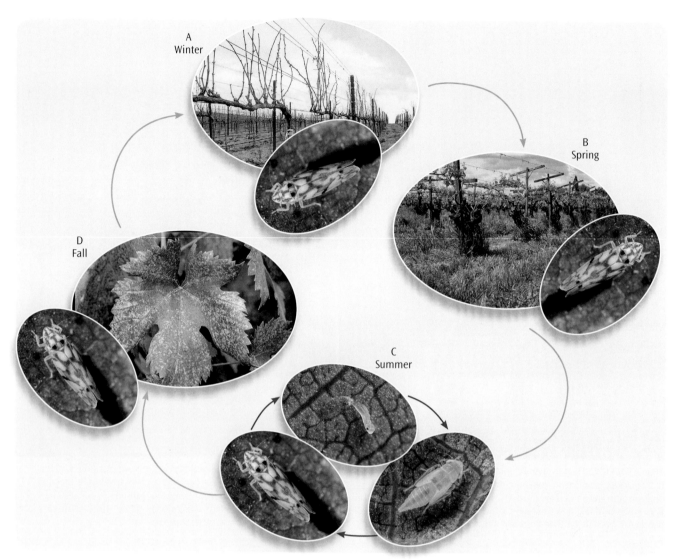

Figure 33.4 Seasonal life history of grape leafhopper. (A) The grape leafhopper overwinters as an adult, feeding on vegetation in or near the vineyard. (B) As shoot growth begins in spring, the adult leafhoppers feed on the new leaves and begin to deposit eggs on the more-mature basal leaves. (C) After egg hatch, the nymphs feed and develop to the adult stage. The number of annual broods ranges from 2 to 5, depending on regional temperature differences. (D) Environmental and vine cues in the fall trigger the adult leafhoppers to begin an overwintering phase, during which they are reproductively dormant but continue to feed on vegetation. *Photos:* K. M. Daane, F. E. Skinner, L. J. Bettiga, and J. K. Clark.

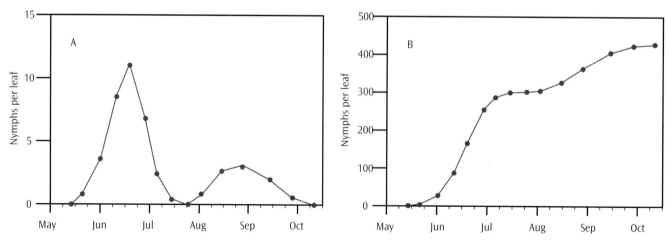

Figure 33.5 Seasonal presence of grape leafhopper nymphs, as depicted for a coastal wine grape vineyard, showing (A) the average number of nymphs per leaf using a conventional sampling program and (B) the accumulated nymphal days (see "Monitoring Guidelines" and table 33.1 for a description of nymphal days).

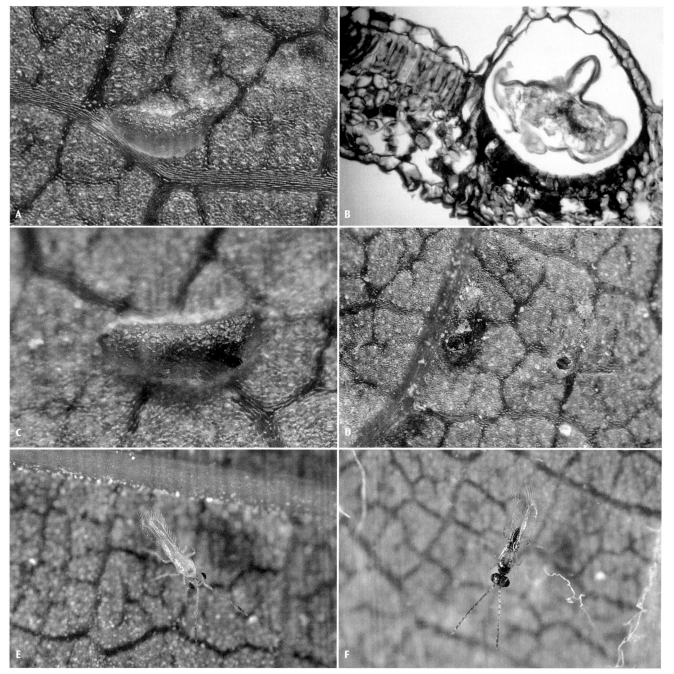

Figure 33.6 Mymarid parasitoids (*Anagrus* species) that attack the grape leafhopper egg, seen from above (A) and in cross-section (B), are the most important grape leafhopper natural enemies. Parasitized leafhopper eggs have a reddish color (C), and after the parasitoid emerges there is a distinct exit hole (D). Adult *Anagrus* species are shown for the female (E) and male (F). *Photos*: F. E. Skinner (A); W. H. Settle (B); F. E. Skinner (C); F. E. Skinner (D); J. K. Clark (E); J. K. Clark (F).

NATURAL CONTROLS

Egg Parasitoids

The most important natural enemies of the grape leafhopper are tiny mymarid wasps (*Anagrus* spp.) (fig. 33.6). The adults are about 0.8 mm (0.032 in) long. The immature *Anagrus* complete their entire development (egg to adult) inside the grape leafhopper egg, consuming the leafhopper egg as they develop.

Recent work has provided better identification of these parasitoids, which were formerly called *Anagrus epos* Girault but are, in fact, a complex of closely related species. Currently, four different *Anagrus* species are known to attack grape leafhopper eggs in North America. The two most common in California are *Anagrus erythroneurae* Triapitsyn and Chiappini and *Anagrus daanei* Triapitsyn. A third species is *Anagrus tretikoviae* Triapitsyn, which is found in warmer regions (e.g., Arizona, New Mexico, Mexico). *Anagrus epos* does attack grape leafhopper eggs, but it is more typically found in colder regions (e.g., Colorado, Canada, and Illinois).

These parasitic wasps are able to locate and attack a high percentage of the grape leafhopper eggs. They develop from the egg to the adult stage more rapidly than do leafhoppers. There can be three or more *Anagrus* generations for each leafhopper generation, making them capable of increasing in numbers quickly, often resulting in parasitization of 90% or more of all leafhopper eggs deposited after July (fig. 33.7).

Anagrus overwinters as an immature larva inside a leafhopper egg, but grape leafhoppers overwinter as adults. Therefore, in order to remain in the vineyard region, adult *Anagrus* emerging from grape leafhopper eggs from late August to October must find and parasitize alternate leafhopper host species that overwinter in the egg stage. In the 1960s, researchers demonstrated that eggs of the blackberry leafhopper (*Dikrella californica* (Lawson)) were suitable overwintering hosts for *Anagrus*. In the 1980s, it was shown that eggs of the prune leafhopper (*Edwardsiana prunicola* (Edwards)) also served as an overwintering host (fig. 33.8). Currently, we know that many leafhopper species overwinter in the egg stage and are suitable hosts for *Anagrus* species attacking grape leafhopper. These include the rose leafhopper (*Edwardsiana rosae* (Linnaeus)) and the white apple leafhopper (*Typhlocyba pomaria* (McAtee)). Undoubtedly, there are still other overwintering hosts, although these host relationships have not yet been identified.

There is evidence that vineyards near riparian areas or prune orchards provide overwintering refuges for *Anagrus*. For example, along rivers where wild blackberries are numerous, *Anagrus* populations can successfully overwinter and then build in numbers in early spring by parasitizing newly laid blackberry leafhopper

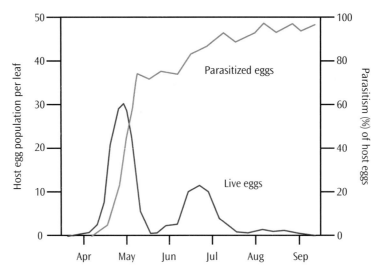

Figure 33.7 An example of the seasonal pattern of grape leafhopper egg parasitism by *Anagrus* species; parasitism begins early, with the development of the first brood and reaches a high percentage during the second and (when present) third broods.

eggs. By late March the *Anagrus* adults can disperse from these riparian areas to vineyards located nearby. There have been attempts to duplicate this benefit by planting blackberries or prune trees near vineyards. To date, however, there is little evidence that these refuge plantings have increased leafhopper egg parasitism throughout the neighboring vineyard. One problem with these refuges may be their small size relative to the vineyard. A small refuge of blackberry bushes or French prune trees will produce a correspondingly small number of blackberry or prune leafhoppers. During the summer and early fall, there can be millions of *Anagrus* in each vineyard block. This onslaught of *Anagrus* will overwhelm the relatively small numbers of leafhoppers in blackberry or prune refuges. The result will be a very high percentage parasitism of blackberry or prune leafhoppers, severely reducing or eliminating those leafhopper populations and providing little or no refuge for overwintering *Anagrus*.

Other management practices that may affect *Anagrus* include the use of cover cropping. Many ground cover species have extrafloral nectaries that can be used by adult parasitoids to increase their longevity. A study in a New York vineyard showed some beneficial impact of cover crops on *Anagrus* populations in vineyards. In California, however, there have been mixed results of cover cropping on *Anagrus* population densities, and more work is needed to understand how to use cover crops to increase leafhopper egg parasitism. The cover crop species used, the growing region, grape cultivar, and leafhopper species (see section 35, "Variegated Grape Leafhopper") might affect levels of egg parasitism and the impact of cover crops.

Nymphal Parasitoids
Aphelopus albopictus Ashmead is a dryinid wasp that attacks grape leafhopper nymphs. In Central

Figure 33.8 Researchers and growers have tried a number of methods to increase natural enemy impact, including adding overwintering refuges for *Anagrus* parasitoids. For example, a number of leafhopper species, such as the blackberry leafhopper (A) and prune leafhopper (B), overwinter in the egg stage and can host the proper *Anagrus* species. Vineyard managers have attempted to increase their numbers in spring by placing rose bushes (C) and prune trees (D) near the vineyard. *Photos*: J. K. Clark (A, B); K. M. Daane (C); K. M. Daane (D).

Valley vineyards, parasitism rates from 0 to 77% have been reported. The female is about 1.8 mm (0.07 in) long and brown to tan. The male is about 1.5 mm (0.06 in) long and black with white mandibles, face, and legs. The adult female parasitizes the larger leafhopper nymphs (third, fourth, and possibly fifth instars) by placing an egg under the leafhopper abdominal segments. The egg does not hatch until the leafhopper nymph molts to the adult stage. The dryinid larva then starts to develop, appearing as an oval mass protruding from the adult leafhopper's first abdominal segment (fig. 33.9). During the parasitoid's larval development, the adult leafhopper is alive and

continues to move and feed; however, the parasitized leafhopper is incapable of reproducing. Eventually, the dryinid larva eviscerates and kills the adult leafhopper. The fully developed parasite larva then drops to the soil, spins a cocoon, pupates, and emerges as a sexually active adult after about 20 days

Generalist Predators

Several generalist predators prey on leafhopper adults and nymphs (fig. 33.10). These include spiders, green lacewings (*Chrysoperla* spp.), brown lacewings (*Hemerobius* sp.), minute pirate bugs (*Orius* sp.), damsel bugs (*Nabis* sp.), lady beetles (*Hippodamia convergens* Guerin-Meneville), and big-eyed

Figure 33.9 The dryinid parasitoid *Aphelopus* attacks late-instar grape leafhoppers, with the parasitoid larva developing externally on the leafhopper. *Photo*: J. K. Clark.

Figure 33.10 A number of predators attack grape and variegated leafhoppers, including the whirligig mite (*Anystis agilis*) (A), various lady beetles (B), spiders (C), and lacewings (D). *Photos*: J. K. Clark (A); F. E. Skinner (B); K. M. Daane (C); K. M. Daane (D).

bug (*Geocoris pallens* Stål). However, the effect of these predators, naturally present in the vineyard, on leafhoppers has not been studied in detail.

In most surveys, spiders comprise more than 90% of the leafhopper predators found in a vineyard. Of the different species of spiders that prey on leafhoppers, most abundant are those of the families Miturgidae (sac spiders), Corinnidae (ant-mimic spiders), Salticidae (jumping spiders), Oxyopidae (lynx spiders), Theridiidae (cobweb weavers), and Araneidae (orb weavers). For more information, see section 35, "Variegated Grape Leafhopper."

Green lacewings are the next-most-common predator group. Lacewing species found on the vines include *Chrysoperla carnea* (Stephens) and *Chrysoperla comanche* Banks, although numbers of these predators are typically low (fewer than one larva per 1,000 leaves). Other green lacewings found in vineyards more commonly reside on the ground cover, and since leafhopper nymphs are on the grapevine these lacewing species do not impact leafhopper populations. These include *Chrysopa oculata* Say, *Chrysopa nigricornis* Burmeister, and *Chrysopa coloradensis* Banks. Lacewing larvae can be voracious leafhopper predators; for example, an individual larva of *C. comanche* killed an average of 252 large leafhopper nymphs over their 9-day development period.

Some growers have released insectary-reared green lacewings to control leafhoppers. In field studies, releases of about 10,000 *C. carnea* eggs per acre (24,700 per ha) from June to July reduced leafhopper densities, but the average reduction was only 9.6%. One possible reason for the poor performance is the high mortality of the released lacewing eggs before the predators hatch. Another possible reason is that feeding by other predators on the lacewing eggs and larvae, as well as cannibalism. Improved release methods are needed before this practice can be recommended. It is also likely that leafhoppers were not as good a target prey for lacewing releases as mealybugs, mites, or scale pests.

The predaceous whirligig mite (*Anystis agilis* (Banks)) attacks small leafhopper nymphs. The adult whirligig mite is large, about 1.5 mm (0.06 in), red, and long-legged. Its common name derives from its rapid and erratic movement. Eggs are small, 0.4 mm (0.016 in), round, yellow-brown, and finely granulated. Eggs are deposited in groups of 6 to 12 and can be found on plant material or debris on the ground or on grape foliage. The whirligig mite is a generalist predator that feeds on any small prey (spiders, mites, and insects), including other whirligig mite nymphs and eggs. Counts in north coast vineyards suggest that two generations occur, one in late spring and one in early fall; a third generation may be present in the warmer San Joaquin and Sacramento Valleys.

The tiger fly (*Coenosia humilis*) is a predator that catches its prey in the air, implying that it will primarily attack leafhopper adults. Immature tiger flies live as maggots in the soil, where they feed on earthworms. While the fly has been commonly found in vineyards and has been observed feeding on adult leafhoppers, there are no studies to date that describe this predator's impact on leafhoppers.

Pathogens

Reports of diseases as mortality agents of grape leafhopper are scarce. Unconfirmed reports of grape leafhopper population declines caused by a fungus, *Beauvaria bassiana,* also need study.

CULTURAL CONTROLS

Habitat Management

Adult leafhoppers maturing in late summer continue feeding on vines until frost and then begin to move to feed on alternate plant species. For example, after fall or winter rains, the adults are commonly found on foxtail, malva, wild mustard, clovers, and filaree. Leafhoppers must have a source of green vegetation to survive in warm weather during their overwintering period. Without these host plants, mortality is high. While overwintering adults have reportedly been found up to a mile from the nearest vineyard, most are found in or close to vineyards. Therefore, reducing overwintering quarters adjacent to vineyards may help control leafhoppers in some circumstances.

Research in the San Joaquin Valley showed that grape leafhopper populations may be reduced by more than 90% by in-row cultivation (French plowing) in late February, disking the adult leafhoppers under the ground (fig. 33.11). Similarly, while not commonly practiced specifically for leafhopper control, the timing of spring mowing or disking ground vegetation can impact leafhopper

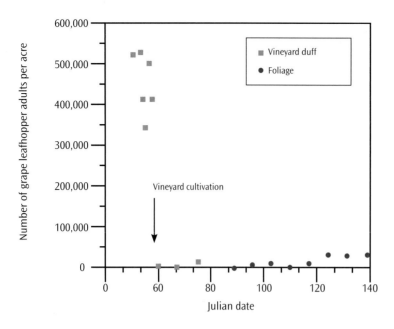

Figure 33.11 The effect of late-winter cultivation on overwintering grape leafhopper adults.

densities. The degree to which leaf-hopper populations are reduced depends on the percentage of the population located in the vineyard ground cover and timing the culti-vation before the adult leafhopper population begins to oviposit in the grape leaves. To be of value, however, the vineyard must be disked early in the morning when temperatures are below the leaf-hoppers' flight threshold, probably below 10°C (50°F). When tempera-tures are warmer, adults will simply move during disking to adjacent crops or weedy areas. Reducing leafhopper populations by cultiva-tion should be weighed against the risk of soil loss with subsequent winter and spring rainfall.

Yellow Sticky Tape

One practice to reduce the num-bers of adult leafhoppers moving into the vineyard is the use of yellow sticky tape strung under the vines, typically on the outer three to five rows of a vineyard block. Few studies have documented the practical efficacy of this pest man-agement practice, and in most regions it is more commonly used to monitor for the glassy-winged sharpshooter or the blue-green sharpshooter. However, one report from the north central wine grape region showed 30% reduction of first-brood nymphs in vineyard blocks employing yellow sticky tape on the outer three rows. The yellow sticky tape is most effec-tive early in the season, when the

adult population is migrating into the vineyard and before the vine canopy begins to cover the tape. High winds can break the tape and debris or soil will build on the tape, usually from cultivation practices, reducing its deadly catch of flying adults.

Leaf Removal

The basal leaves of table and wine grapes are often removed to increase air circulation inside the canopy and reduce the incidence of grape diseases (see section 13, "Bunch Rots," and section 21, "Pow-dery Mildew"). The timing of leaf removal varies among grape-grow-ing regions. However, there is some evidence that when leaf removal for disease management coincides with the emergence or presence of leafhopper nymphs, this practice can also reduce leafhopper num-bers. When infested leaves are dropped to the vineyard floor, most of the leafhopper eggs and nymphs on those leaves die. The biological basis for this practice is that most eggs of the first brood are laid on the first six basal leaves, and the emerging nymphs will not move far from where their eggs were deposited. These small insects are unlikely to walk back up the vine trunk to resume feeding. Timing of leaf removal should, however, be directed toward disease con-trol and fruit quality. In some areas, such as the coastal wine grape regions, leaf removal often coin-cides with the beginning of the first leafhopper brood. Removing leaves too late in the season may, in some vineyards, be too close to closure of the fruit cluster and result in increased risk of sunburn.

Cover Cropping

Cover crops are popularly associated with the attraction of beneficial insects and lower pest densities. Experiments in which cover crops were maintained throughout the growing season typically show no reduction in first- or second-brood leafhopper nymph abundance, but they do show about a 15 to 20% reduction in the third brood. In most instances this level of reduction was too small to be economically important. Further, the mechanism leading to this reduction remains unclear. For a more thorough discussion of cover cropping practices and leafhoppers, please see section 35, "Variegated Grape Leafhopper."

Vine Vigor

Leafhoppers prefer vigorously growing vines; cultural practices (e.g., fertilization and irrigation) or other factors (e.g., vine age, rootstock, soil condition, and available soil moisture) that affect vine vigor may also impact leafhopper densities. Note that maximum vineyard productivity is commonly obtained from moderately vigorous vines, and these are only moderately attractive to leafhoppers. Overly vigorous vines are not desirable, either for their productive potential or their susceptibility to leafhoppers. Fortunately, vines growing with moderate vigor can tolerate fairly large populations without adverse effects. Also note that while stressed vines promote mite outbreaks, proper vineyard management practices that maintain productivity and desired fruit quality but reduce vine vigor will not produce the levels of season-long stress that result in mite

outbreaks. For a more thorough discussion of vine vigor and leafhoppers, please see section 35, "Variegated Grape Leafhopper."

Cultivars

Certain cultivars are likely to suffer greater damage by grape leafhopper populations than others. Late-maturing table grape cultivars, such as Emperor, Autumn Royal, and Crimson Seedless, are likely to have crop damage by late-season leafhopper populations. Similar observations have been made on various wine cultivars. In some regions, late-maturing cultivars produce a continuation of newly matured leaves that are favored by leafhoppers for depositing eggs. Movement out of earlier-maturing cultivars into nearby late-growing cultivars is commonly observed. These migrations may result in the need for treating the late cultivar, particularly rows bordering the earlier cultivar. Such movements may be noticeable in the same vineyard where leafhoppers are attracted to the more vigorously growing vines.

Monitoring Guidelines

Conventional Sampling

The most common sampling plan is based on counts of leafhopper nymphs on leaves. To make these counts accurate, the sampler must know where to sample, when to sample, and which and how many leaves to sample. The suggested sampling program directs the sampler to locations where leafhoppers are most likely to be found. While this provides a biased sample, it also provides treatment decisions based on the higher-density populations of the pest. Biased samples

are, in fact, hard to avoid with grape leafhoppers because their feeding damage can be seen at a distance, often providing a clear signal of which vines and leaves have higher leafhopper densities.

Which leaves to select? The adult leafhopper prefers to deposit eggs in newly mature leaves. The highest densities of the first brood are therefore found on the basal leaves (one to four). First-brood adults move midway on the shoot to lay eggs on the youngest fully developed leaves, and the resulting second-brood nymphs hatch from late June (central San Joaquin Valley) to mid-August (cooler regions), typically on young but fully expanded leaves in the middle of the cane, although a large number are often still found on the first 7 to 10 basal leaves. In regions with three or more broods, the second brood overlaps into the third brood, with nymphs hatching until mid-September. While nymphs can be found on almost any mature leaf during these later broods, adults and nymphs prefer to feed on shaded leaves and, for this reason, leaves on shoots running inside the vine canopy often have higher nymph densities than exposed leaves on shoots growing above or away from the vine canopy and fully exposed to the sun. Similarly, leaves on the shadier side of the vine (the north side in vineyards planted east–west or the east side of rows planted north–south) usually have the highest counts. The vertical shoot positioned trellis systems commonly used in wine grapes groups shoots together and, in these situations, the second- and third-brood leafhopper populations can be found throughout the lower and mid-canopy region. Look for nymphs on both sides of each sampled leaf, making sure to note whether they are grape or variegated leafhoppers. Nymphs can feed on the upper or lower leaf surface, although the underside is preferred. While the sample leaf location is biased toward finding leafhopper nymphs, once leaves selected and the count begins, do not discard any leaf, even if nymphs are absent.

Where in the vineyard should leaves be sampled? Although leafhoppers naturally tend to disperse, there will be patches in the vineyard with higher or lower nymph densities. For example, leafhopper densities tend to be higher on outside rows, on vines with higher vigor or better growth, and on vines closer to overwintering shelters. Therefore, it is best to sample leaves throughout the vineyard to get an accurate count, sampling in 2 to 3 locations for every 10 acres (4 ha), although this requires additional walking and driving time. For smaller vineyards, sample 1 to 2 leaves every fifth row and at least 10 to 15 vines in from the row end. The number of locations and leaves sampled per acre can be reduced for larger, uniformly managed vineyards. For larger vineyards, sample 2 to 3 leaves every 10 to 15 rows of each block (again, at least 10 to 15 vines in from the row end). With this system only one leaf per acre is examined (15 to 40 leaves per block in 10 to 40 acres, respectively).

When should samples be taken? Ideally, each vineyard should be sampled once a week beginning in May and until harvest (no treatment needed); however, with the decreased importance of grape leafhopper and the excellent insecticide controls now available, this intensity of sampling is rarely practiced. Sample blocks every 2 to 3 weeks and, should populations appear to be increasing, additional counts may be necessary. Remember that early nymphal populations do little damage, so a few days' delay in counting or treating does little harm.

Additional Sampling Techniques

A number of sampling programs were developed in the 1980s, when grape and variegated leafhoppers were the primary insect pests in vineyards. Today, many of these programs are not commonly used, a reflection of the leafhoppers' lowered pest priority, effective chemical controls, and a better understanding of sustainable pest control options. Each of these sampling programs, however, provides additional information on leafhopper densities and potential damage or their key natural enemies and are briefly described below.

Presence-absence sampling

An alternative to counting leafhopper nymphs on each leaf is to use presence-absence sampling. This procedure is quick and easy to use. Instead of counting the number of leafhopper nymphs on each leaf, record whether each leaf has any nymphs or none. To determine the proportion of leaves infested, divide the number of infested leaves by the number of leaves sampled. Unlike conventional sampling, presence-absence sampling requires examining a larger number of leaves. Rather than 15 to 40 leaves per block (10 to 40 acres, respectively), 50 to 150 leaves must be examined. This method is usually faster than counting nymphs, since the sampler has only to record whether each leaf has one or more leafhopper nymphs. For 10 to 40 acres, samples usually take only a few minutes per acre. For large commercial acreages (greater than 100 acres), samples can be taken every 15 to 20 rows, driving between rows and blocks rather than walking. Also, because more leaves are examined, a more accurate estimate of the population is made.

One problem with presence-absence sampling is that treatment thresholds have not been clearly determined for different grape commodities based on the proportion of leaves infested. We suggest that a good use of presence-absence sampling may be to determine when to begin the more time-consuming conventional sampling plan. As the season begins or after an insecticide application, use presence-absence sampling until 20 to 30% of the leaves are infested, and then switch to a conventional sampling plan to make treatment decisions based on nymph counts.

Nymphal days

A simple calculation can be made using conventional nymphal counts to provide additional information about the cumulative impact of leafhopper populations by multiplying the number of nymphs per leaf by the number of days of exposure. The resulting calculation, called nymphal days, integrates the combined effect of the leafhoppers over time, so that treatment is not based on only one sample. If a leafhopper monitoring program is based on nymphal counts, accumulating nymphal days becomes fairly straightforward. Table 33.1 provides an example of how to calculate nymphal days using average nymph counts as shown in figure 33.5.

Table 33.1. Grape leafhopper nymphal counts and the calculated nymphal days for a typical vineyard in the north coast region (the data are represented graphically in figure 33.5)

	Sample date	Average nymphs per leaf	Nymphal days*	Accumulated nymphal days†
First brood	May 1	0	0	0
	May 7	0	0	0
	May 14	0	0	0
	May 21	0.8	2.8	2.8
	Jun 1	3.6	24.2	27.0
	Jun 11	8.5	60.5	87.5
	Jun 19	11.0	78.0	165.5
	Jun 29	6.8	89.0	254.5
	Jul 6	2.4	32.2	286.7
Second brood	Jul 15	0.4	12.6	299.3
	Jul 25	0	2.0	301.3
	Aug 2	0.8	4.8	304.1
	Aug 15	2.6	22.1	326.2
	Aug 28	3.0	36.4	362.6
	Sep 14	2.0	42.5	405.1
	Sep 28	0.6	18.2	423.3
	Oct 11	0	3.9	427.2

Notes:

* Nymphal days are determined by averaging the nymph counts over 2 consecutive sampling dates and multiplying by the number of days between sample dates. For example, the nymphal days on June 1 were determined by averaging the May 21 and June 1 counts of nymphs per leaf: (0.8 + 3.6)÷2=2.2; then multiplying by the number of days that elapsed from May 21 to June 1: 2.2 × 11 = 24.2.

† Nymphal days calculated for each period are added to the previous value to give the accumulated nymphal days.

Table 33.2. Guidelines for grape leafhopper tolerance levels in mature Thompson Seedless for raisins or wine and in table grapes

Market use	First brood (nymphs per leaf)	Second and third broods (nymphs per leaf)
raisins or wine grapes	15–20*	15–20
table grapes: early-season cultivars	10	10
table grapes: midseason cultivars	10	5–10
table grapes: late-season cultivars	10	5–8

Note:

* Do not permit more than 20% leaf loss. Tolerance levels are based on damage levels without the presence of *Anagrus;* when the parasitoid is present (numerous red eggs on leaves), tolerance levels in the first brood may be higher since the population is expected to decline in the second brood and (when present) the third brood.

Red eggs

When grape leafhopper is abundant, samplers should also note the presence of red (parasitized) grape leafhopper eggs because *Anagrus* can be a highly effective parasite of grape leafhopper eggs. During the first and second broods, if sampled leaves have red eggs there is a strong likelihood that the subsequent grape leafhopper brood will be naturally reduced. With a high level of parasitism, an insecticide spray is probably not needed.

During the nymphal counts, examine the leaf surface for the presence of red eggs, which are clearly visible on smooth-leafed cultivars such as Thompson Seedless. Use a hand lens to confirm that the eggs are parasitized. Along with the number of leafhopper nymphs per leaf, note the presence or absence of red eggs. Sampling plans have been tested that compare the proportion of parasitized (red) to live (clear) grape leafhopper eggs, with treatment decisions based on this ratio. This practice is not commonly used, however, for several reasons. First, an accurate count of live eggs in the field is difficult, even though the brick-red parasitized eggs can be quite apparent. Second, newly parasitized eggs remain clear for many days and gradually develop a deeper red color as the *Anagrus* completes development, eventually appearing dark yellow to orange just before the adult *Anagrus* emerges from the egg. This makes the accuracy of the count very dependent on when the sample is collected. Third, egg counts in the field are slow.

Adult sampling

The impact of the adult population is not included in any of the sampling methods described above. Because leafhopper adults are so active and difficult to count using conventional monitoring, other methods have been attempted. Yellow sticky cards are available for sampling adult leafhoppers and *Anagrus* adults. There are, however, no thresholds for control decisions based on either adult counts or the combination of adult leafhoppers and *Anagrus*.

MANAGEMENT GUIDELINES

Effect of *Anagrus*

The parasitic wasp *Anagrus* can reduce economic loss from a developing grape leafhopper population, and its presence should be evaluated before a management decision is made. *Anagrus* is easily detected by the brick-red or brown color of the parasitized leafhopper eggs. If parasitized eggs are observed during first-brood surveys, the possibility of grape leafhopper populations remaining within tolerance levels over the rest of the season is good. This is especially true for wine and raisin grapes, which have higher tolerance thresholds. For this reason, targeting the second rather than the first leafhopper brood may provide enough time for the *Anagrus* populations to increase in numbers and have a better opportunity for control. Therefore, the presence of *Anagrus*, especially during the first brood, should always be regarded as a significant natural mortality factor.

Leaf Damage and Vine Tolerance

Treatment guidelines are provided based on nymphal counts using the conventional sampling program (table 33.2). Nymphal counts alone do not, however, provide a complete description of leafhopper density or economic damage. Therefore, assessing treatment thresholds may not be a simple count-and-treat process because vineyard site, commodity, and levels of biological control impact whether the grape leafhopper population increases or decreases from a given time. For example, the same level of leafhopper density (e.g., 12 nymphs per leaf) causes a different level of economic damage depending on grape commodity (wine vs. table), harvest program (e.g., mechanical vs. hand harvest), and vine vigor. Also, nymphal counts more accurately describe the first-brood peak density because this brood's peak is more tightly synchronized than subsequent broods. By this same reasoning, nymphal counts for second or third broods (when present) are not as good a guide for control decisions because these summer generations last 2 months or longer with less-predictable population levels. Furthermore, a brief peak of 30 nymphs per leaf in the first brood may do much less damage than a population of 15 per leaf sustained through the summer.

What broods are most important to suppress? Typically, insecticide treatments are not applied for overwintering adults in order to prevent egg laying and the development of a first summer brood, except where overwintering adults are so high in numbers as to be damaging. Also, adult movement from overwintering quarters to vineyards proceeds for an extended time, and adults are difficult to control; thus, treatment before egg laying often provides only partial population reduction.

First-brood nymphs normally affect a small portion of total leaf surface on a mature vine and should be controlled only if they become numerous enough to cause heavy damage or if the population presents a risk to young vines (less than 3 years old) with relatively small canopies. First-brood nymphs tend to remain on the basal (one to six) leaves where they hatched. Leaves farther out on the shoot often remain free of leafhoppers until the second brood. Feeding by first-brood nymphs does not stunt a mature vine, but with large numbers (20 to 30 per leaf), photosynthesis may be reduced by late May or early June. When treatment is necessary, it is best to delay application until most of the nymphs reach the third or fourth instar. Early-instar nymphs cause little damage, so delaying control has little or no effect on damage. Delaying application provides for better leafhopper control by ensuring that most of the first-brood nymphs have hatched and most of the population is composed of nymphs, which are more susceptible to most insecticides than are eggs or adults. (This is also the best time to do leafing in coastal vineyards.) Delaying the chemical application also allows adequate time to assess the impact of *Anagrus*. If *Anagrus* is active (red eggs are present) at this time, avoiding first-brood treatment may allow the parasite to increase to levels that will provide adequate control of the second brood. If horticultural mineral oils are used for leafhopper management, treatment should be directed at the first brood. A benefit of using oils to manage powdery mildew is a reduction in leafhopper abundance.

Second and (when present) third broods can be the most damaging. Moderate populations can result in spotting on table grape clusters, reducing crop quality. Under the most severe conditions, large populations may defoliate the basal and mid-shoot leaves by mid to late July, resulting in sun exposure to clusters and crop loss, as well as a reduction in yield in the subsequent season. Once second-brood nymphs begin hatching, from June to August, all stages of leafhoppers may be found on the vine at the same time. In general, the smallest number of leafhoppers will be in the protected egg stage or in the more-resistant adult stage if treatments are timed to coincide with most of the leafhoppers being in the third and fourth instars. As mentioned previously, when treatment is delayed into the second or third brood, the parasites will achieve maximum usefulness, and, if treatment is necessary, one treatment is often sufficient. (See "Management Guidelines" in section 35, "Variegated Grape Leaf-hopper," if both variegated and grape leafhoppers are pests.)

Another way to assess leafhopper damage potential is to correlate population density with observed leaf damage and yield or berry quality loss. Trials in the San Joaquin Valley with leaves removed by hand show that vines can lose up to 20% of their leaves without any yield or maturity loss, provided the leaves are not removed until a month after fruit set. In that region, fruit set normally occurs about June 1, so vines can tolerate a 20% loss after July 1. Second-brood nymphs generally do not begin hatching until late June or early July, and this brood will not damage leaves until mid-July. Of course, these levels of leaf loss will vary among regions, vine cultivars, and levels of vine vigor.

Table Grape Tolerance Levels

Excessive spotting or leafhopper droppings determine the economic damage level on table grapes, and this damage occurs long before any reduction in sugar or yield can be measured. As grape leafhopper adults and nymphs often feed on the underside of leaves, their excretions fall on the tops of berry clusters. Such spotting usually starts with the second-brood hatch. Potential damage depends on the length of exposure, which varies with harvest date. Early-maturing cultivars, such as Perlette and Flame Seedless, are exposed for a relatively short time and can tolerate larger leafhopper populations. In comparison, late-season cultivars, such as Crimson Seedless, accumulate spotting for a longer period, which means they tolerate smaller leafhopper populations.

There are no definite standards for "excessive spotting." The U.S. No. 1 Table Grade as set forth by the U.S. Standards of Table Grapes states that berries are damaged "when the appearance is materially affected by the presence of leafhopper residues." Because this description leaves determination of damage to personal opinion, arbitrary maximums have been set at 75 spots per square centimeter for white table grapes and 100 spots per square centimeter for red or black table grapes. Table grapes have been shipped with higher levels of spotting without adverse judgment from inspectors. To monitor spotting, take berries from the most-exposed area of at least 10 (preferably 20) bunches. Use a hand lens to count spots in an area approximately 6 mm (0.24 in) in diameter on each berry. Determine the average number of spots on all berries checked. Multiply this figure by 3.16 to convert to square centimeters.

Little spotting takes place with the first brood unless nymphal populations are more than 15 per leaf. Therefore, spotting counts normally start with the hatch of second-brood nymphs, usually in early July. As the season progresses, some of the spotting weathers off and some is diluted by the growth of the berries. Thus, with a light population of three nymphs per leaf or less, spotting may remain static, weathering off about as rapidly as deposited. Heavy populations may lead to rapid accumulation of spotting up to or past the tolerance level. But when effective treatment or effective parasitism reduces leafhoppers, weathering will reduce spotting considerably.

References

(These references apply to section 33, "Western Grape Leafhopper," and section 35, "Variegated Grape Leafhopper.")

Cate, J. R. 1975. Ecology of *Erythroneura elegantula* Osborn (Homoptera: Cicadellidae) in grape agroecosystems in California. University of California, Berkeley, PhD dissertation.

Costello, M. J., and K. M. Daane. 1995. Spider (Araneae) species composition and seasonal abundance in San Joaquin Valley grape vineyards. Environmental Entomology 24:823–831.

———. 1998a. Effects of cover cropping on pest management: Arthropods. Chapter 8 in C. A. Ingels, R. L. Bugg, G. T. McGourty, and L. P. Christensen, eds., Cover cropping in vineyards: A grower's handbook. Oakland: University of California Agriculture and Natural Resources Publication 3338. 93–106.

———. 1998b. Influence of ground covers on spider (Araneae) populations in a table grape vineyard. Ecological Entomology 23:33–40.

———. 2003. Spider and leafhopper (*Erythroneura* spp.) response to vineyard ground cover. Environmental Entomology 32(5): 1085–1098.

Costello, M. J., M. A. Mayse, K. M. Daane, W. A. O'Keefe, and C. B. Sisk. 1996. Spiders in San Joaquin Valley grape vineyards. Oakland: University of California Agriculture and Natural Resources Publication 21530.

Daane, K. M., and M. J. Costello. 1998. Can cover crops control leafhopper abundance in vineyards? California Agriculture 52(5): 27–33.

Daane, K. M., and L. E. Williams. 2003. Manipulating vineyard irrigation amounts to reduce insect pest damage. Ecological Applications 13(6): 1650–1666.

Daane, K. M., L. E. Williams, S. A. Steffan, and G. Y. Yokota. 1995. Leafhoppers prefer vines with greater amounts of irrigation. California Agriculture 49(3): 28–32.

Daane, K. M., G. Y. Yokota, Y. D. Rasmussen, Y. Zheng, and K. S. Hagen. 1993. Effectiveness of leafhopper control varies with lacewing release methods. California Agriculture 47(6): 19–23.

Daane, K. M., G. Y. Yokota, Y. Zheng, and K. S. Hagen. 1996. Inundative release of the common green lacewing to control *Erythroneura variabilis* and *E. elegantula* (Homoptera: Cicadellidae) in grape vineyards. Environmental Entomology 25: 1224–1234.

Doutt, R. L., and J. Nakata. 1965a. Overwintering refuge of *Anagrus epos* (Hymenoptera: Mymaridae). Journal of Economic Entomology 58:586.

———. 1965b. Parasites for control of grape leafhopper. California Agriculture 19(4): 3.

———. 1973. The *Rubus* leafhopper and its egg parasitoid: An endemic biotic system useful in grape-pest management. Environmental Entomology 2:381–386.

Doutt, R. L., J. Nakata, and F. E. Skinner. 1966. Dispersal of grape leafhopper parasites from a blackberry refuge. California Agriculture 20(10): 14–15.

Gonzalez, D., W. White, C. Pickett, V. Cervenka, M. Moratorio, and L. T. Wilson. 1988. Biological control of variegated leafhopper in grape IPM program. California Agriculture 42(1): 23–25.

Jensen, F. L., D. L. Flaherty, and L. Chiarappa. 1969. Population densities and economic injury levels of grape leafhopper. California Agriculture 23(4): 9–10.

Jensen, F. L., E. M. Stafford, H. Kido, and D. Flaherty. 1965. Surveying leafhopper populations. California Agriculture 19(4): 7.

Kido, H., and E. M. Stafford. 1965. Feeding studies on the grape leafhopper. California Agriculture 19(4): 6–7.

Kido, H., D. L. Flaherty, D. F. Bosch, and K. A. Valero. 1984a. French prune trees as overwintering sites for grape leafhopper egg parasite. American Journal of Enology and Viticulture 35:156–160.

———. 1984b. The variegated grape leafhopper in the San Joaquin Valley. California Agriculture 38(1,2): 31–32.

Lamiman, J. E. 1933. Control of the grape leafhopper in California. University of California Agriculture Extension Service Circular 72.

Mayse, M. A., W. J. Roltsch, and R. R. Roy. 1991. Effects of nitrogen fertilizer on population dynamics of leafhoppers on grapes. In Proceedings, International Symposium on Nitrogen in Grapes and Wine. Seattle: American Society of Enology and Viticulture. 295–299.

Mayse, M. A., R. K. Striegler, W. A. O'Keefe, V. A. Perez-Munoz, F. R. Garcia, and M. S. Njokom. 1995. Sustainable viticulture practices in the San Joaquin Valley of California. Fresno: California Agriculture Technology Institute Bulletin 951201.

McKenzie, L. M., and B. P. Beirne. 1972. A grape leafhopper, *Erythroneura ziczac* (Homoptera: Cicadellidae), and its mymarid (Hymenoptera) egg-parasite in the Okanagan Valley, British Columbia. Canadian Entomologist 104:1229–1233.

Pickett, C. H., L. T. Wilson, and D. L. Flaherty. 1990. The role of refuges in crop protection, with reference to planting French prune trees in a grape agroecosystem. In H. J. Bostanian, L. T. Wilson, and T. J. Dennehy, eds., Monitoring and integrated management of arthropod pests of small fruit crops. Dorset, England: Intercept.

Pickett, C. H., L. T. Wilson, D. Gonzalez, and D. L. Flaherty. 1987. Biological control of variegated grape leafhopper. California Agriculture 41(9): 14–16.

Roltsch, W. R., R. Hanna, F. Zalom, H. Shorey, and M. Mayse. 1998. Spiders and vineyard habitat relationships in central California. In C. Pickett and R. Bugg, eds., Enhancing natural control of arthropod pests through habitat management. Berkeley: University of California Press. 311–338.

Settle, W. H., L. T. Wilson, D. L. Flaherty, and G. M. English-Loeb. 1986. The variegated leafhopper, an increasing pest of grapes. California Agriculture 40(7): 30–32.

Stafford, E. M., and E. L. Jensen. 1953. DDT-resistant leafhoppers: Malathion outstanding for grape leafhopper control in tests in areas where DDT resistance was present. California Agriculture 7(4): 5.

Triapitsyn, S. V. 1998. *Anagrus* (Hymenoptera: Mymaridae) egg parasitoids of *Erythroneura* spp. and other leafhoppers (Homoptera: Cicadeliidae) in North American vineyards and orchards: A taxonomic review. Transactions of the American Entomological Society. 124:112.

Trichilo, P. J., L. T. Wilson, and D. Grimes. 1989. Influence of irrigation management on the abundance of leafhoppers (Homoptera: Cicadellidae) on grapes. Environmental Entomology 19:1803–1809.

Williams, D. W. 1984. Ecology of a blackberry-leafhopper-parasite system and its relevance to California grape agroecosystems. Hilgardia 52(4).

Wilson, L. T., M. M. Barnes, D. L. Flaherty, H. L. Andris, and G. M. Leavitt. 1992. Variegated grape leafhopper. In D. L. Flaherty, L. P. Christensen, W. T. Lanini, J. J. Marois, P. A. Phillips, and L. T. Wilson, eds., Grape pest management. 2nd ed. Oakland: University of California Division of Agriculture and Natural Resources Publication 3343. 202–213.

Wilson, L. T., I. Carmean, and D. L. Flaherty. 1991. *Aphelopus albopictus* Ashmead (Hymenoptera: Dryinidae): Abundance, parasitism, and distribution in relation to leafhopper hosts in grapes. Hilgardia 59(1).

Wilson, L. T., D. L. Flaherty, and W. L. Peacock. 1992. Grape leafhopper. In D. L. Flaherty, L. P. Christensen, W. T. Lanini, J. J. Marois, P. A. Phillips, and L. T. Wilson, eds., Grape pest management. 2nd ed. Oakland: University of California Division of Agriculture and Natural Resources Publication 3343. 140–152.

Zalom, F. G., and R. Hanna. 1992. A fall-winter-spring cover crop system for the integrated management of spider mites and leafhoppers in Thompson Seedless vineyards. In 1991–92 research report for California table grapes. Fresno: California Table Grape Commission.

Zalom, F. G., R. Hanna, C. Elmore, and P. Christensen. 1993. A cover crop for vineyard pest, weed, and nutrition management. In 1992–93 research report for California table grapes. Fresno: California Table Grape Commission.

Hemiptera
*Aphids,
Leafhoppers,
Mealybugs, Scales,
True Bugs,
Whiteflies*

34 POTATO LEAFHOPPER

Larry J. Bettiga and William L. Peacock

Potato leafhopper, *Empoasca* sp. (Hemiptera: Cicadellidae), breeds in large numbers on wild plants and field crops. It occasionally swarms into vineyards as its host plants dry in late spring. In late summer and fall, the leafhoppers can migrate to citrus groves to overwinter, and migration into adjacent vineyards can also occur at this time. Moreover, some vineyards appear to have resident populations that reproduce and increase to injurious levels. In the San Joaquin Valley, the potato leafhopper is a novelty, but on rare occasions it can cause economic damage, particularly when young vines are being established and trained.

DESCRIPTION

Potato leafhoppers are small, green, slender insects, usually about 3 mm (0.13 in) long with inconspicuous white spots on the head and pronotum (fig. 34.1). They are characterized by bristlelike antennae in front of and between the eyes and two parallel rows of spines along the hind tibiae (legs). The small, wingless nymphs (immatures) are also wedge shaped and green and move rapidly forward, backward, and from side to side. Nymphs and adults are similar in size and appearance to grape and variegated leafhopper but stand out because of their green color. Populations are much lower, however, and several shoots may have to be surveyed before the potato leafhopper is detected.

ACTUAL SIZE: POTATO LEAFHOPPER

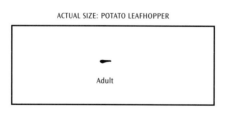

Adult

Figure 34.1 Potato leafhopper adult. *Photo*: J. K. Clark.

INJURY

The presence of potato leafhopper on vines is rare in the San Joaquin Valley, but when they are active, feeding damage on foliage is striking. The leafhopper prefers feeding on young, newly developing leaves. Injury is characterized primarily by ruffled, misshapen leaves, with light green patches on the blade. Shoot internodes are shortened and zigzag, sometimes with bumpy, slightly purple discoloration. With high populations in the spring, many of the vine leaves are distorted, and damage may be mistaken for that caused by drift of a growth regulator or similar material. The presence of adults or light green nymphs confirms the injury. This can occur even when numbers appear low, as they evidently inject a toxin when feeding. Late-season feeding on leaves causes a white to yellowish stippling on the leaves.

Cultivars vary in susceptibility. In the southern San Joaquin Valley, Princess and Thompson Seedless are favorite hosts. Although rare, damage can be severe enough to stunt vine growth, and control is warranted. Normally, damage to vines is slight, limited to the vineyard's edge, and of no economic significance.

The potato leafhopper is controlled by the same materials used to control grape and variegated leafhoppers. Populations are rarely evident later than June. This leafhopper prefers juvenile tissue, which limits late-season activity.

SEASONAL DEVELOPMENT

Information related to migration into vineyards or to development of populations in vineyards has not been developed.

NATURAL CONTROL

Applicable information on natural control is not available.

MONITORING GUIDELINES

No monitoring guidelines have been developed.

MANAGEMENT GUIDELINES

Because potato leafhopper is a minor pest, treatment of its source (open fields) or of the vineyard is not generally necessary.

Hemiptera
Aphids,
Leafhoppers,
Mealybugs, Scales,
True Bugs,
Whiteflies

35 VARIEGATED GRAPE LEAFHOPPER

Kent M. Daane, Richard L. Coviello, Walter J. Bentley, Philip A. Phillips, Serguei V. Triapitsyn, and Jay A. Rosenheim

Variegated grape leafhopper (*Erythroneura variabilis* Beamer) (Hemiptera: Cicadellidae) was first reported in southern California in 1929. It became established in the San Joaquin Valley in the 1980s, was soon the most common leafhopper pest of grapes south of Merced, and became the most important grape pest in the 1980s and early 1990s. While the variegated leafhopper is also found in some vineyards in the northern interior wine grape region, as well as in some central coast vineyards, its infestations are most severe in the warmer table and raisin grape regions of the southern San Joaquin Valley.

In areas where variegated leafhopper is present, all vineyards may be infested, although damage by variegated leafhopper varies according to cultivar, plant vigor, season, and levels of biological control. Moreover, whereas in the 1980s to early 1990s it was common for variegated leafhopper populations to defoliate vines by midsummer, populations rarely reach damaging levels when proper treatments are applied against leafhoppers, and many of the insecticides used for mealybugs also kill leafhoppers. As a result, continuing assessment of insecticide resistance, environmental safety, and changes in pesticide use are the most important issues in leafhopper management. A closely related species, grape leafhopper (*Erythroneura elegantula* Osborn), can be found throughout the San Joaquin Valley and coastal and foothill wine grape regions (see section 33, "Western Grape Leafhopper").

DESCRIPTION

The adult variegated leafhopper is about 3 mm (0.12 in) long. It is richly mottled in brown, red, white, and yellow, making its appearance darker and clearly distinguishable from that of the grape leafhopper (fig. 35.1). The color patterns on the wings and head are more intense in winter adults than in summer and spring adults. Note that newly molted adult variegated leafhoppers have white wings with pale markings for up to 3 days until their characteristic dark markings develop. A helpful hint is that these new adults do not fly.

Eggs are laid singly in the epidermal tissue of upper and lower leaf surfaces. Each egg is minute, about 0.8 mm (0.03 in) long. The egg location in the grape leaf is the primary difference between variegated and grape leafhopper eggs. Most variegated leafhopper eggs are inserted adjacent to or within leaf veins; eggs of the grape leafhopper are mainly laid in interveinal areas. More important, variegated leafhopper eggs are imbedded

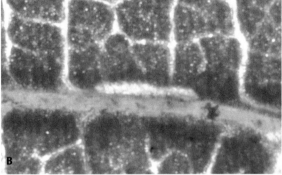

Figure 35.1 Variegated leafhopper adult (A), egg (B, embedded into the leaf just above the vein running horizontally), third instar (C), and fifth instar (D). *Photos*: J. K. Clark.

more deeply into leaves than are grape leafhopper eggs (fig. 35.2). For this reason, variegated leafhopper eggs are difficult to see without a hand lens and a light source from underneath the leaf. Also, while the variegated leafhopper egg is about the same length as the grape leafhopper egg, it is more slender.

The nymph, which emerges through a slit in the egg and leaf tissue, is almost transparent to pale white with prominent red eyes. By the second instar, the variegated leafhopper is easily distinguished from the grape leafhopper nymph by its darkening color. There are five nymphal stages; each resembles the previous one, except for increases in size and darkening from yellow to reddish brown. Also, the variegated leafhopper's abdomen points up at an angle and its developing wings (called wing pads) become more pronounced in the third, fourth, and fifth stages. By the fifth stage, nymphs are about 2.5 mm (0.1 in) long. Similar to the grape leafhopper, although nymphs molt five times, cast-off skins of only the fifth molt stick to leaves. These skins can be mistaken for live leafhoppers by an inexperienced sampler.

INJURY

Nymphs and adults feed on grape leaves, puncturing leaf cells and sucking out the contents. Each feeding puncture leaves a white spot where the leaf mesophyll cell was killed. As feeding damage increases, the photosynthetic activity of damaged leaves decreases, more or less proportionally to the area damaged. Severely damaged leaves lose their green color, dry up, and fall off the vines. Excessive fruit spotting from leafhopper excrement in table grapes can lead to economic loss before any effect on soluble solids or yield is noted. As with the grape leafhopper, pickers at harvest may be annoyed by high adult populations flying in their faces, making leafhoppers a nuisance pest as well. Mechanical harvesting for wine and raisin grapes largely eliminates this problem.

Shortly after variegated leafhopper invaded the San Joaquin Valley, University of California personnel noticed that damage appeared to be more pronounced than that caused by grape leafhopper. Data collected in Fresno County (fig. 35.3) confirm this observation and show that one variegated leafhopper can damage approximately 57% more leaf area than can one grape leafhopper.

SEASONAL DEVELOPMENT

Variegated leafhoppers overwinter as adults; similar to the grape leafhoppers, their reproductive biology is closely tied to the development of the grapevine. During most of the winter, the adult leafhoppers are active and feed during warm weather on weeds or other succulent vegetation, including citrus and alfalfa. In cold weather, they are found in protected areas, such as under dried leaves, dead grass, old paper trays, in debris along ditches, and in windbreaks. Although active, the adults are in a state of reproductive diapause during the late fall and winter. As spring approaches, egg production (ovigenesis) in the female begins, but the ovaries do not completely mature until the female has fed on grape foliage. This biological requirement synchronizes egg maturation and deposition (oviposition) with the availability of suitably mature grape leaves.

Expect to see adult variegated leafhoppers move from their winter quarters onto grapevines as soon as newly developed grape leaves are available. All adults do not move into the vineyard at once; they may take a month or so to move gradually out of winter quarters (including the ground cover or debris in the vineyard). During this transition period, they may feed on grape leaves during warm hours of the day and retreat to the ground cover or other protected shelter under the vines at night. Their reproductive organs mature in synchrony with leaves pushing out on the vine, typically in late February in the Coachella Valley and mid-March in the San Joaquin Valley. Overwintered females lay eggs in grape leaves for about 6 weeks. Depending on the temperature, eggs of the first brood may take up to 3 weeks to hatch, beginning in early April in the Coachella Valley and in late April or early May in the San Joaquin Valley. Egg hatch in the summer broods may occur less than 1 week after they are deposited in the leaves.

Once in the vineyard, the seasonal development of variegated leafhopper populations depends largely on temperature. As with grape leafhopper, the lower developmental threshold is 10.3°C (50.5°F). Research conducted in the San Joaquin Valley near Fresno indicates that first-brood nymphs appear in vineyards by late April or early May, with the first generation peak occurring 210 degree-days Celsius (DDC) (378 degree-days Fahrenheit, or DDF) later. Each subsequent nymphal peak occurs approximately every 849 DDC (1,528 DDF). Therefore, at an average temperature of 32°C (90°F), it takes 28 days to complete one generation. Because development is tied to temperature, insect activity and the number of broods differ between regions. Activity begins sooner in the Coachella Valley and there are more broods (five to six per season), while in the San Joaquin Valley activity begins later and ends earlier, and there are fewer broods (three to four) (fig. 35.4). In the cooler southern and coastal wine grape–producing regions, two broods are more common, often with a partial third brood. Later-season broods start to overlap, and by August all stages of the leafhopper can be found on infested vines.

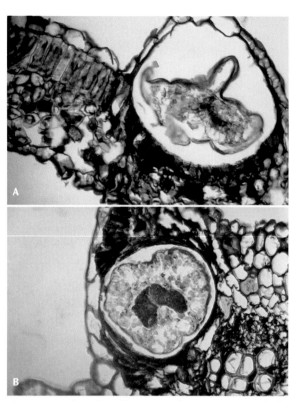

Figure 35.2 When viewed in cross-section, the variegated leafhopper egg (B) is embedded deeper into the leaf tissue than the grape leafhopper egg (A). *Photos*: W. H. Settle.

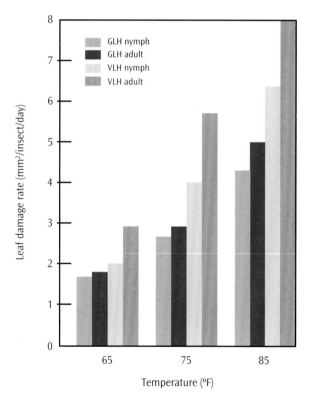

Figure 35.3 Effect of temperature on variegated leafhopper damage.

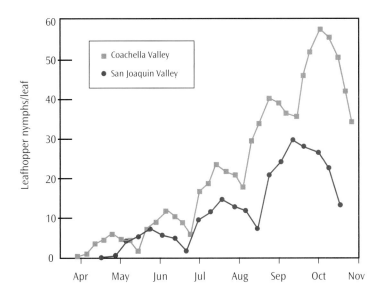

Figure 35.4 Phenology of the variegated leafhopper in San Joaquin Valley and Coachella Valley Thompson Seedless vineyards.

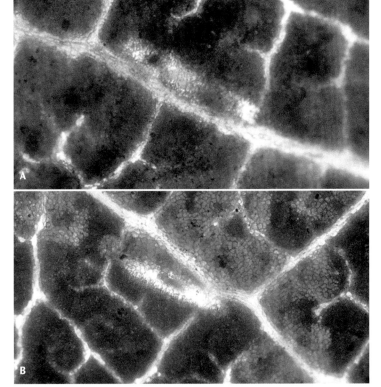

Figure 35.5 Parasitized variegated leafhopper eggs turn reddish brown, similar to those of the grape leafhopper. However, because the variegated leafhopper egg is placed deeper in the leaf tissue, the parasitized egg is more difficult to distinguish. Photo (A) shows a well-developed parasitoid, a nearly completely formed adult ready to emerge with its head and an eye visible. Photo (B) shows what could be the initial development of the parasitoid larva, a small, cigar-shaped darker area in the middle of the leafhopper egg. *Photos*: J. K. Clark.

Natural Control

Parasites of Eggs

The most important natural enemies of variegated leafhopper are the tiny mymarid wasps (*Anagrus* spp.), also known as egg parasitoids. As described in the grape leafhopper section (see section 33), *Anagrus erythroneurae* Triapitsyn and Chiappini and *Anagrus daanei* Triapitsyn are commonly found in most California vineyards, while *Anagrus tretikoviae* Triapitsyn is found more commonly in warmer regions (Coachella, Arizona, New Mexico, and Mexico). The immature *Anagrus* complete their entire development (egg to adult) inside the leafhopper egg; the larva consumes the leafhopper egg as it develops. Parasitized eggs eventually turn red to golden brown. *Anagrus* pupates inside the leafhopper egg, and the adults chew a round hole in the egg to emerge (compared with the slit produced by a live leafhopper nymph pushing its way out of the egg). The adult *Anagrus* is less than 0.7 mm (0.028 in) long. These parasitic wasps are able to locate and attack a high percentage of the grape leafhopper eggs (see section 33, "Western Grape Leafhopper"). However, they have not been nearly as effective against the variegated leafhopper. As a comparison, in the San Joaquin Valley, parasitism of grape leafhopper eggs often exceeds 90% early in the second brood but rarely exceeds 40% at that time for variegated leafhopper eggs.

Lower parasitism levels of variegated leafhopper compared with grape leafhopper are thought to result from the egg location. Variegated leafhopper oviposits most of its eggs adjacent to or within leaf veins, and the eggs laid under leaf epidermal cells are deeper in the leaf tissue than the grape leafhopper eggs (fig. 35.5). As a result, the adult *Anagrus* has more difficulty finding the variegated leafhopper eggs. Observations reveal that the adult female *Anagrus* spends most of her time in the interveinal areas, searching for leafhopper eggs. When she encounters the grape leafhopper egg blister, near the leaf surface, she usually stops to quickly insert her ovipositor and deposit an egg, and then immediately resumes the search for other leafhopper eggs. The variegated leafhopper egg is also more slender than the grape leafhopper egg, which might make it a less desirable host.

To improve biological controls of the variegated leafhopper, an importation program was conducted from 1985 to 1992. Vineyards in northwestern Mexico and the southwestern United States were sampled, and three different genera of egg parasitoids were imported. The egg parasitoids were in the families Mymaridae (which include *Anagrus* species and biotypes, described previously) and Trichogrammatidae (*Itysella* sp. and *Paracentrobia* sp., which did not apparently establish in the San Joaquin Valley). As with grape leafhopper, the Achilles' heel of these egg parasitoids may be their overwintering requirement: the wasps spend the winter months in leafhopper eggs, while the variegated leafhopper overwinters in the adult stage. Because no variegated leafhopper eggs are found in the vineyard from October to March, the parasitoid numbers drop dramatically in the fall when emerging adult *Anagrus* must search outside the vineyard for alternate leafhopper hosts, such as the prune leafhopper (*Edwarsina prunicola* (Edwards)). The prune leafhopper overwinters in the egg stage. For more information, see the discussion in section 33, "Western Grape Leafhopper," on the importance of overwintering refuges such as prune trees.

Parasites of Nymphs and Adults
There are no known effective parasitoids of variegated leafhopper nymphs. In contrast, *Aphelopus albopictus* Ashmead, a dryinid wasp, is an effective parasitoid of grape leafhopper nymphs (see section 33, "Western Grape Leafhopper"), but it is not known to attack the variegated leafhopper. There are probably nymphal parasitoids capable of attacking variegated leafhopper nymphs, but these have not yet been identified.

Generalist Predators
Several generalist insect predators prey on variegated leafhopper nymphs and adults. Among the most abundant insect predators are *Chrysoperla* spp. (green lacewings), *Orius* spp. (minute pirate bugs), *Nabis americoferus* Carayon (damsel bug), *Hippodamia convergens* Guérin-Méneville (lady beetle), *Geocoris pallens* Stål (big-eyed bug), *Hemerobius* spp. (brown lacewings), and tiger flies (*Coenosia humilis* Meigen and *Coenosia* nr. sp. *tigrina* Fabricius). The tiger flies are predaceous in the adult stage, catching their prey in flight, and spend their larval period in the soil as predators of other soft-bodied organisms. Therefore, their role may be both beneficial (as adults) and potentially destructive (as larvae). First-instar leafhopper nymphs have also been observed being attacked by the predaceous mite *Anystis agilis* (Banks).

For most of these predators, little is known about their impact on variegated or grape leafhoppers. While they attack leafhoppers and other vineyard pests, none has been shown to be directly responsible for leafhopper control. Densities of most of these predators are difficult to manipulate, and only different densities of green lacewings have been tested for leafhopper control (for a discussion on the effectiveness of an augmentative release of green lacewings, see section 33, "Western Grape Leafhopper").

In most surveys, spiders comprise more than 90% of the insect predators found in a vineyard (fig. 35.6). There are more than 50 spider species in San Joaquin Valley vineyards; however, fewer than 10 species comprise most of the spiders found on the vines. Spiders are often grouped by their size and mode of hunting prey. Large nocturnal hunters locate prey by tarsal contact; these include two species of *Cheiracanthium*, *C. mildei* Koch and *C. inclusum* (Hentz) (Miturgidae); *Trachelas pacificus*

Figure 35.6 The most common leafhopper predators on the vine and in the cover crop are spiders: a ground-dwelling wolf spider (A); a western lynx spider (*Oxyopes scalaris*) (B); and a dwarf spider (C). *Photos*: K. M. Daane.

(Chamberlin and Ivie) (Corinnidae); *Anyphaena pacifica* Banks and *Hibana incursa* Chamberlin (both Anyphaenidae). Medium-sized diurnal spiders are often visually oriented toward their prey and include species in the family Salticidae, which can jump many times their body length to pounce on and capture leafhoppers. Examples of medium-sized spiders are *Oxyopes scalaris* Hentz (Oxyopidae) and *Platycryptus californicus* (Peckham and Peckham) (Salticidae). The most obvious spiders on the vine are often the sit-and-wait web builders such as the small cobweb weavers (*Theridion dilutum* Levi and *Theridion melanurum* Hahn) (Theridiidae) and dwarf spiders (*Erigone dentosa* (O.P.-Cambridge)) (Lyniphiidae), which construct a fine, irregular network of webbing, typically on the underside of leaves. Another sit-and-wait web builder is a funnel weaver (*Hololena nedra* Chamberlin and Ivie) (Agelenidae), which constructs a large, funnel-shaped web. One of the largest and visually apparent spiders is an orb weaver (*Neoscona oaxacensis* (Keyserling)) (Araneidae); small, immature *N. oaxacensis* spin webs on the grape foliage or trellis wire, but as this species matures, it strings its web between grapevine rows.

All spiders are predators, but what and how much they eat is quite variable among species. Each species has a distinct life history, feeding behavior, and habitat preference. Therefore, the spider species complex and the extent of leafhopper control can vary dramatically between vineyards. For example, most spider species kill leafhoppers, but their effectiveness varies. In the laboratory, *Trachelas*

and *Cheiracanthium* ate an average of 12 leafhoppers per day per spider, the small cobweb weavers killed only 1 to 2 nymphs per day, the funnel weaver fed only on leafhopper adults, and a common jumping spider, *Sassacus vitis* (Cockerell), would not feed on leafhoppers. Exclusion experiments (removing spiders from the vines) have shown that spiders can reduce leafhopper numbers. However, consistent economic control of leafhopper populations using spiders is difficult to evaluate.

A difficulty in assessing spiders as natural enemies is that the species present and their numbers are difficult to manipulate. Although increasing diversity with cover crops may favor predators such as *Trachelas* at certain sites, what makes *Trachelas* the dominant species at one site but other spider species dominant in nearby vineyards depends on many factors: vine cultivar, trellis system, soil type, regional climate, and management practices (e.g., pesticide use). Another consideration is that spider density tends to remain fairly stable with respect to leafhopper density. In other words, when leafhopper populations increase or decrease rapidly, there is no corresponding change in spider density. This results, in large part, because most vineyard spiders have only 1 to 3 generations per year, creating a slow response. Spiders are also commonly territorial, reducing their numbers on any vine through competition with other spiders either through avoidance, competition for food and shelter, or "spider on spider predation" (spiders are commonly the best predators of other spiders). One group of spiders that

does seem to respond numerically to leafhopper densities is the small cobweb weavers. Unfortunately, these spiders tend to build to large numbers at the end of the season in response to large numbers of leafhoppers, rather than earlier in the season when their predation on leafhoppers might help suppress damaging populations.

Pathogens
Reports of diseases, such as those caused by the fungus *Beauvaria bassiana*, as mortality agents of variegated leafhopper are sketchy and need confirmation. It is conceivable that this pathogen may exert some control over both variegated and grape leafhoppers.

Cultural Controls

Habitat Management
Adults maturing in late summer continue feeding on vines until the season's end and then begin to move to feed on alternate plant species. For example, after fall or winter rains, the adults are commonly found on foxtail, malva, wild mustard, clovers, and filaree. Leafhoppers must have a source of green vegetation to survive during their overwintering period. Without this source, mortality is high. While overwintering adults have reportedly been found up to a mile from the nearest vineyard, most are found in or close to vineyards. Therefore, reducing overwintering quarters adjacent to vineyards may help control leafhoppers in some circumstances. As discussed with the grape leafhopper (see section 33, "Western Grape Leafhopper"), there is evidence that leafhopper populations may be reduced by late-February French plowing and cultivation, basically disking the

adult leafhoppers under the ground. The degree to which leafhopper populations are reduced depends on the percentage of the population located in the vineyard ground cover, and the farm manager being able to cultivate the ground cover before the adult leafhopper population begins to oviposit in the grape leaves as well as temperatures cold enough to prevent the leafhoppers from escaping by flying temporarily away.

Yellow Tape

One practice to reduce the numbers of adult leafhoppers moving into the vineyard is the use of yellow sticky tape strung under the vine (fig. 35.7), typically on the outer three to five rows of a vineyard block. Few studies have documented the effectiveness of this tool, and it is not commonly practiced. However, one report from the northern interior wine grape region showed 30% reduction of first-brood nymphs in vineyard blocks employing yellow sticky tape on the outer three rows. The yellow sticky tape is most effective early in the season, when the adult population is migrating into the vineyard and before the vine canopy begins to cover the tape. High winds can break the tape and debris or dirt carried by the wind will build on the tape, reducing its deadly catch of flying adults.

Cover Crops

Many grape growers are managing floor vegetation, either in the form of sown cover crops or resident vegetation, to help control insect and mite pests (fig. 35.8). The role of cover crops in vineyard pest management is not well understood, however. In theory, natural enemy populations

Figure 35.7 Yellow sticky tape has been used to catch and kill adults moving into the vineyard in spring, when they disperse from their overwintering sites. *Photo*: K. M. Daane.

Figure 35.8 Some vineyard managers use ground cover to attract or support beneficial predators or parasitoids that might help suppress variegated and grape leafhopper populations. *Photos*: K. M. Daane.

increase because cover crops (or other ground vegetation) provide natural enemies with additional habitat (e.g., shelter), food (e.g., nectar and pollen), and alternate prey (e.g., aphids for ladybird beetles). In one study, ground covers maintained throughout the year in San Joaquin Valley juice, table, and wine grape vineyards resulted in lower third-brood leafhopper densities in seven of eight trials. The level of leafhopper reduction was often not economically important, however, ranging from 0 to 30% (fig. 35.9), and the reduction in leafhoppers was seen only in the third brood. The addition of vineyard ground covers produces a number of changes, but there was rarely a consistent change in predator densities. For example, total spider abundance on the vine was similar in vineyards with and without ground covers (fig. 35.10). Of course, there were more predators in the vineyard (vines and ground cover), but spiders in the ground cover rarely hunt insect prey on the vine. However, ground covers can change the kinds of predator species present. For example, the spider *Trachelas pacificus* and the whirligig mite were more abundant in vineyards with ground covers.

Ground covers may impact leafhopper densities by changing vine vigor. For example, some species of year-round ground covers, especially weedy grasses, can compete with the vines for water and nutrients; under some circumstances, a reduction in vine vigor can lower leafhopper densities without reducing yield. Other ground cover species may add nitrogen to the soil, and native grass species have even been shown to improve water

penetration to the lower soil horizon and water amounts in this root zone; these changes may increase vine vigor. Regardless, cover cropping by itself cannot be relied on for leafhopper control from one year to the next. While there is evidence that cover crops play a role in vineyard pest management, the benefits of cover crops must be determined for each vineyard separately and should be primarily considered for how ground covers improve vine health (e.g., balancing vine vigor) and vineyard management (e.g., improving soil health, reducing erosion).

Refuges

There is evidence that vineyards near large riparian areas or prune orchards provide overwintering refuges for *Anagrus*. There have been numerous attempts to duplicate this effect by planting blackberry or French prune tree "refuges" near or in the vineyards. The primary failure of these refuges

appears to be their small size relative to the vineyard. A small refuge of blackberry bushes or prune trees will produce a correspondingly small number of blackberry or prune leafhoppers and therefore provide little actual refuge. For a discussion of refuge impacts, see section 33, "Western Grape Leafhopper."

Vine Vigor

Leafhoppers prefer vigorously growing vines; cultural practices (e.g., fertilization) or farm conditions (e.g., vine age, soil conditions) that affect vine vigor may also change leafhopper densities. As an example, one practice that can reduce vine vigor is irrigation amounts. In an experimental San Joaquin Valley vineyard, different irrigation amounts were supplied to Thompson Seedless vines. Results show that excess irrigation amounts (resulting in too much vine vigor and reduced crop yields) resulted in higher leafhopper

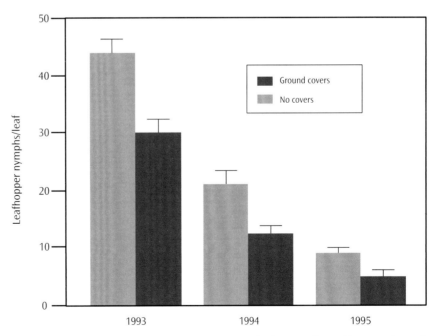

Figure 35.9 Density of third-brood leafhopper nymphs in Flame Seedless table grape vineyard blocks with and without season-long ground covers.

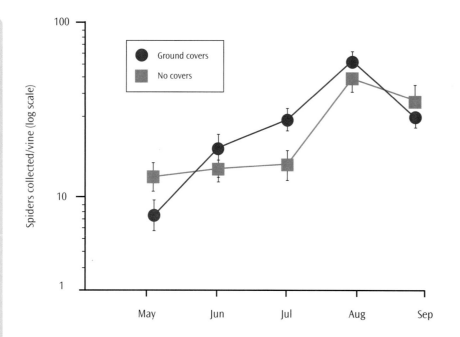

Figure 35.10 Density of spiders on the vine in Flame Seedless table grape vineyard blocks with and without season-long ground covers.

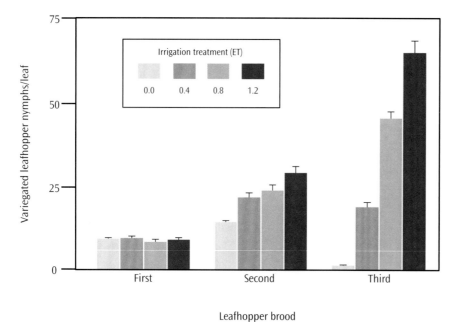

Figure 35.11 Variegated leafhopper densities under different levels of irrigation amounts in a Thompson Seedless vineyard. Peak leafhopper nymph densities in each of the three summer broods show that differences in leafhopper densities among irrigation treatments increased as the season progressed. Irrigation treatments represent fractions of water applied to vines growing in a lysimeter.

densities (fig. 35.11). Perhaps more important for leafhopper control were results showing that dispersing adults were collected in greater numbers and deposited more eggs on vines with excess irrigation amounts. Additional studies indicate that properly timed deficit irrigation practices in wine grapes can greatly reduce leafhopper densities while also improving crop quality. Where practical, therefore, leafhopper abundance may be reduced, particularly in overly vigorous vineyards, by manipulating irrigation amounts.

Caution must be advised before undertaking irrigation management for leafhopper control. For example, water-stressed vines have been associated with mite pest problems (see section 79, "Spider Mites"). While susceptibility of vineyards to Pacific spider mite may be alleviated by cultural practices that increase vine vigor, vigorous vines promote higher leafhopper populations. But a proper balance can be achieved. Maximum productive crop capacity is obtained from moderately vigorous vines, and these are only moderately attractive to leafhoppers and moderately susceptible to Pacific spider mite attack.

Grape Cultivars

Variegated leafhopper populations, in the absence of proper management practices, tend to increase during the season and are higher on vines with greater vigor. Therefore, vines that continue growing late into summer or fall provide female leafhoppers a continuation of newly matured leaves that favor egg laying. This is most apparent on late-season cultivars, such as Ribier and Emperor (and possibly

Autumn Royal and Crimson Seedless), which continue to produce nymphal populations late in the season. Similarly, high-vigor cultivars or vines grown on vigorous rootstocks, such as Ramsey (Salt Creek), support higher numbers of leafhoppers than do vines grown on their own roots or vigor-suppressing rootstocks.

Leaf Removal

The basal leaves of table and wine grapes are often removed after bloom to open air circulation and reduce the incidence of grape diseases (see section 13, "Bunch Rots"). When properly synchronized with the emergence of leafhopper nymphs, this practice can also reduce first-brood leafhopper numbers by dropping infested leaves and leafhoppers to the vineyard floor, where both will dry up and die. Most eggs of the first brood are laid on the first six basal leaves, and the emerging nymphs will not move far from where their eggs were deposited. These small insects are unable to walk up the vine trunk to resume feeding. If leafhoppers are to be considered, it is best to perform leaf removal after egg deposition and hatch are complete. Otherwise, the adults will deposit eggs on the remaining leaves.

Pesticide Use

One of the best methods to increase the number of natural enemies in a vineyard is to reduce the use of pesticides. While this is not practical for many vineyards, it should be noted that all pesticide materials used in the vineyard may have beneficial (e.g., reduction of the target pest) and negative (e.g., removal of beneficial organisms, costs, preharvest intervals)

impacts. For example, there is evidence that sulfur dust applications are toxic to *Anagrus* species egg parasitoids, potentially reducing its numbers; on the other hand, sulfur is a valuable resistance management tool in powdery mildew management programs.

Monitoring Guidelines

Variegated leafhopper populations may be surveyed in the same manner as is discussed in section 33, "Western Grape Leafhopper," and only the conventional sampling method will be reviewed here.

Conventional Sampling

The most common sampling plan is based on counts of leafhopper nymphs on leaves. To make these counts accurate, the sampler must know where to sample, when to sample, and which and how many leaves to sample. The suggested sampling program directs the sampler to locations where the leafhopper is most likely to be found. While this provides a bias sample, it also provides treatment decisions based on the higher-density populations of the pest.

In each block, pick one to two leaves for examination every fifth row and go in anywhere from the fifth to the tenth vine. Avoid outside rows and the two end vines, as these usually have higher-than-normal populations. To observe first-brood nymphs, select a basal leaf on the shoot (second through sixth leaves give the highest counts). For second and third broods, select a mid-shoot leaf. Variegated leafhoppers also oviposit on older leaves; as a result, nymphs of second, third, and later broods can be found on older leaves deep within the

vine's canopy. Leafhoppers prefer to feed on the shadier leaves, so sample leaves from the east side of rows planted north and south or from the north side of rows planted east and west. Although the small stages tend to feed on the leaf's underside, count leafhopper nymphs on both sides of the sampled leaves. Once leaves are selected and the count begins, include each leaf in your assessment, even when nymphs are absent. Separate variegated leafhopper counts from grape leafhopper counts.

For any block, count nymphs on a minimum of 15 leaves. Add nymph numbers and divide by the number of leaves examined to obtain the average number of nymphs per leaf. Keep separate counts for each block. Previously, samples were taken weekly, but with the availability of effective insecticides and the frequent use of insecticides for mealybug that also kill leafhoppers, vineyard managers now sample less frequently for leafhoppers.

Management Guidelines

Impact on Yield

Studies that correlate leafhopper density to yield have been conducted on only a limited number of grape cultivars, and typically in the San Joaquin Valley. In a Thompson Seedless vineyard, reductions in yield or sugar did not occur even when populations of first and second broods reached peaks of 20 nymphs per leaf. Among other reasons, grapevines are able to tolerate such apparently high leafhopper populations because:

- Leafhoppers are small insects and are not able

to cause much injury relative to the total leaf area of a vine.

- As leafhoppers prefer to feed on shaded leaves in the interior of the canopy, much of the damage is to leaves that are less photosynthetically active.

- During each season, vines can lose up to 20% of their leaves without any yield or maturity loss, provided the leaves are not removed until about a month after fruit set. Generally, one leafhopper causes a 1% leaf loss per vine during its lifetime.

- As with most perennial crops, grapevines store energy in the form of remobilizable carbohydrates, primarily in their trunks and roots. This provides vines with a buffering capacity. Although leafhopper damage may be extreme during a season, the vines are able to compensate by remobilizing these stored carbohydrates. Repeated high levels of damage over a 2- or 3-year period may, however, affect a vineyard's long-term vigor and productivity.

Economic Thresholds

Table 35.1 provides suggested treatment thresholds for raisin, wine, and table grapes based on conventional sampling counts and provides the corresponding calculated values for presence-absence and nymphal-day calculations. These thresholds are suggestions; management decisions will be based not only on leafhopper density but on commodity, region, and vine vigor, as well as each manager's personal comfort with some level of leafhopper damage. Moreover, work in a Thompson Seedless vineyard in the San Joaquin Valley showed that the same leafhopper counts (e.g., 15 nymphs per leaf) produced very different levels of vine damage depending on the amount of irrigation water provided. Vines with more vigor and more shoot growth had less vine damage, while water-stressed vines had more leaf damage with the same number of leafhoppers per leaf.

Raisin and wine grapes

For raisin and wine grapes, tolerance levels are set either by the amount of damage to the vine and the resulting decline in yield or by the amount of productivity lost during harvest operations because of leafhopper presence. If leafhopper densities are high enough to reduce the leaf canopy, there may also be problems from increased sun exposure on the clusters, resulting in some sunburn. Treatment thresholds for the variegated leafhopper typically range from 15 to 20 nymphs per leaf during the second or third brood (see table 35.1).

Table grapes

As adults and nymphs feed, their excretions fall on the tops of the berry clusters and cause aesthetic damage. Excessive spotting or leafhopper droppings determine the economic damage level on table grapes because this aesthetic

Table 35.1. Guidelines for variegated and grape leafhopper treatment thresholds in vineyards

Market use	First-brood threshold	Second- and third-brood threshold
raisins or wine grapes	10–15 nymphs per leaf	15–20 nymphs per leaf
table grapes	7–10 nymphs per leaf	early-season cultivars: ≥ 10 nymphs per leaf
		midseason cultivars: ≥ 7 nymphs per leaf
		late-season cultivars: ≥ 5 nymphs per leaf

Note: Treatment thresholds provided here are based on work conducted in leafhopper populations on Thompson Seedless grapes. Tolerance levels will vary among vineyards and are influenced by the presence of natural enemies, vine vigor, and grower decisions on pest density and insecticide use.

damage occurs long before any reduction in sugar or yield can be measured. For these reasons, economic injury levels for second-brood leafhoppers are typically set between 5 to 10 nymphs per leaf, using the conventional sampling program (see table 35.1). Accumulated nymphal days, based on counts from the conventional sampling program, is a useful index of leafhopper berry spotting. Use of this index is described in "Table Grape Tolerance Levels" in section 33, "Western Grape Leafhopper."

Regional Impacts

Variegated leafhopper damage levels are influenced by the grape-growing region. Warmer regions have a longer growing season for both the vine and its leafhopper pests, resulting in more broods per year and higher leafhopper densities if leafhoppers are not controlled.

In the Coachella Valley, variegated leafhopper has as many as six broods annually, and levels of natural control are relatively poor. This can result in large and damaging populations. For this reason, an insecticide treatment against the first leafhopper brood is the common practice. Overwintering adults typically begin egg deposition in early spring (March 15 to 25). A control treatment can be applied soon after egg deposition begins or scheduled against the first nymphal brood. A second opportunity comes when this first generation has completed development and the resulting adults are present and producing the overlapping second-generation eggs and nymphs. This usually occurs

between May 15 and 25. Additionally, a postharvest treatment for leafhoppers is sometimes required to prevent midsummer defoliation as three to four generations can develop after harvest.

In the San Joaquin Valley and coastal and upland regions where variegated leafhopper is found, overwintered leafhopper adults typically begin to move into the vineyard in March (warmer areas) and April (cooler areas) and begin to deposit eggs after the first flush of vine growth. The first nymphs are commonly seen in early May, depending on seasonal temperatures. It is not recommended to treat vines to kill overwintering adults or first-brood nymphs unless these populations are so damaging as to require treatment. In most of these regions, the grape leafhopper can also be found, and it is important to consider both grape and variegated leafhopper populations when making treatment decisions. While both leafhopper species have a high reproductive potential, predators and parasites can negate most of the potential of grape leafhopper, but they can affect only part of the reproductive potential of variegated leafhopper. As discussed in section 33, the presence of red eggs, indicating parasitism by *Anagrus*, in the first brood suggests the probability that grape leafhopper populations will remain within tolerance levels and that there will be some suppression of variegated leafhopper populations. Even when a variegated leafhopper population is above tolerance level for the first brood, it is generally best to

delay treatment until the second or later broods so that *Anagrus* and other natural enemies can express good control of grape leafhopper and partial control of variegated leafhopper. First-brood nymphs normally affect a small portion of the total leaf surface on a vine, typically remaining on the basal six to eight leaves where they hatched. New leaves remain free of leafhoppers until the nymphs mature and move to them. Feeding by nymphs does not stunt a vine, but with high numbers (20 to 30 per leaf), photosynthesis may be reduced by late May or early June.

Insecticide Management

When treatment decisions are made, insecticide selection must take into account resistance management. Historically, the variegated leafhopper has developed resistance to common insecticides. Currently, less-disruptive and very effective insecticides are available for leafhopper management in vineyards (see the UC IPM Grape Pest Management Guidelines, www.ipm.ucdavis.edu/PMG/). While novel, related compounds are being tested, cross-resistance to these new materials might still be an issue, jeopardizing future insecticide effectiveness. A few simple guidelines can be used for resistance management. First, use chemical controls only when deemed necessary. Second, rotate insecticides among materials that have different modes of action. Third, do not spray multiple types of materials each season in an attempt to kill every pest in the vineyard; this might only increase the percentage of the resistant population.

Organic Materials

Soaps, narrow-range oils, and botanicals can reduce leafhopper numbers, but these materials are generally not as effective as the more recently registered insecticides applied for leafhoppers. If oils are used, first-brood populations should be considered for control. Careful attention must be made to timing and spray coverage because these materials work best against the smaller nymphs and have less impact on eggs or adults. For this reason, treatments of later broods are less effective because of the greater overlap of different leafhopper developmental stages. Also, first-brood nymphs are mostly confined to basal leaves on shoots where treatment coverage is fairly easy, while summer broods are spread over the vine, reducing the likelihood of complete coverage and direct contact that is needed with most of these materials. More studies are needed to determine how effective these materials are on a wide range of vineyard pests, as well as their impact on natural enemies and grape quality, including their effect on berry bloom when treatments are either dilute or concentrate sprays. As more oils are used for powdery mildew control, leafhopper management will be improved.

Secondary Impacts

The vineyard ecosystem is complex, and many factors combine to influence pest and natural enemy densities. Because natural pest control must take place in a blend of migrating and resident pests and natural enemies, vineyard cultural practices, vineyard age, soil characteristics, and regional characteristics, it is important to consider how insecticide applications will impact not only the target pest but other pests and natural enemies as well.

REFERENCES

See the references for section 33, "Western Grape Leafhopper."

Hemiptera
*Aphids,
Leafhoppers,
Mealybugs, Scales,
True Bugs,
Whiteflies*

36 VIRGINIA CREEPER LEAFHOPPER

Lucia G. Varela and Kent M. Daane

The Virginia creeper leafhopper (*Erythroneura ziczac* Walsh) (Hemiptera: Cicadellidae) was first reported in California in Butte County in 1984. Since then it has been sporadically detected in northern California vineyards from the Oregon border to Sacramento, Solano, and Yolo Counties in northern Sacramento Valley; in the northern Sierra foothills and Mono County; and by 2012 in Lake and Mendocino Counties in the north coast. This species was originally described from grapevines in Illinois and is most commonly found in northern Midwestern states, but it has spread throughout Canada's grape-growing regions and to Washington State. It is also reported in large numbers on Virginia creeper (*Parthenocissus quinquefolia*) and Boston ivy (*Parthenocissus tricuspidata*).

DESCRIPTION

Virginia creeper leafhopper is similar in appearance to the western grape leafhopper (*Erythroneura elegantula*) (referred to as grape leafhopper in this publication). Adults are 2.8 to 3.1 mm (0.11 to 0.12 in) long, with reddish brown zigzag markings on a pale white to yellow background and reddish brown eyes (fig. 36.1). Kidney-shaped eggs are deposited beneath the epidermis on the underside of fully expanded leaves. The eggs are usually laid side by side in groups of two to seven, but they can be laid singly as well. The eggs are made more noticeable by their covering with a bluish gray deposit called brochosomes (fig. 36.2A). Young nymphs are pale yellow with reddish brown eyes. Mature nymphs have a pair of dark reddish brown spots on the outside edge on the segment immediately behind the head and a pair of reddish brown spots on the third thoracic segment (fig. 36.2B).

INJURY

Leafhopper nymphs and adults prefer to feed on the underside of leaves, puncturing leaf cells and sucking out the contents with piercing mouthparts. Feeding punctures leave white spots that appear as stippling on the upper side of the leaf. Heavily damaged leaves lose color and may dry up and drop. As with grape leafhopper, some leafhopper feeding damage is tolerable.

Figure 36.1 Virginia creeper leafhopper adult female (A) and adult male (B). *Photos:* J. K. Clark (A); M. L. Poe (B).

SEASONAL DEVELOPMENT

The biology and life cycle of Virginia creeper leafhopper is similar to that of grape leafhopper. It will probably have two full generations in northern California, although in Kansas it is reported to have three and a partial fourth generation; this may be more typical if populations reach the San Joaquin Valley. Adults spend the winter in the leaf litter in and around the vineyard. In the spring they disperse, feeding on vegetation in or near the vineyard, then move to grapes when leaves appear. The development of the broods is similar to that of grape leafhopper, with the first brood developing on basal leaves and subsequent broods developing on young but fully expanded leaves in the middle of the shoot.

NATURAL CONTROL

Eggs of Virginia creeper leafhopper

are reported to be parasitized by *Anagrus tretiakovae* Triapitsyn in Washington and by *A. daanei* in Washington and British Columbia. Further studies are needed to evaluate the species of *Anagrus* parasitizing Virginia creeper leafhopper in California and the impact of other natural enemies on populations.

MONITORING GUIDELINES

Follow the conventional sampling plan for grape leafhopper.

MANAGEMENT GUIDELINES

As with grape leafhopper, treatment thresholds depend on vineyard site, commodity, levels of biological control impact, and vine vigor. Insecticide control programs used for the grape leafhopper and variegated grape leafhopper should also work for the Virginia creeper leafhopper.

REFERENCES

Fairbairn, V. M. 1928. The life history of *Erythroneura ziczac* Walsh (Homoptera, Cicadellidae). Journal of the Kansas Entomological Society 1(4): 79–84.

Olsen, K. N., W. W. Cone, and L. C. Wright. 1998. Influence of temperature on grape leafhoppers in southcentral Washington. Environmental Entomology 27(2): 401–405.

Triapitsyn, S. V., P. R. Rugman-Jones, G. Jeong, J. G. Morse, and R. Stouthamer. 2010. Morphological and molecular differentiation of the *Anagrus epos* species complex (Hymenoptera: Mymaridae), egg parasitoids of leafhoppers (Hemiptera: Cicadellidae) in North America. Zootaxa 2428:1–21.

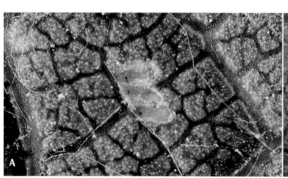

Figure 36.2 Virginia creeper leafhopper eggs (A) and nymph (B). *Photos*: J. K. Clark.

Hemiptera
Aphids,
Leafhoppers,
Mealybugs, Scales,
True Bugs,
Whiteflies

37 *PSEUDOCOCCUS* MEALYBUGS
(Grape, Obscure, and Longtailed Mealybugs)

Walter J. Bentley, Kent M. Daane, Philip A. Phillips, Mark Battany, and William L. Peacock

Five species of mealybug cause economic damage to grapes in California. Three of these belong to the genus *Pseudococcus*: grape mealybug (*Pseudococcus maritimus* (Ehrhorn)); obscure mealybug (*Pseudococcus vibruni* (Signoret)); and the longtailed mealybug (*Pseudococcus longispinus* (Targioni Tozzetti)). Each of these species has different biological attributes, hosts, geographic ranges, and natural enemy complexes.

Grape mealybug was the only mealybug of consequence until the 1980s. At that time, economic losses in Edna Valley wine grapes in San Luis Obispo County led to discovery of obscure mealybug. Later, in the 1990s, longtailed mealybug also was found to be associated with grapes in San Luis Obispo County. All three species were subsequently found in northern Santa Barbara County. Longtailed mealybug has not been detected infesting grapes in areas other than the California central coast.

In 1910, E. O. Essig identified grape mealybug from infested grapes grown in Fresno. Attempts to control it date back to the 1920s, when vines were fumigated with sulfur under tarps or treated with whale oil sprays. Before the 1940s occasional infestation occurred in table grapes, but these infestations usually disappeared the following year. More-persistent grape mealybug populations were noted in the late 1940s, starting in the southern San Joaquin Valley near Delano and Earlimart. Extensive use of DDT and other synthetic pesticides used to control grape leafhopper had apparently disrupted natural enemies of grape mealybug.

Although mealybug infestations increased with general use of synthetic pesticides, the organophosphate insecticides used after DDT seemed less disruptive. In fact, grape mealybug populations noticeably subsided in the late 1950s and 1960s. Individual vineyards still suffered losses but less severely; in many cases, sprays were reduced or eliminated. More recently, outbreaks of grape mealybug in table grapes appear to be related to changes in cultural practices such as no-tillage and the use of drip or microsprinklers for irrigation. These practices provide an undisturbed habitat for gray field ant (*Formica aerata* Franceour), Argentine ant (*Linepithema humile* (Mayr)) and southern fire ant (*Solenopsis xyloni* McCook).

237

These ant species reduce the success of parasitoids that normally provide grape mealybug control.

DESCRIPTION

Grape Mealybug

Grape mealybug was originally described from specimens collected in Santa Cruz, California, on *Eriogonum latifolium*. It has a soft, oval, flattened, and distinctly segmented body. The divisions of the head, thorax, and abdomen are not distinct. The adult female can grow to 5 mm (0.2 in) long and appears smoothly dusted with a white, mealy wax secretion (fig. 37.1). The long wax filaments along the lateral margin of the body become progressively shorter toward the head. As many as 150 eggs are laid in an ovisac that looks like a small, loose, cottony sac attached to the posterior end of the female's body. The yellow-orange, oval eggs can be seen within the sac with the

Figure 37.1 Grape mealybug female and nymphs. Note color of ostiolar fluid. *Photo:* J. K. Clark.

ACTUAL SIZE: GRAPE MEALYBUG

Egg   Adult Female

naked eye (fig. 37.2). The crawlers that hatch from the eggs are yellow to brown and are free of the waxy coating characteristic of later growth stages (fig. 37.3). Females and males appear similar in the early development stages. All stages of the female are similar. The male passes through three nymphal instars, then forms a flimsy, thin, cottony cocoon about 3 mm (0.12 in) long in which the pupa is formed. The cocoon is usually visible in the striations of the bark interior. The adult male has a pair of clear wings, a pair of halteres (highly reduced hind wings) provided with hooks (not visible), and two long, white anal filaments. The antennae are relatively long and composed of beadlike segments.

Obscure Mealybug

In form, obscure mealybug is identical in appearance to grape mealybug. A simple field diagnostic test can be used to separate obscure mealybug from grape mealybug. Both species possess a pair of ostiolar pores on the anterior and posterior ends of the body. When prodded with a sharp needle, the pores exude a fluid. The fluid of grape mealybug is a deep orange color while that of obscure mealybug is clear. The bodies of both are light gray and thinly covered with white powder (fig. 37.4).

Longtailed Mealybug

Longtailed mealybug is also similar in appearance to the two species described above. However, the anal filaments are much longer (as long or longer than the body) than those of grape or obscure mealybug. The lateral filaments are relatively short. The body of longtailed

mealybug is also shorter than the other two species, not exceeding 3.6 mm (0.14 in) long (fig. 37.5). It is yellow to light gray and heavily waxed (fig. 37.6). The longtailed mealybug does not lay eggs; it produces live young, holding the eggs in the reproductive ducts until they are ready to hatch (a reproductive method called ovoviviparity). It is thought to be native to Europe and is now found throughout the world.

INJURY

All three species of *Pseudococcus* mealybugs are phloem feeders and cause similar damage. Cottony ovisacs, immature stages, adults, honeydew, and black sooty mold contaminate fruit (fig. 37.7). Occasionally, soft scales and other scale insects infest vines and produce honeydew that is confused with that produced by mealybugs. These scale insects include European fruit lecanium (*Parthenolecanium corni* Bouche), cottony cushion scale (*Icerya purchasi* Maskell), cottony maple scale (*Neopulvinaria innumerabilis* Rathvon), frosted scale (*Parthenolecanium pruinosum* Coq.), and black scale (*Saissetia oleae* Olivier). Carefully searching the vine will reveal the damaging species.

In San Joaquin Valley table grape vineyards, mealybug presence and honeydew result in fruit cullage. Virtually no contamination is tolerated. Of the three species of *Pseudococcus* mealybugs, only grape mealybug infests table and raisin grapes. This appears to be due to climatic conditions where these two types of grape production occur. Table grapes are generally more severely infested than are raisin or wine grapes.

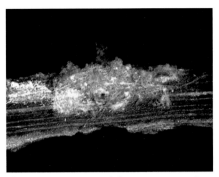

Figure 37.2 Grape mealybug egg mass under bark. *Photo*: L. Strand.

Figure 37.3 (A) Grape mealybug nymphs as seen on berries. (B) Nymphs and their honeydew seen in greater detail. *Photos*: J. K. Clark.

Insecticides, more often used in table grapes, have been demonstrated to reduce grape mealybug parasitoid abundance. Raisin and wine grapes may be heavily infested, at times, but populations fluctuate greatly. Also, higher numbers of mealybug can be tolerated because the raisin and wine grapes are processed.

Severity of infestation also varies by cultivar and depends on vine growth and fruiting characteristics, fruit maturation date, and type of pruning. Vigorous vines are more likely to be infested than are weak ones. Cultivars such as Ruby Seedless and Ribier that produce clusters close to the base of the shoot with fruit touching old wood (arms or cordons) (fig. 37.8) are likely to have more severely infested clusters than cultivars for which clusters hang freely.

Clusters on cane-pruned cultivars (Thompson Seedless) hang free of old wood and are less likely to be seriously infested than fruit on spur-pruned vines. This is because mealybugs primarily overwinter on old wood, and the immature stages have to disperse farther over the vine to reach fruit in cane-pruned cultivars. Thus, cane pruning protects the fruit

somewhat in relation to its position on old wood, where most mealybug eggs are laid.

Early-harvested cultivars (Perlette, Flame Seedless, Superior Seedless, and Exotic) are much less likely to have serious fruit damage than are late-maturing cultivars (Emperor, Autumn Royal, Christmas Rose, and Crimson Seedless) because they are harvested prior to the complete development of second-generation mealybugs.

Heavy infestations of obscure mealybug along the central coast have been reported to cause severe stunting of shoot growth. Longtailed mealybug infestation may also be implicated in this type of damage.

All three species can transmit leafroll viruses. The presence of these viruses more severely impacts wine grapes grown under cooler climatic conditions, such as in the north and central coast. Leafroll viruses result in grapes with lower soluble solids and uneven ripening. Consequently, lower-quality wines are produced. Leafroll viruses have not had as severe an impact on raisin and table grape cultivars grown in California's warm San Joaquin Valley.

Figure 37.4 Obscure mealybug adult females and nymph. *Photo*: K. M. Daane.

MEALYBUG SIZE COMPARISON

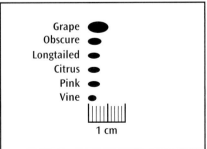

Figure 37.5 Comparison of mealybug sizes.

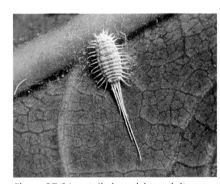

Figure 37.6 Longtailed mealybug adult. *Photo*: D. Rosen.

Figure 37.7 Emperor bunch that made contact with the bark shows various contaminants of grape mealybug infestation (A) and mold growth on berry surfaces (B). *Photos*: J. K. Clark (A); L. J. Bettiga (B).

SEASONAL DEVELOPMENT

Grape mealybug overwinters on old wood under the loose bark of vines. In the late fall the egg stage predominates, but by late December first-stage nymphs (crawlers) are more commonly found. Both stages are still within the cottony egg sac. Beginning on warm days in February, the crawlers can be found moving to the base of spurs and canes and later onto expanding leaves. In mid-June, in the San Joaquin Valley, adult females can be found at the base of spurs and canes where egg sacs will be found by late June. The eggs hatch in early July. These summer-generation crawlers then move out to the green portions of the vine to feed on fruit and foliage. It is this

Figure 37.8 Grape mealybug–infested Emperor bunches touching bark. *Photo*: J. K. Clark.

generation that infests the bunches. Some females maturing in late August and September lay their eggs on fruit and leaves, but most return to the old wood to lay wintering eggs (fig. 37.9). Each female produces from 50 to 150 eggs.

A small number of grape mealybugs never leave the protection of the old wood. They survive by feeding at the base of spurs, on callus tissue at the site of girdle wounds, and underneath the old bark. They feed on live tissue, producing visible honeydew.

The overwintering generation that moves to foliage in March and April is usually present in low numbers and, if biological control is to be achieved, it must establish in this generation. The summer generation, hatching in June and July, may create a population explosion without earlier biological control.

Seasonal development of obscure mealybug has not been thoroughly studied on grapevines. Its development differs from grape mealybug in that continual reproduction is possible throughout the year. Obscure mealybug tolerates a relatively narrow temperature range. It does not survive freezing temperatures, nor does it do well under extremely warm conditions of the San Joaquin Valley. It is primarily a problem in commercial glasshouses. Unlike the grape mealybug, all stages of obscure mealybug are present during the winter, and multiple generations are possible. Each female can produce up to 500 eggs.

The longtailed mealybug also is known as a pest of ornamentals and glasshouse-grown plants. It is considered a tropical or subtropical mealybug and has multiple generations per year, with as many as six occurring in southern

Figure 37.9 Seasonal development of grape mealybug on grapevine.

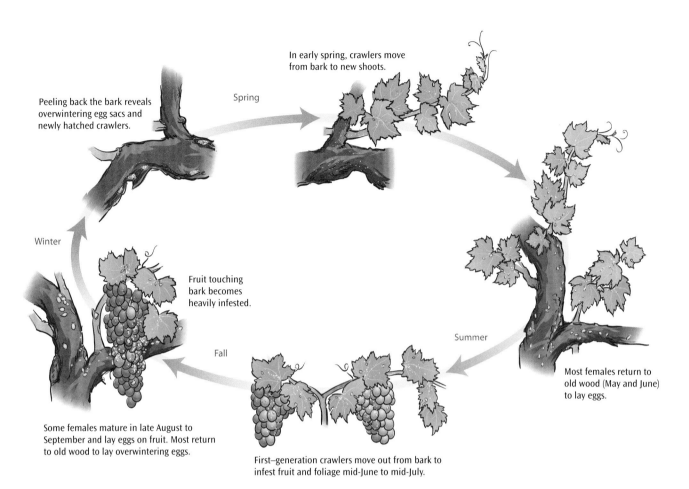

In early spring, crawlers move from bark to new shoots.

Spring

Peeling back the bark reveals overwintering egg sacs and newly hatched crawlers.

Winter

Fruit touching bark becomes heavily infested.

Fall

Summer

Most females return to old wood (May and June) to lay eggs.

Some females mature in late August to September and lay eggs on fruit. Most return to old wood to lay overwintering eggs.

First–generation crawlers move out from bark to infest fruit and foliage mid-June to mid-July.

California. All stages can be found on vines during the winter. This species does not lay eggs in sacs, but produces live young. Over 200 crawlers have been recorded from a single female.

Natural Control

Grape Mealybug

The effectiveness of natural enemies of grape mealybug has been studied closely for a number of years. Natural enemies have been demonstrated to be responsible for keeping populations at low levels. The following parasitic wasps (parasitoids) have been identified as attacking grape mealybug in the San Joaquin Valley: *Acerophagus*

notativentris (Girault) (fig. 37.10), *Acerophagus angelicus* (Howard) (fig. 37.11), *Zarhopalus corvinus* (Girault), *Anagyrus subalbicornis* (Girault), *Pseudleptomastix squammulata* (Girault), and *Anagyrus clauseni* Timberlake. More recently, only three parasitoids have been commonly found. These are *A. notativentris, A. angelicus,* and *Z. corvinus. Acerophagus notativentris* is the dominant species in spring and summer, and *A. angelicus* is more common in the fall in the San Joaquin Valley.

The gray field ant (*Formica aerata* and *Formica peripilosa* Wheeler), the Argentine ant (*Linepithema humile*) (fig. 36.12),

and the southern fire ant (*Solenopsis xyloni*) (fig. 37.13) tend grape mealybug. In so doing, they protect mealybugs from the action of parasitoids, resulting in greater levels of infestation. The practice of nontillage and the use of drip irrigation in grape production have facilitated better establishment of these ant species in vineyards and may account for the reduced level of parasitism now experienced. *Formica aerata* has been managed in table grapes by using a common vetch (*Vicia sativa*) cover crop planted between the vine rows. The extrafloral nectaries on common vetch are more attractive than the honeydew produced by the

Figure 37.10 Adult of the encyrtid wasp *Acerophagus notativentris,* a parasitoid of grape mealybug. *Photo*: J. K. Clark.

Figure 37.11 Adult of the encyrtid wasp *Acerophagus angelicus,* a parasitoid of grape mealybug. *Photo*: J. K. Clark.

Figure 37.12 Argentine ant tending obscure mealybug on a Chardonnay cluster in a central coast vineyard. *Photo*: J. K. Clark.

Figure 37.13 Southern fire ant tending several grape mealybugs in a San Joaquin Valley Thompson Seedless vineyard. *Photo*: J. K. Clark.

mealybug. Although populations of the ant persist, they do not tend the mealybug but visit the extra-floral nectaries instead, allowing for increased parasitization of grape mealybug.

Predators play a lesser role in management of grape mealybug. The well-known mealybug destroyer (*Cryptolaemus montrouzieri* Mulsant) (fig. 37.14) does not overwinter in the colder regions of California. It is commonly found in California's north and central coast wine grape–growing areas. Other coccinellid beetles, including *Scymnus binaevatus* Mulsant and *Hyperaspis* nr. sp. *lateralis,* also can be found preying on grape mealybug, but control has not been demonstrated.

The larvae of a small cecidomyiid fly have been found to be frequently associated with grape mealybug infestations in the San Joaquin Valley, but this fly has not provided the control needed in table grape vineyards (see fig. 38.8B).

The green lacewings *Chrysopa carnea* (Stephens), *Chrysopa oculata* Say, *Chrysopa nigricornis* Bermeitster, *Chrysopa coloradensis* Bermeister, and *Chrysoperla comanche* Banks can be found associated with grape mealybugs. They do prey on the early growth stages, but honeydew production by later mealybug growth stages fouls lacewing mouthparts. They are not considered dominant predators.

Brown lacewings (Hemerobiidae) are considered to be more important predators of grape mealybug than are green lacewings. *Symnpherobius barberi* Barber is a particularly important lacewing predator in the West. Brown lacewings are subject to parasitism by *Dibrachys daphne* (Girault), and this reduces their effectiveness.

A varied assortment of spiders has been studied in central California vineyards, but none regulated grape mealybug populations.

Obscure Mealybug

The obscure mealybug has only one parasitoid associated with it. In 1994, *Pseudaphycus flavidulus* (Brethres) was imported from Chile and released in California's central coast vineyards. This parasitoid has been found in coastal California vineyards, but the abundance is low. A more important beneficial appears to be *C. montouzieri*, the mealybug destroyer. It has been found preying on obscure mealybug more regularly than any other predator or parasitoid. As with grape mealybug, ants protect obscure mealybug from predators and *P. flavidulus*.

Longtailed Mealybug

No parasitoids were found to be associated with longtailed mealybug when grapes were surveyed for this pest in 1999. The longtailed mealybug is the most common species found infesting grapes in Australia and New Zealand. Seven parasitoid species are known to attack it on the Australasian continent. The three most important include *Coccophagus gurneyi* Compere, *Alamella mira* Noyes, and *Anagyrus fusciventris* (Girault). *Coccophagus* is reported in California but has not been found parasitizing longtailed mealybug in grapes. Predators found in North America that are known to feed on longtailed mealybug include *C. montrouzieri* and *Scymnus loewi* Mulsant.

Monitoring Guidelines

Grape mealybug monitoring has been studied closely, but this is not true for longtailed and obscure mealybug. Monitoring information is based on work done on table grapes in the southern San Joaquin Valley. It involves sampling at bud swell, during June, and at harvest. Grape mealybug is more often found on vigorous vines; therefore, these should be sampled preferentially over weak vines. Obscure and longtailed mealybug do not have a preference for vigorous vines.

Spring Monitoring

Vines that were infested and marked at harvest should be examined closely during the early spring. Grape mealybug crawlers respond to warm weather (above 15.5°C, or 60°F) by moving from hidden areas beneath the bark to the spurs and expanding shoots. Select a single regrowth spur from each of 100 vines per 40 acres (16 ha). The vines should be selected from areas that have shown infestation during the previous harvest. Examine each spur for 1 minute, peeling back loose areas of papery bark. Look closely at the juncture of the spur and the old wood. If more than 5 spurs out of 100 sampled are found to be infested with crawlers, an insecticide application should be made if grapes are harvested for the fresh market. Higher infestation is tolerated for wine and raisin grapes.

Summer Monitoring

In late May or early June, examine the base of spurs, canes, or arms for the presence of mature females. Monitoring can be aided by looking for ant activity on the vine. Another clue is to look for vines with wetted areas on the bark or on the leaves,

indicating mealybug feeding (fig. 37.15). In particular, the gray field ant or Argentine ant will be tending mealybugs actively. Following ants to sites at the base of spurs will aid in detecting the presence of mealybugs. The females may have egg clusters attached to the posterior end of the body. Sample 100 vines per 40 acres (16 ha). Each vine should be searched for 1 minute. If more than 10 live females are found per 100 vines, or cluster contamination is occurring, a treatment should be made.

Figure 37.14 *Cryptolaemus* larva (right) and adult beetle (left) feed in a mealybug aggregation. *Photo:* J. K. Clark.

Figure 37.15 Bark wet from honeydew from a high population of grape mealybug (A) and sooty mold on the foliage (B) of a cane below the vine indicate that honeydew is dripping from mealybugs above. *Photos:* L. J. Bettiga (A); J. K. Clark (B).

Pheromone Monitoring

UC entomologists have recently identified the pheromones for grape, longtailed, and obscure mealybugs. The pheromone components for each species appear to be very selective to males of the particular species. The use of monitoring traps as described for vine mealybug will greatly aid in identifying sites of infestation and possibly lead to improved methods of timing insecticide applications. The use of pheromones for monitoring *Pseudococcus* species are relatively new; in time and with more field experience, guidelines will be developed for their field use.

Harvest Monitoring

If grape mealybug was detected in the summer monitoring, train the harvest crew to recognize cluster and vine infestation. Provide the crew with marking tape and instruct them to tag vines when infested clusters are detected. This will greatly aid in delineating overall vineyard establishment of mealybugs and serve to narrow the focus of intensive monitoring in the following year. Infestation of more than 2% of the clusters will require preventative chemical control in subsequent years.

Parasitoid Monitoring

Of the three *Pseudococcus* mealybug species, only grape mealybug has been controlled biologically. Monitoring for parasitoids can provide clues as to the need for and the type of insecticide management. Wasps of both *Ascerophagus notativentris* and *A. angelicus* can be detected easily. These species can superparastize hosts, and more than one individual wasp will develop within the body of the host mealybug. For example, *A. notativentris* attacks all

stages of grape mealybug, and the number of wasps emerging from a parasitized mealybug will range from 1 to 20, depending on the growth stage that is attacked (fig. 37.16). The average emergence is 7 per mealybug. If live grape mealybugs are collected and held in small gelatin capsules, the emergence of multiple wasps from a single individual will indicate the presence

of one of these two species of parasitoids. If the parasitoid is bright yellow, the species is *A. notativentris*. If distinctive parasitized mummies are found in the clusters or beneath the bark, there is no need to collect live grape mealybugs (fig. 37.17). A single large emergence hole from the dorsum of grape mealybug indicates parasitization by *Z. corvinus*.

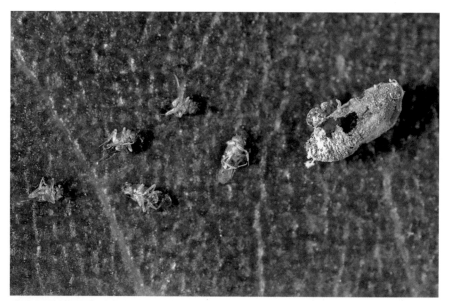

Figure 37.16 Dead adult *Acerophagus notativentris* wasps that have emerged from a grape mealybug mummy. *Photo*: J. K. Clark.

Figure 37.17 Grape mealybug infestation with four mummified mealybugs. *Photo*: J. K. Clark.

Management Guidelines

For the most part, spraying grape mealybug depends on the previous history of infestation. However, problem areas should be closely monitored because infestations can decline dramatically as a result of biological control.

Insecticides are available that provide selective control of mealybugs while not harming parasitoids. These can be applied during the spring or summer. The delayed-dormant spray has been an effective treatment but does not incorporate the possibility of biological control in determining the need for treatment.

If summer treatments are to be made, they should be done prior to veraison, when sprays still can penetrate clusters. Summer treatments should be based on a June sampling program. A close relationship exists between the number of spurs infested and subsequent cluster infestation: roughly, for every spur infested in June, a single cluster will be infested at harvest. Treatment for grape mealybug is best during the crawler stage. In the San Joaquin Valley, this occurs in late June. If unacceptable infestation occurs, the vines should be checked for live eggs or young mealybugs after harvest, indicating the potential for continued infestation the following year.

A number of insecticides with different modes of action are available for mealybug management. Each should be incorporated into an IPM program to avoid insecticide resistance, which occurred when parathion was repeatedly used to control mealybugs prior to the banning of the insecticide.

Organic growers must rely on biological control and careful training of vines to lessen the impact of *Pseudococcus* mealybugs. Horticultural mineral oil and calcium polysulfide, allowable for organic growers, have not provided adequate management of mealybugs. Experimentation with bark removal is currently being tested for organic grape production.

To enhance biological control, ants must be prevented from tending mealybugs. If gray field ants (*Formica* spp.) are tending grape mealybugs and protecting them from parasitoids, planting a cover crop of common vetch (*Vicia sativa*) can help. Common vetch has an abundance of extrafloral nectaries that attract the ants away from grape mealybug, exposing the mealybugs to parasitoids. In research studies, common vetch was fall seeded as 80% common vetch and 20% Merced rye (*Lolium multiflorum*). The cover crop established itself in late fall and winter so that by early spring it was ready to attract the ants. A heavy seeding rate of 120 pounds per acre (about 134 kg/ha) helps ensure a good stand. The effect of other nectary-bearing cover crops on attracting ants has not been evaluated.

Chemical control of ants by soil application and through the use of baits has been demonstrated in grapes. At present new and non-disruptive methods of application are being developed.

Very little work has been conducted on the management of obscure mealybug. Research has demonstrated that ant management could significantly reduce obscure mealybug abundance and infestation. General predation is enhanced in the absence of ants.

References

Ben-Dov, Y. 2009. ScaleNet, Pseudococcidae. ScaleNet website, http://www.sel.barc.usda.gov/SCALNET/SCALENET.HTM.

Bentley, W. J., L. G. Varela, F. G. Zalom, R. J. Smith, and A. H. Purcell. 2008. Insects and mites. In B. L. Ohlendorf and M. L. Flint, eds., UC IPM Pest management guidelines: Grapes. Oakland: University of California Agriculture and Natural Resources Publication 3448. UC IPM website, www.ipm.ucdavis.edu/PMG/.

Geiger, C. A. and K. M. Daane. 2001. Seasonal movement and distribution of the grape mealybug (*Homoptera: Pseudococcidae*): Developing a sampling program for San Joaquin Valley vineyards. Journal of Economic Entomology 94(1): 91–301.

Geiger, C. A., K. M. Daane, W. J. Bentley, G. Y. Yokota, and L. A. Martin. 2001. Sampling program for grape mealybugs improves pest management. California Agriculture 55(3): 19–27.

Godfrey, K. E., K. M. Daane, W. J. Bentley, R. J. Gill, and R. Malakar-Kuenen. 2002. Mealybugs in California vineyards. Oakland: University of California Agriculture and Natural Resources Publication 21612.

Flaherty, D. L., L. P. Christensen, W. T. Lanini, J. J. Marois, P. A. Phillips, and L. T. Wilson, eds. 1992. Grape pest management. 2nd ed. Oakland: University of California Agriculture and Natural Resources Publication 3343.

McKenzie, H. L. 1967. Mealybugs of California. Berkeley: University of California Press.

Hemiptera
*Aphids,
Leafhoppers,
Mealybugs, Scales,
True Bugs,
Whiteflies*

38 *PLANOCOCCUS* MEALYBUGS (VINE MEALYBUG)

Kent M. Daane, Walter J. Bentley, Rhonda J. Smith, David R. Haviland, Edward A. Weber, Mark Battany, Carmen Gispert, and Jocelyn G. Millar

The vine mealybug (*Planococcus ficus* (Signoret)) (Hemiptera: Pseudococcidae) is an invasive insect that is now found in California and Mexico. In 1994, vine mealybug was first identified as a vineyard pest in North America when it was found in commercial table grapes in the Coachella Valley (Riverside County), although it probably entered the state years before. After this initial detection, surveys found that the vine mealybug had spread throughout the Coachella Valley, infesting approximately 80% of grape acreage by 1998. Soon afterward, similar reports were made of vine mealybug finds in table grapes in Hermosillo, Mexico. By 1998, the vine mealybug was found in the San Joaquin Valley in Kern and Fresno Counties. From that point, its dispersal into new regions was dramatic, as isolated populations were found in vineyards in Santa Barbara County in 2000, San Luis Obispo County in 2001, and in El Dorado, Madera, Monterey, Napa, Sacramento, Sonoma, San Joaquin, and Stanislaus Counties in 2002.

Circumstantial evidence suggests this rapid dispersal resulted from movement of infested vineyard equipment (mechanical harvesters, bins, tractors, etc.); through sales of infested nursery stock from 1998 to 2003; and through the natural dispersal of mealybugs by wind, birds, and rodents. Regardless of how it was spread, by the end of 2003, vine mealybug had been found in 16 counties in California. Currently, all vineyard regions in the state are at risk.

The vine mealybug has long been associated with vineyards. It was first identified as a new species in Crimea in 1868, where it was found infesting grapes. Vine mealybug has been found in grape-growing regions of Europe, North and South Africa, Argentina, the Middle East, and Mexico. Its past invasive nature suggests that noninfested grape-growing regions in California are still vulnerable to inoculation events as a result of the movement of infested plants or equipment.

DESCRIPTION

The adult female vine mealybug is about 4 mm (0.17 in) long, and the body shape is an elongated oval that is somewhat flattened from top to bottom (fig. 38.1A). After each molt, wax secretion from hundreds of small pores on the dorsum (top) begins to cover the mealybug. This gives it a white, cottony appearance, even though the mealybug's body color actually ranges from faded pink to purple. Along the lateral margin, the wax secretion forms filaments that look like small spines, with a pair of slightly longer posterior "tail" filaments near the anus.

Just before eggs are laid, mature adult females begin to secrete wax to form an ovisac, a shelter for the eggs. The ovisac resembles loose cotton threads and can be 1 cm (0.4 in) long, appearing larger than the female. Eggs are deposited underneath the ovisac. Over 1,000 eggs have been recorded in a single female's ovisac, although most contain between 150 and 400 eggs. Each egg is minute, about 0.4 mm (0.016 in) long, elongate oval, and pale yellow to pink. The ovisac helps to cluster the developing eggs and protects them from natural enemies and desiccation. The deposited ovisac sticks to the vine and will remain there long after the eggs hatch and the crawlers leave, especially ovisacs deposited under the bark.

The first-instar nymph hatches from the egg and leaves behind a white, collapsed eggshell. The newly hatched mealybug is small, about 0.6 mm (0.024 in) long, and pale yellow because it is not yet covered in white wax (so there are no lateral or tail filaments) (fig. 38.1B). Viewed from above, it is elongate oval, but from the side it is flat. It moves quickly to find a feeding spot, hence its common name, crawler. There are three molts, resulting consecutively in the second instar, third instar, and the immature adult (before the ovaries have developed). Each of these stages resembles the previous except for an increasing size and amount of wax secretion that results in a thicker wax pelt or covering (fig. 38.1C). The mature, or gravid, adult female begins to grow as the ovaries mature and the body fills with developing eggs (fig. 38.1D). By the time the mature female starts construction of the ovisac, she is not as flattened dorso-ventrally and she rarely moves. As eggs are deposited into the ovisac, the female begins to shrink. Essentially, the mature female is storing hundreds of eggs in her ovaries, and as the eggs are deposited over the course of several days or even weeks (depending on temperature), the female body decreases in size, shifting the parent's resources to the offspring.

Male vine mealybugs have a different life cycle than that of females. From egg to third instar, the males generally resemble the females, with the exception that the males are slightly more elongate and narrow. After the third instar, the male develops to a prepupa and then to a pupa, from which a winged adult male

Figure 38.1 The vine mealybug adult (A) on a grape pedicel shows the classic shorter tail filaments as compared with adult females of *Pseudococcus* species. Crawlers (first-instar nymphs), just emerged from their eggs, are seen clustering on a vine stem between two leaf petioles (B). The crawlers will eventually disperse to find preferred feeding sites. On the grape leaf in (C), there are approximately 1,000 first- to third-instar vine mealybugs; this picture shows a more accurate view of the mealybugs' appearance without the aid of magnification. Mealybugs mature to either an adult female, shown in (D) beginning the formation of an ovisac, or a winged adult male, also shown in (D). *Photos*: K. M. Daane.

emerges. The adult male is the only mealybug stage with wings. It is about 1.5 mm (0.06 in) long, with a brown body and multisegmented antennae that are about half the body length. Most evident are the long, opaque wings that cover the body and extend well beyond the abdomen, which has a long pair of pale white filaments (caudal filaments). The adult male is fragile, not a strong flyer, does not feed, and lives for only a few days in summer when peak temperatures reach more than 38°C (100°F) in some regions; at room temperature, adult males have been kept alive for more than a week.

Comparison with Other Mealybugs

The vine mealybug is similar in size and appearance to other grape-infesting mealybug species (see section 37, "Pseudococcus Mealybugs"). However, the vine mealybug is more closely related to the citrus mealybug (*Planococcus citri* (Risso)) than to other mealybugs commonly found in the vineyard such as the *Pseudococcus* species (e.g., grape mealybug). Not surprisingly, it has very different biological characteristics, leading to differences in pest status, geographic range, and control strategies. In the field, the vine mealybug can be easily separated from these other common mealybugs. The wax filaments surrounding the body are not as long as those found on the *Pseudococcus* species, and there is a faint dorsal median stripe on mature females, appearing as though less wax is present there than on the remainder of the body.

INJURY

The vine mealybug feeds on vine roots, trunk, cordon, shoots, leaves, and fruit. Moderate to high population densities can result in defoliation and infested fruit clusters, both of which reduce crop quality and yield (fig. 38.2A). Untreated vines can become heavily infested and, after 3 to 4 years of repeated mealybug feeding and damage, will have reduced crop yield and may die.

Mealybugs are phloem feeders, using long, slender mouthparts to suck out plant fluids. The phloem fluid contains more carbohydrates than the mealybug needs, and it eliminates the unused material as a sugary fluid (honeydew). The

mealybug actually flicks beads of honeydew away from its location. Vine mealybug produces far more honeydew than other vineyard mealybugs, such as the grape mealybug. The sticky honeydew can accumulate on all vine parts. As it dries and concentrates, honeydew can form a hard, white to brown crystalline layer that covers infested plant parts (fig. 38.2B). The carbohydrate-rich honeydew also supports the growth of sooty molds, which can build up on the leaves and shoots, significantly reducing photosynthesis, and in heavily infested vines defoliation may occur. Infested clusters are more prone to bunch rots. Defoliation and feeding inside the clusters also cause the fruit to raisin on the vine.

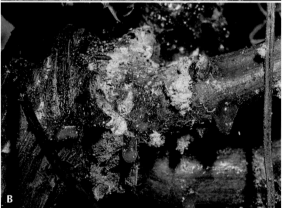

Figure 38.2 Vine mealybug damage can be severe if the population is not treated (A). This mealybug readily feeds on grape leaves, even during the summer in most regions, causing leaf damage and drop, which can result in raisining of the fruit when fully exposed to the sun. The mealybug will get into the clusters early in the season, causing direct contamination and promoting bunch rot. The mealybug produces a large amount of honeydew, which can cover fruit, leaves, and shoots, often resulting in a waxlike buildup on the vine (B). *Photos*: K. M. Daane.

Similar to some other mealybug species, the vine mealybug can transmit grapevine viruses that cause leafroll and corky bark diseases and therefore can be an economic pest even at low densities. As vectors, mealybugs typically carry the virus for short periods, losing the virus after each molt. The smaller stages (first and second instars) may be the most effective life stages in terms of their efficiency at acquiring leafroll viruses (feeding on an infected plant and picking up the virus) and transmitting the virus (placing the pathogen in another plant while feeding). This means that crawlers can acquire the pathogen from an infected vine, move into a clean field some distance away (e.g., blown by the wind), feed for a short time and transmit the virus to the clean vine, then die from natural causes that same day, all without leaving a noticeable trace of their presence. Disease symptoms showing that the vine is infected may not be apparent until the next season. Because of the serious consequences associated with viral diseases in some grape-growing regions, growers may choose to apply control measures against mealybugs at low densities in order to limit virus spread. For more information, see section 24, "Grapevine Virus Diseases."

SEASONAL DEVELOPMENT

The vine mealybug can infest all parts of the vine, including the roots, at any time of the season, and all life stages can be found on the vine, especially when older populations begin to develop asynchronous generations. There are, however, regional abundance and dispersal patterns that influence where most of the population will be found on the vine. These patterns, in turn, influence the amount of mealybug feeding damage and the effectiveness of chemical and biological controls.

In the Coachella Valley, vine mealybug abundance is relatively low during the winter months. Activity typically starts in late February or March, when the over-wintered mealybugs increase their feeding and development and deposit ovisacs. In late March or April, a steady increase in mealybug abundance begins with the egg hatch of the first generation. After several more generations, the population reaches peak abundance in May or early June at levels that can be more than ten times greater than levels during overwintering. The rapid increase in spring is often followed by an equally fast decline, beginning just after harvest (late May to June) and continuing through the period when summer temperatures are often in excess of 43°C (110°F) (July and August). In some vineyards, a second, smaller rise in abundance is found from September to October, when cooler fall temperatures are better suited to mealybug survival and before the populations recede to their low winter densities.

Along with the seasonal changes in mealybug density, the mealybugs' location on the vine changes as well (fig. 38.3). In winter, the population is primarily found under the bark of the trunk or cordon. If tending ants are present, most mealybugs are found on the lower trunk or roots. In spring, as the mealybug population increases, it moves up the vine to the new shoots and leaves and, as soon as fruit ripening begins, into the clusters. Management becomes a race

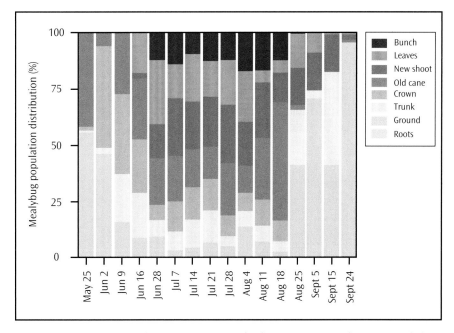

Figure 38.3 The location of vine mealybug on the vine from May to September was recorded on Thompson Seedless vines near Fresno, California. The pattern shows the mealybug population moving from its overwintering area underneath the bark of the trunk and canes and onto the new shoots, leaves, and fruit. In this vineyard, high levels of parasitization in August and September increased the percentage of the population residing under the bark, as most of the exposed mealybugs on the leaves were killed.

between the table grape harvest date (May to June) and the time when mealybugs reach the clusters. After harvest, as the mealybug population decreases it also retreats back toward the trunk and roots, where the declining population can find some shelter from the summer heat.

In the San Joaquin Valley studies of mealybug populations, the overwintering vine mealybug can be found anywhere on the vine, although in most vineyards the population is primarily found on the lower trunk. The location depends on factors such as vine age and pruning system. During early spring, the population follows vine growth, and the greatest proportion of the vine mealybug population may be on the upper trunk, cordons, or fruiting canes of older vines that provide plenty of feeding sites. As temperatures increase, the population moves up to the shoots, leaves, and fruit clusters. Unlike in the Coachella Valley, mealybug abundance continues to increase throughout the summer, and they can remain on the leaves until leaf senescence. This pattern suggests that summer temperatures in the San Joaquin Valley are not high enough to cause significant vine mealybug mortality. Their presence on leaves and shoots is important because these more exposed mealybugs cause more damage than the population located under the bark. Note that researchers have found vine mealybug on all parts of the vine throughout the entire season, including under the bark of the lower trunk and on the roots (the latter is especially true in sandy soil or where ants are actively tending the mealybugs). The more-hidden locations (e.g., under the bark) help protect mealybugs from most natural enemies and some pesticide treatments.

There is less information on mealybug abundance and location patterns in coastal, foothill, and northern interior wine grape regions, but the vine mealybug appears to follow a pattern similar to that described for the San Joaquin Valley, albeit with fewer summer generations.

Regional temperatures affect mealybug damage levels by influencing the number of annual generations, the feeding location on the vine, and the mortality from extreme temperatures. At constant temperatures, developmental times for one complete generation (from egg

hatch to the adult stage and the subsequent production of a new ovisac) range from about 130 days at 16.5°C (62°F) to about 22 days at 26°C (79°F) (fig. 38.4). Research also shows mortality rates increased above a constant 32°C (90°F), and no mealybugs survived to develop egg sacs at a constant 34°C (93°F). Similarly, the mealybug could not complete development at a low constant temperature of 12°C (53.5°F). The optimal development temperature, at which mortality was relatively low and the development rate was relatively fast, was near 26°C (79°F), with mealybug survival higher than 85%, egg production greater than 350 eggs per female, and

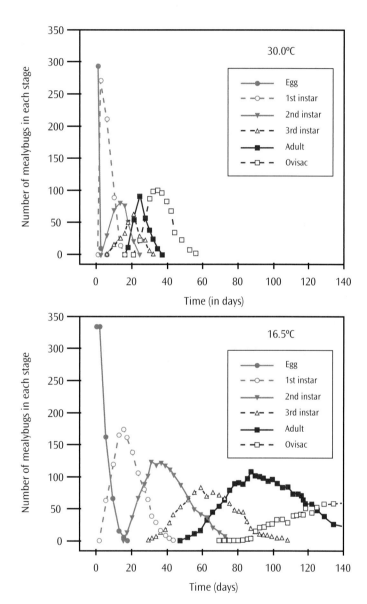

Figure 38.4 Vine mealybug developed on potted Thompson Seedless vines and held at constant temperatures shows the development times for each stage from egg to adult and the production of the ovisac. At 30°C (86°F), the mealybug ovisacs were produced in less than 30 days, whereas at 16.5°C (62°F), many of the ovisacs were not formed even after 100 days. At both temperatures, most mortality occurred in the first instar as the crawlers were finding feeding sites.

the ratio of female to male off-spring at 8 to 1.

The number of annual generations and mortality (from harsh weather conditions only) in various grape-growing regions have been estimated using degree-day calculations. The desert table grape region in the Coachella Valley had the highest number of annual generations (more than nine per year), with population growth limited because of the high mortality during the summer months. The southern region of the San Joaquin Valley had six to seven generations per year, while the northern region of the San Joaquin Valley had four to five generations per year. The coastal wine grape regions are cooler, and there was a corresponding decrease in the number of generations, with about four in the central coast and only three in regions near Monterey. Using these data, researchers predict that the vine mealybug may continue to spread, potentially infesting vineyards in Oregon, Washington, and even Canada.

NATURAL CONTROLS

Natural enemies play a key role in regulating vine mealybug in other parts of the world, and they are becoming increasingly important in California vineyards.

Parasitoids

The most important natural enemies of mealybugs are parasitoids. Evidence of parasitoid activity in the vineyard is the presence of mummified mealybugs. These are rounded rather than flattened, and they lose their wax covering, changing to a golden brown, leathery (or mummified) skin. The mummy helps protect the developing parasitoid inside. Parasitization levels range widely among regions and vineyards. In Coachella Valley table grapes, 5 to 20% of late-season (August to October) mealybugs can be parasitized. In the San Joaquin Valley, where much of the mealybug population remains exposed on the leaves and grape clusters from July through September, parasitization levels as high as 90% have been reported in August and September surveys.

Encyrtid wasps in the *Anagyrus* nr. sp. *pseudococci* (Girault) complex account for more than 85% of the parasitoids recovered from vine mealybug in California; it has been reported as a vine mealybug parasitoid in Israel, Egypt, Europe, Argentina, and South Africa. In California, *A. pseudococci* alone has not provided complete control, but it helps reduce late-season vine mealybug populations. The adult *A. pseudococci* typically lays an egg into second- or third-instar mealybugs, where the larva develops and eventually devours the mealybug from the inside. When the egg is first deposited, the mealybug is still active (walking and feeding). As the parasitoid larva develops, the mealybug becomes sluggish and soon ceases movement altogether as the parasitoid larva eats away at the mealybug's internal tissues. Soon afterward, the parasitoid pupates inside the mealybug. The fully formed adult wasp emerges by chewing a round hole through the mummified mealybug (fig. 38.5).

Anagyrus pseudococci is an effective parasitoid in the summer months due to its ability to rapidly reproduce during warm weather. At a constant 34°C (93°F), *A. pseudococci* completed development from egg to adult emergence in 10 to 12 days, suggesting that there

Figure 38.5 A number of natural enemies help lower vine mealybug densities. The most important are those in the *Anagyrus pseudococci* complex. The adult female of *A. pseudococci* is golden brown with distinctive black and white antennae, as seen after emerging from the mealybug mummy (A); the adult male is smaller, black, and has hirsute (hairy) antennae (B). *Photos*: K. M. Daane.

can be two to three parasitoid generations to each vine mealybug generation. However, it appears that *A. pseudococci* has an overwintering requirement that reduces its presence and effectiveness early in the season by delaying the period when it emerges (fig. 38.6).

Augmentation, the release of insectary-reared natural enemies, can circumvent some of the biological limitations of natural enemies. Experiments testing augmentative release of *A. pseudococci* in a San Joaquin Valley Thompson Seedless vineyard showed that vine mealybug abundance and damage could be reduced by 50% with releases of adult *A. pseudococci* from June to July, but the per-acre release rate of parasitoids was quite high, and this practice was not as cost effective as many insecticide control options.

Other parasitoid species in California include the encyrtid wasps *Leptomastidea abnormis* (Girault), *Leptomastix dactylopii* (Girault), and *Coccidoxenoides peregrinus* Girault, and the platygastrid *Allotropa* species. Together, these species typically account for less than 15% of the parasitoids recovered. Other parasitoids reared from mealybugs include *Chartocerus* species, which are hyperparasitoids, probably attacking *A. pseudococci*. Ongoing biological control programs are seeking to import parasitoid species that are better adapted to regional conditions in California, including other strains of *A. pseudococci*, which may later be shown to be separate species.

Predators

The mealybug destroyer (*Cryptolaemus montrouzieri* Mulsant) is the most well known mealybug predator (fig. 37.14). This lady beetle was collected from Australia in 1892 and imported into California to help control mealybugs on citrus. Although a voracious predator, mealybug destroyer populations often drop sharply during the winter in California's cooler vineyard regions due to an inability to survive winter temperatures in some vineyard regions. In 1996, a cold-hardy strain of the mealybug destroyer was collected in southern Australia and released in California, where it is now found throughout coastal wine grape regions. Mealybug destroyer larvae have waxlike filaments similar to those of mealybugs. This camouflage allows beetle larvae to feed among mealybugs without too much disturbance from mealybug-tending ants. This predator is especially effective against mealybug eggs in the ovisac, where eggs are often protected from other predator species. Releases of adult

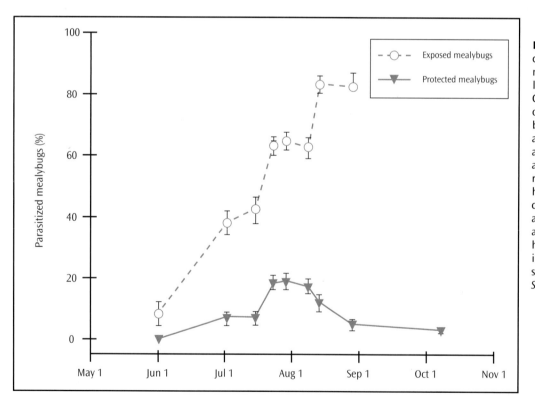

Figure 38.6 Average percentage parasitization of vine mealybug in a Flame Seedless vineyard near Fresno, California, showing the levels of parasitization of mealybugs collected in exposed areas (such as on the leaves) and in protected areas (such as under the bark). The results show that although high levels of parasitization can be reached, parasitoid activity is greatest in August and September, often after harvest, and mealybugs in protected areas escape some of the natural enemies. *Source*: Daane et al. 2004.

mealybug destroyers are commonly made and appear to reduce exposed mealybug populations on leaves and fruit; however, there is little research that documents the effectiveness of this program. Adult mealybug destroyers search for mealybug ovisacs into which they deposit their eggs. If mealybug ovisacs are not present, the adult beetle is likely to fly away. Timing the predator release with the presence of ovisacs should help retard the dispersal of the released beetles.

Other lady beetles closely associated with vineyard mealybugs include *Scymnus* and *Hyperaspis* species (fig. 38.8A). Larvae of these lady beetles are also covered with wax, and they are often mistaken for the mealybug destroyer. In some vineyards, *Scymnus* and *Hyperaspis* are more common than the mealybug destroyer on mealybug-infested vines.

A number of midge species (i.e., predaceous flies in the family Cecidomyiidae) are found in vineyards, with their larvae feeding on mealybugs (fig. 38.8B). Midge larvae are commonly found in or near the mealybug ovisac feeding on mealybug eggs and nymphs. The fly larvae typically pupate in the ground, and the adult is not predatory. The most common midge in California is *Dicrodiplosis californica* Felt. The larva is cream to orange colored and maggot shaped. When examining an ovisac, the midge larvae will be slowly moving among the mealybug eggs. Unfortunately, very little is known about the effectiveness of these predators.

Several generalist insect predators prey on mealybugs in the vineyards, including green lacewings (*Chrysoperla* spp.), brown lacewings (*Hemerobius* spp.), minute pirate bugs (*Orius* spp.), damsel bugs (*Nabis americoferus* Carayon), ladybird beetles (*Hippodamia convergens* Guérin-Méneville), big-eyed bugs (*Geocoris pallens* Stål), and European earwigs (*Forficula auricularia* Linnaeus). Predaceous mites have been observed feeding on mealybug eggs and crawlers in the laboratory, but little is known about their impact in vineyards. Spiders comprise more than 90% of the insect predators found in a vineyard. Although some spiders, such as *Theridion* species, have been observed feeding on mealybugs in vineyards, there are no studies of their impact on mealybug populations.

The mealybug can find refuge from both parasitoids and predators in some of the more protected regions on the vine. For example, parasitization levels by *A. pseudococci* are lower for mealybugs located under the bark than for those exposed on the leaves. Ants can also create a biotic refuge because they tend mealybugs and protect them from many of the common natural enemy species. In the San Joaquin Valley, a new biotic refuge has been identified: the larvae of a species of *Givira*, a moth in the family Cossidae, have been found feeding on the vine trunk just underneath the bark. Their feeding creates small, bored-out depressions in the trunk, and the vine mealybug has moved in with these moth larvae. In these

Figure 38.7 *Leptomastix abnormis* is a relatively polyphagous parasitoid that can attack the vine mealybug, although it has rarely been found in significant numbers. This parasitoid, like many other species, kills mealybugs as both a parasitoid and a predator. Here an adult of *L. abnormis* is seen using her ovipositor to slash a hole in a first-instar mealybug (A) and then turn around and feed on the exuding fluids (B), a practice known as host feeding. *Photos*: K. M. Daane.

moth-made shelters, research-ers have yet to find a parasitized mealybug.

MONITORING GUIDELINES

There are no simple and effec-tive methods to monitor vineyard mealybug species. Current monitoring methods consist of time-consuming and often labori-ous examination of plant material for the presence of live mealybugs. A faster sampling method specific to the vine mealybug is the use of sticky traps baited with the vine mealybug sex pheromone to lure in and trap adult males. Both conven-tional sampling and pheromone trapping have advantages and dis-advantages and, for that reason, both methods should be used.

Pheromone Traps

Adult vine mealybug males can be monitored using delta (tent-shaped) sticky traps loaded with a synthetic form of the vine mealybug sex pheromone. Using commercially available pheromone-baited traps, new

infestations have been found throughout California's grape-growing regions.

Recorded trap catches in com-mercial vineyards have ranged from 0 to 1,200 males per trap per week. The catch number is influ-enced not only by the mealybug density but by a number of fac-tors, such as the insecticides used in the vineyard (adult males are fragile and easily killed), the popu-lation's sex ratio, the time of year, wind direction, and other factors. For this reason, the traps are best used to determine whether vine mealybug is present in or near the vineyard. Traps are less valuable at providing estimates of mealy-bug density, especially early in the season. For these reasons, not every block needs to be trapped. Use two traps in small (less than 40 acres) or isolated vineyards. For larger vineyards with multiple blocks, place two traps every 80 to 120 acres (32 to 48 ha), select-ing sites that are most likely to be infested, such as near roads,

nursery material, culled grapes, and pomace piles from harvest operations. The pheromone-baited traps should be hung inside the vine canopy, typically on an inner trellis wire at the height of the fruit clusters. Be sure that the open ends of the trap are not obstructed by the vine. The pheromone lure inside the trap attracts the male vine mealybug, not the color of the trap. Most insects are not attracted to the red color of the trap (as opposed to yellow, which attracts many insect species), so it captures fewer unwanted insects.

Trap only during the primary flight season. Males do not fly during the winter, so there is no need to trap at that time. A small flight typically occurs in March in the Coachella Valley, April in the San Joaquin Valley, and April or May in coastal vineyards. Trap catches during these periods are very low and represent males that overwintered out of synchrony with most of the population, which overwinters primarily as mated

Figure 38.8 Several generalist mealybug predators also provide some control (some of these were highlighted in section 37, "*Pseudococcus* Mealy-bugs"). Other predators found feeding on vine mealybug include a number of lady beetles, such as the *Hyperaspis* species (A) and the cecidomyiid larvae (B). *Photos*: K. M. Daane.

females. The first significant male flight occurs after overwintered females deposit their ovisacs and the resulting offspring develop to adult males and females. This typically occurs between April and May in the Coachella Valley and June in the San Joaquin Valley and coastal vineyards. Growers should wait until these periods to deploy traps; earlier trapping is not as productive. Once deployed, traps should be inspected every 2 weeks, replacing the delta trap and transferring the lure to the new trap. Lures should be replaced every 2 months. Peak catches are often from August to October. During this period, peak counts of fewer than 30 males per trap per week suggest that there is a new infestation in or near the traps; moderate counts with multiple peaks between 20 to 60 males per trap per week indicate that there are infested vines nearby and a vine search and spot treatment may be needed; high counts of greater than 60 males per trap per week indicate a more widespread infestation that may require a postharvest treatment or a treatment the following season.

Properly reading the traps (counting the number of male mealybugs caught) requires some training. The males are extremely small and may be confused with other small insects (e.g., thrips). With practice and a dissecting microscope (30×), male mealybugs can be identified in the sticky traps and separated from other small insects. However, it is difficult to separate vine mealybug males from other male mealybug species, such as grass mealybugs (*Phenococcus sp.* and *Chorizococcus* sp.), that are occasionally trapped (see section 39, "Adult Male Mealybug Identification"). Setting up the delta traps properly, with the ends folded in, will help reduce the number of insects other than mealybugs in the trap, which makes the analysis easier.

Recording trap catches on a consistent, biweekly basis will permit relative changes in mealybug numbers to be seen as the season progresses. There are no economic thresholds based on trap counts of adult males, and numbers caught can vary greatly during the season and even between vineyards with similar mealybug densities. Trap counts of 10 or fewer mealybugs per trap per week are especially difficult to correlate to mealybugs in the block and may consist of males that were blown in from some distance away: males have been caught 750 m (2,460 ft) from the nearest infested vine. Because the males are not strong fliers and live for only a few days during the summer months, it is probable that they were transported by the wind. Conversely, traps placed close to an infested vine but upwind may have very low counts. Other factors that can lower trap catches in vineyards with moderate female populations are the mealybug sex ratio, which can be 95% female; pesticide applications, which can reduce the fragile, exposed adult males without greatly impacting the female population under the bark; old lures that were not properly stored (lures should be stored in a cooler or freezer until they are used); and seasonal changes, for example, unusually cold or hot periods can impact male trap captures. If only a few males are caught and the infested vines cannot be found, one suggested method of reducing the chance that males are from far away is to set out traps in the morning hours and to remove them before the wind picks up in the afternoon.

Traps help answer the important question "Is the vine mealybug present somewhere in my neighborhood?" If trap placement, catch numbers, timing, and other factors point to the likelihood that an infestation is nearby, the traps have done their job, and it is time to focus on finding the female mealybugs and preventing an increase in mealybug population density, damage, and movement. When managers of neighboring vineyards work together and share trapping results, it is more likely that infestations can be located.

Conventional Sampling
In most vineyards, finding and counting mealybugs using standard sampling programs is not cost efficient, especially when the population density is low. Mealybug populations spend much of the year hidden under bark and have a clumped distribution, meaning that thousands of mealybugs can be on one or two vines in the vineyard and very few will be found on nearby vines. For that reason, randomly selecting and sampling a specific number of vines per block is not an effective plan. Rather, population signals (see below) should be used to select vines for further search. Infestations become more apparent as harvest approaches. However, locating infested vines and reducing vine mealybug populations prior to picking fruit can reduce the movement of mealybugs to un-

infested areas of the vineyard that results from contaminated harvest equipment or infested leaves that are pulled off the vine. Fieldworkers should be trained to spot the signs of vine mealybug infestations at any time of the year and to mark infested vines while performing activities such as suckering, leaf removal, fruit thinning, harvest, and pruning.

Ants are closely associated with vine mealybugs, as they tend the pests for their honeydew. Look for ants actively moving up and down the vine trunk or along the cordon. Sample vines with high ant activity. Honeydew can also be a good signal of an infested vine. Vine mealybugs under the bark produce so much honeydew (sugary liquid waste excretion) that the infested region will have a darker, wet appearance. Strip back this bark and look for mealybugs. When mealybugs begin to move onto the leaves, their honeydew accumulates, making the leaf appear wet or shiny and providing a signal for further sampling on that vine. Black sooty mold may grow on the honeydew and provide further evidence of an infestation. When the mealybug numbers increase, their feeding damage may cause leaves to turn yellow, then brown, and finally drop from the vine. Look for dropped leaves under the canopy that have a dried appearance and use a hand lens to determine whether these leaves have mealybugs. If so, sample the nearby vines. The vine mealybug prefers to feed in the ripe fruit clusters. In winter, infested vines usually have black sooty mold on large portions of the cordons that is visible during pruning.

MANAGEMENT GUIDELINES

Economic Thresholds

No specific economic thresholds have been established for vine mealybug populations. Several factors make vine mealybug much more damaging and difficult to control than other common vineyard mealybugs. As a result, tolerance for any population level of vine mealybug has been set quite low.

- The vine mealybug reproduces at a higher rate than other species (more eggs per female and more generations per year), enabling small numbers of mealybugs to reach damaging levels in a single season.

- All life stages can be found on vines from May to November. This makes chemical control more difficult, as some insecticides are most effective against specific stages (primarily the younger stages).

- Vine mealybug produces much more honeydew than other species.

- Vine mealybug can feed on all parts of the vine throughout the year. By hiding under bark or on the roots, it is protected from most foliar insecticides and natural enemies. Such well-established populations may require repeated insecticide treatments to bring them to manageable levels.

- Vine mealybug has been reported to feed on subtropical (e.g., figs, citrus) and tropical (e.g., avocados, mangos) crops as well as a number of common weeds. These plants may provide a refuge for vine mealybugs to survive away from grapevines.

- Uncontrolled populations reduce crop quality and yield and may even result in vine death after years of uncontrolled infestations.

Cultural Controls and Habitat Management

Ant controls

Controlling vineyard ants can greatly reduce mealybug abundance and damage. Ant species vary in dominance in vineyard regions. The Argentine ant (*Linepithema humile* (Mayr)) is one of the world's more damaging invasive insects and is now commonly found in coastal vineyards and some northern interior wine grape locations. In San Joaquin Valley vineyards, the native gray ant (*Formica aerata* Francoeur) is most common, whereas in the Coachella Valley, *Formica peripilosa* Wheeler and *Solenopsis xyloni* McCook are the dominant vineyard ant species. All these ants tend vineyard mealybugs for their honeydew, some species more aggressively than others. The mutualistic association has clear benefits for the ants, which are provided with a carbohydrate food source, and ant tending has been credited with protecting mealybugs from natural enemies. For more on vineyard ants, see section 60, "Ants."

Cluster thinning

Clusters that touch the vine trunk or vine cordon have higher levels of mealybug damage. As the mealybugs move from the trunk and cordon to better feeding sites, ripening clusters touching the trunk or cordon are quickly infested. During thinning operations, clusters touching the trunk or cordon should be dropped or repositioned. Table grape growers can reduce mealybug infestations of clusters by structuring the trellis systems so that fruit clusters hang far from the trunk or cordon.

Bark stripping

Mealybugs feed underneath the bark of the trunk, cordon, spurs, and fruiting canes. These locations provide some protection from insecticides, natural enemies, and environmental conditions. Stripping the bark from the trunk and cordon exposes the mealybugs to these mortality factors. Common treatments after bark stripping include synthetic or organic pesticides, as well as flaming, to kill the mealybugs, or banding the trunk with a sticky barrier (e.g., Stickum or Tanglefoot) to reduce the movement of mealybugs and ants. While these techniques effectively lower mealybug density, they are labor intensive and costly.

Sticky barriers

Because mealybugs overwinter primarily on the trunk, cordon, canes, or spurs, they must move to the shoots, leaves, or clusters at some time during the season. In a commercial Flame Seedless vineyard, researchers covered each spur before budbreak with Tanglefoot, and in a commercial Thompson Seedless vineyard they placed a 5 cm (2 in) ring of Stickum around the upper trunk. In both vineyards, these temporary barriers prevented a significant number of mealybugs from moving up the vine and onto the leaves or clusters, but like bark stripping, the practice is labor intensive and costly.

Cover cropping

Cover crop systems have been used to improve soil health and lower pest densities by increasing natural enemy numbers or diversity (see section 35, "Variegated Grape Leafhopper"). There is little information on the impact of cover cropping for mealybug control, although a vetch-barley cover crop has been shown to reduce native gray ant activity on vines by providing vetch nectar as an alternate food source. The mealybug natural enemies most likely to benefit from cover cropping would be the parasitoids that could use the cover crop nectar as a food source to increase adult longevity and the generalist predators, such as lacewings and some lady beetle species, that could use other herbivores in the cover crop as an alternate food source. Which cover crop species should be planted specifically for optimal mealybug management is not known.

The vine mealybug can feed on a number of plant species, including some very common ground covers. The vine mealybug has been found on common weeds such as malva (*Malva parviflora*), burclover (*Medicago polymorpha*), black nightshade (*Solanum nigrum*), sowthistle (*Sonchus* spp.), and lambsquarters (*Chenopodium album*). Whether these are temporary feeding sites or reproductive hosts is not known. In California vineyards, both the obscure mealybug and the vine mealybug have been found on the roots of many broadleaf weeds.

Vine vigor

Overly vigorous vines can increase mealybug populations in two ways. First, excess nitrogen has been shown to increase the size of mealybug females and the number of eggs in each ovisac. Second, the increased foliage associated with overly vigorous vines provides better shelter for the mealybugs by reducing temperatures inside the vine canopy and may also reduce the amount of applied foliar insecticide that reaches the mealybugs.

Grape cultivars

Mealybug populations, in the absence of proper management practices or natural controls, increase during the season in the San Joaquin Valley, coastal, Sacramento Valley, and Sierra foothill regions. Therefore, cultivars with later harvest dates have fruit clusters that are exposed to mealybugs for a longer period. In some regions, cultivars with an early harvest date may not need an in-season application to keep mealybugs out of the cluster, which is harvested before the mealybugs move from the trunk and into the cluster.

Limiting Dispersal

An important component of vine mealybug management is preventing further spread and reinfestation of vines. Some grape-growing regions implement localized eradication of the vine mealybug, and every region should strive to reduce mealybug spread. As discussed previously, dispersion of vine mealybug throughout the state was aided by infested equipment and nursery material. In response, university researchers and the nursery industry developed protocols to reduce the incidence of infested dormant cuttings moving through the nursery production process, including the use of hot water immersions of dormant grape cuttings and rootings. Today, commercial nurseries use a 5-minute immersion in each of three water tanks: preheating at 30°C (86°F); hot water at 52.8°C (127°F); and cooling at 23°C (73.4°F). In tests, this commercial procedure provided 99.8 to 100% mealybug control. Nursery practices also include insecticide applications to green-growing plants and nursery mother blocks. State regulations do not require nurseries to take all these steps, so it is prudent for buyers to discuss vine mealybug control practices prior to purchasing plants. Furthermore, while hot water treatments for dormant wood can provide excellent control, insecticide treatments of green-growing plants have not yet been thoroughly tested.

Because of better nursery controls, the movement of vine mealybug on nursery stock is now less of an issue than it was prior to 2003. Currently, vine mealybug dispersal most commonly occurs as a result of natural spread from infested vines (e.g., wind, birds) and the movement of contaminated fruit, vineyard equipment, and workers. Leaves that fall from infested vines may still support a large number of vine mealybugs. Over 1,000 small mealybugs have been counted on a single dislodged leaf. These leaves are easily blown by the wind or moved by equipment. As the leaf dries, the mealybugs crawl off the leaf and

onto the nearest vegetation (often ground covers). Many find their way onto vines.

Wind is also important in the direct spread of mealybugs, especially the small crawlers. These first-instar mealybugs are very mobile, lightweight, and shaped like an elongate-oval disc. On heavily infested vines, crawlers seek better feeding sites, and many move up onto the more exposed leaves to feed, where the wind can catch and carry them. Birds and rodents have also been implicated in natural spread of vine mealybugs between sites.

The sticky nature of the honeydew produced by vine mealybug greatly facilitates its spread. All parts of the vine get very sticky: leaves, shoots, berries, clusters, cordons, and trunks. Adult insects, nymphs, and eggs can get stuck to tractors, bins, picking pans, and gloves, for example, and be moved to other locations. Machine harvesters pose a significant risk because they operate in vineyards when mealybug populations are high and on the leaves and fruit clusters. The harvesters have considerable contact with foliage and are frequently moved from vineyard to vineyard. If operated in an infested block and then moved without thorough cleaning, mealybug spread can easily occur. Operators need to be made aware of any vine mealybug infestations in blocks they are harvesting, and growers should discuss equipment sanitation practices if using a contract harvesting service. Similarly, mechanical pruning and leaf removal can contribute to distribution throughout a vineyard and to

other vineyards if machinery is not cleaned.

Grape clusters harvested from infested vineyards can also lead to spread of vine mealybug if stems and press loads are spread back into vineyards. Research has shown that mealybugs can survive whole cluster pressing. However, if fresh pomace (the unfermented skins, seeds, and stems) is securely covered with clear plastic for a week, the population of vine mealybug is significantly reduced because the mealybugs are killed by the heat. Cluster stems (generated from a crusher-destemmer) will likely still contain mealybug eggs and larvae as well. Composting infested stems and pomace at an appropriate distance from vines should provide adequate control, as long as the composting process follows state regulations and proper temperatures are reached within the compost piles (above 54.4°C, or 130°F) for specified time periods. Further research is needed to confirm the effects of composting on winery waste infested with vine mealybug.

Mating Disruption

Female mealybugs produce a sex pheromone, and the winged adult male mealybugs can follow the odor plume to the females. Mating disruption uses this behavior to prevent males from finding females and successfully mating. This is accomplished by applying synthetic sex pheromone to the treated field in amounts that are millions of times greater than that produced naturally by the insects. Males cannot locate females because the sex pheromone plume is hidden in a fog of synthetic sex pheromone.

Although mating disruption studies are still ongoing, several factors may contribute to the success of this approach. The adult males are short-lived and are poor fliers; the synthetic sex pheromone is relatively inexpensive to produce (compared with that of other mealybug species) and is very attractive to male mealybugs; there is a seasonal flight period (typically from April to October); and vines are low and relatively compact (as compared with large trees), so coverage with a synthetic sex pheromone might be more complete than with tree crops. Researchers have also observed increased levels of parasitization in vineyards with mating disruption and hypothesize that the sex pheromone increases activity of *Anagyrus pseudococci* searching for vine mealybug.

In field trials, the synthetic sex pheromone was applied in a sprayable microencapsulated formulation and also in plastic membrane dispensers. The sprayable formulation provided better coverage on the vine. This may be critical as the mealybug population is clumped together and males often need to travel only a short distance to find females. The disadvantage is that the sprayable formulation tested had a very short residual time, lasting about 21 to 28 days in San Joaquin Valley trials before reapplication was needed. The membrane dispensers last the entire season, but there is less control of the release of the synthetic pheromone. Mating disruption was most effective when the mealybug density was low, suggesting that for best results

a combination of an insecticide application and mating disruption may be necessary, at least initially.

Insecticide Management

Vine mealybug is often the target of numerous insecticide applications annually. Table grapes have a low threshold for fruit infestation, and because mealybugs can also vector grapevine leafroll associated viruses, wine grapes in cool-climate regions may also require similar low tolerance levels to prevent virus spread. Some regions have also attempted to locally eradicate the vine mealybug, but success so far has been observed only in a limited number of vineyards with high rates of insecticide treatments under conditions conducive to insecticide efficacy.

In the 1990s, the recommended insecticide program for vineyard mealybugs was a delayed-dormant organophosphate insecticide and in-season application(s) of a short-residual organophosphate or carbamate. Although these insecticides can provide adequate vine mealybug control, their repeated use may also kill vineyard natural enemies, reducing the level of biological control for all pests. The recent development of novel insecticides has greatly improved mealybug control programs, while diminishing the negative impacts on other insect species. Some of the alternative materials include the neonicotinoid insecticides, insect growth regulators, and short-residual enzyme inhibitors. For updated information on registered materials, see the UC IPM Grape Pest Management Guidelines, www.ipm.ucdavis.edu/PMG/.

Several products are very effective against the vine mealybug, but application timing and delivery are critical to successful control. For example, most insecticidal soaps can kill mealybug crawlers, but their residual activity is very short and the mealybug egg hatch can last for weeks, initially, and then months. Once overlapping generations develop during the late-summer months, the timing of multiple soap sprays makes this material impractical for most operations. Mealybugs located under the bark or on the roots are very difficult to kill with a foliar application of products that do not have a fuming action; however, the recent focus on volatile organic compounds (VOCs), which contribute to the formation of ground-level ozone, may result in the reduced use of these compounds. Drip irrigation greatly improved the effectiveness of a soil-applied neonicotinoid insecticide compared with furrow irrigation. The establishment of baseline susceptibilities to insecticides is an important element of a proactive resistance management program.

Resistance management

When treatment decisions are made, insecticide selection must take into account resistance management. It is important to use insecticides only when needed and to time applications against the most susceptible portion of the vine mealybug population. Using different types of insecticides during the season can help to prevent the development of resistant populations.

REFERENCES

Bentley, W. J., L. G. Varela, and K. M. Daane. 2005. Grapes, insects, ecology and control. In D. Pimental, ed., Encyclopedia of pest management. doi: 10.1081/E-EPM-120041132. New York: Taylor & Francis. 1–8.

Bentley, W. J., L. G. Varela, F. G. Zalom, R. J. Smith, A. H. Purcell, P. A. Phillips, D. R. Haviland, K. M. Daane, and M. C. Battany. 2008. Insects and mites. In University of California IPM Grape pest management guidelines. Oakland: University of California Division of Agriculture and Natural Resources Publication 3448. UC IPM website, www.ipm.ucdavis.edu/PMG/.

Daane, K. M., W. J. Bentley, V. M. Walton, R. Malakar-Kuenen, J. G. Millar, C. A. Ingels, E. A. Weber, and C. Gispert. 2006. New controls investigated for vine mealybug. California Agriculture 60(1): 31–38.

Daane, K. M., M. L. Cooper, S. V. Triapitsyn, J. W. Andrews Jr., and R. Ripa. 2008. Parasitoids of obscure mealybug, *Pseudococcus viburni* (Signoret) (Hemiptera: Pseudococcidae) in California vineyards: Establishment of *Pseudaphycus flavidulus* (Brèthes) (Hymenoptera: Encyrtidae) and discussion of reared parasitoid species. BioControl Science and Technology 18:43–57.

Daane, K. M., M. L. Cooper, S. V. Triapitsyn, V. M. Walton, G. Y. Yokota, D. R. Haviland, W. J. Bentley, K. E. Godfrey, and L. R. Wunderlich. 2008. California vineyard managers and researchers seek sustainable solutions for mealybugs, a changing pest complex. California Agriculture. 62(4): 167–176.

Daane, K. M., R. Malakar-Kuenen, and V. M. Walton. 2004. Temperature development of *Anagyrus pseudococci* (Hymenoptera: Encyrtidae) as a parasitoid of the vine mealybug, *Planococcus ficus* (Homoptera: Pseudococcidae). Biological Control 31(1): 123–132.

Godfrey, K. E., K. M. Daane, W. J. Bentley, R. J. Gill, and R. Malakar-Kuenen. 2002. Mealybug in California vineyards. Oakland: University of California Division of Agriculture and Natural Resources Publication 21612.

Haviland, D. R., W. J. Bentley, and K. M. Daane. 2005. Hot water treatments to control *Planococcus ficus* (Hemiptera: Pseudococcidae) in grape nursery stock. Journal of Economic Entomology 98(4): 1109–1115.

Millar, J. G., K. M. Daane, J. S. McElfresh, J. Moreira, R. Malakar-Kuenen, M. Guillen, and W. J. Bentley. 2002. Development and optimization of methods for using sex pheromone for monitoring the mealybug *Planococcus ficus* (Homoptera: Pseudococcidae) in California vineyards. Journal of Economic Entomology 95(4): 706–714.

Walton, V. M., K. M. Daane, W. J. Bentley, J. G. Millar, T. E. Larsen, and R. Malakar-Kuenen. 2006. Pheromone-based mating disruption of *Planococcus ficus* (Hemiptera: Pseudococcidae) in California vineyards. Journal of Economic Entomology 99(4): 1280–1290.

Walton, V. M., K. M. Daane, and K. L. Pringle. 2004. Utilizing the sex pheromone of *Planococcus ficus* to improve pest management in South African vineyards. Crop Protection 23:1089–1096.

Hemiptera
Aphids,
Leafhoppers,
Mealybugs, Scales,
True Bugs,
Whiteflies

39 ADULT MALE MEALYBUG IDENTIFICATION

Lucia G. Varela

In mealybug insects, the nymphs and adult females are similar in appearance. However, the adult males are very different in shape from the immatures and females, having the three distinct body divisions (head, thorax, and abdomen) typical of most other insects, three pairs of fully functional legs, and one pair of wings. The adult males of most mealybugs are very small, only about a third or less the size of the adult females of the same species.

Mealybug females produce a pheromone (a species-specific scent) that allows the adult males to locate them. Research has identified the pheromone for vine, grape, longtailed, and obscure mealybugs. Vine and grape mealybug pheromone lures are commercially available and are used in red delta traps to monitor for males. Each lure is specific for the targeted mealybug. Using red delta traps (with closed ends leaving small openings) reduces the number of other species entering the trap, since insects are not drawn to red as they are to yellow traps. However, other male mealybug species are occasionally caught on the traps, and it is important to be able to distinguish them. Correct identification is critical when using the traps to determine whether a species is present at a new location. A microscope with 30× magnification is required for proper identification.

The adult males of armored and soft scale insects can be easily distinguished from adult male mealybugs by the shape of the male genital capsule at the tip of the abdomen. The male genital capsule of the soft scale insects is elongated, and in the armored scales, it is almost as long as the rest of the abdomen (fig. 39.1). The terminal structure (genital capsule) of the adult male of mealybug species is short and triangular.

The adult male mealybug is amber brown. It has one pair of wings, but they may not be visible if they are embedded in the trap stickum. The thorax is wider than the abdomen, and the antennae are beaded. The triangular genital capsule has an opening on the ventral side through which the aedeagus (male copulatory organ) is extruded. Some character differences between species can be distinguished while in the trap stickum. However, to identify differences on the genital capsule or the type of setae (hairs), it is necessary to remove the specimen from the trap, clean away the stickum, and mount the adult male on a microscope slide.

The vine mealybug male (*Planococcus ficus* Signoret) is approximately 0.8 mm (0.03 in) long. The antennae are as long as the head and thorax. The length of each leg is approximately 60% of the body length. On each side of the eighth abdominal segment is a pair of caudal setae (tail

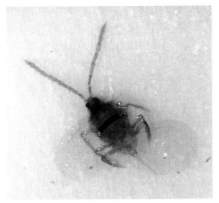

Figure 39.1 Armored scale adult male with long genitalia capsule. *Photo*: B. Grafton-Cardwell.

filaments). When they land on the stickum, the two setae on each side appear as one dark hair, thus the setal pairs are visible through the stickum as though one filament. The genital capsule appears as a triangle with sides of equal size (fig. 39.2) with two lobes whose setae are inwardly directed toward the capsule opening.

The grape mealybug (*Pseudococcus maritimus* (Ehrhorn)) male cannot be morphologically distinguished from the obscure mealybug (*Pseudococcus viburni* (Signoret)) male. The pheromone is specific for each species. In the laboratory, grape mealybug pheromone does not attract obscure mealybug males, and vice versa. If a grape mealybug lure is used, the males caught that look like either grape or obscure mealybug are probably grape mealybug. However, if either of these species males blunders into traps with a vine or longtailed mealybug lure, it can be differentiated from the targeted male, but the exact species cannot be ascertained. The males of grape and obscure mealybugs are about 0.8 mm (0.03 in) long, and the length of the antennae and legs as well as the caudal filaments are similar to those of vine mealybug. The genital capsule is longer on the sides than at the base, and the distal end of the genital capsule covering the tip of the aedeagus is broad and rounded (fig. 39.3).

Longtailed mealybug (*Pseudococcus longispinus* (Targioni Tozzetti)) has long, fleshy setae on the thorax and abdomen, along with hairlike setae. The distal end of the genital capsule is apically truncated (fig. 39.4).

Vine mealybug lures have been available since 2002, enabling growers and researchers to acquire more field experience with them than with other mealybug lures. The adult male mealybugs most commonly found accidentally in vine mealybug traps are grass mealybugs of the genus *Phenacoccus*, grape and obscure mealybugs, and bermudagrass mealybug (genus *Chorizococcus*). None of these species are attracted to the vine mealybug traps. Thus, with the exception of *Phenacoccus*, when they accidentally enter a trap they are found in low numbers, fewer than 10 per trap. On occasion adult males of *Phenacoccus* have been found in large numbers, but they can be distinguished readily from other mealybugs while still on the trap.

The *Phenacoccus* adult male mealybug is about 1 mm (0.04 in) long, slightly larger than vine mealybug or *Pseudococcus* mealybug males (fig. 39.5). The antennae are as long as the body. The legs are approximately 85% of its body length and are longer than vine mealybug legs. They do have a pair of caudal setae on abdominal segments seven and eight, but these caudal setae are not visible in the stickum. The genital capsule is narrow and pointed.

Adult males of *Chorizococcus* species have short, fleshy setae on most antennal segments (fig. 39.6); these setae are much shorter and broader than the hairlike setae on the antennal segments of other mealybug males.

REFERENCES

Gill, R. 2004. Guide to the identification of common adult male mealybugs. California Department of Food and Agriculture Plant Pest Diagnostics Branch. Misc. Training Guide.

Millar, J. G., K. M. Daane, J. S. McElfresh, J. A. Moreira, and W. J. Bentley. 2005. Chemistry and applications of mealybug sex pheromones. In R. Petroski, ed., Semiochemicals in pest management and alternative agriculture. ACS Symposium Series 906. Washington, D.C.: American Chemical Society. 11–27.

Millar, J. G., K. M. Daane, J. S. McElfresh, J. A. Moreira, R. Malakar-Kuenen, M. Guillen, and W. J. Bentley. 2002. Development and optimization of methods for using sex pheromone for monitoring the mealybug *Planococcus ficus* (Homoptera: Pseudococcidae) in California vineyards. Journal of Economic Entomology 95(4): 706–714.

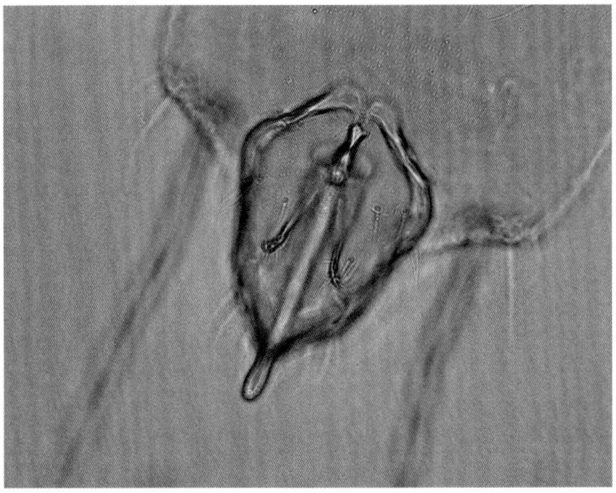

Figure 39.2 Vine mealybug genitalia capsule is triangular, with all sides approximately equal in length; also, two lobes with setae inwardly directed toward the capsule opening. *Photo*: W. J. Bentley.

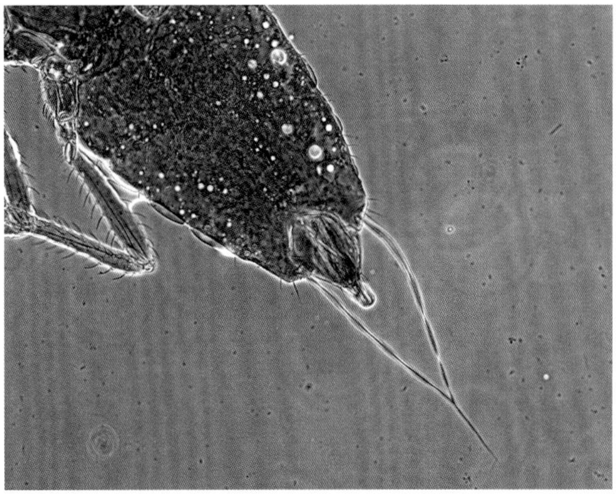

Figure 39.3 Grape or obscure mealybug male genitalia capsule is triangular, with the sides longer than the base; also, distal end broad and round. *Photo*: W. J. Bentley.

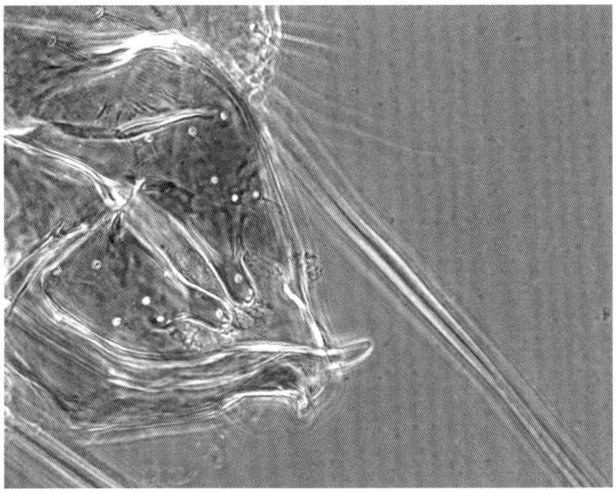

Figure 39.4 Longtailed mealybug genital capsule is apically truncated. *Photo*: W. J. Bentley.

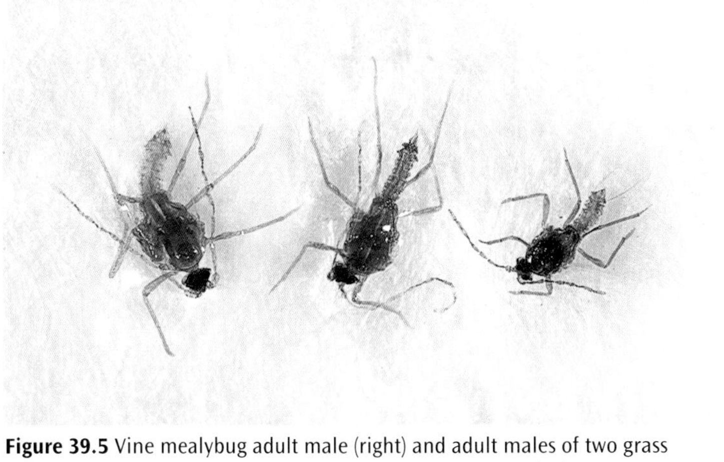

Figure 39.5 Vine mealybug adult male (right) and adult males of two grass mealybugs (*Phenacoccus* spp.) (center and left). *Photo*: J. K. Clark.

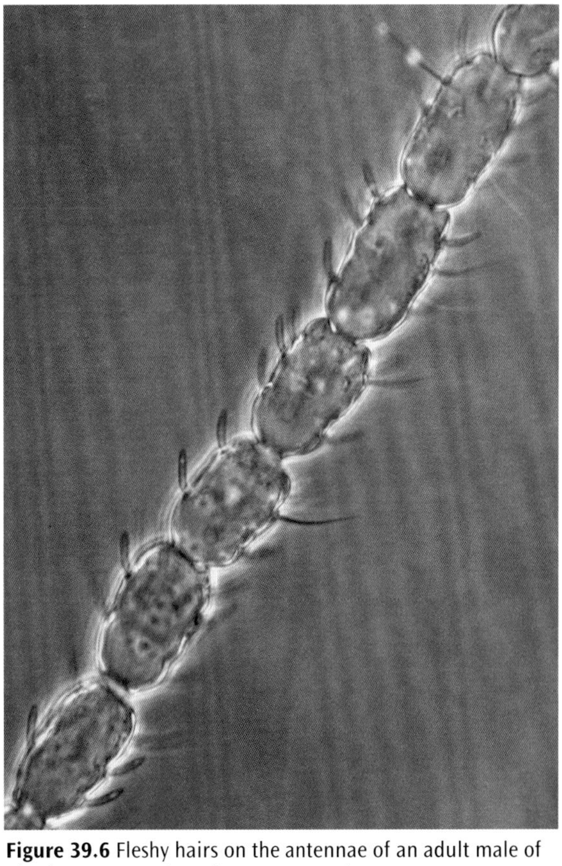

Figure 39.6 Fleshy hairs on the antennae of an adult male of *Chorizococcus* species. *Photo*: L. G. Varela.

Hemiptera
Aphids,
Leafhoppers,
Mealybugs, Scales,
True Bugs,
Whiteflies

40 *FERRISIA* (GILL'S MEALYBUG)

David R. Haviland, Lynn R. Wunderlich, and Kent M. Daane

Gill's mealybug (*Ferrisia gilli* Gullan) (Hemiptera: Pseudococcidae) is most commonly a pest of deciduous trees and shrubs but has become an emerging pest in vineyards in the Sierra foothills and the northern coast (Lake County). The pest was first documented in California in the late 1990s in a pistachio orchard in Tulare County. It was initially considered to be the striped mealybug (*Ferrisia virgata* (Cockerell)); however, differences in adult morphology and its biological importance prompted a closer examination. The mealybug was soon described as a new species (*F. gilli*). Since the initial description in 2003, it has been found in 12 California counties and recorded as a pest in pistachios, almonds, persimmons, fruitless mulberry, and grapes. The Gill's mealybug probably has a greater distribution in California, but prior to 2003 it may have been misidentified as the striped mealybug. Generally, infestations in vineyards have been rare; however, studies conducted from 2008 to 2011 have shown that Gill's mealybug appears to be spreading in El Dorado County vineyards and that the full potential for its range expansion is not known. Gill's mealybug can be controlled using insecticide programs that are timed for the mealybug immature stages as they move onto leaves, where it is most exposed to spray coverage, as well as through the action of natural enemies that can provide biological control in grape production systems.

DESCRIPTION

Adult female Gill's mealybugs are flat and oval; their body is faded pink and covered with white wax (fig. 40.1). Wax patterns on the body surface give it a striped appearance. Gill's mealybug can be distinguished from other grape-infesting mealybugs in that it has no lateral filaments and has two broad white tails (caudal filaments) that can be up to half the body length. More distinctive is that the Gill's mealybugs are often covered by white, crystalline filaments 5 to 10 mm (0.2 to 0.4 in) long that have the appearance of long, glassy rods. Adult males are rarely seen in the field; they are very small, less than 2 mm (0.08 in) long, and have wings. Gill's mealybug, like the longtailed mealybug (see section 37, "*Pseudococcus* Mealybugs"), is ovoviviparous, holding the eggs in the reproductive tract and giving birth to first-instar mealybugs rather than depositing eggs. As crawlers are born they remain for a few days underneath the protection of the adult female and mass of glasslike rods (fig. 40.2). They then

Figure 40.1 Adult female Gill's mealybug. *Photo*: D. R. Haviland.

disperse to better feeding sites and continue their development. The crawlers are tiny and orange and are indistinguishable from those of other mealybug species. Immature mealybugs pass through several developmental stages, with each successive instar resembling the previous, but slighter larger. These nymphal stages can also be covered by the glasslike filaments.

INJURY

Gill's mealybugs are primarily phloem feeders that insert their mouthparts into plant tissues to suck out liquids. During the summer they feed under the bark of permanent and fruiting wood, on leaves, and, eventually, within the fruit cluster, contaminating the crop and and making grape clusters unmarketable. High populations of mealybugs on the vine may render much of the crop unmarketable due to excessive amounts of honeydew and sooty mold (as well as the mealybugs themselves) contaminating the fruit. Laboratory studies done in 2011 found that Gill's mealybug is

Figure 40.2 Adult female Gill's mealybug produces crawlers that initially remain underneath the adult female, then begin to move out on their own. *Photo*: K. M. Daane.

able to acquire and transmit grapevine leafroll associated virus strain 3 (GLRaV-3).

SEASONAL DEVELOPMENT

Gill's mealybug phenology and development were studied from 2008 to 2011 in El Dorado County vineyards. There, Gill's mealybug produced two broods of crawlers and completed two generations. In foothill vineyards, Gill's mealybug overwinters as nymphs (second to third instars), and by May late-instar nymphs and adult females are found under the bark of arms and spurs and at the base of new shoots. After mating occurs, adult females spin a filamentous waxy sac and begin to produce crawlers in late June to early July. These crawlers pass through their nymphal development, moving out to leaves and giving rise to adults during late July to early August. A portion of the mealybug population moves into grape clusters beginning in July, but most of the mealybugs return under the bark of arms and spurs. From late August to September, a second generation of crawlers is produced by adult females, and these crawlers develop into older nymphs during the fall, moving from the spurs to leaves and clusters. Depending on vineyard location and temperature, a partial third generation may be produced in fall. Late-instar nymphs overwinter under bark on the trunk and migrate in spring up to the cordons and arms. Honeydew production was observed to be most evident in late summer.

In studies in pistachios in the San Joaquin Valley, Gill's mealybug has three fairly discrete generations: the first summer generation

from early June to mid-July, the summer and fall generation from mid-July through September, and the third generation beginning in September with crawlers that molt to older overwintering nymphs that develop to the adult stage in May.

NATURAL CONTROL

Natural enemies in California can provide effective control of Gill's mealybug. The most important are small encyrtid wasps, parasitoids in the genus *Acerophagus*, that typically attack the second and third instars of the mealybug. These parasitoids have been naturally found to be associated with Gill's mealybug infestations in almond and persimmon orchards in Tulare County and vineyards surveyed in El Dorado County. Observations suggest that they can be quite effective and can suppress Gill's mealybug populations within several years after their arrival. Parasitized mealybugs, most commonly found under the grapevine trunk bark in early spring and in untreated clusters prior to harvest in the fall, can be distinguished as mummies that turn yellow to amber brown and do not move. The mealybug is dead at this time, and the parasitoid larva or larvae are developing inside; the adult parasitoid pupates inside the mummified mealybug and eventually chews an exit hole through the mummy and emerges.

Other biological control organisms also help in the control efforts. These include two additional parasitoids in the genera *Chrysoplatycerus* and *Anagyrus* as well as several species of generalist predators. These predators include green lacewings and a small brown cocci-nellid (ladybird) beetle whose larva mimics the appearance of a mealy-bug. To date, this beetle has not been identified, though it is a close relative of the mealybug destroyer (*Cryptolaemus montrouzieri* Mul-sant), which can be common in vineyards.

Research has not yet been con-ducted to provide clear guidelines on the optimal conditions for bio-logical control of Gill's mealybug. It is known, however, that common insecticides used in pistachios, particularly permethrin-based materials, have a detrimental impact on biological control, whereas certain other insecticides, such as insect growth regulators and lipid biosynthesis inhibitors, have minimal impacts on Gill's mealybug natural enemies. Leav-ing a few vineyard rows completely untreated, if possible, has been shown to conserve the parasitoids present in most vineyards.

Monitoring Guidelines

Gill's mealybug can be found under the bark of spurs and arms in early spring. By mid to late May, adult females move to the base of new vine growth (fig. 40.3). This is an ideal time to monitor, since shoot-thinning crews can be trained to identify the relatively large adult females at the base of growing shoots, and these vines can then be flagged and revisited to look for the crawlers. By late June to early July, the mealybug crawlers move for a brief period out onto leaves to feed. The crawler stage is the most vulnerable to insecti-cide treatment, and leaves should be monitored during this period to effectively time treatments.

Unless the infestation is heavy, Gill's mealybug does not tend to produce large amounts of hon-eydew until late summer and fall, when the mealybugs are easiest to find. Look for honeydew and ants on the vines as indications that mealybugs are present. Be sure to identify the species of mealybug, since all produce honeydew and have associations with ants. If har-vest is done by hand, train harvest crews to flag infested clusters or those that are suspect, since most mealybugs will be within the clus-ter during harvest. Parasitization levels are also easy to assess at this time by looking for emergence holes in mummies found within the clusters.

Management Guidelines

Manage Gill's mealybug by not dis-rupting biological control with broad-spectrum insecticides. In cases where biological control does not provide sufficient control, consider making an insecticide treatment. Applications of a regis-tered insect growth regulator are highly effective if used in late June

to early July, when the majority of the crawlers of the first summer generation have emerged from underneath the adult females and migrated to the leaves. Treatments targeting the second generation are not as effective. If insecticide applications are well timed, it is likely that treatment for Gill's mealybug will be warranted only once every few years, as mealybugs require time to build noticeable populations in the canopy and clusters. Other insecticides that are effective on vine, grape, obscure, or longtailed mealybug are also effec-tive, although these materials may be detrimental to natural enemies.

References:

Haviland, D., R. Beede, K. Godfrey, and K. Daane. 2006. *Ferrisia gilli*: A new mealybug pest of pistachios and other deciduous crops. University of Califor-nia Division of Agriculture and Natural Resources Publication 8207. UC ANR Communication Services website, http://anrcat-alog.ucdavis.edu/pdf/8207.pdf.

Figure 40.3 Adult female Gill's mealybug moves out to the base of shoots in the spring (May). This is an ideal time to monitor before crawlers are produced. *Photo*: L. R. Wunderlich.

Hemiptera
*Aphids,
Leafhoppers,
Mealybugs, Scales,
True Bugs,
Whiteflies*

41 *RHIZOECUS* (GROUND MEALYBUG)

David R. Haviland

Several species of ground mealybugs belonging to the genus *Rhizoecus* (Hemiptera: Pseudococcidae) have been reported in California. The two species most widespread and economically important are *Rhizoecus falcifer* Künckel d'Herculais, found mostly along the coast from San Diego to Humboldt County, and *Rhizoecus kondonis* Kuwana, found in Sonoma, Sutter, San Joaquin, Contra Costa, and Yolo Counties. Both species are similar in activity, host range, and seasonal development.

Considered a minor pest of grapes, ground mealybug has not been found in commercial vineyard plantings and has been found only occasionally in home or backyard plantings of grapes. Knowing that both species feed on grape roots and that they are occasionally capable of causing serious economic losses to other commercial crops in close proximity to vineyards makes them suspect for possible injury to commercial grape plantings. Ground mealybugs have been found to be feeding on many other plants, including grasses, broadleaved annuals, citrus, cacti, and shrubs.

DESCRIPTION

Ground mealybug is a white, small, slender insect 2 to 3 mm (0.1 in) long (fig. 41.1). Along with vine mealybug, it is the only mealybug species on grapes that is found belowground. However, unlike vine and other aerial (aboveground) species, they have no waxy rods or filaments projecting from the body surface. The body, covered uniformly with a white, waxy powder, has no longitudinal depressions or fringe. The internal body liquid is light colored compared with the pink, reddish brown, green, wine purple, or amber of other mealybugs. The antennae are noticeably short and small and have five segments. With a hand lens, the insects can be seen as small, sluggish, flattened, elongate, oval bodies thinly covered with a white, powdery wax.

Figure 41.1 Adult female ground mealybug. *Photo:* J. K. Clark.

ACTUAL SIZE: GROUND MEALYBUG

Adult Female

267

Injury

These entirely subterranean mealybugs insert their slender mouthparts into small feeder roots and suck out liquids. Where large numbers are found feeding on roots of trees, shrubs, vines, or grasses, they are suspected of causing the decline of these plants. Loss of feeder roots has resulted in zinc and potassium deficiencies; introduction of root rot pathogens may follow root injury, causing further loss.

Seasonal Development

Little is known about the life cycle of ground mealybugs, but both nymphs and adults are found all year in infested areas.

Natural Control

There is very little information on natural control of ground mealybugs.

Monitoring Guidelines

Monitoring should be based on examining weakened grapevines under stress, considering all possible causes, such as nematodes, pathogens, irrigation, soil types, and insects. When looking for ground mealybugs, look for white, waxy powder masses in the soil or around roots of vines.

Management Guidelines

There is no known economic treatment threshold for ground mealybugs. Plants growing in areas where frequent summer and fall irrigations are practiced may not be susceptible to attack. California's San Joaquin and Sacramento Valleys, where frequent summer irrigations are applied, would have less chance of damaging infestations than would north coast and central coast areas.

Chemical control of ground mealybug has not been necessary in commercial vineyards in California. Where infestations have been found in nursery plantings and backyard vines, insecticide drenches have successfully controlled this insect. Preplant soil fumigation in nurseries is also effective.

Hemiptera
*Aphids,
Leafhoppers,
Mealybugs, Scales,
True Bugs,
Whiteflies*

42 *MACONELLICOCCUS* (PINK HIBISCUS MEALYBUG)

Larry J. Bettiga

The pink hibiscus mealybug (*Maconellicoccus hirsutus* (Green)) (Hemiptera: Pseudococcidae) is a serious pest on a wide range of hosts in tropical and subtropical regions of the world. It is established in Africa, Asia, Australia, South America, the Caribbean Islands, the northern Mexicali Valley in Mexico, Hawaii, Florida, and the southern Imperial Valley of California. A wide range of economically important hosts makes this insect a potential pest of grape if introduced into the growing regions of California.

DESCRIPTION

The adult female is about 2 to 3 mm (0.1 in) long; after molting it is lightly covered by white waxy excretions with a reddish to brown body color (fig. 42.1). In contrast to other mealybug species found on grape, this mealybug does not have waxy filaments around the lateral margins of the body and has two very short caudal filaments. Females lay eggs in a white ovisac that has an outer layer of matted fibers. Eggs are 0.35 mm (0.014 in) long. Newly laid eggs are orange but turn pink just prior to hatching. After hatching, females have three nymphal instars. Males have four nymphal instars, the first two appearing similar to female nymphs. At the end of the second instar, males form a cottony cocoon (puparium) in which the third (prepupal) and the fourth (pupal) stages develop. The adult male is the only stage with wings. It is about 1.5 mm (0.06 in) long, with a pinkish body. Males have opaque wings that extend well beyond the abdomen and a long pair of white caudal filaments.

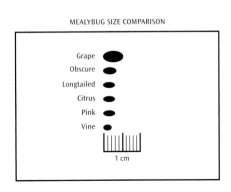

MEALYBUG SIZE COMPARISON

Grape
Obscure
Longtailed
Citrus
Pink
Vine

1 cm

Figure 42.1 Pink hibiscus mealybug adults (some with ovisacs) and crawlers. *Photo*: J. K. Clark.

INJURY

Where pink hibiscus mealybug is present on grape, feeding on the foliage and fruit can result in stunting, fruit contamination from honeydew and subsequent mold growth (fig. 42.2), and shriveling of heavily infested clusters.

SEASONAL DEVELOPMENT

Pink hibiscus mealybug overwinters in its various life stages in protected parts of the host plant. After hatching, the motile crawlers move to feeding sites to begin their development. Nymphs develop into adults in approximately 30 days. Regional temperatures affect the number of generations per year: a range of 3 to 10 generations has been estimated for California grape-producing regions. As temperatures become cooler, the females search for protected areas to lay their eggs.

NATURAL CONTROL

The parasitoid wasps *Anagyrus kamali* Moursi (Encyrtidae), *Gyranusoidea indica* Shafee, Alam and Agarwal (Encyrtidae), and *Allotropa* sp. nr *mecrida* (Walker)

(Platygastridae) have been released in the Imperial Valley. This biological control effort has reduced the populations of pink hibiscus mealybug to low levels.

The mealybug destroyer (*Cryptolaemus montrouzieri* Mulsant) (Coccinellidae) is the most well known predator that feeds on pink hibiscus mealybug. For more information on general predators of mealybugs, see section 38, "*Planococcus* Mealybugs."

MONITORING GUIDELINES

No specific monitoring guidelines have been developed for grape. A sex pheromone specific for pink hibiscus mealybug males has been developed. Pheromone traps can be an effective tool in determining the presence of mealybugs. Visual survey and identification is critical for pest detection.

MANAGEMENT GUIDELINES

Mealybugs are spread by wind, birds, ants, or more commonly the movement of infested plant material and equipment into noninfested areas. For more information on sanitation practices, see section 38, "*Planococcus* Mealybugs."

When mealybugs are found in a vineyard, it is important to identify which species are present. If you find adult mealybugs with no waxy filaments around the lateral margins of the body with two very short caudal filaments, it could be a new infestation of pink hibiscus mealybug. A sample that includes adult females should be submitted to the local University of California Cooperative Extension office or the county agricultural commisioner for identification.

REFERENCES

Godfrey, K. E., K. M. Daane, W. J. Bentley, R. J. Gill, and R. Malakar-Kuenen. 2002. Mealybugs in California vineyards. Oakland: University of California Division of Agriculture and Natural Resources Publication 21612.

Roltsch, B. J., D. E. Meyerdirk, R. Warkentin, et al. 2006. Classical biological control of the pink hibiscus mealybug, *Maconellicoccus hirsutus* (Green), in southern California. Biological Control 37:155–166.

Figure 42.2 A pink hibiscus mealybug infestation on a branch with two ants attending the mealybugs. *Photo*: J. K. Clark.

Hemiptera
Aphids,
Leafhoppers,
Mealybugs, Scales,
True Bugs,
Whiteflies

43 MINOR CICADA

Philip A. Phillips

Cicadas (Hemiptera: Cicadidae) are well known because of the loud clicking or buzzing noises they make on warm summer afternoons. Although everyone has heard them, few have seen them despite their large size. When approached, they dodge around a limb away from the observer. One of the smaller species, the minor cicada (*Platypedia minor* Uhler), occasionally injures grapes.

DESCRIPTION

Minor cicada adults are about 19 mm (0.75 in) long with black or bronze-black bodies and two pairs of large, colorless, transparent wings (fig. 43.1). They produce a loud, rapid, high-pitched whining sound that gradually increases in intensity and then suddenly stops.

INJURY

Females cause damage during egg laying. Each puncture of the grape cane is made conspicuous by slivers of wood protruding from it. Whether the young cicadas feed on grape roots has not been proven. They do feed on French prune roots, and when both prunes and grapes are available the females prefer to lay their eggs in grapes. This would indicate that young cicadas probably do feed on the vine roots.

Figure 43.1 Adult cicada female (Okanagana spp.), found in a central coast vineyard, is similar in size to the minor cicada. *Photo*: L. J. Bettiga.

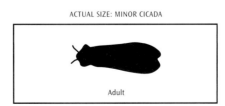

ACTUAL SIZE: MINOR CICADA

Adult

SEASONAL DEVELOPMENT

Egg laying begins late in April when the adults emerge. Females are provided with a strong, saw-toothed rod on the hind end of their abdomen with which they can drill holes into the hardest wood. They drill holes into grape canes to prepare niches to hold their eggs. After a hole has been cut, the female lays four or five eggs in it, then moves forward about a quarter of an inch and repeats the performance, until a row of 5 to 10 such punctures results.

Eggs hatch in a week or two, and nymphs make their way to the ground and burrow in. Front legs of young cicadas are greatly enlarged for digging in the soil. They may burrow 3 or 4 feet deep to feed on roots.

From 2 to 3 years are spent belowground before the young are fully grown and ready for transformation into winged adults. Young cicadas then leave the soil and crawl up a few inches on grass, fence posts, etc., their skins split down their backs, and the adults emerge, leaving their old skins intact and firmly attached to their support.

NATURAL CONTROL

No information is available on the natural control of cicadas in vineyards.

MONITORING GUIDELINES

No monitoring guidelines have been developed.

MANAGEMENT GUIDELINES

Control is reportedly achieved by normal cultivation. When young cicadas are fully grown, they make their way upward through the soil during February to positions 2.5 to 5 cm (1 to 2 in) below the surface. Disking the soil before the emergence of adults during the last 2 weeks of April crushes many of them and appears to interfere with their emergence. Pruning canes to short spurs in winter, thereby removing many visible egg punctures, is of no value in controlling this pest because the eggs have long since hatched. It has also been reported that this insect is tolerant to many insecticides.

Hemiptera
Aphids,
Leafhoppers,
Mealybugs, Scales,
True Bugs,
Whiteflies

44 SCALE INSECTS

Lucia G. Varela, Kent M. Daane, Philip A. Phillips, Larry J. Bettiga, and Serguei V. Triapitsyn

Scale insects are rarely of economic importance on grapes in California. A number of them, however, have been found living on grapevines, and control measures are occasionally necessary, especially in some coastal vineyards where Argentine ant is established.

Scale insects found on grapevines may be separated into three groups: giant scales (Hemiptera: Monophlebidae); unarmored or soft scales (Hemiptera: Coccidae); and armored or hard scales (Hemiptera: Diaspididae).

Giant and soft scales may feed on more than one part of the vine, and all secrete sugary liquid excrements (honeydew). Other grape pests that produce honeydew are mealybugs and whiteflies. The cottony cushion scale (*Icerya purchasi* Maskell, a giant scale), and the following soft scales are found on grapes: brown soft scale (*Coccus hesperidum* L.), cottony maple scale (*Neopulvinaria innumerabilis* (Rathvon)), cottony vine scale (*Pulvinaria vitis* (L.)), European fruit lecanium scale (*Parthenolecanium corni* (Bouché)), frosted scale (*Parthenolecanium pruinosum* (Coquillett)), and black scale (*Saissetia oleae* (Olivier)). When mature, soft scales are 5 mm (0.2 in) or more in diameter. The *Neopulvinaria* and *Pulvinaria* species are very similar in appearance and biology and are easily confused. Cottony maple scale is native to North America, while cottony vine scale is of European origin and has been known in North America since 1987. Cottony maple scale is a polyphagous species (feeding on several hosts) but appears to be most abundant on maple (*Acer* spp.), false acacia (*Robinia* spp.), and grape (*Vitis* spp.). Cottony vine scale has been reported on birch (*Betula* spp.), alder (*Alnus* spp.), hazel (*Corylus* spp.), poplar (*Populus* spp., including aspen and cottonwood), willow (*Salix* spp.), hawthorn (*Crataegus* spp.), and *Vitis* species, but it is a pest only on vines. Cottony maple scale is found in the Lodi area and coastal Santa Barbara County. Cottony vine scale has been found in Napa County.

DESCRIPTION

The adult European fruit lecanium female soft scale is from 3 to 5 mm (0.12 to 0.20 in) long and nearly hemispherical; it is slightly longer than broad, smooth, and shiny brown (fig. 44.1). The soft scale's oval eggs are found beneath the female body. They are pearly white when first laid, turning yellow to pink as they are about to hatch (fig. 44.2). The first nymphal stage, or crawler, emerges from beneath the female body as the eggs hatch. The nymphs are small, flat, oval and vary from yellow in the summer months to

pale brown in winter (fig. 44.3). Males have not been observed.

The cottony maple (fig. 44.4) and cottony vine scales are very similar in appearance. The adult female of both species is flat and ovoid to circular, with the cottony maple scale 3 to 10 mm (0.12 to 0.40 in) long and the cottony vine scale 3 to 7 mm (0.12 to 0.28 in) long. The females lay eggs under their body in cottony masses that can be 10 mm (0.4 in) long, causing the female body to tilt at an angle from the vine surface.

Vines heavily infested with grape scale, an armored scale, appear dirty white. The female is circular, pale yellowish brown with a pale yellow nipple to one side of center, and from 1 to 2 mm (0.04 to 0.08 in) long. The male scale is smaller, narrower, and more convex than the female. Males pupate and emerge as delicate, two-winged adults. The first immature stage (crawlers) lose their legs a day or two after hatching, settle down, and form a hard cover that is separate from the scale's body. The second nymphal stage secretes an enlargement to its cover, forming concentric rings.

INJURY

European fruit lecanium scale produces honeydew that covers the grape leaves and clusters, leaving a sticky residue and allowing for sooty mold growth, causing blackened areas on leaves and fruit in the same manner as honeydew produced by mealybugs. When European fruit lecanium occurs in abundance, it may severely stunt vine growth. The European fruit lecanium scale and cottony vine scale can transmit viral pathogens. Most armored scales do not excrete honeydew. Very high populations of grape scale may stunt or retard vine growth.

SEASONAL DEVELOPMENT

Soft Scales

European fruit lecanium adult females are mostly found on 1- to 3-year-old wood under the bark on the underside of woody canes, cordons, and spurs, where they remain for the rest of their lives. Females reproduce without mating (parthenogenetically), and eggs are laid in spring beginning in April beneath the female's body. Egg laying for the overwintering generation lasts approximately 6 weeks, until mid-May. As more eggs are laid, the female's entire body is converted to eggs; the walls of the scale's body become hard, forming a hard shell; and the female dies. If populations are high, as the nymphs develop into adults and begin to lay eggs their bodies can overlap. Each female lays about 1,500 eggs.

Figure 44.1 European fruit lecanium scales. *Photo:* J. K. Clark.

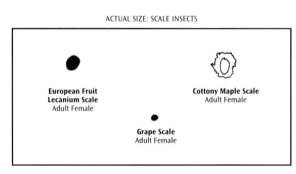

ACTUAL SIZE: SCALE INSECTS

European Fruit Lecanium Scale Adult Female

Cottony Maple Scale Adult Female

Grape Scale Adult Female

Figure 44.2 European fruit lecanium female flipped to reveal eggs under her body (A); close-up of eggs and crawlers (B). *Photos*: J. K. Clark.

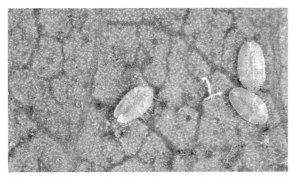

Figure 44.3 European fruit lecanium nymphs. *Photo*: J. K. Clark.

Figure 44.4 Cottony maple scale. *Photo*: L. J. Bettiga.

Crawlers hatch from May through most of June in the north coast and from mid-April into July in the central coast. They move from under the female's shell to the shoots and underside of basal leaves of the current season's growth. After all the crawlers have emerged, the empty shell of the dead female remains attached to the 1- to 3-year-old wood where she developed. From June to July the crawlers molt to second instars and can be found higher up in the canopy.

In the north coast a portion of the second-instar population continues development and becomes adult females that produce a second generation. These females develop on leaf veins, petioles, current-season shoots, bunch stems, or berries. The females of this summer generation lay on average 50 eggs, far fewer than produced by the previous generation's overwintering females. Crawlers of the second generation may be found on leaf petioles, leaves, and shoots in August.

Beginning in September, second-instar nymphs from both the first and second generations migrate back to 1- to 3-year-old wood. They overwinter under the bark in the second-instar stage. At this time of the year, they are pale brown, which is the color of the wood, and are very difficult to distinguish. Early in the spring, the second instars molt to the third instars and then quickly develop into mature females that begin laying eggs in April and May. Usually, there is only one generation each year, but a portion of the population in the north coast has two generations.

Both cottony maple and vine scale have one generation per year. Cottony maple scale overwinters as a mated female on the vine trunk and cordon. Cottony vine scale overwinters as immatures. Female *P. vitis* are parthenogenetic; males are unknown. The females of both species are found on canes, cordons, and trunks. Females lay eggs in masses in May and June. As the scale continues to lay eggs, the sac enlarges. Each female lays about 3,000 eggs. The sac remains for some time after the female has died and crawlers have dispersed to the undersides of the leaves. Immature scales feed by inserting long, thin mouthparts into the living plant tissue to suck juices. In late July and early August, males of cottony maple scale develop into adults. After mating, wingless cottony maple scale females crawl back to the cordon or trunk for overwintering. The immature cottony vine scale moves away from the leaves onto the cordons in the fall.

Armored Scales

Infestation can occur at any place on trunks, arms, or canes where the grape scales can reach living tissue with their sucking mouthparts. When abundant, most scales are found on 2-year-old wood. Most armored scales species have several generations each year. Grape scale has two generations per year. They overwinter as mated nearly mature females under loose bark on canes and trunks. Females complete development in the spring. Females both lay eggs and give birth to 35 to 50 living young (crawlers). First-generation crawlers emerge in mid-May through June. Crawlers are mobile for 24 to 48 hours, crawling under the loose bark of the previous season's growth and settling mostly in rows. After settling, this scale is permanently fixed and does not move to feed on other spots on the vine. Second-generation crawlers emerge in July and August. Overwintering females mate in the fall.

Natural Control

European fruit lecanium scale is attacked by several species of parasitoids, including *Aphytis* spp., *Encarsia* spp., *Coccophagus lycimnia* (Walker), *Metaphycus luteolus* (Timberlake), *M. insidiosus* (Mercet), and *Blastothrix longipennis* Howard. Frequently, second-instar scales may be heavily parasitized in February and March, preventing them from maturing to adult females.

The ladybird beetle *Chilocorus orbus* Casey has been observed feeding on cottony maple scale. Ants, including native gray and Argentine, have been observed feeding on cottony maple scale. However, ants, while actively foraging for honeydew from soft scales, also protect them from most natural enemies.

Monitoring Guidelines

Scale populations take several years to build. Monitor closely throughout the year and make a map of infested areas in the vineyard. For European fruit lecanium, monitor 1- to 3-year-old wood in early March through April for the presence of parasitism, denoted by a round exit hole, on second-instar scale nymphs. In April, monitor for female development under the bark of cordons, arms, upper trunk, and vine head. Monitor for crawler emergence in May by placing double-sided sticky cellophane tape around smooth 1-year-old wood near the female, or by turning over the females and looking for the crawlers. The crawler is the stage most susceptible to chemical treatment. When using summer oil sprays, treatments should be timed to coincide with at least 50% crawler emergence and then again around 90% emergence. When using sticky tape to monitor crawler emergence, change tape weekly and observe when crawler activity peaks and drops off rapidly. To determine when 50% of the females have crawlers, remove 10 females, turn them upside-down and look for crawlers with a hand lens. Crawlers have legs and are moving. Determine how many females have one or more crawlers and how many females only have eggs. Calculate the percentage emergence by dividing the number of females with crawlers by the total number of females examined. Crawlers emerge for a period of from 6 to 11 weeks starting in mid-May in the north coast and in mid-April in the central coast. Continue monitoring until 90% emergence is observed.

Management Guidelines

If overwintering European fruit lecanium female populations are high, crawlers of the summer generation can be controlled with summer oil. Apply the first treatment of oil when 50% of the females have crawlers and another 2 to 3 weeks later at approximately 90% emergence. High temperatures in the summer months may reduce populations. If populations are high in September and grapes have been harvested, second-instar nymphs can be controlled with a treatment before mid-October.

If honeydew-seeking ants are present, they must be controlled to allow natural enemies of scale to aid in its control.

Armored scales infesting grapevines are best controlled with delayed-dormant oil sprays.

Hemiptera
*Aphids,
Leafhoppers,
Mealybugs, Scales,
True Bugs,
Whiteflies*

45 SHARPSHOOTERS

Lucia G. Varela, Rhonda J. Smith, Alexander H. Purcell, Jennifer M. Hashim, Edward A. Weber, and David R. Haviland

Pierce's disease is caused by the bacterium *Xylella fastidiosa*, which multiplies in the water-conductive tissue (xylem) of the plant, causing blockages that may limit the vine's ability to transport water and nutrients. The bacteria are spread (vectored) from plant to plant by xylem-feeding insects. The primary insect vectors are sharpshooters, a subfamily of the leafhopper family Cicadellidae. Some spittlebugs (family Cercopidae) can also vector *X. fastidiosa*, but they are not known to be of great importance in causing Pierce's disease.

The importance of different sharpshooter species varies geographically. The blue-green sharpshooter (*Graphocephala atropunctata* (Signoret)) is native to California and is the most important vector in coastal vineyards. The glassy-winged sharpshooter (*Homalodisca vitripennis* (Germar)) was introduced into southern California around 1989 and became the most significant vector in that region. Since then it has spread to several counties in the southern third of the state. The smoke-tree sharpshooter (*Homalodisca liturata* Ball) is native to the desert of southern California and is not considered a major vector. However, it may become a more important vector in the Coachella Valley because it is found in many of the same host plants as glassy-winged sharpshooter. Additional vectors in the San Joaquin Valley are the green sharpshooter (*Draeculacephala minerva* Ball) and the red-headed sharpshooter (*Xyphon fulgida* Nottingham). Under certain circumstances they can also contribute to the spread of *X. fastidiosa* in coastal regions. The willow sharpshooter (*Graphocephala confluens* (Uhler)) is found in willows in riparian areas throughout California and may move the bacteria to adjacent vineyards, although it is seldom found feeding on grapevines.

Grape, variegated, and Virginia creeper leafhoppers, pests of grapevines, do not feed on xylem fluid and do not spread the bacterium that causes Pierce's disease.

DESCRIPTION

Sharpshooters are named for their behavior of hiding behind a stem or leaf when disturbed and swaying their body from side to side while standing in place. Since xylem fluid is under negative pressure, insects tapping into it must have strong muscles to operate the sucking pump in their mouthparts. These bulky muscles give the face a swollen appearance, which differentiates xylem feeders from other sucking insects (fig. 45.1).

Most xylem-feeding insects require succulent plant tissue or rapidly growing plants as food sources. These plants are found primarily in habitats where soil moisture promotes vigorous plant growth. Grapevines are a good feeding host for the vectors because they are pruned every winter and produce succulent new growth annually.

Blue-Green Sharpshooter

The blue-green sharpshooter adult (fig. 45.2A) is approximately 7 mm (0.28 in) long, dark green to bluish green, and has characteristic black lines and spots on the back of the head and thorax and a yellow triangle between the wings at the thorax. The legs and underside are light yellow. The immature stages (nymphs) are wingless and are translucent white (fig. 45.2B).

In coastal regions, riparian habitats are the principal breeding areas for blue-green sharpshooters (see table 45.1), which have been collected from over 150 species of plants. These insects shift their feeding preferences throughout the year, seeking succulent plant growth. At the end of summer, when succulent growth is unavailable, sharpshooters may be found feeding on unusual host plants such as boxelder or even leafless buckeye trees. Blue-green sharpshooters can also be found in ornamental plants in parks and near residences or commercial buildings. When pruned in winter, woody ornamentals produce vigorous, succulent spring growth. Insects are attracted to this growth even when the same plants would otherwise be minor feeding hosts. For example, live oak is normally an occasional feeding host for the blue-green sharpshooter in the spring; however, when the tree is heavily pruned, the insect is highly attracted to suckers for feeding and laying eggs.

Glassy-Winged and Smoke-Tree Sharpshooters

The glassy-winged sharpshooter is so named because its wings are translucent (fig. 45.3A). The adult is a large insect, almost 13 mm (0.5 in) long. The wings are clear with red venation but appear dark brown due to the body coloration beneath them. The underside of the body is ivory colored. The upper parts of the head and back are stippled with yellowish spots. Before laying eggs, the female secretes a chalky white substance consisting of microscopic particles. Using her legs, she transfers it from the anal region to the upper wings, forming two large white spots called brochosomes. After laying eggs, she covers them with this chalky material by transferring it from the wings. Thus, the white spots on the wings are visible on females only shortly before laying a batch of eggs and are not present on males.

Eggs are laid in a mass on the underside of leaves, usually in groups of 10 to 12 and ranging from 1 to as many as 30 eggs. Eggs are laid side by side in a single layer (fig. 45.3B). Each egg is inserted independently of the others, leaving the oviposition punctures aligned in a straight line or very slight arc.

Figure 45.1 Sharpshooters belong to the leafhopper family but can be distinguished from other leafhoppers by the swollen shape of the face plate (highlighted by the dotted line). Side view of a grass-feeding leafhopper (left), *Thamnotettix zeleri,* and the blue-green sharpshooter (right). *Photo*: J. K. Clark.

Figure 45.2 Blue-green sharpshooter (*Graphocephala atropunctata*) adult (A) and nymph (B). *Photos*: J. K. Clark.

Table 45.1. Pierce's disease vectors: bacterial transmission efficiency, habitats, and monitoring methods

	Blue-green sharpshooter	Willow sharpshooter	Glassy-winged sharpshooter	Smoke-tree sharpshooter	Green sharpshooter	Red-headed sharpshooter	Spittlebugs
Bacteria transmission efficiency	high	high	low	low	low	high	high
Breeding habitat	riparian areas, some ornamental landscapes	riparian areas	crops, riparian areas, ornamental landscapes, native woodlands, weeds	ornamental landscapes, native woodlands in southern desert	grasses in wet areas	grasses in wet areas, but tolerates drier conditions	riparian areas, ornamental landscapes, weeds
Breeding hosts	woody perennials	willows	woody perennials, herbaceous plants	woody perennials, herbaceous plants	sedges, nutgrass, watergrass, ryegrass, fescue	bermudagrass, semiaquatic grasses	grasses, herbaceous plants
Occurrence in breeding habitat	frequent	sporadic	very frequent	sporadic	frequent	sporadic	frequent
Movement into vineyard	along riparian edge	from willows along riparian edge	widespread	widespread	along irrigated pastures and ditches	along irrigated pastures and ditches; may breed on bermudagrass in vineyards	only adults along riparian edge; carried by wind beginning in May
Most common monitoring methods used	yellow sticky traps; visual inspection, sweep net	yellow sticky traps	yellow sticky traps; visual inspection; beating trays	yellow sticky traps; visual inspection; beating trays	sweep net (not attracted to yellow sticky traps)	sweep net (not attracted to yellow sticky traps)	yellow sticky traps; visual inspection

Each individual egg appears as a greenish blister beneath the epidermis of the leaf, and the entire egg mass is covered with the white chalky material, evidently used to discourage parasitism by minute egg-laying wasps. In her lifetime, the female can lay from 800 to 1,500 eggs. The upper leaf surface above an egg mass may develop a yellowish elongated blotch. After hatching, the old egg mass appears as a tan to brown scar on the leaf. Glassywinged sharpshooter nymphs are wingless, uniformly olive gray, and have prominent bulging red eyes (fig. 45.3C).

Closely resembling the glassy-winged sharpshooter, the smoke-tree sharpshooter can be distinguished by the upper parts of the head and back, which are

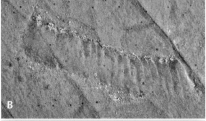

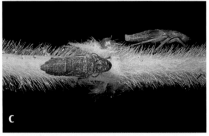

Figure 45.3 Adult glassy-winged sharpshooter (*Homalodisca vitripennis*) (A), eggs (B), and nymphs (C). *Photos:* J. K. Clark.

covered with wavy, light-colored lines (fig. 45.4A), rather than being stippled with yellow spots (fig. 45.4B). Eggs are similarly laid in a mass with an average of 9 eggs per group and are covered by the female with the chalky material. In her lifetime, a female can lay from 30 to 300 eggs. Smoke-tree sharpshooter nymphs are also wingless and uniformly olive gray.

The glassy-winged sharpshooter ranges over many habitats, including agricultural crops, urban landscapes, native woodlands, and riparian vegetation. It is reported to feed on hundreds of plant species. It will feed on growth that is less succulent than that preferred by other sharpshooters, including shoots and woody stems, but still prefers succulent plant tissue. It can increase to unusually high numbers in citrus. Other preferred hosts include acacia, ash, azalea, blackberry, camellia, crape myrtle, elm, eucalyptus, *Eugenia, Euonymus*, hibiscus, locust, mulberry, oleander, olive, pittosporum, and sumac among many others. Host plant preferences change as often as several times per day according to availability and nutritional value of the plant and species diversity in a given location.

The smoke-tree sharpshooter also feeds on many different ornamental plants and native shrubs and occupies a wide range of habitats. Some of the preferred host plants are pittosporum, acacia, cottonwood, citrus, yucca, pyracantha, wisteria, pepper tree, and *Baccharis*. It is found in southern California south of the Tehachapi Mountains and is most abundant in the dry inland areas.

Green and Red-Headed Sharpshooters

The green sharpshooter is approximately 8 mm (0.3 in) long and is green on the top side with tan to dark brown legs and underside (fig. 45.5A). Males are smaller, with black undersides. In some southeastern parts of the Central Valley, adults of the green sharpshooter are brown during the fall (fig. 45.5B). Nymphs are translucent pale tan, the same shape as adults without wings (fig. 45.5C). The red-headed sharpshooter is approximately 5 mm (0.2 in) long, with green wings and thorax. The sharply pointed head is reddish at its apex (fig. 45.6). Both species feed primarily on grasses.

In the Central Valley, grasses and certain annual weeds found in irrigated pastures, weedy alfalfa fields, or along ditch banks are the principal feeding and breeding

Figure 45.4 The smoke-tree sharpshooter (*Homalodisca liturata*) (A) has wavy white lines on its head. The glassy-winged sharpshooter (B) is distinguishable by the numerous small, ivory to yellowish spots on its head. *Photos:* J. K. Clark.

Figure 45.5. Green sharpshooter (*Draeculacephala minerva*) shown here as (A) green summer phase adult, (B) brown winter phase, and (C) a nymph. *Photos*: J. K. Clark.

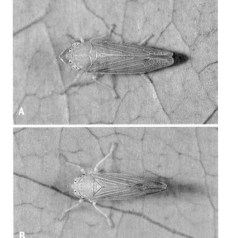

Figure 45.6 Red-headed sharpshooter (*Xyphon fulgida*) adult female (A) and as an adult male (B). *Photos*: J. K. Clark.

habitats of the green sharpshooter and red-headed sharpshooter (see table 45.1). Grapes are only an accidental host of grass-feeding sharpshooters. These sharpshooters can be a source of Pierce's disease in coastal and valley vineyards located adjacent to their breeding habitat. The green sharpshooter breeds and feeds primarily on watergrass (*Echinochloa crusgalli*), bermudagrass (*Cynodon dactylon*), perennial rye (*Lolium perennae*), and fescue (*Festuca* sp.). The red-headed sharpshooter breeds and feeds primarily on bermudagrass. It is not as common as the green sharpshooter but can be found in drier locations.

Willow Sharpshooter

The willow sharpshooter is approximately 7 mm (0.28 in) long, gray, and mottled with small, cream-colored spots (fig. 45.7). In southern California, willow sharpshooters have much darker, almost black, wings and upper body. The upper part of the head is marked with heavy black lines. The underside of the body is dark gray. The nymph is cream colored with black stripes on the thorax. They can occur in large numbers on willows and occasionally on other riparian plants such as California mugwort (*Artemesia douglasiana*). This

Figure 45.7 Willow sharpshooter (*Graphocephala confluens*), adult. *Photo*: J. K. Clark.

sharpshooter can vector the bacteria to vines close to willows at the edge of a vineyard. They may also play a role in spreading the bacteria within riparian vegetation and increasing the bacterial reservoir.

INJURY

Sharpshooter feeding alone rarely damages vines. Damage to grapevines is due to the development of Pierce's disease following transmission of *X. fastidiosa* bacteria by the insect vectors. The number of insects present in a vineyard is usually quite low; however, low sharpshooter numbers may cause significant Pierce's disease incidence. Xylem-feeding insects can acquire *X. fastidiosa* while feeding on infected plants. Bacteria attach to the internal structure of the mouthparts and sucking pump (foregut) and multiply to form a bacterial plaque. During subsequent feeding, bacteria may dislodge from the insect's mouthparts and enter the host's xylem. Vector transmission can occur within minutes of acquiring the bacteria.

The efficiency of bacterial transmission to grape varies among sharpshooter species (see table 45.1). Sharpshooters and spittlebugs are able to transmit bacteria almost immediately after acquiring them from an infected plant. Less than 100 bacteria per insect are required for efficient transmission. An infectious blue-green sharpshooter has about a 90% chance of transmitting the bacteria to grape during a day's feeding. In contrast, the glassy-winged sharpshooter has a 5 to 20% chance of transmitting the bacteria in the same time period.

Once the adult acquires the bacterium, the insect remains capable of transmitting it through-out its life. Immature insects are able to transmit until they molt, at which time the bacteria are shed with the lining of the mouthparts. Newly molted insects must reac-quire the bacteria by feeding on an infected plant. The bacterium is not transferred from infected females to their eggs.

Seasonal Development

Blue-Green Sharpshooter
This vector has only one generation per year in most areas. There is a second generation in warmer areas like the Central Valley and a small second generation in southern coastal regions. Adults overwin-ter in or near riparian habitats but may also be distributed among ornamental trees and shrubs. Pre-ferred breeding hosts in riparian habitats are Himalayan black-berry (*Rubus discolor*), California blackberry (*Rubus ursinus*), wild grape (*Vitis* sp.), periwinkle (*Vinca major*), California mugwort (*Artemisia douglasiana*), stinging nettle (*Urtica dioica*), mulefat (*Baccharis salicifolia*), and blue elderberry (*Sambucus mexicana*).

Eggs are laid singly beneath the epidermis of green leaves and stems beginning in April, depend-ing on temperature. Most adults (80 to 90%) breed in riparian areas. During the spring when tempera-tures exceed 15.5°C (60°F), a small proportion of adults migrate to vineyards immediately adjacent to riparian habitats. Their disper-sal into the vineyard increases as riparian vegetation dries. These adults lay their eggs on vines that are within 90 m (300 ft) of the edge of the riparian vegetation. Most overwintering adults die by early June.

The flightless nymphs emerge from late April or early May through July and remain on the same plant where the eggs were laid. Nymphs become adults between late June and the end of August. In summer, new adults disperse deeper into the vineyard than did the original spring migra-tion. At the beginning of September, when grape foliage is less succulent, sharpshooters begin to move back into nearby natural habitats, where they overwinter. Adults acquiring *X. fastidiosa* in the fall remain infec-tive through the winter and can spread the bacteria to new plants the following spring.

Glassy-Winged and Smoke-Tree Sharpshooters
The glassy-winged sharpshooter has two generations per year in southern California and in the San Joaquin Valley. It overwinters as an adult, feeding throughout the winter on various plants and trees. It reproduces on a large number of native plants, agricultural crops, ornamentals, and weeds. Ovi-position (egg laying) occurs in late February through May and again in mid to late summer. First-generation eggs are commonly found on nondeciduous hosts such as citrus and ornamentals where adult females have overwintered. Nymphs go through five immature stages. The first-generation adults begin to appear in May through late August. Second-generation egg masses are laid June through late September, and these will develop into overwintering adults.

Smoke-tree sharpshooter also has two generations per year and overwinters as an adult, with egg-laying periods similar to those of glassy-winged sharpshooter.

Green and Red-Headed Sharpshooters
Green sharpshooter has three generations per year in central Cal-ifornia and overwinters as an adult. Females insert eggs into the leaves of winter annuals or perennial grasses from late February to early March. Second-generation eggs are laid beginning in April or early May. Nymphs from the second gen-eration reach maturity during the latter part of June through July, when third-generation eggs are deposited.

Red-headed sharpshooter has four generations per year and also overwinters as an adult. Females insert small groups of eggs just below the grass leaf epidermis, pri-marily on bermudagrass. Eggs of each generation are laid in mid-March, mid-May, early July, and mid-August. In the warm summer months it takes approximately 25 days to develop from egg to adult.

The overwintering adults of both species do not live long (no later than March or April); thus, it is probably the first-generation adults that migrate to neighboring vineyards in the largest numbers.

Willow Sharpshooter
The willow sharpshooter has one generation per year, and its sea-sonal development is similar to that of the blue-green sharpshooter. It breeds on all willow species and occasionally on mugwort.

Natural Control

Blue-green sharpshooter popu-lations are under good natural biological control from generalist predators and egg parasites, and they rarely appear in high numbers in vineyards. Unfortunately, it is such an efficient vector that only a small number is needed to cause damaging levels of Pierce's disease. Biological control alone cannot reduce vector populations enough to prevent the spread of *X. fastidiosa*.

Egg parasites frequently attack glassy-winged and smoke-tree sharpshooter egg masses. The predominant parasitoid, *Gonatocerus ashmeadi* Girault (Mymaridae), is a tiny wasp (fig. 45.8) that achieves up to 50% egg parasitism early in the spring and as high as 80 to 95% in the summer months. Parasitized eggs are identified by the small circular hole left by the emerged parasite at one end of the egg (fig. 45.9). Related species have also been found parasitizing glassy-winged sharpshooter eggs in low numbers. Promising egg parasite species are being imported from the native range of glassy-winged sharpshooter and released in California. Several *Gonatocerus* species have been released. Other egg parasitoids being studied are *Ufens* and *Zagella* species (both Trichogrammatidae).

MONITORING GUIDELINES

It is important to monitor blue-green sharpshooters in riparian vegetation and ornamental landscaping to determine which plants are sources of insects and to time chemical control measures in the vineyard. Early detection of the glassy-winged sharpshooter in areas where it is not known to be established is critical for developing control strategies. Blue-green, willow, glassy-winged, and smoke-tree sharpshooter adults can be monitored with yellow sticky traps or tape (see table 45.1). Beating trays and sweep nets are useful for finding adults in cool weather, when they are less likely to be flying, as well as nymphs, which are unable to fly. Visual inspection of plants is used to detect egg masses of the glassy-winged sharpshooter, as well as nymphs and adults of blue-green and glassy-winged sharpshooters.

If diseased vines are observed next to lush grasses, monitor the grasses for green or red-headed sharpshooters with a sweep net. These two vectors are not attracted to yellow sticky traps, although they are occasionally captured on them.

Yellow Sticky Traps and Tape

Place yellow sticky traps shortly before budbreak. Check traps once a week initially and more frequently after 2 or 3 days of warm weather. The temperature must exceed 15.5°C (60°F) for sharpshooters to fly. Remove insects from traps after counting them. Replace traps when they become excessively dirty or discolored by moisture.

To monitor blue-green and willow sharpshooters' movement, place sticky traps on the edge of the vector's habitat, such as riparian areas and ornamental landscapes, as well as 15 m (50 ft) into an adjacent vineyard. Place traps 30 to 60 m (100 to 200 ft) apart along the edge of the vineyard. When vector populations are low, it is important to have many traps; however, the purpose of the yellow sticky traps is to determine insect abundance and not to reduce populations. Use double-sided yellow sticky traps no smaller than 10 by 18 cm (4 by 7 in). Continue monitoring through May.

As you begin to detect blue-green sharpshooters in the traps, you may want to place a continuous yellow sticky plastic tape along the edge of the vineyard to detect hot spots. The tape allows you to determine where the greatest concentrations of blue-green sharpshooters are entering the vineyard from surrounding vegetation. Tapes may need to be replaced every 2 to 4 weeks, depending on how frequently they get wet or soiled. Support tape every 3 to 5 m (10 to 15 ft) with a grape stake, fence post, or sturdy tree trunk. Tapes are not effective for mass trapping of sharpshooters for control purposes.

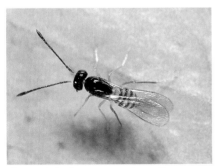

Figure 45.8. *Gonatocerus ashmeadi* parasitizes the eggs of the glassy-winged sharpshooter. *Photo*: J. K. Clark.

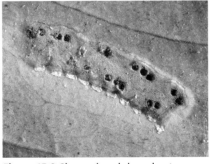

Figure 45.9 Glassy-winged sharpshooter parasitized eggs. *Photo*: J. K. Clark.

For early detection of glassy-winged and smoke-tree sharpshooters, place traps at the interface of the vineyard and all adjacent vegetation (e.g., other crops, native woodlands, ornamental landscape, and riparian vegetation). Glassy-winged sharpshooter adults tend to move among plants throughout the day, as well as seasonally. Thus, monitoring between different plant types and habitats increases the probability of detecting this vector.

For glassy-winged sharpshooter, place a minimum of one trap per 10 acres (4 ha) from the edge to throughout the vineyard. Traps should be placed on or above canopy height. To prevent traps from becoming obscured by foliage, they should be moved as vine growth occurs. For glassy-winged sharpshooters, it is better to use larger sticky cards, 18 by 23 cm (7 by 9 in), that contain more sticky material. Continue monitoring throughout the season until daytime high temperatures remain below 18.5°C (65°F).

Continuous yellow sticky tape is useful in early detection of glassy-winged sharpshooters when their numbers are very low, particularly along interfaces between citrus and grapevines. The larger the trapping surface area, the higher the probability of catching the insect, provided the tape is changed frequently to maintain stickiness.

Beating Tray Samples

Beating tray samples can be used to locate nymphs on plants where insects breed. They can also be used to find adults as long as the temperature is lower than that required for them to fly. Monitor for glassy-winged sharpshooters early in the morning when the ambient temperature is below 15.5°C (60°F). Place a large white sheet of fabric under the host plant to be sampled. Beat or shake the plant with moderate force. Adults and immatures will drop to the white sheet and remain nearly stationary. This sampling method may be used for detection, population monitoring, and collecting. At warmer temperatures, insects either jump or fly away before dropping to the sheet.

Visual Inspection

To identify vector host plants, or for early detection, make direct observations of vegetation. For glassy-winged sharpshooter, it is recommended not to rely solely on sticky trap counts. Do weekly foliage inspections in vineyard areas where infestations are known to occur or are suspected. Make inspections early in the morning when daytime temperatures are low.

Look for sharpshooter adults and immatures on host plants and on grapevines. For blue-green sharpshooters, search the leaf blades. To be able to see the vector on both sides of the leaf, position yourself so that the leaves are back-lit. Blue-green sharpshooters are most likely to be found on younger leaves. They do not normally reside on stems.

For glassy-winged sharpshooter, search leaf petioles, stems, and small branches of grapevines and host plants for the presence of immature and adult sharpshooters. Glassy-winged sharpshooters may be found on any aged leaves and often will congregate along stems. In the vineyard, inspect the outer third of the canopy on 15 consecutive vines in three areas for each 10 to 40 acres (4 to 16 ha). Try not to disturb the plants, since sharpshooters tend to hide when disturbed. Egg masses of this vector can be found on the underside of leaves, and each may appear as a chlorotic spot on the upper leaf surface. Inspect 50 leaves per 15 consecutive vines for egg masses.

During feeding, glassy-winged sharpshooters excrete small droplets that fall as a mist, coating the plants on which they feed. When these droplets dry, they form a white residue on leaves and fruit. High populations of glassy-winged sharpshooters can cause plants to have a whitewashed appearance from the accumulation of this residue.

Sweep Net

A sweep net is the best sampling method to monitor adult green and red-headed sharpshooters along pastures and ditches, but sweeping is a poor method for detecting nymphs of these vectors. Blue-green and glassy-winged sharpshooter adults and nymphs can be sampled on their preferred host plants with the use of a sweep net. Make 15 sweeps per sample and take at least four samples. To look at the net's contents, turn the net inside out to empty the catch into a clear plastic bag. Specimens are easier to observe in the plastic bag.

MANAGEMENT GUIDELINES

Sharpshooters are pests of grapevines only due to their role as vectors of *X. fastidiosa*. If there is little or no risk of Pierce's disease in your vineyard, there may be no need to control these insects.

Pierce's disease is complex, and several management strategies may be used against it (see section 9, "Pierce's Disease"). Listed below are management guidelines specific to the main insect vectors.

Blue-Green Sharpshooter

Insecticide treatments aimed at controlling blue-green sharpshooters on the vineyard edge and on ornamentals adjacent to vineyards can reduce Pierce's disease incidence by reducing the number of sharpshooters migrating into the vineyards from early spring through May. The degree of control has not been sufficient for extremely susceptible cultivars such as Chardonnay and Pinot Noir or for vines less than 3 years old. Regulations prohibit the use of most insecticides in riparian habitats.

Ideally, blue-green sharpshooter chemical control should be done when warm weather increases vector foraging activity. Cool weather immediately following treatments may decrease the effectiveness of insecticides in controlling this vector. Consider treatment if there is a sharp increase in trap counts after several successive warm days—above 15.5°C (60°F)—or if you see more than one sharpshooter per vine. Treat ornamental plants where you observe the vectors and treat the edges of the vineyard if new vine shoot growth is greater than a few inches. Replace traps after treatment if they are no longer sticky. Continue monitoring traps and vegetation until late April or for a month after treatment to make sure the vector population is reduced. Re-spray if trap catches indicate another population increase. Monitor vector habitat from May through July with a sweep net and visually search for nymphs to learn where sharpshooters are reproducing.

Vegetation management may also be used to reduce populations of blue-green sharpshooters (see section 9, "Pierce's Disease").

Glassy-Winged Sharpshooter

Management of glassy-winged sharpshooter in vineyards adjacent to other host crops is best done on an area-wide basis. This approach relies on monitoring agricultural crops and other plant species, and treating overwintering hosts. Early-season systemic insecticide treatments to citrus have been very effective at reducing migration of sharpshooters into adjacent vineyards in late spring and summer. Overwintering glassy-winged sharpshooters prefer to lay their eggs in citrus. As nymphs hatch, they feed on the treated citrus and die before reaching the winged adult stage that can migrate into vineyards.

Riparian vegetation management or removal of ornamental plant hosts is not recommended for the control of the glassy-winged sharpshooter. This insect feeds and breeds on an extremely wide range of host plants. If preferred host plants are not present, it will exploit other plants. The removal of all host plants is not feasible.

Where an area-wide approach is not possible, insecticide treatments to vineyards should be made if any glassy-winged sharpshooter life stage is discovered or if there is potential for movement of this pest into vineyards from adjacent hosts.

A contact insecticide application at the edge of the vineyard may be needed if monitoring indicates overwintering adults moving into the vineyard. Within the vineyard, nymphs are best controlled with systemic insecticides applied early in the season to control first-generation nymphs. Some insecticides reduce sharpshooter feeding, which might reduce vector transmission of the bacterium, but more evidence is needed to confirm effects on Pierce's disease spread.

Green and Red-Headed Sharpshooters

Monitor for the presence of these vectors using sweep nets. Prevent them from breeding by controlling lush grasses rather than attempting to control the vectors with insecticide applications. Insecticides are not effective against green and red-headed sharpshooters because eggs, which are not killed by insecticides, are present from early spring through fall due to overlapping generations. Where Pierce's disease appears to be associated with these insects, remove grasses and sedges growing along ditches and roads prior to budbreak in grapes, if feasible. Alfalfa fields free of grass weeds do not support significant populations of these sharpshooters. Irrigated pastures associated with Pierce's disease hot spots in nearby vineyards cannot be managed to prevent sharpshooter breeding. If possible, avoid planting vineyards adjacent to pastures in regions with Pierce's disease. Growers with a high incidence of Pierce's disease near permanent pastures may consider planting a buffer crop between pasture and vineyard to increase the distance from the vector source.

Hemiptera
Aphids,
Leafhoppers,
Mealybugs, Scales,
True Bugs,
Whiteflies

46 TREEHOPPERS

Rhonda J. Smith

Treehoppers (Hemiptera: Membracidae) are occasionally found in coastal and Sierra foothill vineyards where the injury they cause may be mistaken for symptoms of leafroll virus. Members of this insect family can cause economic damage in legume crops, young fruit trees, and shrubs. Damage is caused by both feeding and egg laying in stems and petioles. Three-cornered alfalfa hopper (*Spissistilus festinus* (Say)) (fig. 46.1) and buffalo treehopper (*Stictocephala bisonia* (Kopp and Yonke)) are common, widespread treehoppers, and injury on grapevines in coastal and foothill regions has been attributed to both insects.

DESCRIPTION

Adult treehoppers are triangular when viewed from the front because of their large pronotum, which extends upward and posteriorly over the abdomen. Various shapes of the pronotum cause treehoppers to be bizarre-looking, hump-backed insects. Adults are about 6 to 8 mm (0.24 to 0.30 in) long. The five nymphal stages have the same general shape as the adults but lack the prominent pronotum. Nymphs of the three-cornered alfalfa hopper are covered with projections, spines, and hairs. The egg of that species is quite small, about 1 mm (0.04 in) long and 0.35 mm (0.01 in) wide.

INJURY

Plant damage caused by three-cornered alfalfa hopper has been described only for alfalfa and other legumes; however, damage to grapevines is similar. Like grape leafhopper, it has piercing-sucking mouthparts. Damage to grapevines results when there is a concentration of feeding punctures in a continuous line that encircles a petiole or lateral shoot, girdling these structures. Girdling resulting from feeding is more often caused by late-instar nymphs than by adults. The restriction of water and nutrients to the leaf blade distal to the girdle reduces chlorophyll production, and in red cultivars, the entire blade will turn red (fig. 46.2). Symptoms are less noticeable in white cultivars. The buffalo treehopper adult inserts its eggs into a shoot, which also results in girdling. If the girdle occurs on a young shoot, it will cease to grow. Although rare, damage caused by either treehopper can be severe if significant feeding or oviposition occurs in shoots of young vines that are being trained.

Figure 46.1 Three-cornered alfalfa hopper. *Photo*: J. K. Clark.

ACTUAL SIZE: TREEHOPPERS

Adult Female

SEASONAL DEVELOPMENT

Both the three-cornered alfalfa hopper and buffalo treehopper overwinter as eggs in and around the vineyard, but they can occasionally overwinter as adults. Eggs are laid by adults in spring on young, tender shoots of several host plants. The elongated eggs are inserted nearly parallel to the long axis of stems. Severity and duration of winter temperatures determine how soon egg laying begins and whether eggs of the first brood are deposited in grape shoots. There may be three to four generations annually depending on area climate.

NATURAL CONTROL

In host plants other than grapes, damsel bug (*Nabis* spp.) and big-eyed bug (*Geocoris* spp.) feed on three-cornered alfalfa hopper nymphs, and egg parasitoids attack the eggs. Predaceous mites and spiders are also reported to be natural enemies. The extent of their control in vineyards is not known.

MONITORING GUIDELINES

No monitoring guidelines have been developed for treehoppers in vineyards.

MANAGEMENT GUIDELINES

Treehoppers are a minor pest in California's coastal and Sierra foothill vineyards. Treatment of vines, cover crops, or weedy areas surrounding vineyards is not recommended.

Figure 46.2 Feeding damage from treehoppers can cause a reddening of shoots in red cultivars. *Photo*: L. J. Bettiga.

Hemiptera
Aphids,
Leafhoppers,
Mealybugs, Scales,
True Bugs,
Whiteflies

47 GRAPE WHITEFLY

Lucia G. Varela, Edward A. Weber, and Serguei V. Triapitsyn

Grape whitefly, *Trialeurodes vittata* (Quaintance) (Hemiptera: Aleyrodidae), is a sporadic pest of commercial grapes. Native to California, this species is found in both the coastal and interior valley regions. Infestations may occur in grapevines and native host plants in Butte, Lake, Los Angeles, Marin, Mendocino, Napa, Santa Barbara, Santa Clara, Santa Cruz, Sonoma, and Yuba Counties.

Grape whitefly infestations usually occur in vineyards close to chaparral or ornamental shrubs that are suitable as overwintering hosts. Because it overwinters in nymphal stages on leaves, an evergreen host plant is needed during the winter. The only known evergreen host plant is coffeeberry (*Rhamnus californica* Eschscholtz), native to southwest Oregon, California, Arizona, and New Mexico. It is a dark green shrub, commonly 1 to 3 m (3.3 to 10 ft) high, with a green berry that turns red and finally black when ripe. During spring and summer, grape whitefly prefers deciduous host plants including European grapes (*Vitis vinifera* L.), American grapes (*Vitis* spp.), and deciduous hawthorn (*Crataegus* spp.)

DESCRIPTION

The adult is a small, white-winged insect. It can be readily identified by its size, about 1.5 mm (0.06 in) long, and an intense whiteness that is caused by a dense, white, waxy powder covering the body and wings. Adults hold their wings tilted somewhat vertically, or rooflike, over the body.

Adults lay most eggs on the edge and lower surface of grape leaves and a few on the upper surface (fig. 47.1). Each egg is attached to a leaf by a very short stalk. Eggs are tiny, elongated, and cigar shaped. They are green when first laid and turn black when they are about to hatch. A hand lens is necessary in order to see the eggs. When eggs hatch, larvae crawl a short distance and settle down to a motionless nymphal stage. Nymphs of grape whitefly are oval and almost translucent when seen on the dark leaf of grape or coffeeberry. However, under a hand lens, early-instar nymphs show lemon-yellow spots inside the body, which is circled by a narrow, white, waxy fringe (fig. 46.2). It is difficult to distinguish this stage from immature

ACTUAL SIZE: GRAPE WHITEFLY

Nymph   Adult

Figure 47.1 Grape whitefly eggs. *Photo*: J. K. Clark.

soft scale insects such as European fruit lecanium (*Parthenolecanium corni* (Bouché)). They can be identified as grape whitefly by bending the leaf sharply beneath them to make them more visible. Whitefly nymphs have a slightly raised profile, while European fruit lecanium nymphs are flat. The last instar develops into a naked, dark pupal case about 1 mm (0.04 in) long, with a narrow, white marginal fringe. As an adult emerges it makes a slit in the pupal case. Discarded pupal cases remain attached to the leaf, often in great numbers on the underside of leaves.

INJURY

Whitefly nymphs feed on phloem and flick droplets of honeydew away from their bodies. Damage to vines is caused by the excreted honeydew that accumulates on leaves and fruit and fosters the growth of black sooty mold fungus (fig. 47.3). Under high population pressures, foliage and fruit may turn black. This can cause fruit to be unmarketable. High populations of whitefly can also be a nuisance to fieldworkers. Ants do not tend whitefly nymphs.

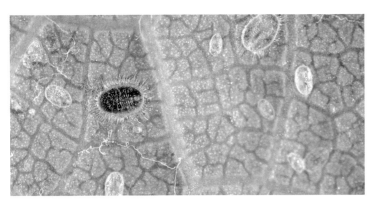

Figure 47.2 Grape whitefly nymphs and pupae. *Photo*: J. K. Clark.

Figure 47.3 Sooty mold contamination caused by whitefly nymphs. *Photo*: J. K. Clark.

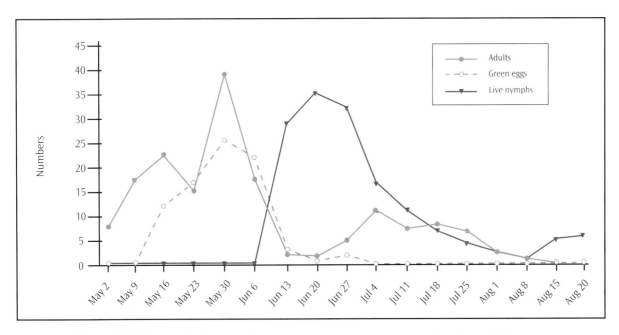

Figure 47.4 Whitefly adults, first-generation eggs, and nymphs on grapevines in Napa County, 2006.

SEASONAL DEVELOPMENT

Grape whitefly has several generations per year. It overwinters on coffeeberry in the nymphal stage. In early spring, these nymphs develop into dark brown pupal cases. Adults emerge from late April to mid-May and fly to new foliage on grapevines or hawthorn in order to lay eggs. Large numbers of whiteflies can be found on grapes near coffeeberry plants.

Eggs are laid on grapevines starting in May. Newly hatched nymphs can be seen on grape leaves in June (fig. 47.4). They settle down to a motionless existence and feed on leaves until they reach the pupal stage. First-generation adults begin emerging in early July. Several generations follow on deciduous host plants and may build up to large populations. Eggs are laid preferentially on new growth. Thus, young vines and vigorous vines that continue to develop new growth throughout the summer will tend to support more generations of whiteflies and will have higher populations. In the fall, adults migrate in large numbers to nearby coffeeberry plants. Swarms of whiteflies can be found around individual coffeeberry plants in woodland settings. Adults lay eggs on coffeeberry leaves, where they develop into overwintering nymphs. Grape whitefly is not found on grapes, hawthorn, or other deciduous species during winter.

NATURAL CONTROL

Grape whitefly is parasitized by two primary aphelinid parasitoid wasps: *Encarsia meritoria* Gahan and *Eretmocerus corni* Haldeman. In many situations, these two parasitoids keep populations under good biological control. The parasitoids make a round exit hole to emerge from the pupal case (fig. 47.5), as compared with the slit that a whitefly makes. Thus, parasitism can be evaluated by examining exited pupal cases starting in July. In the Napa Valley, a signiphorid hyperparasitoid, *Signiphora coquilletti* Ashmead, has been found parasitizing primary parasitoids of grape whitefly in the fall. This hyperparasitoid may be very abundant when whitefly densities are high and several primary parasitoids are present.

MONITORING GUIDELINES

Use yellow sticky traps on vineyard borders to monitor the adult spring migration from coffeeberry or make weekly observations of new grapevine foliage in mid to late spring for nymphal infestations. Monitoring should be concentrated along borders adjacent to native coffeeberry. In mid to late May, look for nymphs on the underside of new grape leaves with a 14× hand lens. In fall, observations can be made of the adult movement back to the evergreen winter host plants. Damaging levels are determined by watching the progress of large numbers of nymphs and adults depositing sticky excrement on grapes in advance of black, sooty fungus development.

MANAGEMENT GUIDELINES

Removing coffeeberry plants reduces infestations in adjacent vineyards. In lieu of removal, treatment of overwintering nymphal populations on coffeeberry may also reduce vineyard infestations. Treating the edge of the vineyard may be warranted if significant adult migration into the vineyard is observed and nymphs are present on the leaves. Treatment should target the first-generation nymphs that are present in June.

Figure 47.5 Grape whitefly pupa with parasite exit hole. *Photo*: J. K. Clark.

Hemiptera
*Aphids,
Leafhoppers,
Mealybugs, Scales,
True Bugs,
Whiteflies*

48 SILVERLEAF WHITEFLY

Charles G. Summers and William L. Peacock

The silverleaf whitefly (*Bemisia argentifolii* Bellow and Perring) (Hemiptera: Aleyrodidae) was first recognized in southern California in 1990. In 1992, it was observed infesting numerous crops in Kern County, and it subsequently spread through the entire southern San Joaquin Valley. By the summer of 1993, silverleaf whitefly was found throughout Kern, Kings, Tulare, Fresno, and Madera Counties. Currently, damaging populations appear to be confined to southern California, including the Imperial and Coachella Valleys and the southern San Joaquin Valley. Silverleaf whitefly has been found in low numbers in the Sacramento Valley but causes little or no damage. It does not occur in the coastal regions.

Silverleaf whitefly has an extensive host range, attacking over 500 plants, including crop, ornamental, and weed species. It was first reported infesting grapes in 1992 in the Coachella Valley. In 1994 silverleaf whitefly was reported infesting a commercial nursery in Kern County containing rooted cuttings of table and wine grape cultivars. Wine grape cultivars were more heavily infested than were table grape cultivars. Of several wine grape cultivars examined, Zinfandel was the most heavily infested and Merlot the least infested. In controlled experiments involving several table grape cultivars, Thompson Seedless was the most susceptible to silverleaf whitefly colonization, followed by Flame Seedless, Perlette, Ruby Seedless, Christmas Rose, and Redglobe. Based on field observations, it appears that all cultivars are potential hosts for silverleaf whitefly, but there are definite differences in susceptibility. Factors such as vine vigor, parentage, and rootstock may all affect individual cultivar response to silverleaf whitefly susceptibility and colonization.

DESCRIPTION

Whiteflies are small insects, about 1.5 mm (0.06 in) long (fig. 48.1). The wings of the adult are covered with a fine, whitish, powdery wax that is opaque in appearance. Silverleaf whitefly adults hold their wings somewhat vertically tilted, or rooflike, over their body. When at rest, with the wings folded over the back, a slight gap exists between the wings through which the yellowish body can be seen. While some whiteflies lay eggs in definitive patterns, including circles or clusters, the tiny, oval eggs of the silverleaf whitefly are scattered over the underside of a leaf in a random

Figure 48.1 Adult silverleaf whiteflies on the underside of a grape leaf. Notice how the wings are folded tentlike over the body, exposing the yellowish abdomen. *Photo*: J. K. Clark.

ACTUAL SIZE: SILVERLEAF WHITEFLY

Nymph   Adult

fashion (fig. 48.2). The eggs hatch into first-instar nymphs called crawlers. This instar has legs and antennae, and it actively crawls about the leaf surface, looking for a suitable leaf vein on which to begin feeding. After the first molt (shedding of the skin), the legs and antennae are lost and subsequent stages remain fixed to the leaf surface. The nymphs are oval, whitish, and appear like small raised bumps on the underside of the leaf. They grow slightly larger with each molt but remain attached to the same spot on the leaf. At each molt, the mouthparts are withdrawn from the leaf and reinserted immediately upon completion of the molt. The last nymphal instar, often called the pupa or the red-eyed nymph, is the easiest stage to identify. As the name implies, it has large red eyes, easily observable with a 10× hand lens. The edge of the pupa tapers down to the leaf surface and has few or no waxy filaments around the edge. When the adult emerges, the pupal skin (exuvia) remains attached to the leaf and has a T-shaped slit in the back through which the adult has crawled out.

Silverleaf whitefly nymphs can be easily distinguished from grape whitefly nymphs by their color and the presence or absence of waxy filaments. Grape whitefly nymphs are lemon yellow and have a narrow fringe of short, waxy, white filaments encircling the body. Silverleaf whitefly nymphs are white or very pale yellow and lack the fringe (fig. 48.3). The pupa of the grape whitefly is black, while the pupa of the silverleaf whitefly is white or pale yellow.

INJURY

Damage is caused by direct feeding by both nymphs and adults and by honeydew deposits that support the growth of sooty molds. Feeding removes nutrients from the plant and introduces salivary toxins that affect plant physiology. In cases of severe infestations, the leaves lose their green color and become dry and brittle, and premature defoliation can occur (fig. 48.4), resulting in reduced carbohydrate reserves in the trunk and roots, which can delay budbreak and shoot growth in the spring. Silverleaf whitefly colonizes only the leaves, not the wood or the fruit.

Leaves covered by sooty molds have a reduced photosynthetic capacity. This has been observed in Perlette and Flame Seedless grapes in the Coachella Valley and Thompson Seedless in the southern San Joaquin Valley. In the San Joaquin Valley, significant damage usually occurs from late August through October. Honeydew dripping onto the fruit from nymphs colonizing the leaves (figs. 48.5–48.6), as well as the subsequent overgrowth of sooty molds, leads to a significant decrease in grape quality, sometimes resulting in product rejection. In the southern San Joaquin Valley, late-season table grape cultivars Crimson Seedless, Autumn Royal, and late-harvested Redglobe and Thompson Seedless are at greatest risk of sooty mold causing aesthetic damage to the fruit. Sooty mold is most apparent on green cultivars, followed by red and then black cultivars.

In recent years, silverleaf whitefly populations have been low to moderate in the San Joaquin Valley, but this insect has a reputation for adaptability, and it could again become a problem in the future. While silverleaf whitefly is the vector of several plant viruses, it does not vector any virus diseases of grapes.

SEASONAL DEVELOPMENT

Silverleaf whiteflies overwinter as nymphs on citrus, winter weeds, and cool-season vegetables. In the spring, the adults emerge and seek out new hosts. Grapes may be infested at any time during the growing season but are most often attacked during late summer and early fall. Silverleaf whitefly has several generations per year;

Figure 48.2 Silverleaf whitefly eggs on the underside of a grape leaf. The eggs are small yellowish spheres. The larger white spheres are whitefly nymphs. *Photo*: R. Coviello.

Figure 48.3 Silverleaf whitefly nymphs on the underside of a grape leaf. Notice the smooth edges of the nymphs and that they lack any hairs or filaments. *Photo*: J. K. Clark.

during the hot summer season, it may have two generations per month. Grapes planted near preferred hosts such as cotton, melons, squash, tomatoes, and citrus are the most likely to become infested. This is particularly true when these crops are harvested or as the foliage senesces.

MONITORING GUIDELINES

Monitoring should begin in early summer. Check vines along the edge of the vineyard. Examine the underside of newly expanded leaves for the presence of eggs and nymphs. Particular attention should be paid to vineyards in close proximity to cotton, cucurbits, or citrus. Yellow sticky cards can be used along the vineyard edge to detect flights of adults entering the area. Since the adults are small, sticky cards should be examined with a binocular microscope or 10× hand lens to determine whether the small insects encountered are whitefly adults. Because other species of whiteflies may also be captured on the sticky cards, the presence of silverleaf whitefly should be confirmed by examination of the foliage for eggs and nymphs. Eggs are visible with a 10× hand lens, and the nymphs are visible to the unaided eye. Check for the presence of shiny honeydew on leaves and the presence of black sooty molds.

NATURAL CONTROL

Silverleaf whitefly is attacked by parasites and predators. Parasitic wasps of the genera *Encarsia* and *Eretmocerus* are distributed throughout California and attack both silverleaf whitefly and other whitefly species. Parasitized nymphs are slightly darker than healthy ones and have a papery look. When mature, the adult parasite cuts a circular hole in the back of the nymph and emerges. The presence of this circular hole, as opposed to the T-shaped slit cut by the emerging adult in the exuvia, is the easiest way to determine whether an individual has been parasitized (fig. 48.7). Whitefly nymphs are also preyed on by big-eyed bugs, lacewing larvae, minute pirate bugs, *Nabis* spp., and lady beetles.

Figure 48.4 Thompson Seedless vineyard in Tulare County in which the leaves have been killed by silverleaf whitefly feeding in September and October. *Photo*: W. L. Peacock.

Figure 48.5 Grape leaves (top) covered with sooty mold from silverleaf whitefly feeding; compare with the clean grape leaves (bottom). *Photo*: C. G. Summers.

Figure 48.6 A young grapevine covered with sooty mold from silverleaf whitefly feeding. *Photo*: C. G. Summers.

Figure 48.7 An adult *Encarsia* spp. parasite of silverleaf whitefly. Note the exuvia below the parasite. The T-shaped slit indicates that an adult whitefly has emerged from this pupa. The exuvia at the bottom left has a circular hole, indicating that a parasite has emerged from it. *Photo*: J. K. Clark.

MANAGEMENT GUIDELINES

Currently, chemicals offer the only practical control of silverleaf whitefly in grapes. No more than a 30% loss of leaf area should be allowed before September 1, or 50% before October 1. The action level for table grapes is lower than with raisin or wine grapes since the primary concern with table grapes is the buildup of honeydew and sooty molds on the fruit. Table grape fruit should be closely monitored. Applications should be made if sooty mold is forming on the leaves or if honeydew is beginning to drip onto the clusters.

REFERENCES

Natwick, E. T., C. G. Summers, C. C. Chu, T. J. Henneberry, C. E. Bell, and L. D. Godfrey. 2000. *Bemisia argentifolii* hosts in Imperial and southern San Joaquin Valleys, California. Southwestern Entomologist 25:243–254.

Summers, C., and B. Peacock. 1997. Silverleaf whitefly: A new potential pest of grapes in the San Joaquin Valley. Tulare County Cooperative Extension Grape Notes. September–October: 1–2.

Summers, C. G., P. Elam, and A. S. Newton Jr. 1995. Colonization of ornamental landscape plants by *Bemisia argentifolii* Bellow & Perring (Homoptera: Aleyrodidae). Pan-Pacific Entomologist 71:190–198.

Summers, C. G., A. S. Newton Jr., and K. R. Hanson. 1995. Susceptibility of selected grape cultivars and tree fruit to silverleaf whitefly (*Bemisia argentifolii*) colonization. HortScience 30:1040–1042.

49 THRIPS

Philip A. Phillips, Rhonda J. Smith, Larry J. Bettiga, Jennifer M. Hashim, and William L. Peacock

Thrips species (Thysanoptera: Thripidae) found on grape usually present only minor problems; however, table grape cultivars are at risk for economic damage by thrips. During bloom and early postbloom, table grapes may be damaged by western flower thrips (*Frankliniella occidentalis* (Pergande)), resulting in unmarketable, scarred fruit. Some foliar damage also occurs, but it is rarely economic in the southern San Joaquin Valley. In the northern San Joaquin Valley and in coastal counties, western flower thrips occasionally stunts young shoots in early spring and thus requires control. Grape thrips (*Drepanothrips reuteri* Uzel) may also stunt young shoots in spring. Summer damage to foliage by grape thrips is common, but it usually is not considered troublesome unless leaf area is insufficient or compromised for other reasons. Occasionally, grape thrips severely scars or leads to cracking of the fruit of some table grape cultivars. Other thrips species found on grapes are rarely considered pests.

DESCRIPTION

The two major species of thrips considered to be grape pests are western flower thrips (*Frankliniella occidentalis*) (fig. 49.1) and grape thrips (*Drepanothrips reuteri*). Citrus thrips (*Scirtothrips citri* (Moulton)) is reported as a pest in the Coachella Valley. Bean thrips (*Caliothrips fasciatus* (Pergande)), minute flower thrips (*F. minuta* (Moulton)), and onion thrips (*Thrips tabaci* Lindeman) may be found occasionally on grapevines but are not damaging. Predaceous sixspotted thrips (*Scolothrips sexmaculatus* (Pergande)) and black hunter thrips (*Leptothrips mali* (Fitch)) are also found on grapevines. They are important predators of Pacific spider mites and other small insects. Western flower thrips has also been observed feeding on Pacific spider mite eggs.

Thrips are small, with a slender elongate body about 0.8 to 1 mm (0.03 to 0.04 in) long. They have a square head with compound eyes at the anterior sides, a pair of antennae projecting forward, and asymmetrical mouthparts (the left mandible is developed but the right mandible is vestigial). The most distinctive characteristic of adult thrips is two pairs of long, narrow wings fringed with long hairs carried lengthwise over the body when not in use. Thrips commonly found on grapes can be identified by using table 49.1 and figure 49.2.

Figure 49.1 Western flower thrips adult. *Photo*: J. K. Clark.

ACTUAL SIZE: THRIPS

-

Adult

Table 49.1 Key to thrips on grapes

If specimen shows	Proceed to
Step 1. Abdomen with dorsal-lateral microsetae (**A in fig. 49.2**)	Step 2
Abdomen without dorsal-lateral microsetae	Step 3

Step 2. If antennae are six-segmented, the thrips is
       Drepanothrips reuteri Uzel (**A in fig. 49.2**)
If antennae are seven-segmented, the thrips is
       Thrips tabaci Lindeman
If antennae are eight-segmented, the thrips is
       Scirtothrips citri (Moulton) (**B in fig. 49.2**)	

Step 3. If body is reticulated, the thrips is *Caliothrips fasciatus* (Pergande) (**C in fig. 49.2**)	
If body is not reticulated	Step 4
Step 4. If pronotum has prominent setae at anterior corners, but midlateral setae are long and forewings have six dark spots, the thrips is *Scolothrips sexmaculatus* (Pergande) (**D in fig. 49.2**) If pronotum has prominent setae at anterior corners, but midlateral setae are short and forewings are without spots	Step 5

Step 5. If interocellar setae are long, the thrips is
       Frankliniella occidentalis (Pergande) (**E in fig. 49.2**)
If interocellar setae are short, the thrips is
       Frankliniella minuta (Moulton)	

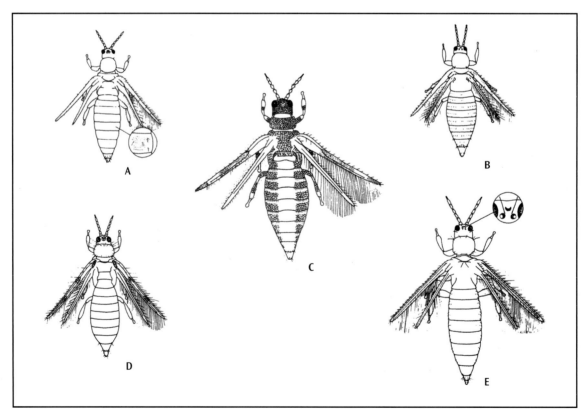

Figure 49.2 The following thrips are reported to occur in grapes and are identified by using the above key. (A) The grape thrips (*Drepanothrips reuteri*) (inset shows detail of dorsal-lateral microsetae; (B) the citrus thrips (*Scirtothrips citri*); (C) the bean thrips (*Caliothrips fasciatus*); (D) the sixspotted thrips (*Scolothrips sexmaculatus*); and (E) the western flower thrips (*Frankliniella occidentalis*) (inset shows detail of relative length of interocellar setae). *Source:* UC IPM.

INJURY

Western flower thrips cause injury to the fruit by ovipositing (inserting eggs) into the tissue of small berries) and feeding. All thrips have piercing-sucking mouthparts: they make a hole in the epidermis with their single mandible, puncturing cells with stylets and sucking the sap that oozes out of the punctured cells. Feeding results in various tissue responses, including scar formation and distorted growth. Damage on grapevines consists of halo spotting (fig.49.3) and berry scarring, both of which can make the fruit of certain white table grape cultivars unsightly and unmarketable; berry cracking increases susceptibility to late-season *Botrytis* infections, shoot stunting, and foliage damage (fig. 49.4).
Grape thrips is mainly responsible for summer foliage damage, although it occasionally causes fruit scarring and shoot stunting (fig. 49.5).

Research conducted in the San Joaquin Valley in the early 1970s on the white table grape cultivars Almeria, Calmeria, Italia, and Thompson Seedless provided a clear understanding of the nature of thrips damage. That work forms the basis for management strategies in current popular cultivars and future USDA table grape cultivar releases.

Western Flower Thrips Fruit Damage

Halo spots

Halo spots are the result of thrips oviposition (fig. 49.6). A small dark scar is produced at the site of the puncture. Berry tissue becomes whitish in a roughly circular area around the puncture. As grapes grow, these spots may show growth cracks on large-berried cultivars.

No cullage results if only a few halo spots are evident, as is the case with most table grape cultivars. However, some cultivars are prone to halo spotting, and these include the white or green cultivars Almeria, Calmeria, and Italia. Halo spotting is most serious with Italia and Redglobe because rot develops when the berry skin at the spot cracks during ripening. On other cultivars, rot does not normally result from halo spots.

Studies of Italia show that halo spotting is produced during bloom and up to fruit set or shortly thereafter. This period may last from 10 days to 2 weeks or more, depending on the temperature. With Italia, the occurrence of halo spotting is about equally divided between bloom and postbloom up to fruit set. In Calmeria, most damage occurs from 70% bloom to fruit set. Other cultivars have not been studied.

In red or black cultivars, halo spotting is generally not a serious problem because the spots are obscured when color develops. The small dark scar in the center of the halo spot remains visible but is not unsightly. Some red cultivars may not develop a deep or uniform enough color to obscure all the halo spots, but most are not evident.

Cultivar susceptibility apparently explains the differences in the incidence of ovipositing and resultant halo spots in a few cultivars. The number of adult thrips

Figure 49.3 Halo spot on young berry (A, arrow). (B) shows a close-up of halo spot. *Photos*: J. K. Clark.

SECTION 49: THRIPS

Figure 49.4 Flower thrips stunted growth of Chardonnay vine in foreground: normal growth appears on the next vine (A). Close-up of flower thrips damage to young shoots of Colombard (B). *Photos*: A. N. Kasimatis.

Figure 49.5 Leaf bronzing of Riesling from summer population of grape thrips. *Photo*: L. J. Bettiga.

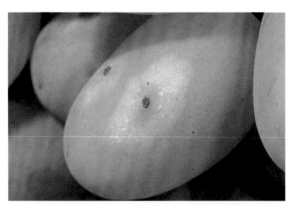

Figure 49.6 Halo spots on mature Calmeria table grapes with scar from oviposition puncture in center. *Photo*: J. K. Clark.

Figure 49.7 Typical starfish pattern of berry scarring on Thompson Seedless (A) and Chardonnay (B). *Photos*: A. N. Kasimatis (A); L. J. Bettiga (B).

298

attracted to flower clusters has not been found to be different between susceptible and less-susceptible cultivars. In susceptible cultivars, a higher percentage of eggs are oviposited in berries, whereas in other cultivars, ovipositing occurs in the cluster stem structure.

On cultivars subject to severe halo spotting, many small, dark scars are sometimes seen without the surrounding halo. The source of this type of scar is not known for certain, but it is believed to be associated with thrips because these scars do not occur when western flower thrips populations are absent or controlled. When a few halo spots are present, the number of dark scars is usually well below the number of halo spots. However, when halo spots are prevalent, an equal number of dark scars may occur. Scarring without halo spots is most likely the result of probing by the female without egg deposition; similar scars have been produced by puncturing berries with a fine wire. Other possible explanations for such scars include the deposition of an infertile egg or an ovipuncture made near the end of the egg-laying period, when response of berry tissues may be different than earlier in the season.

It should be noted that fruit scarring from wind abrasion and spray damage can look similar to the scarring from thrips activity. The cause of scarring can be easily misdiagnosed.

Starfish scarring on Thompson Seedless caused by western flower thrips
In the late 1960s and early 1970s, table grape growers in Kern County's Arvin-Edison district saw a unique type of berry scarring on Thompson Seedless; in addition,

reduced incidence of a similar injury was seen in a few vineyards in Tulare and Fresno Counties. Called starfish, or sunburst, scarring because of the pattern (fig. 49.7), the scar frequently, but not exclusively, surrounded the stylar scar.

Although this type of berry scarring had always been evident, it did not become a problem until use of the plant growth regulator gibberellin began in about 1959 and increased in about 1966. In the Arvin-Edison district, berry scarring was a serious problem from 1968 through 1972, when substantial cullage resulted on 3,000 to 5,000 acres (1,212 to 2,024 ha). Losses in other areas were much less severe, although damage did occur, particularly in 1971 and 1972. In the following seasons, little loss was seen in any district. The cause and prevention of this scarring were largely discovered in trials conducted from 1971 to 1974.

The starfish pattern of scarring is caused by western flower thrips larvae feeding under the calyptras (caps) and damaging the surface tissue of young berries. Larvae cause this scarring only when the flower parts fail to shed normally (fig. 49.8). Usually the cap sticks at the stylar end of the berry. Less commonly, the cap stretches from the base of the berry to the stylar end, leading to feeding scars on the side of the berry.

The larvae begin to appear toward the end of bloom and reach peak levels at about fruit set (fig. 49.9). Adhering flower parts finally get pushed off by growth of berries at about set or shortly after. Damage occurs between the late bloom stage (about 70%) and fruit set or slightly beyond.

Factors involved in the frequency and amount of berry scarring include persistent flower parts, thrips larval populations, and gibberellin sprays. Gibberellin increases the size and visibility of scarred tissue. Other factors that may be involved include the length of time between late bloom and fruit set. Warm temperatures promote rapid berry development, thus much less scarring occurs than with cool temperatures and a longer exposure to thrips feeding damage.

When there are no persistent flower parts, larvae feed on the stem structure, particularly the pedicels and cluster lateral stems. While these may be heavily scarred, no fruit damage results.

A similar starfish pattern of scarring has also been observed on Chardonnay in the cooler areas of the central coast. This damage is seen when persistent calyptras occur and cool bloom period temperatures allow for extended feeding by thrips. This type of damage is rarely economically significant for wine grapes.

Effect on fruit set
Thrips are sometimes accused of causing a poor set in grapes. This belief has apparently arisen because of the large population of adult thrips occasionally taken from flower clusters. In University of California trials conducted in the San Joaquin Valley, no adverse effect from thrips populations on fruit set has been observed.

Grape Thrips Fruit Damage
Fruit damage by grape thrips occurs soon after fruit set, reportedly when the berries are 3 mm (0.12 in) in diameter. Damage is attributed to feeding by larvae and, to a lesser extent, adults. Feeding

on fruit discontinues in summer, when thrips move to new vegetative growth. Injury is found scattered within districts and within vineyards. Exposed bunches on the vine are apparently preferred. Malaga grapes are particularly susceptible to fruit scarring by grape thrips (fig. 49.10A), and in cases of severe scarring, Malaga berries crack as they grow. Redglobe and Ruby Seedless are susceptible to grape thrips activity, which leads to berry cracking and susceptibility to late-season *Botrytis* infection. Only occasionally are Thompson Seedless grapes scarred enough to render them not marketable as table fruit. Generally, scarring by grape thrips is of little importance in raisin and wine grape production (fig. 49.10B).

Western Flower and Grape Thrips Shoot and Foliar Damage

Damage in early spring

Thrips occasionally cause shoot and foliar damage in early spring when shoots are less than 30 cm (12 in) long. This damage is seldom severe enough to warrant control in the southern San Joaquin Valley. From Merced County north in the valley and in coastal counties, vines may sustain economic damage because young shoots are stunted. The severity of this damage depends on temperature. Cool springs slow shoot growth rates, resulting in concentrated feeding activity on limited shoot tissue. Damage to the growing tip may cause distortion and abnormal shoot growth (fig. 49.11). Crimson Seedless and Princess are particularly susceptible to early shoot damage by thrips, and treatment is required in some years to ensure normal budbreak and shoot development. Feeding at the tip of the shoot on developing leaves will cause bronzing. Subsequent scarring of affected shoots and foliage develops. Populations do not have to be extraordinarily high for damage to occur. White grape cultivars such as Colombard, Chenin blanc, Trousseau gris, Palomino, Sylvaner, and Chardonnay are reported to be preferred by thrips. However, black cultivars like Grenache and Barbera may also be attacked. Effective treatment reduces the thrips population and allows normal growth to resume.

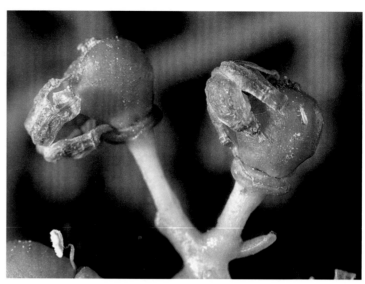

Figure 49.8 Persistent flower caps. Note adult thrips (right). *Photo*: J. K. Clark.

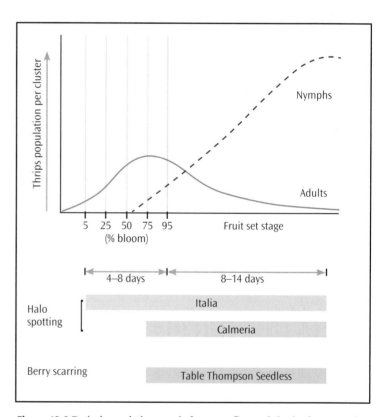

Figure 49.9 Typical population trend of western flower thrips in clusters and periods when halo spotting and berry scarring are produced on susceptible cultivars.

Figure 49.10 Grape thrips damage to White Malaga (A) and Pinot noir (B) berries. *Photos*: J. K. Clark (A); L. J. Bettiga (B).

Figure 49.11 Grape thrips damage to Thompson Seedless shoot tip and developing leaves in summer. *Photo*: L. J. Bettiga.

Western flower thrips and, occasionally, grape thrips are primarily responsible for shoot and foliar damage, along with lesser numbers of minute flower thrips, bean thrips, and perhaps other species. Grape thrips usually do not produce much foliar damage in early spring because their populations are too low. Species as well as populations undoubtedly vary from vineyard to vineyard.

Vineyards with grass or other vegetation in or nearby usually support larger populations of thrips, with the exception of grape thrips, and are more likely to show foliar damage. Grape thrips feed almost exclusively on grapevines. However, other species such as western flower thrips may move into vine canopies when cover crops are mowed or disked. They may also migrate into vineyards from nearby areas when resident vegetation dries.

Damage in late spring and summer

The cultivar Salvador is particularly vulnerable to grape thrips, and shoot tips of this cultivar may be damaged in May. Damage to shoot tips is most obvious in midsummer in Crimson Seedless, Princess, Redglobe, Thompson Seedless, Flame Seedless, Calmeria, Italia, and Chardonnay (see fig. 49.11). Canopy damage can be serious enough on Crimson Seedless that fruit becomes overexposed to sunlight. In Chardonnay, incidence of grape thrips can be specific to clone. Growth is stunted; populations of thrips usually subside after a brief peak, and normal vine growth resumes. In succeeding weeks, leaves fail to expand to normal size, often curl upward, and are bronzed. Internodes are shortened and scarred.

Adults and larvae can be found in damaged shoot tips if they are examined when feeding is occurring. Often, the population has decreased by the time damage becomes obvious. Growers may be hesitant to believe that foliar symptoms were produced by the few thrips remaining.

In most cases the peak population of grape thrips occurs too late in the season to warrant treatment. Vines have usually developed a sufficient leaf surface by mid-July to mature the crop and accumulate a good reserve for the next year. Damage on vigorous vines that are still growing may appear peculiar since it is limited to new tip growth, but such vines can easily tolerate damage and in only a few cases is control warranted. Young vines that are being trained may need to be protected, as should weak vines when the loss of leaf area would reduce their capacity to mature the crop.

Citrus Thrips Damage

Citrus thrips (*Scirtothrips citri* (Moulton)) reportedly is a pest of grapes only in Riverside County's Coachella Valley. Populations high enough to distort tip growth are most often encountered in late summer and fall. Occasionally, citrus thrips may scar young grape berries in the first few rows adjoining citrus groves. Their feeding is not usually considered damaging and they seldom require control.

Seasonal Development

Western Flower Thrips

Western flower thrips, found throughout California on many plant species, reportedly has five to seven generations per year. The adult population peaks in May, coinciding with grape bloom (see fig. 49.9). Western flower thrips overwinters in the adult and larval stages in weeds or cover crops in the vineyard, in nearby crop hosts that remain growing during the winter, or in native vegetation.

Reproduction may be either sexual or asexual. Minute eggs are laid singly in soft tissues, particularly in flowers. Each female lays about 20 eggs, which hatch in about 5 days. Larvae feed on the host through two larval stages lasting a total of 7 to 12 days. After feeding, larvae drop to the ground, where they continue development. Their prepseudopupal and pseudopupal stages last a total of 4 to 5 days in soil debris. Then, as adults, thrips emerge and are attracted to grape flower clusters at bloom, possibly by fragrance and light color.

Adults feed on pollen, but it is not clear to what extent they feed on stem or fruit tissue. Larvae feed only on stem tissue if flower parts have been shed, or they feed on both stems and fruit tissue if flower parts persist.

Usually only a few thrips are found on leaves, except shortly before and for about a month after bloom. They can, however, be found feeding on young shoots in early spring, especially if the vineyard has a resident or grass cover crop or adjoins weedy areas or alfalfa.

There are three color forms of the adult female: light, intermediate, and dark. The dark form is predominant in early spring; the light and intermediate forms are most common later. The light form generally is the most numerous. Males are numerous only in spring.

Grape Thrips

Grape thrips originated in Europe, reportedly reaching North America in 1926. Only virgin females overwinter. They hibernate in the soil in small numbers, emerging when grapevines begin growth. The first generation is produced asexually. By midsummer there are about eight females to one male; by fall, males disappear.

In California, grape thrips has only been collected on grapevines and poison oak. In general, it prefers white grape cultivars and especially tender foliage. Eggs are laid in leaf and stem tissue. Larvae begin to appear in early April. By early May, adults begin to appear, most commonly on the upper surfaces of young leaves. Their population usually peaks in July, but the peak may vary from mid-June to mid-August. During this period, thrips concentrate on shoot tips, especially on the tops of vines. Young leaves may be severely distorted, and new growth restricted. Populations usually decline sometime after midsummer, with only a few thrips remaining after early October (fig. 49.12).

There are five to six generations per year in the southern San Joaquin Valley; about 22 days are required for a generation in midsummer. Average stage lengths are egg, 7 days; larva (both stages),

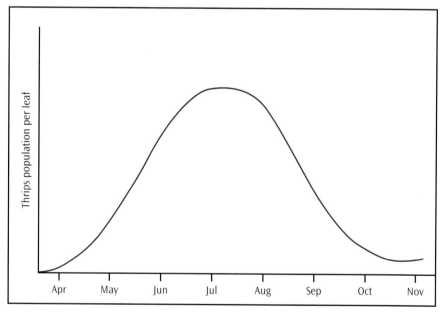

Figure 49.12 Generalized population trend of grape thrips on grape leaves in the southern San Joaquin Valley. Peak populations are usually reached about mid-July. Timing of the population peak as well as thrips numbers vary from year to year.

7 days; prepseudopupa, 1 day; pseudopupa, 2 days; preoviposition period, 5 days.

Like western flower thrips, grape thrips larvae drop to the soil to pupate after completing feeding. They continue to develop in debris under vines or on the soil surface.

Natural Control

While little is known about natural control of thrips in vineyards, a number of natural enemies feed on thrips, including minute pirate bug, predatory mites, black hunter thrips, lacewings, and spiders. Minute pirate bug (*Orius tristicolor*) nymphs and adults may play an important role in keeping thrips populations in check. Adult minute pirate bugs are small, 2 to 5 mm (0.08 to 0.20 in) long, oval, and black to purplish with white markings and a triangular head. Nymphs are pear shaped, tan, yellow, or reddish brown, with red eyes. They are generalist predators and are often one of the first predaceous insects to appear in the spring. Black hunter thrips have a slender, sharply pointed body. The larvae are reddish brown, and adults are black with white wings. They prey on thrips, mites, scale crawlers, and other small pests and are more active and larger (1.75 mm, or 0.07 in, long) than phytophagous thrips.

Monitoring Guidelines

Fruit

Western flower thrips populations are determined by counting adults or larvae knocked out of flowers or fruit clusters. This is done by sharply striking attached clusters three times against the flat surface of an 8½-by-11-inch piece of cardboard. During early cluster development, adults are fairly easily dislodged by this method, but larvae are not. Once berry size reaches a diameter of 8 to 13 mm (0.3 to 0.5 in), fruit becomes difficult to manipulate and fewer thrips can be knocked out of the clusters.

Using this method, adults are easily and quickly counted, but larvae are barely visible, especially at their first stage. To count larvae, tip the counting board to let large flower parts fall off. Then turn the board almost parallel to the sun's rays so that the larvae cast shadows. It takes practice to distinguish slowly crawling larvae from pollen grains and small flower parts. To make counting easier, use a counting board with a grid pattern. Also, larvae are more easily seen on light blue cardboard. Normal populations of western flower thrips range from 5 to 25 adults and from 10 to 50 larvae per cluster. Peak counts are in excess of 150 adults and 300 larvae per cluster.

Specific monitoring guidelines have not been developed that specify grape thrips population levels that are likely to scar fruit. Vineyards with histories of fruit damage by grape thrips bear careful watching for activity on young fruit. Either grape thrips or western flower thrips may be present on young fruit. Identification is important on Thompson Seedless because western flower thrips pose a threat only if there is a persistent-cap problem, as previously discussed. Examine clusters exposed to direct sunlight, which are preferred by grape thrips. Grape thrips also appear to be more active than the slower-moving western flower thrips. Positive identification is made by using the key in table 49.1 or by submitting a sample to the county agricultural commissioner's office.

Foliage

Western flower and occasionally grape thrips may cause early-season damage to shoots, especially during cool weather conditions after budbreak, and must be monitored by direct observation. In the spring, monitoring thrips by using cardboard as described above is not practical because the shoots may be quite short and this method may cause shoot breakage. Instead, close inspection of stunted shoots is necessary to reveal large thrips populations feeding on the developing leaves at the shoot tip or their heavy bronzing of developing leaves.

Because grape thrips is not usually considered troublesome during late spring and summer, no monitoring guidelines have been developed. However, a heavy grape thrips population may threaten Crimson Seedless and Salvador from late spring through early summer and other cultivars during early summer.

Management Guidelines

Fruit Injury

The amount of thrips damage allowed for the U.S. No. 1 Table Grade as set forth by the U.S. Standards for Grades of Table Grapes is not easy to specify. Standards allow a total of 8% tolerance (by weight of damaged berries) for defects. Included are scarring by thrips, discoloration, heat injury, Almeria spot, mildew, or other insect injury or infestation. The standards define damage as "any defect which materially detracts from the appearance, or edible or marketing quality." Thus, there is a subjective factor in interpretation of severity of damage. As foreign markets open, quarantines may alter the thresholds for thrips damage in countries where they are not found.

Italia

Most Italia vineyards require annual pesticide treatment for western flower thrips because halo spotting is frequently severe enough to lead to bunch rot. Unless past experience has shown little loss without control, begin treatments at the 5 to 10% bloom stage and repeat as necessary to keep adult populations below five per cluster until fruit set (see "Monitoring Guidelines," above).

Calmeria

Halo spotting is not as severe as in Italia, nor does rot normally develop from the halo spots. Many growers who have never treated suffer little loss; others are concerned because of the potential for high cullage. Based on limited experience, treatment is believed to be warranted only with a population of 10 adults or more per cluster in vineyards with histories of thrips injury. When treatment is needed, apply insecticides at about 70% bloom. Most halo spotting occurs from this point until about fruit set. More than one treatment may be needed.

Table Thompson Seedless

If caps persist in vineyards with a history of fruit scarring, treat when larvae appear, at about 70% bloom stage. One treatment should be enough, but this may depend on the insecticide used. Severe damage can occur with peak populations of 10 adults per cluster and many persistent flower parts.

Redglobe and Ruby Seedless

Redglobe grapes seem to be particularly susceptible to oviposition spotting, and in certain years multiple punctures can be observed on individual berries. Oviposition spots often bleach from sulfur dioxide treatment in cold storage, further degrading appearance. However, more extensive damage occurs when vineyards are weedy or located adjacent to rangeland undergoing summer dry-down. In these cases, populations of western flower thrips should be closely monitored. Ruby Seedless cultivar is very susceptible to late-season *Botrytis* infections, and thrips damage to fruit exacerbates this problem by providing injury points for infection.

With the high standards of table grape quality, grape thrips increasingly pose problems for table grape growers; however, little is known regarding the timing of chemical control measures or the relationship between thrips damage on fruit and bunch rot (sour rot and Botrytis) incidence.

Foliage injury

Treatment might be needed only when thrips feeding on developing leaves delay normal shoot growth during prolonged cold weather in the spring.

REFERENCES

Yokoyama, V. Y. 1974. Thrips associated with table grapes and their effect on fruit quality. Ph.D. dissertation. University of California, Berkeley.

———. 1977. *Frankliniella occidentalis* and scars on table grapes. Environmental Entomology 6:25–29.

Coleoptera
Beetles

50 BLACK VINE WEEVIL

Philip A. Phillips

The black vine weevil (*Otiorhynchus sulcatus* (Fabricius)) (Coleoptera: Curculionidae) is primarily nocturnal and tends to hide beneath loose trunk bark or in debris at the base of vines during the day. The adult is flightless, its forewings being fused together, and parthenogenetic; males are unknown. When ample food is present, weevils tend to migrate very little. However, they have been shown to move 55 m (180 ft) in 3 days in a mark and release study.

DESCRIPTION

The adult is a roughened, hard-shelled beetle, approximately 1.3 cm (0.5 in) long, black with small patches of white scales on the forewings (fig. 50.1). As is typical of weevils, the front of the head projects into a long, broad snout.

INJURY

Adults feed on foliage and any portion of the inflorescence or cluster rachis, especially just before unfertilized berries drop. Foliar feeding is apparent in the distinctive notching along leaf margins. On later-maturing varieties, where budbreak coincides with adult emergence, a high percentage of primary buds and new shoots may be destroyed. Larvae, or grubs, feed in the soil on roots with no apparent damage to the vines.

SEASONAL DEVELOPMENT

Oviposition begins 2 to 3 weeks after adult emergence and continues for 6 to 8 weeks. A single female may lay as many as 500 eggs in the soil. These eggs hatch into legless, white grubs that feed on roots. Larvae require approximately 10 to 11 months of development before pupation in the soil during late winter. Adult emergence occurs as temperatures rise in spring. Along the California coast, adult emergence generally begins the first week in April and continues through May.

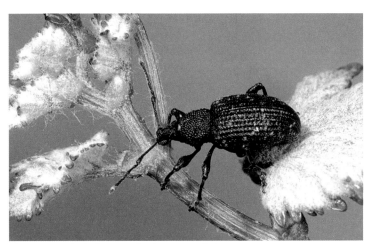

Figure 50.1 Black vine weevil. *Photo*: J. K. Clark.

ACTUAL SIZE: BLACK VINE WEEVIL

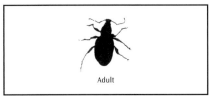

Adult

NATURAL CONTROL

Significant natural controls are not known. Entomopathogenic nematodes look promising for controlling black vine weevil in potted plants. Trials in commercial vineyards have not been successful. Black widow spiders have been observed with numerous black vine weevil carcasses in their webs beneath the loose vine trunk bark, but their overall impact seems to be negligible.

MONITORING GUIDELINES

Adults are easily monitored by first stripping loose bark from a section of vine trunk 45 cm (1.5 ft) long and wrapping a corrugated cardboard "tree wrap" around the cleaned area, using a plastic tie to hold it in place. During the day, adults will hide between the wrap's corrugations and the smooth vine trunk, generally clinging to the wrap when removed for inspection (fig. 50.2). Weevils are thus easily counted, discarded, and the wrap replaced. Twice-a-week inspections are recommended in mid to late March to detect first emergence, followed by weekly inspections thereafter.

As shown by this technique, adult activity between the soil and vine generally peaks in mid to late May and is generally complete by early July.

MANAGEMENT GUIDELINES

In weevil-free vineyards, avoid introducing black vine weevil through the introduction of potted landscape plants such as roses, a

Figure 50.2 Corrugated cardboard trap band used to monitor adult emergence. *Photo*: P. A. Phillips.

favorite nursery host, from infested nurseries for wineries or vineyard row ends. Commercial nurseries are generally the initial source of new infestations, as the weevil cannot fly. Because there is considerable weevil movement between the vine canopy and soil, control measures should target the vine trunk and soil adjacent to the trunk. Additionally, trunk spray treatments can be effective. Whole-vine foliar treatments are not necessary and should be avoided, as they are likely to disrupt biological control of other pests.

Among cover crops, creeping red fescue supports black vine weevil larvae populations while oats, vetch, and alfalfa do not.

REFERENCES

Bedding, R. A., and L. A. Miller. 1981. Use of a nematode, *Heterorhabditis heliothidis,* to control black vine weevil, *Otiorhnychus sulcatus,* in potted plants. Annals of Applied Biology 99:211–216.

Phillips, P. A. 1989. Simple monitoring of black vine weevil in vineyards. California Agriculture 43(3): 12–13.

51 BRANCH AND TWIG BORER

Frank G. Zalom, Larry J. Bettiga, and Rhonda J. Smith

Branch and twig borer (*Melalgus confertus* (LeConte)) (Coleoptera: Bostrichidae) is a member of a family of wood-boring beetles. Found throughout California and Oregon, the branch and twig borer is associated with many species of cultivated and native trees and shrubs.

Larvae of this beetle typically mine the heartwood of dead trees and shrubs, contributing to the natural recycling of plant material. Branch and twig borer becomes a pest when the adult burrows into twigs of cultivated plants at a crotch or bud axil, destroying the bud and weakening the twig. In grapevines, adults burrow into canes or spurs at bud axils, giving this species the more appropriate common name grape cane borer.

A sporadic grape pest, branch and twig borer can become a chronic problem in vineyards where it becomes established. Most injury has been reported in north and central coast counties, where it has been known to kill more than half of all new shoots in some vineyards under extremely high population pressure.

Establishment of branch and twig borer in a vineyard may be attributed to one or two factors: proximity to habitat with host plants suitable to the insect, such as riparian or woodland areas, old orchards, or unmaintained vineyards, and failure to destroy or adequately remove dead or damaged wood, including injury from disease (such as Eutypa and Pierce's disease) or cultural practices such as T-budding, lowering of arms, or mechanical pruning.

Figure 51.1 Branch and twig borer adult. *Photo*: L. J. Bettiga.

DESCRIPTION

The adult is a cylindrical, dark brown beetle, with the pronotum wider near the head than at its base (fig. 51.1). The adult female is 12 to 16 mm (0.47 to 0.63 in) long; the adult male is 7 to 8 mm (0.28 to 0.31 in) long. Eggs are smooth and white, cylindrical, and slightly pointed at one end. Adult females lay eggs singly in cracks and crevices in rough bark, on cordons, or on the trunk. After hatching, a larva bores into wood at an old pruning wound or at an injured area of the vine, where it develops over a period of 10 months.

Typically curved in a C shape, the larva is white and covered with fine hair; the head is small and brown (fig. 51.2). The larva's anterior end is enlarged, although the entire body is bulbous. Three pairs of small legs are found on the thorax

ACTUAL SIZE: BRANCH AND TWIG BORER

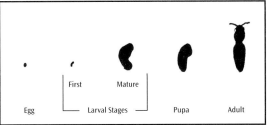

Egg · First · Mature · Larval Stages · Pupa · Adult

Figure 51.2 Branch and twig borer larva. *Photo*: J. K. Clark.

Figure 51.3 Branch and twig borer pupa. *Photo*: J. K. Clark.

Figure 51.4 (A) Branch and twig borer on grape shoot; (B) effect of adult feeding on the same shoot 10 days after photo (A). *Photos*: J. K. Clark.

near the head. The pupa is 10 mm (0.4 in) long, white, and cylindrical (fig. 51.3). It remains inactive and may be found within the tunnel excavated by the larva.

INJURY

Adult and larval stages of branch and twig borer can cause injury to grapevines. Adults burrow into the canes at the bud axil or into the crotch formed by the shoot and the spur. During bud swell, adults have been observed feeding on buds and boring into canes directly through the bud. Feeding is often deep enough to completely conceal the adult in the hole. When the adult makes a hole adjacent to the base of the shoot, the shoot may wilt and die (fig. 51.4). When shoots reach a length of 20 to 25 cm (8 to 10 in), a strong wind can

cause infested canes to twist and break at the feeding site (fig. 51.5), resulting in significant loss of vine growth and, possibly, in yield. Portions of canes so damaged often remain attached to the remainder of the cane.

Damage by adults is most serious in cane-pruned vineyards where early-season loss of a portion of one cane may result in significant yield loss to an individual vine; generally two to six canes (12 to 16 buds per cane) are retained after pruning. On spur-pruned vines, 12 to 20 two-bud spurs are retained; therefore, loss of a spur represents much less crop loss than the loss of a cane. Vigorous vines and cultivars may compensate for early-season injury more readily than vines that are less vigorous.

Larvae bore into wood at dead or dying parts of vines, often in old pruning scars (fig. 51.6). Once established, they feed on both living and dead wood. Larvae burrow slowly, plugging the tunnel behind them with frass and chewed wood. In chronically infested vineyards, when many larvae are present, their burrows can weaken vine structure, causing canes, spurs, or even whole cordons to break (fig. 51.7).

SEASONAL DEVELOPMENT

Adult branch and twig borers are present in vineyards from early March through May, and they are often seen walking on canes and cordons or feeding on bud axils or shoot crotches. Males are frequently found attending females while they feed. Eggs are laid singly in protected areas. Larvae emerge in May or June and bore into dead wood, where they continue to feed. The larva remains in its burrow for 10 months. It then prepares a hollow cell in which to pupate. Adults emerge from pupae within 2 weeks of pupation.

NATURAL CONTROL

Little is known about the natural enemies of branch and twig borer; however, the many species of general predators found under bark and on the vines may assist in maintaining lower population levels. Some especially important predators include those in the families Rhaphidiidae, Carabidae, and Ostomidae.

University of California researchers have shown that the entomophagous nematode (*Steinernema feltiae* (Filipjev)) can move through frass tubes to infect larval branch and twig borers. Field studies conducted to determine the nematode's potential as an agent for control have proven disappointing.

MONITORING GUIDELINES

Infestations can be detected by searching vines for active feeding sites and by looking for adult beetles in spring. Examine old pruning scars and dead parts of vines for brown frass and fine wood dust filling the holes left by borer larvae (fig. 51.8). Holes not plugged with frass are probably exit holes of adult beetles. Borer holes are detected more easily during the dormant season, particularly during pruning. Inspect vines and prunings annually for evidence of borer activity in vineyards where damage has been observed previously. Early detection of an active vine infestation can facilitate control.

Beginning in early March, adults can be observed on trunks and canes and are most visible before shoots have reached a length of 15 to 20 cm (6 to 8 in). Examine crotches or bud axils where adults burrow, as very often the beetle may be entirely within a feeding hole. Broken or wilted shoots in the vineyard in early spring warrant further inspection to determine whether branch and twig borers are the cause of the damage.

No control action thresholds have been established for this pest; however, it is unlikely that chemical treatment will be necessary in cordon-pruned vineyards if good vineyard pruning and sanitation are practiced. Damage by adult beetles in cane-pruned vineyards is related to the total number of canes that have twisted and snapped and the ability of the grape cultivar to compensate for loss of bunches by increasing bunch weight elsewhere on a vine. Cane-pruned vineyards with a history of borer injury may require treatment.

MANAGEMENT GUIDELINES

Cultural Control

To manage branch and twig borers in vineyards, prevent their invasion and establishment with cultural methods. Remove and destroy dead or dying portions of vines while pruning (fig. 51.9). Remove all prunings from berms on vine rows and destroy them to optimize sanitation. Completely remove wood and brush piles of any kind of trees or shrubs from the vineyard or burn them before emergence of adult beetles in March. If mechanical cane chipping or cutting is used for pruning disposal, incorporate

Figure 51.5 Canes twist (A) and break (B) where weakened by branch and twig borer feeding. *Photos*: J. K. Clark (A); L. J. Bettiga (B).

Figure 51.6 Frass (arrow) on old pruning wounds helps identify branch and twig borer infestations. *Photo*: F. Zalom.

Figure 51.7 A severe branch and twig borer infestation may result in damage to cordons. *Photo*: J. K. Clark.

Figure 51.8 Frass-filled holes (arrow) at old pruning scars indicate activity by branch and twig borer larvae. *Photo*: J. K. Clark.

the residue into the soil before adult emergence. Good vine health helps reduce sites of borer establishment in vineyards.

Chemical Control

Chemical control is normally not necessary if good cultural controls are practiced. However, if a damaging resident population of borers is present in a vineyard, chemical

treatment may be needed. Spring treatment for cutworms at or soon after bud swell offers some control of adult branch and twig borers. Under very high population pressure, multiple applications may be necessary due to the extended emergence period of adult feeding activity.

Figure 51.9 Accumulation of prunings or leaving dead vines (A) in the vineyard provides breeding sites for the branch and twig borer (B). *Photos*: L. J. Bettiga.

52 CLICK BEETLE

Larry J. Bettiga

Click beetles (**Coleoptera: Elateridae**) are known throughout California as wireworms because of their appearance in the immature, or larval, stage. They are common in vineyard soils, but apparently they feed mostly on roots of weeds and cover crops. Occasionally, the adult is reported as a pest in vineyards on grape buds.

Click beetles are easily recognized by a characteristic action and sound. If one of these long, slender, hard-shelled beetles is held between the thumb and finger, it will arch its body backward, then straighten out with an audible snap.

Of the hundreds of species of wireworms in California, only Pacific Coast wireworm (*Limonius canus* LeConte) is regularly injurious to grape buds. Other species are frequently found in vineyards, but they emerge too late in spring to damage opening buds.

DESCRIPTION

Females may attain a length of 13 mm (0.5 in), males a length of about 10 mm (0.4 in) (fig. 52.1). Wing covers (elytra) of the females are reddish brown, and the head and thorax are dull brown. Wing covers of the males lack the distinct reddish tinge and are a dull, grayish brown. The prothorax has pointed posterior tips on both sexes.

Larvae have slender, hard, cylindrical bodies that are yellowish to brown and about 2 cm (0.8 in) long when full grown. These larvae are well named because the long, slender, hard, polished body suggests a piece of wire.

INJURY

Damage to buds in early spring is difficult to distinguish from that of bud beetles. Unlike cutworms and bud beetles, however, click beetles may be seen feeding at the apex of buds in full daylight. Because they have wings and fly readily, they reach the spurs by flying instead of walking as do cutworms and grape bud beetles. Their flight activity is particularly noticeable in late afternoon on warm days.

Figure 52.1 Click beetle adult. *Photo*: J. K. Clark.

ACTUAL SIZE: CLICK BEETLE

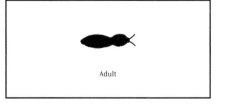

Adult

SEASONAL DEVELOPMENT

Pacific Coast wireworm adults hibernate in winter under surface debri on the ground and emerge to feed on warm days in March. They are often found in various flowers. It lays its eggs in the soil. In 2 or 3 weeks, eggs hatch into minute wireworms. Wireworms complete their life cycle in 3 to 4 years. When a wireworm is fully grown, it constructs a cell in the soil and transforms into an adult. Most of the time is spent in the larval stage, but all stages may be present at once.

NATURAL CONTROL

Applicable information is not available on the natural control of click beetle in vineyards.

MONITORING GUIDELINES

Monitoring guidelines have not been developed.

MANAGEMENT GUIDELINES

Click beetles are reportedly controlled at the same time as are cutworms and bud beetles. Alone, they seldom occur in sufficient numbers to warrant chemical control measures.

53 DARKLING GROUND BEETLE

Walter J. Bentley and Philip A. Phillips

Figure 53.1 Darkling ground beetle adult. *Photo*: J. K. Clark.

ACTUAL SIZE: DARKLING GROUND BEETLE

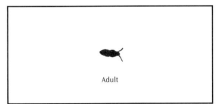

Adult

On rare occasions, darkling ground beetles in the genus *Blapstinus* (Coleoptera: Tenebrionidae) damage young vines. The larvae live in the soil and are called false wireworms. They feed on the roots of grasses and occasionally damage field and vegetable crops; they do no damage to grapevine roots. They prefer to remain in the dry, upper 5 to 7.5 cm (2 to 3 in) of soil and do not penetrate to the depth of the vine roots. Only the adult beetle damages the vine.

DESCRIPTION

Adults are black or bluish black, often with reddish legs. These beetles are about 5 to 6 mm (0.20 to 0.25 in) long (fig. 53.1). They are most often seen in great numbers and can migrate from neighboring weedy fields.

INJURY

Darkling beetles damage young vines by feeding on trunk wounds made by cultivating tools. They may start to feed on fresh, succulent tissue exposed by a recent cut, or if a wound has started to heal, they will feed on callous tissue. In either case, they extend a wound slowly around the trunk and to a lesser extent up and down the trunk, eventually girdling the vine. Such girdles are often 5 to 7.5 cm (2 to 3 in) wide.

In the southern San Joaquin Valley, these beetles have been known to defoliate and kill vines grown for propagation. Another similar beetle, *Eleodes* spp. (Coleoptera: Tenebrionidae), has been a problem in areas bordered by native rangeland throughout the southern San Joaquin Valley. It is much larger than the darkling ground beetle, and the tip of the abdomen is pointed.

SEASONAL DEVELOPMENT

Studies on seasonal development have not been made in vineyards. However, there is only one generation per year. In cotton, spring migration of adult beetles from nearby range or weedy, uncultivated fields results in plant death.

NATURAL CONTROL

Information on natural control is not available.

MONITORING GUIDELINES

No monitoring guidelines have been developed.

MANAGEMENT GUIDELINES

Bait formulations of insecticides have been most effective in controlling ground beetle and least disruptive to nontarget organisms. In newly planted vineyards that have not been fumigated, beetles can often be found accumulating inside cardboard trunk barriers. Care should be taken to apply controls inside such areas.

Coleoptera
Beetles

54 FLEA BEETLE

Walter J. Bentley

Flea beetle is so named because it can jump like a flea. Several different species are known to attack grapes in different parts of the United States, but in California the grapevine flea beetle (*Altica torquata* LeConte) (Coleoptera: Chrysomelidae), also called the steel-blue beetle, is the only species of importance. It has been found in the desert areas of Kern County. New plantings near Ridgecrest have been heavily attacked. Movement occurs primarily from evening primrose, a native host. Otherwise, this beetle is rarely reported as pest of grapes; in 1926, it was reported in countless numbers in vineyards in New Mexico, Arizona, and southern California. In the eastern United States the grape flea beetle (*Altica chalybia* Illiger) is the common species.

DESCRIPTION

Adults are shiny and metallic blue or purple, about 4.8 mm (0.19 in) long with enlarged hind femur (thigh) used for jumping (fig. 54.1). Fully grown larvae are about 8.5 mm (0.33 in) long and are yellowish brown with black markings.

INJURY

Upon emerging from hibernation in spring, adults feed on swelling and opening grape buds and may completely destroy them. In abundance, this pest has been known to destroy all buds in a vineyard. Attacks have usually been concentrated in only part of a vineyard. Abundant populations feeding on young vines also cause leaf loss.

ACTUAL SIZE: FLEA BEETLE

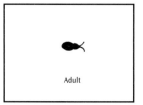

Adult

Figure 54.1 Flea beetle adult. *Photo*: J. K. Clark.

SEASONAL DEVELOPMENT

Adults overwinter in surface debris and become active in spring when grape buds swell and open. After feeding for a few days to up to 2 weeks, females mate and lay small, light brown eggs in cracks in the vine bark or at the base of buds. Eggs hatch when new leaves are expanding. Newly emerged larvae feed on the upper surface of expanding leaves for 3 to 4 weeks, eating out irregular holes. At maturity they drop to the soil, penetrating to about 1 inch (2.5 cm) and forming cells in which to transform to adult beetles. A week or two later, in late July and August, new adults emerge, move to the vine, and feed sparingly on the leaves for the rest of the summer. There is only one generation each year.

NATURAL CONTROL

Applicable information in not available.

MONITORING GUIDELINES

No monitoring guidelines have been developed. In a vineyard with a history of flea beetle damage sample during bud-swell to early shoot growth.

MANAGEMENT GUIDELINES

No guides are available.

Coleoptera
Beetles

55 GRAPE BUD BEETLE

Walter J. Bentley

Grape bud beetle (*Glyptoscelis squamulata* Crotch) (Coleoptera: Chrysomelidae) is native to North America and occurs throughout the western United States, including most counties of California's Central Valley and southern California. Adult beetles have been collected on poplar, willow, tamarisk, mesquite, desert mallow, cheeseweed, beans, corn, alfalfa, rose, peach, and wild grapes. Grapes are the only commercial host where the beetle is considered a pest.

In 1922, grape bud beetle adults were found seriously damaging grape buds in all vineyards in Las Vegas Valley, Nevada. The following year they were found on grapes in California's Coachella Valley. Agricultural officials have reported beetle damage in vineyards in the Imperial Valley (1926), in the San Joaquin Valley along the Kings River (1936), and in a vineyard in the Sacramento Valley (1950). During this period, some vineyards in southern California suffered 80% crop loss, greatly limiting grape plantings and production.

By the late 1940s, grape bud beetle was no longer considered an important pest of grapes, although occasional damage was reported in the Coachella Valley. The beetle went virtually undetected during the 1950s and 1960s until infestations increased in the late 1970s. The marked decrease in grape bud beetle abundance may have been partially caused by widespread use of DDT after 1945. DDT was used to control variegated grape leafhopper (*Erythroneura variabilis* Beamer) and citrus thrips (*Scirtothrips citri* (Moulton)), and these sprays likely affected grape bud beetle. Treatment in March for these two pests coincided with peak emergence of beetle adults from the soil. In addition, a commonly used nematicide, 1, 2-dibromo-3-chloropropane (DBCP), registered for use in 1957, may have lowered populations of soil-inhabiting larvae. Removal of DDT for use on grapes in 1972 and of DBCP in 1979 was likely responsible for the increased beetle levels in the late 1970s.

DESCRIPTION

Male and females beetles are both 6 to 10 mm (0.25 to 0.40 in) long and 5 to 6 mm (0.20 to 0.25 in) wide (fig. 55.1). Young adults are normally covered with light gray scales. Scales may be rubbed off as adults crawl through soil to emerge or from brushing against the inside of vine bark or cracks in vine supports, where they hide during daytime. Older beetles turn dark brown when scales have been removed but are light gray when scales are present. There is no reliable method of sexing adults other than observing mating pairs or dissecting them to observe the reproductive organs.

ACTUAL SIZE: GRAPE BUD BEETLE

Adult

Figure 55.1 Light gray grape bud beetles are seen easily on a green leaf. *Photo*: M. Badgley.

315

Larvae are whitish gray, with the last larval stage slightly larger than adults. The yellowish orange eggs are about 2 mm (0.08 in) long and 0.5 mm (0.02 in) wide (fig. 55.2).

INJURY

Adult grape bud beetles cause fruit loss by feeding on opening buds and eating the bud center (fig. 55.3), which contains immature leaves and flower cluster primordia (fig. 55.4). One or both lateral growing points of the bud are often left intact (fig. 55.5), but these are usually sterile. Once shoots are 2.5 to 4 cm (1.0 to 1.5 in) long, feeding damage is negligible.

SEASONAL DEVELOPMENT

Grape bud beetle has one generation per year. Larval stages are spent in soil, feeding on grape roots. Larval feeding appears not to cause any noticeable loss in vine vitality based on initial observations of this pest, but this has not been experimentally demonstrated. More than 300 beetles have been collected in 3-by-3 ft (90-by-90 cm) adult emergence cages placed between grapevines; 300 grubs per 9 square feet (250 per m²) appear to reduce vine vigor.

Adults mate soon after emergence. Males are extremely aggressive toward females. Early in the season, mating pairs are easily seen both at night and during the day. Although mating occurs early, females do not begin egg deposition until 1 to 2 weeks after emergence. They lay one to three batches of 12 to 44 eggs each. There are usually 16 to 18 eggs in a batch. Females held at 21°C (70°F) lay an average of 77 eggs, while females held at 16°C (61°F) lay an average of 158 eggs.

The female projects a long ovipositor to insert eggs under bark or between layers of grape bark; as a result, the eggs are difficult to find. On hatching, larvae drop to the ground and immediately enter the soil (fig. 55.6). Larvae have been found 60 to 90 cm (2 to 3 ft) below the soil surface but more often are found at half this depth range.

Results of monitoring emerging adults from soil (1983 to 1987) showed that peak emergence is not synchronized with budbreak, the susceptible vine stage. For example, in 1983, vines completed budbreak 2 to 3 weeks earlier than in 1982 because of above-average January temperatures in the Coachella Valley. Few treatments for grape bud beetle were necessary in 1983, while many vineyards were treated in 1982.

The Coachella Valley, where bud beetle is a common pest, is a saucer-sloping valley surrounded on three sides by mountains. Air temperature inversion layers occur throughout the valley. Grapevines can be completely budded out on the higher slopes of the valley, and three-fourths of a mile away, at the bottom of the valley, the same cultivar will be just beginning budbreak. Thus, budbreak and grape bud beetle presence have to be monitored in individual vineyards to determine the potential for damage.

Adult Emergence

Adult beetles can be found on vines in infested vineyards by mid-January in southern California. An hour or more of daytime searching may be required to find adults hiding in spaces between the grape stakes and crossarms or in holes in the crossarms used to support wire trellises. Beetles are long-lived,

Figure 55.2 The female grape bud beetle has a long, thin ovipositor and lays batches of 12 to 44 eggs between the thin layers of grape bark, shown here with the top layers of bark removed. *Photo*: M. Badgley.

Figure 55.3 Adult grape bud beetles can seriously damage grapes by feeding on opening buds. *Photo*: V. M. Stern.

Figure 55.4 Cross-section of a bud with the leaf and flower cluster primordia in top center of photo. The beetles eat the top center portion of the bud. Lateral shoots grow, but they are mostly sterile. *Photo*: V. M. Stern.

with numbers increasing until about mid to late March (fig. 55.7). When adults emerge from the soil, they crawl upward and onto vines. Because adults are fluorescent and tend to be exposed, searching during the night with ultraviolet light can give a better estimate of beetle populations (fig. 55.8). There often is a wide range of time (2 weeks or more) between budbreak with different cultivars. This should be taken into account when considering beetle damage and need for treatment.

Activity and Dispersal

Beetles that emerge in February are still alive in March and often remain on the same vine. Beetles become active about 1 hour after sundown. In full darkness, during February and early March, adults come out of their daytime hiding places. They can be found feeding on opening buds and small shoots of early-developing spur-pruned cultivars. On cane-pruned grapes (Thompson Seedless), beetles follow the same activity pattern at night, even though vines have not started budbreak. Adult activity is not interrupted even on cold, windy nights.

During the day, adults can be found hiding under bark or in cracks of wooden stakes and crossarms and in debris at the base of vines. As vine foliage develops, more beetles are found hiding in the canopy during the day, but they cause little damage.

Beetles occasionally may be seen flying in and around vineyards during the day, but they are not active fliers. When vines are vigorously shaken on warm days in March and early April, many adults fall to the ground and feign death or fly to adjacent vines. Adult beetles tend to remain on the same vines and vine supports, dispersing very little if not disturbed. There is little discernible movement between vineyards.

Distribution in Vineyards

Adult emergence studies show considerable variation in the number present in different parts of a vineyard. Distribution may be attributed to the sedentary behavior of adults and to the fact that eggs are laid in batches. After hatching, larvae drop to the ground and enter the soil.

New vineyards in the Coachella Valley planted on virgin desert

ground or land previously growing nonhost crops are seldom infested for many years. Generally, however, beetle populations increase as vineyards age.

Grape roots remain alive for a few years after vines have been removed. These roots provide food for developing larvae. When old vines are removed during summer or fall and replanted the following spring, monitor shoots closely for presence of adults. Where a broadly toxic fumigant for nematode control is used before replanting, bud beetle populations are eliminated.

Changing cultivars by way of budding or grafting may expose the few available buds to large numbers of emerging beetles.

MONITORING GUIDELINES

An important part of managing grape bud beetle is keeping accurate yearly records of infested vineyards. Beetles will be present in the same vineyard the following year. Indeed, high densities tend to remain in localized areas of a vineyard year after year. Since beetles are not equally distributed, survey all parts of a vineyard.

The time of peak beetle emergence is not related to budbreak for any grape cultivar. Air temperature inversion layers, as described earlier, can affect the time of budbreak within the same cultivar. Beetle emergence is not affected by these air temperatures. Thus, budbreak and adult presence must be monitored throughout each vineyard.

Figure 55.5 Bud center eaten by an adult grape bud beetle, with sterile lateral shoot developing. *Photo*: V. M. Stern.

Figure 55.6 Grape bud beetles hatch about the same time and drop to the ground on a fine silken thread. They enter the soil and feed on the grape roots. *Photo*: V. M. Stern.

Management Guidelines

Treatment decisions for adults are complex. For example, unusually warm weather can push the buds out rapidly, or cold weather may delay budbreak and provide longer exposure of buds to beetle feeding. For all cultivars grown in the Coachella Valley, a portion of the buds never open.

Several spur-pruned table grape cultivars have earlier budbreak. Beauty Seedless and Perlette bud out first; Flame Seedless vines, 10 to 14 days later. These cultivars have about half as many buds per vine as do Thompson Seedless vines, which bud out 3 to 4 weeks after Beauty Seedless and Perlette. However, compared with the later budbreak of cane-pruned cultivars, fewer beetles will generally have emerged at budbreak of spur-pruned cultivars.

During budbreak, monitor vineyards frequently for the presence of adults and bud damage. In Thompson Seedless vineyards treatment is suggested when there are one to three beetles per vine and bud damage is noticeable.

Treatment is suggested in Beauty Seedless, Perlette, and Flame Seedless vineyards at one to two adults per vine and when bud damage is noticeable.

Once new shoots are an inch or more long, ignore feeding. Although no further damage will occur during the current year, beetles will return the following year. Therefore, when beetles are present in large numbers, a timely chemical application around peak emergence can suppress adults and reduce oviposition, providing benefit in subsequent years.

References

Stern, V. M., and J. A. Johnson. 1984a. Biology and control of the grape bud beetle, *Glyptoscelis squamulata* (Coleoptera: Chrysomelidae), in southern California table grapes. Journal of Economic Entomology 77:1327–1334.

———. 1984b. New data on the grape bud beetle. California Agriculture 38(5): 22–24.

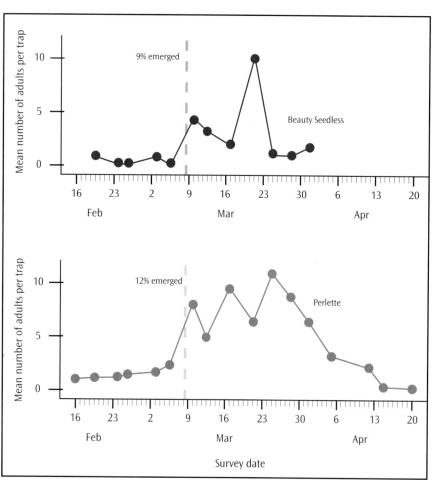

Figure 55.8 While trying to follow night movement of grape bud beetles that had been marked with fluorescent orange dye, it was discovered that unmarked beetles glow silvery blue under UV light. *Photo:* V. M. Stern.

Figure 55.7 Emergence of grape bud beetles from two Coachella Valley vineyards in 1983. The same emergence pattern occurred in different vineyards from 1984 to 1986. Emergence traps show that about 10% of the beetles emerge by the first week in March, with peak emergence in the latter half of March. Essentially all vineyards complete budbreak before peak beetle emergence. Nearly 300 beetles were found in some traps, but only a few beetles were found in other traps in the same vineyard.

56 HOPLIA BEETLE

Walter J. Bentley

Hoplia beetles (*Hoplia callipyge* LeConte) (Coleoptera: Scarabaeidae) are often noticed on flowers of many plants, including grapes, but they do not reproduce within vineyards. They are particularly attracted to white or yellow flowers: roses, lilies, and blossoms of orange, olive, and deciduous fruit trees. When disturbed, these beetles are quick to feign death and fall to the ground, even though they are strong fliers. Hoplia beetles entering a vineyard often feed in groups, so damage may be spotty. In certain regions of the San Joaquin Valley, however, crop loss has been severe at times.

DESCRIPTION

Adults are 6 to 8 mm (0.25 to 0.30 in) long and robust (fig. 56.1). The abdomen of females is thicker than that of males, which is almost flat. The upper side of these beetles is mostly reddish brown, with a darker head; the underside is silvery and shiny. Large variations in color and size occur, however, even among beetles that have emerged from the ground in the same area. Larvae (grubs) are whitish and C shaped with six short legs at the anterior end and a swollen, bulbous posterior.

INJURY

About the time new grape shoots are 30 to 35 cm (12 to 14 in) long, beetles fly into the vineyard from adjacent areas and feed on developing flower clusters and younger leaves. Partial destruction of developing clusters results in small, misshapen bunches at harvest.

About 1 or 2 weeks after beetles first appear in vineyards, certain vines, often at the ends of rows, may show considerable foliage damage from the beetles' gregarious feeding. By this time, beetles have stopped feeding on developing fruit, and vines produce foliage so rapidly that there is little additional damage.

ACTUAL SIZE: HOPLIA BEETLE

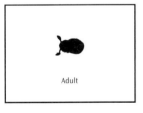

Adult

Figure 56.1 Hoplia beetle adult. *Photo*: J. K. Clark.

SEASONAL DEVELOPMENT

During June, adult females move out of the vineyard to areas with suitable host plants and lay their eggs in the ground, and then die. Grubs hatching from the eggs feed on the roots of alfalfa, lawns, and other plants, including roses. The grubs overwinter, then pupate in the soil in early spring and grow into adults. On emerging from the soil in spring, new adults often leave round exit holes. They immediately fly some distance to flowers and vines to feed and mate. Often, they pass over good sources of food in this dispersal flight. Some females return to their hatching sites to lay eggs, however, as hoplia beetles have been observed emerging year after year from the same limited areas.

NATURAL CONTROL

Little or no information is available on natural control.

MONITORING GUIDELINES

A monitoring program has not been developed.

MANAGEMENT GUIDELINES

In many cases spot treatment of infested vines is sufficient.

319

57 LEAD CABLE BORER

Walter J. Bentley and Paul S. Verdegaal

Lead cable borer (*Scobicia declivis* (LeConte)) (Coleoptera: Bostrichidae) is not a common pest of grapes, but it can be found where vineyards border native hardwood forests or abandoned fruit orchards. Most often, lead cable borers have been found in grape-growing areas of the north coast and in the Lodi district of San Joaquin County. They attack limbs and small branches of oak, acacia, maple, and California laurel. In the past, the most common problem caused by this insect was boring into oak barrels stored in outdoor areas, it being attracted by the scent of oak, alcohol, and wine. However, the larvae have been known to mine the canes of grapevines.

DESCRIPTION

The lead cable borer is about 6 mm (0.25 in) long and is relatively cylindrical, with the head hidden below the prothorax when viewed from above (fig. 57.1). It is dark brown to black, with the antennae, legs, and lower body parts more rusty red. The eggs are approximately 2 mm (0.08 in) long and are elongate and thin, with a small stipe protrusion; eggs are cream colored and have a somewhat roughened surface. They are laid in wood. The larvae are dirty white and curved. The head end appears swollen and is much larger than the rear end.

INJURY

The adults bore into living vine tissue that has been cut or broken. There they lay eggs, and the larvae continue feeding into canes and arms, killing them. The beetle also has been a major problem when found in wine casks made from oak. It is attracted to the smell of newly cut oak as well as the smell of alcohol and wine. Adult beetles bore into the casks and feed, eventually causing the casks to leak.

ACTUAL SIZE: LEAD CABLE BORER

Adult

Figure 57.1 Close-up of adult lead cable borer, showing the position of the head, which is mostly hidden by the hoodlike pronotum when viewed from above. *Photo*: J. K. Clark.

SEASONAL DEVELOPMENT

Borers are first found attacking vines in May. Adult activity extends to September, but the greatest activity occurs during July and August. The female bores through bark into the cambium, where it feeds in tunnels at right angles to the grain, then lays eggs in the wood pores. The eggs require about 20 days to hatch; grubs continue to feed on the wood tissue for about 9 months. Pupation occurs in a hollow wood cell, and the adult bores out in about 1 month. There is only one generation per year.

NATURAL CONTROL

No natural controls are known.

MONITORING GUIDELINES

Alcohol bait pans can be used to attract emerging beetles, but vine infestation is very difficult to observe.

MANAGEMENT GUIDELINES

Broad-spectrum insecticides, usually registered for other pests, have been used, but no formal tests have provided information. Once borers are in the wood, chemical control is not possible.

58 LITTLE BEAR BEETLE

David R. Haviland

Little bear beetle (*Paracotalpa ursina* Horn) (Coleoptera: Scarabaeidae) is periodically found feeding on grapes in the southern San Joaquin Valley, where climate and other factors favor its development. However, experienced viticulturists do not consider this beetle to be economically important; they report it only as a curiosity.

DESCRIPTION

Adults have broad, thick, hard bodies like other scarab beetles and range from 1.3 to 2.5 c m (0.5 to 1 in) long (fig. 58.1). The wing covers of most are dark reddish brown, but in a few cases they may be black or light brown. The head and thorax are black and in certain lights suggest a purple sheen.

INJURY

Adults occasionally feed on young, tender grape leaves in late March and April in the southern San Joaquin Valley. There have been no reports of adult beetles feeding on shoots or developing clusters. No case of injury to roots or grapevines by soil-living grubs has been discovered.

SEASONAL DEVELOPMENT

During late March through April, adult beetles congregate in groups on the foliage of grapevines. Males are attracted to females by a sex pheromone, and adults on the vine are commonly engaged in the mating process. After mating, females lay their eggs at or near the ground, and white, six-legged grubs spend their entire lives in the soil. It is not known whether grape is a host for grubs; they most likely feed on the roots of grasses, weeds, or shrubs in riparian areas surrounding vineyards where adult beetles are found.

NATURAL CONTROL

No information on natural control is available.

MONITORING GUIDELINES

No information on monitoring guidelines is available.

MANAGEMENT GUIDELINES

Little bear beetles are not reported to feed on clusters and do not do enough damage to significantly reduce leaf canopy. Therefore their presence should cause little concern.

ACTUAL SIZE: LITTLE BEAR BEETLE

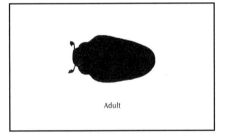

Adult

Figure 58.1 Little bear beetle adults. *Photo*: D. R. Haviland.

Coleoptera
Beetles

59 WESTERN GRAPE ROOTWORM

Walter J. Bentley and David R. Haviland

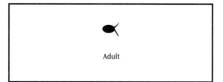

ACTUAL SIZE: WESTERN GRAPE ROOTWORM

Adult

Figure 59.1 Western grape rootworm adult, black phase. *Photo*: J. K. Clark.

Figure 59.2 Western grape rootworm adult, brown phase. *Photo*: J. K. Clark.

Western grape rootworm (*Bromius obscurus* (L.)) (Coleoptera: Chrysomelidae) was at one time one of the most serious pests attacking grapes in the San Joaquin Valley. Effective control was accomplished as cultivation and flood irrigation became well established in the early 1900s. These cultural techniques break the pest cycle by destroying and drowning larvae and pupae, in the soil, before emergence in the spring. Now, as grape growers move from cultivation to nontillage and drip irrigation, grape rootworm is again being found attacking grapes throughout the San Joaquin Valley. The pest has worldwide distribution.

Description

Adult beetles are approximately 5 mm (0.2 in) long and have two color phases. One form is completely black (fig. 59.1) and covered by a very fine gray pubescence. In the second form, the elytra (hard wings), the base of the antennae, and the tibial segment of the legs are brown (fig. 59.2). The body is covered with fine gray hairs. When viewed from above, the head is not visible; the thorax is narrower than the elytra. Eggs are pale yellow and elongated. Larvae are C shaped with six true legs. Mature larvae are approximately 6 mm (0.25 in) long with a white body and light brown head. Pupae can be found in the spring inside smooth-walled, oval soil cells near the ground surface. Pupae average 6 mm (0.25 in) long and are white. They have four rows of relatively large spines on the upper front area of the thorax, near the head, and anal hooks are present at the tip of the abdomen.

Injury

The most severe damage results from larvae feeding on roots. Small roots can be eaten entirely. Larger roots will have deep, long holes gouged through the bark and outer wood, leaving a channel filled with frass and chewed wood. If the feeding channel spirals around and girdles the root, the root may die. The majority of root damage occurs in late summer and fall. Where larvae populations are abundant, vines can be killed due to root feeding.

Adult beetles feed on the upper surface of leaves and on berries from late May through June. Leaf feeding results in characteristic slits 18 mm (0.7 in) long that, when numerous, give the leaves a lacy appearance (fig. 59.3). Whole vines can be defoliated. Feeding on the berries is also common and results in small gouges on the fruit (fig. 59.4). As the berry develops, the gouged areas crack, leaving a crescent-shaped wound.

SEASONAL DEVELOPMENT

Adult beetles are active at night and can be found on grape leaves from May through June. After mating, females lay eggs in clusters under the old, loose bark. These clusters contain 4 to 30 eggs; a single female can lay up to 70 eggs. Two to three weeks are required for hatching.

Upon hatching, the small larvae crawl or drop to the ground and quickly move into the soil, where they begin feeding on the fine root hairs. As they grow, larvae move and feed on progressively larger roots. Larvae mature and complete their development in the fall and winter, 2 feet (60 cm) or more below the soil surface. They overwinter in the soil as larvae. In March and April, the mature larvae burrow upward and pupate within 1 foot (30 cm) of the soil surface and 2 feet of the main trunk. Pupation requires approximately 2 weeks. There is one generation per year.

NATURAL CONTROL

No information on natural control is available.

MONITORING GUIDELINES

Monitor leaves for the characteristic slitlike feeding cuts caused by adults. These are most commonly seen on the basal leaves first. Looking for feeding damage is the only effective monitoring method for grape rootworm.

MANAGEMENT GUIDELINES

Manage western grape rootworm by tilling or disking vine middles and berms in April or early May, when pupae can be crushed near the soil surface. Flood irrigation also suppresses the development of young larvae near the soil surface. Where grape growers are practicing nontillage, traditional broad-spectrum insecticides are effective in killing adult beetles. Sprays should be applied as leaf feeding becomes evident but prior to oviposition. Insecticides directed at the soil-inhabiting larval stage are not effective.

REFERENCES

Essig, E. O. 1947. Insects of western North America. 7th ed. New York: Macmillan.

Quayle, J. H. 1908. The California grape rootworm. University of California College of Agriculture Bulletin No. 195.

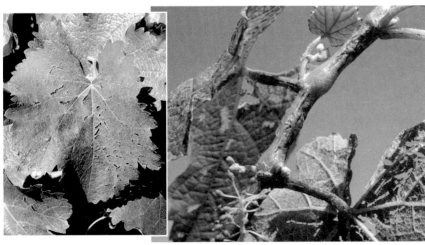

Figure 59.3 Feeding injury to leaves and shoots caused by western grape rootworm adults. *Photos*: J. K. Clark (left); L. J. Bettiga (right).

Figure 59.4 Berry damage caused by adult western grape rootworm feeding. *Photo*: J. K. Clark.

60 ANTS

Philip A. Phillips, Monica L. Cooper, Kent M. Daane, John H. Klotz,
and Mark Battany

As a group, ants (Hymenoptera: Formicidae) are among the most abundant of terrestrial animals. Like many species of wasps and bees and all termites, ants are eusocial and therefore cannot survive alone but must live and work in a colony. Larvae are confined to the nest and rely on adult workers for grooming, transport, and nourishment. Whereas individual ants may live only a few weeks or months, a colony's lifespan may extend over multiple years. In some species, nest locations can be quite ephemeral, with the colony moving to a more favorable location in response to disturbance.

Intraspecific (same species) and interspecific (between species) aggression and competition for resources are common in ants and help to regulate colony size and territorial range. When nonnative ant species are introduced into new areas without their competitors, they may build large populations and become pests in their introduced ranges. Nests of invasive species, such as the Argentine ant (*Linepithema humile* (Mayr)), may have multiple queens (polygyny) and lack intraspecific aggression (unicolonialism). In the absence of aggression and territoriality, more resources can be directed to colony growth, domination of food and nesting resources, and displacement of native ants during direct, aggressive encounters. These traits, among others, contribute to their success as invasive species.

With the exception of certain urban and agricultural pests, ants are generally beneficial, especially as predators, scavengers, and seed dispersers. Of the approximately 270 ant species in California, only a small percentage have noxious habits of economic importance, mainly due to their association with phloem-feeding hemipterans (aphids, mealybugs, and scale insects). The ants disrupt biological control by protecting hemipterans from natural enemies and in turn collect nutrient-rich honeydew as a food source. In California's coastal vineyards, the Argentine ant has been implicated in outbreaks of mealybugs, including the grape (*Pseudococcus maritimus*), obscure (*Pseudococcus viburni*), longtailed (*Pseudococcus longispinus*), and vine (*Planococcus ficus*) mealybugs, as well as European fruit lecanium scale (*Parthenolecanium corni*). In addition to reducing vine vigor and affecting fruit marketability, these hemipterans may vector viral diseases.

ACTUAL SIZE: ARGENTINE ANT

Adult

Figure 60.1 Native gray ant (*Formica aerata*).
Photo: J. K. Clark.

Description

Of the many vineyard ant species, the field ants (*Formica* spp.) are among the most prevalent in warmer, interior regions of the state and include *Formica aerata* Françoeur (commonly called the native gray ant) (fig. 60.1), *F. perpilosa* Wheeler, and *F. cinerea* Mayr. These ants are medium to large, 4 to 7.5 mm (0.17 to 0.29 in) long, and have a red thorax and gray or dark brown abdomen. The gray ant's abdomen may appear shiny in the sunlight. They tend to be solitary foragers and move in jerky and apparently random fashion. Each has unique biological characteristics and geographic ranges: for example, *F. aerata* is more common in the San Joaquin Valley, whereas *F. perpilosa* is common in the Coachella Valley. They should not be confused with the similar-sized harvester ant species. Harvester ants are innocuous seed and dead insect feeders and leave telltale seed chaff around the entrance to their nests. The California harvester ant (*Pogonomyrmex californicus* (Buckley)) (fig. 60.2) is shiny red, does not move in trails, and can bite or sting painfully. The

jet black harvester ant (*Veromessor pergandei* (Mayr)) follows trails in morning and evening, is less active during midday, and does not sting but can bite. The field ant species are generally protein feeders, but they are also known to tend hemipterans for their honeydew.

The Argentine ant (fig. 60.3) is by far the most prevalent and damaging of the honeydew-seeking ant species found in coastal California vineyards. These small (2 mm, or 0.08 in), dull brown to dark gray ants have pale stripes visible on their abdomens when distended with honeydew. They can also be recognized by the musty odor emitted when crushed. The Argentine ant is a faithful trail-following species, and ants are often seen moving rapidly in lines along irrigation tubing or trellis wires. Once it enters a vineyard, this aggressive species displaces other ants until it becomes the predominant ant species in the vineyard. Unlike many native ant species, Argentine ant nests within an area are functionally interconnected. For instance, over 50% of the workers found in one nest will be exchanged with workers from nearby nests over a

5-day period. This unicolonialism gives the Argentine ant a distinct advantage over native ants in that nests share resources instead of competing for them. For many native ant species, intraspecific aggression and competition for resources are common and tend to limit their populations.

Less-common vineyard ant species include those in the genus *Paratrechina*. This includes the "crazy ant" species found in the southern San Joaquin Valley and named for its erratic movement. *Cardiocondyla mauritanica* Forel and the pavement ant (*Tetramorium caespitum* L.) may be found in close association with the Argentine ant. Although these three species are highly aggressive toward each other, they may jointly displace native ants. The southern fire ant (*Solenopsis xyloni* McCook) (fig. 60.4) is native to southern and western North America; ranging in California from the south to the Sacramento Valley. Workers range in size (polymorphism) from 2.5 to 5 mm (0.1 to 0.2 in) and are bicolored, with a shiny red head and thorax and a black abdomen. The southern fire ant has generalized

Figure 60.2 California harvester ants (*Pogonomyrmex californicus*) are found in vineyards and should not be confused with the *Formica* species. *Photo*: J. K. Clark.

Figure 60.3 Argentine ant (*Linepithema humile*). *Photo*: J. K. Clark.

Figure 60.4 Southern fire ant (*Solenopsis xyloni*). *Photo*: J. K. Clark.

foraging habits (seeds, insects, and honeydew), is active in the morning and evening, and will sting when provoked. Other native California ant species found in the vineyard include the thief ant (*Solenopsis molesta* Say), the winter ant (*Prenolepis imparis* Say), and *Pheidole californica* Mayr. The tiny (1.8 mm, or 0.07 in), pale yellow to golden-colored thief ants often nest near or within the colonies of other ant species and feed on their eggs and larvae. Thief ants and winter ants may be found collecting honeydew from mealybugs on grapevines, although neither has been reported to disrupt biological control. As their common name implies, winter ants are specialized for foraging in cooler weather and are more commonly found in coastal vineyards. The ground-dwelling *P. californica* prefers open, dry habitats and is mainly a seed harvester. Carpenter ants belong to one of the most abundant and widespread genera (*Camponotus*) worldwide. Although found in vineyards, they are not considered damaging. They typically nest in live or dead wood (or landscaping material) and are generalist scavengers and predators, feeding on dead and live insects, nectar, fruit juices, and honeydew.

Injury

In vineyards, the detrimental effects of certain ant species outweigh their benefits for pest management. These species disrupt biological control by protecting hemipterans from predation and parasitism by their natural enemies. The ants, in exchange, are rewarded with a sugar-rich food source (honeydew) excreted by the hemipterans. In coastal California vineyards, the Argentine ant is the major species of concern because it has been shown to elevate the pest status of certain insects (especially the grape, obscure, and vine mealybugs) (fig. 60.5). For example, in vineyards populated with obscure mealybug, parasitism levels of the mealybug were five times greater on vines from which Argentine ants were excluded, as compared with vines tended by ants, resulting in dramatically lower mealybug densities (fig. 60.6). Similarly, the gray ant, pavement ant, and *F. perpilosa* have been associated with higher mealybug and scale populations in vineyards where they are the predominant species. Ants can also interfere with certain generalist predators such as adult ladybeetles and the larvae of syrphid flies, lacewings, and dusty wings. Not all natural enemies are equally disturbed by foraging ants. One exception is the larvae of mealybug destroyer beetles (*Cryptolaemus montrouzieri* Mulsant and *Scymnus* sp.) that escape some detection by mealybug-tending ants because they are physically similar to mealybugs with respect to body shape, waxy cuticle, and hairs. Some of the native ant species, including *S. molesta*, *S. xyloni*, and *P. imparis*, use honeydew as a food source but have not been reported to significantly disrupt natural enemies. The southern fire ant also feeds directly on tender canes, bark, and leaves of young vines, sometimes girdling and killing them. It can damage drip irrigation tubing in its search for water.

Seasonal Development

The Argentine ant generally nests in the bare soil on the berm directly at the base of the vine. These nesting sites provide the needed warmth and sun exposure during winter and cooling shade during summer. Proximity to the irrigated root zone maintains the nest area at a higher relative humidity than the surrounding soil. Argentine ants prefer a warm, dry climate with access to free water to protect them from desiccation; they lose two to three times more water than native California ant species. They are especially common in irrigated landscapes, although foraging may be limited under excessively wet conditions associated with large amounts of rainfall. The extreme aridity of chaparral and oak-pine woodland habitats during the summer may explain why the Argentine ant has not successfully colonized these areas.

Figure 60.5 Argentine ants foraging on honeydew secreted by vine mealybugs. *Photo*: M. Battany.

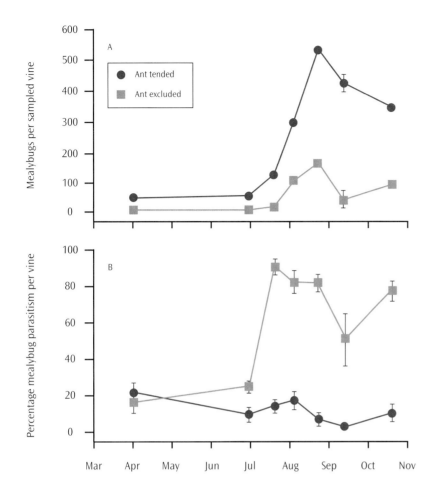

Figure 60.6 Season-long counts of (A) obscure mealybugs per 3-minute vine search (± SEM) and (B) percentage parasitism of obscure mealybug in a central coast vineyard for vines with ant exclusion (■) and ant tending (●) of the obscure mealybugs.

Argentine ants do not build obvious aboveground nests; they live in chambers excavated in the soil. The majority of the colony is generally located in the top 20 to 30 cm (8 to 12 in) of the soil, although the colony may reach depths of 60 cm (24 in). Argentine ant colonies begin to expand in size and range as temperatures warm and food resources (such as mealybug honeydew) become more plentiful. The size of each individual nest varies from hundreds to many thousands of workers and from one to dozens of queens. However, individual nest size is somewhat irrelevant, as Argentine ants are unicolonial: all nests within an area

are functionally interconnected and workers move freely between nests. The result is supercolonies that span large geographic regions and may contain tens of millions of Argentine ants. Ant nests may grow and shrink in response to environmental conditions; ants tend to recede into fewer, larger nests during the winter and expand into a greater number of smaller nests during the summer. Argentine ant colonies typically contain female reproductives (queens), winged males, and sterile female workers. Developing ants go through four larval stages and a pupal stage before reaching adulthood. Queens lay the first cycle of eggs in late

winter, giving rise to reproductives (males and new queens) in early spring. Eggs laid in early spring are reared as sterile females (workers) that comprise the majority of the colony during the summer months (fig. 60.7). Worker ants may live at least 9 months in a colony containing a queen and survive up to 6.5 months in a queenless colony.

The southern fire ant builds nests with entrances of loose mounds or numerous scattered, flattened craters. Nests are located in warm, shaded areas. Fire ants generally aggregate in smaller numbers than do Argentine ants, but they can also be found in large colonies.

Most species of *Formica* are polygynous (more than one queen), and some are polydomous (occupying more than one nest), however, this varies even within a species. They are ground-nesting ants with omnivorous diets. The native gray ant, *F. aerata*, is considerably larger than the other two species and builds its nests in topsoil or under rocks or debris, usually at the base of the vine.

Natural Control

Little is known about natural control of ants in vineyards. In their native range, a combination of factors limits ant populations, including environmental, inter- and intra-specific competition, predation, parasitism, and biological agents (fungi). In their introduced environments, Argentine ants have few natural enemies. Competition with other ant species will limit populations, although the Argentine ant's unicolonial nest structure, high population density, and efficient foraging strategy and use of resources provide an advantage in interspecific competition. As a result, Argentine ants typically displace native ants and often disturb other invertebrate and some vertebrate species.

MONITORING GUIDELINES

In order to have ample time to implement management strategies, ant monitoring should be done in the spring, although monitoring in summer months can be useful to plan treatment for the following season. Ant nests are often found in bare soil areas or on the vineyard berms and can be seen in spring shortly after a light rain, when nest excavation brings dark,

moist soil to the surface, where it contrasts with the lighter, dry surface soil. Because Argentine ants do not build obvious aboveground nest structures, they may be difficult to detect. Poking or prodding the berm soil with a sharp object (screwdriver or soil probe) will disturb the nest, sending workers (often carrying brood) scurrying out.

While ant nests may be difficult to locate, foraging ants are more easily spotted, especially when they are searching the vines for honeydew. Sampling for foragers is most fruitful in mid to late morning on warm days in early spring. Foragers are most active

from 15° to 30°C (59° to 86°F). Ants trailing beneath the bark or inside hollow metal stakes may be more difficult to spot. Gently tapping the vine disturbs the ants, prompting them to break their trails and scurry about the vine in a defensive response. Trailing ants may be difficult to locate on the vineyard floor; they are often more obvious along drip irrigation lines, trellis wires, and trunk sections, which may become veritable "ant highways" during periods of heavy trailing.

Argentine ants may nest in irrigated landscapes or noncrop areas abutting vineyards. Since these can be starting points for invasions into a vineyard, it is important to sample and potentially manage populations in these areas. Within the vineyard, Argentine ants are often found at lower elevations, especially surrounding streams, reservoirs, and other water sources. Monitoring and management may be concentrated in these hot spots, where water is more available during the summer.

MANAGEMENT GUIDELINES

Vineyard ant communities can be quite diverse, therefore the ants should be properly identified before a management strategy is developed or implemented. Cultural and chemical tactics are most often employed in ant management, although there have been some successful reports of biological control with invertebrate or microbial agents. There is no single cultural control that is effective against all of the different ant species. Flooding and frequent soil disturbances help limit ant populations, although the Argentine ant can thrive in highly disturbed

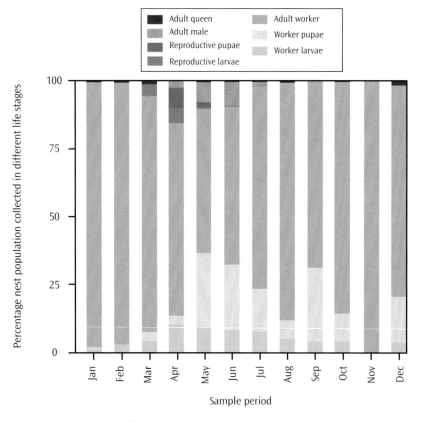

Figure 60.7 Argentine ant life cycle in coastal California vineyards, based on averaged data from nest collections in a San Luis Obispo County vineyard, 2004–2006. Data are presented as the percentage of the nest population in recognized life stages. Ant bait should be deployed in early spring, when larvae are present in the nest. Workers may not recruit heavily to bait in late summer (July-August), because there are fewer larvae in the nest and hemipteran honeydew and ripening grapes are more attractive foraging options. *Source*: Cooper et al. 2008.

soil, and flooding is often not possible in many coastal vineyards where this species is found. Cover crops have been shown to promote southern fire ant populations, yet they may inhibit *Formica aerata* from tending mealybugs. With limited cultural and biological control options, most ant control relies on chemical strategies, including broad-spectrum barrier sprays and toxic ant baits. Broad-spectrum insecticide sprays should be directed at the nests, trails (if present), and the base of each vine. These sprays may provide effective ant control but have several drawbacks: they disrupt natural enemies, target only foraging workers, require repeated application (every 1 to 3 months), and are not always compatible with IPM programs.

Baits (an attractant combined with an insecticide) can be an effective means of delivering a toxicant to the ant colony while reducing undesirable environmental impacts. Unlike contact sprays, baits target nest populations because the baits are foraged by workers and distributed to other workers, queens, and larvae through trophallaxis (food exchange with colony members). Therefore, even the members of the colony not feeding directly on the bait are impacted by the toxicant. Baits also take advantage of foraging habits, especially the Argentine ants' ability to outcompete other species for control of the bait stations. These baits must be slow acting (killing ants in 1 to 4 days), so that foraging ants do not die before exchanging bait with colony members. If the concentration of active ingredient is too high, dead ants will pile up outside bait stations and foraging activity at

the station will diminish or cease. Because baits are slow acting and cannot often be dispersed at each vine, it may take 2 to 3 years to reduce a large ant population, and the ant population may never be eradicated from an area.

Ant baits are typically formulated as gels, granules, or liquids. Gels are popular in household ant control. Granular baits are commonly formulated with a protein or soybean oil attractant, whereas liquid baits typically use sugar as the attractant (fig. 60.8). The choice of attractant should be based on a particular species' dietary preference. Argentine ants, for example, imbibe liquids containing high concentrations of sugar: as much as 99% of the material carried to the nest by foragers on citrus trees was either citrus nectar or honeydew produced by the citrus mealybug. Therefore, Argentine ant baits are often formulated as liquids with a sugary attractant. Conversely, protein baits have been shown to be effective against southern fire ants, and experimental anchovy-based bait significantly reduced foraging activity of *F. perpilosa* in vineyards in the Coachella Valley.

University of California researchers have worked with chemical companies to develop baits for Argentine ants and *Formica* species. Baits are most effective when deployed in early spring (March to April), when developing larvae must be fed (see fig. 60.7) and there are few alternative resources available to foraging ants. This coincides with the seasonal biology of the ants: the most active time for larval development is spring, and targeting the colony at this time will

Figure 60.8 Liquid bait stations registered for use on ants in vineyards and orchards by the ChemSAC arm of the U.S. EPA (fall 2005) include the UC-designed PVC station (A) with bait reservoir (B) and the KM AntPro station (C). *Photos*: M. L. Cooper (A, C); Central Coast Vineyard Team (B).

impact the summer populations. In late summer, the nest is dominated by the worker population, and demand for resources drops because there are few larvae in the nest at this time. Additionally, in late summer, hemipteran honeydew and ripening grapes are increasingly attractive food resources, resulting in a sharp drop in ant activity at bait stations. Therefore, proper timing is essential to the success of the ant baiting program. There will be no significant effect on ant or mealybug populations in the current season if baits are deployed in July instead of April; although the effects will be apparent in subsequent years if baiting continues.

In experimental trials for Argentine ant control, a variety of toxicants have been incorporated into a bait matrix. All toxicants have resulted in season-long, significant decreases in ant populations, as long as the bait matrix remains attractive to the Argentine ant and the concentration of active ingredient is not too high. Not all toxicants have been incorporated into commercially available bait products. Several companies are interested in developing bait for the agriculture market, and more options may become available (see the UC IPM Grape Pest Management Guidelines, www.ipm.ucdavis.edu/PMG/, for updated information).

In the future, the management methods described here may be supplemented by the use of semiochemicals that modify ant behavior. For example, the use of trail pheromones or other chemical attractants could be used to enhance recruitment to bait or permit the use of fewer bait stations in a given area. Alternatively, studies focusing on the chemical ecology of Argentine ants may reveal methods for disrupting Argentine ant foraging or for inducing aggression among nestmates.

REFERENCES

Cooper, M. L., K. M. Daane, E. H. Nelson, L. G. Varela, M. C. Battany, N. D. Tsutsui, and M. K. Rust. 2008. Liquid baits control Argentine ants sustainably in California vineyards. California Agriculture 62(4): 177–183.

Coot, T. W. 1953. The ants of California. Palo Alto: Pacific Books.

Daane, K. M., M. L. Cooper, K. R. Sime, E. H. Nelson, M. C. Battany, and M. K. Rust. 2008. Testing baits to control Argentine ants (Hymenoptera: Formicidae) in vineyards. Journal of Economic Entomology 101:699–709.

Daane, K. M., K. R. Sime, J. Fallon, and M. L. Cooper. 2007. Impacts of Argentine ants on mealybugs and their natural enemies in California's coastal vineyards. Ecological Entomology 32:583–596.

Daane, K. M., K. R. Sime, B. N. Hogg, M. L. Bianchi, M. L. Cooper, M. K. Rust, and J. H. Klotz. 2006. Effects of liquid insecticide baits on Argentine ants in California's coastal vineyards. Crop Protection 25:592–603.

Ebling, W. 1975. Urban entomology. Berkeley: University of California Division of Agricultural Sciences.

Greenberg, L., and J. H. Klotz. 2000. Argentine ant (Hymenoptera: Formicidae) trail pheromone enhances consumption of liquid sucrose solution. Journal of Economic Entomology 93:119–122.

Hooper-Bui, L. M., and M. K. Rust. 2000. Oral toxicity of abamectin, boric acid, fipronil, and hydramethylnon to laboratory colonies of Argentine ants (Hymenoptera: Formicidae). Journal of Economic Entomology 93:858–864.

Ingram, K. K. 2002. Plasticity in queen number and social structure in the invasive Argentine ant (Linepithema humile). Evolution 56:2008–2016.

Klotz, J., L. D. Hansen, H. Field, M. K. Rust, D. Oi, and K. Kupfer. 2009. Urban pest management of ants in California. Oakland: University of California Agriculgure and Natural Resources Publication 3524.

Klotz, J. H., L. D. Hansen, R. Pospischil, and M. K. Rust. 2008. Urban ants of North America and Europe. Ithaca: Cornell University Press.

Klotz, J. H., M. K. Rust, L. Greenberg, H. Costa, P. Phillips, C. Gispert, D. A. Reierson, and K. Kido. 2003. Directed sprays and liquid baits to manage ants in vineyards and citrus groves. Journal of Agricultural and Urban Entomology 20:3140.

Markin, G. P. 1970. The seasonal life cycle of the Argentine ant, Iridomyrmex humilis (Hymenoptera: Formicidae), in Southern California. Annals of the Entomological Society of America 63:1238–1242.

Nelson, E. H., and K. M. Daane. 2007. Improving liquid bait programs for Argentine ant control: Bait station density. Environmental Entomology 36:1475–1484.

Phillips, P. A., and C. J. Sherk. 1991. To control mealybugs, stop honeydew-seeking ants. California Agriculture 45(2): 26–28.

Rust, M. K., D. A. Reierson, and J. H. Klotz. 2004. Delayed toxicity as a critical factor in the efficacy of aqueous baits for controlling Argentine ants (Hymenoptera: Formicidae). Journal of Economic Entomology 97:1017–1024.

Tollerup, K. E., M. K. Rust, K. W. Dorschner, P. A. Phillips, and J. H. Klotz. 2004. Low-toxicity baits control ants in citrus orchards and grape vineyards. California Agriculture 58:213–217.

Tollerup, K., M. K. Rust, and J. H. Klotz. 2007. *Formica perpilosa*, an emerging pest in vineyards. Journal of Agricultural and Urban Entomology 24:147–158.

Tsutsui, N. D., A. V. Suarez, and R. K. Grosberg. 2003. Genetic diversity, asymmetrical aggression, and recognition in a widespread invasive species. Proceedings of the National Academy of Sciences 100:1078–1083.

Vega, S. J., and M. K. Rust. 2001. The Argentine ant: A significant invasive species in agricultural, urban, and natural environments. Sociobiology 37:3–25.

Ward, P. S. 2005. A synoptic review of the ants of California (Hymenoptera: Formicidae), Zootaxa 936. Auckland, New Zealand: Magnolia Press.

Wheeler, W. M. 1960. Ants: Their structure, development, and behavior. New York: Columbia University Press.

61 SOCIAL WASPS AND HONEY BEES

Eric C. Mussen and Rhonda J. Smith

An estimated 10,000 to 12,000 species of wasps and 2,000 species of bees live in California. Nearly all of them are solitary and more likely to be beneficial to farming operations than harmful. However, social wasps and honey bees establish large colonial populations in individual nests. Social wasps are defensive around their nesting sites and can interfere with grape harvest. Wasps and honey bees, attracted to grape flowers during bloom in the spring and to flowering weeds or planted cover in the summer, are usually not considered problematic. But they can be a nuisance when they forage on injured grapes as a source of sugar syrup in late summer through fall, when nectar-producing flowers are scarce.

DESCRIPTION

Paper Wasps

These are the wasps most frequently found nesting in orchards and vineyards. Adult paper wasps (fig. 61.1A) can be seen foraging on flowers and later on injured fruit. Their umbrella-shaped nests are commonly suspended from grapevines, branches and twigs of trees, eaves of buildings, and ceilings of attics, barns, and sheds. The golden paper wasp (*Polistes fuscatus aurifer* Saussure) is the most abundant and widespread native species in California. The worker is about 18 mm (0.7 in) long, with a yellow face and abdomen and legs that are brown near the body and yellow toward the ends. A second native species, the Apache wasp (*Polistes apachus* Saussure), is becoming more abundant in California. The workers are about 20 mm (0.8 in) long, with a golden brown color and yellow stripes. Paper wasps tolerate a certain degree of disturbance before reacting, but once they begin defending their nests, they do so pugnaciously.

The most rapidly growing population of paper wasps in California is an introduced species, the common European paper wasp (*Polistes dominulus* (Christ)). First identified in Massachusetts in the late 1970s, it has moved across the country and has become quite a nuisance. Often confused with yellowjackets because of its striped, bright yellow coloration, like other paper wasps the European paper wasp is a bit more elongated than a yellowjacket and is about 15 mm (0.6 in) long, with a black X on the anterior of its abdomen. In flight, it dangles its hind legs in typical paper wasp fashion. At rest, it can be distinguished by its yellow or orange antennae; antennae of yellowjackets are black. European paper wasps nest in either open or protected locations, building small to large vertical and curved nests as well as the usual horizontal nests. These wasps are rather easily disturbed and tend to sting with little provocation.

Figure 61.1 Common European paper wasp (*Polistes dominulus* (Christ)) (A) compared with a western yellowjacket (*Vespula pensylvanica* (Saussure)) adult worker (B). Note that the antennae of the paper wasps are yellow or orange and those of yellowjackets are black. *Photos*: K. K. Garvey.

Yellowjackets

Commonly occurring in California, yellowjackets (*Vespula* and *Dolichovespula* spp.) are frequently observed foraging in vineyards and orchards, and they occasionally nest in those sites. They are named after the black and yellow striped abdominal coloring of the majority of the species, although some species have a very pale whitish yellow substituted for the deeper yellow. Yellowjackets can be distinguished by the color patterns primarily on the abdomen and also by facial morphology.

Aerial-nesting yellowjackets

Nests of the common aerial yellowjacket (*Dolichovespula arenaria* (Fabricius)) can often be seen attached to the outside of buildings. Nests are as small as a golf ball or as large as softball, with a thumb-sized opening at the bottom. The baldfaced hornet (*Dolichovespula maculata* (Linnaeus))—a black-bodied yellowjacket rather than a hornet—builds nests as large as a basketball and tends to live at moderate elevations in the Sierra and along California's north coast; it is infrequently found in the Central Valley. Workers of both species are 12 to 16 mm (0.45 to 0.63 in) long. The adult *D. maculata* can be distinguished from the adult *D. arenaria* by its black body with white markings on the face, thorax, and tip of the abdomen.

Ground-nesting yellowjackets

The most common and most pestiferous yellowjacket from a human interaction point of view is the western yellowjacket (*Vespula pensylvanica* (Saussure)) (fig. 61.1B). It is predatory when prey is abundant but becomes an efficient scavenger when necessary. This wasp occurs throughout the western states and can become extremely abundant in Sierra foothill locations. The workers are 15 mm (0.6 in) long, and their sting usually results in painful swelling and subsequent itching. The nest often is begun in an abandoned rodent hole or rotting log. The cavity is enlarged by the wasps, and the nest is surrounded by a paper wrapping that is similar to that of the aerial yellowjackets.

Honey Bees

It is very unlikely that honey bees (*Apis mellifera* L.) (fig. 61.2) will nest in a vineyard, unless the property includes a structure containing a substantial cavity in which they can build wax combs. More recently, with colony collapse disorder and infestations of tracheal and varroa mites, these feral colonies are becoming less common. Honey bees are believed to be a vegetarian offshoot of the yellowjacket line, so they are the size and shape of those wasps but are covered with hair for collecting pollen grains. Honey bees vary from banded yellow and black through brown and gray to solid black.

INJURY

In some cases wasps have been observed biting holes in intact grapes (fig. 61.3). Wasps also collect juice leaking from injured grapes and prey on other insects attracted to that food source. Normally, honey bees visit previously wounded grapes to extract the juice from the fruit. If fruit injury is from feeding by other insects, bird damage, or microbial attack, or if splitting is substantial, honey bee and wasp visitation can become quite high.

Figure 61.2 Honey bee (*Apis mellifera*) attracted to grape juice. *Photo*: J. K. Clark.

Figure 61.3 Yellowjackets feeding on berries close to harvest (A) and the damage they can cause (B). *Photos*: L. J. Bettiga.

SEASONAL DEVELOPMENT

Depending on the species of social wasp, the mated female, or foundress, comes out of hibernation in the spring and starts building a paper nest in the ground, in leaf litter on the ground, or considerably above ground. She chews wood or paper to get fibers from which to form the paper to construct her nest. The female raises her first brood alone, hunting for prey and feeding the macerated bodies to her larvae. After rearing a few daughters, which are sterile, the female reproductive assumes the role of a queen (sole egg layer), and her daughters serve as workers. The population increases until late summer, when males and fertile females are produced. In temperate regions, the bulk of the colony then dies, leaving only the newly mated females to reside in protected places over the winter.

The number of individuals in a wasp nest varies with the species of wasp and also with availability of food. A nest of ground-nesting yellowjackets may have many thousands of workers, while a nest of paper wasps frequently has fewer than 100 workers. Protein sources tend to be other insects and spiders for predatory species and bits of meat for scavenger species. Fly larvae in decaying fruits are particularly attractive to some wasps.

NATURAL CONTROL

No natural controls are known that can be applied in the field. Sometimes, birds visit paper wasp nests and eliminate the populations. Wet, long winters appear to reduce wintering populations of many wasp species.

MONITORING GUIDELINES

Monitoring guidelines have not been developed.

MANAGEMENT GUIDELINES

Little can be done about paper wasps short of traveling through the vineyard and eliminating nests individually by knocking them down or spraying them with a rapid knock-down wasp and hornet spray. Burning nests may provide satisfaction, but it is no more effective. Eliminating the nests at night may be preferable, since all the wasps tend to be on the nest at night, and they are less likely to fly in the dark. Protective clothing and a flashlight covered with red cellophane would be prudent choices for this work.

Eliminating the emerging foundress of ground-nesting yellowjackets in the spring reduces the number of nests that are established. This can be accomplished with commercially available yellowjacket traps baited with pheromone. Once the nest is started, it is nearly impossible to find the nesting site unless someone walks too close and is stung or notices high-density foraging flight late in the season. At the end of the season, yellowjacket traps can catch hundreds of workers per day, but they cannot significantly reduce the population.

Aerial-nesting yellowjackets and wasps are equally susceptible to wasp and hornet sprays, but the chemical must be directed upward, through the entrance, into the paper nest. Avoid standing directly under the nest during application, because the liquid chemical splashes down very soon after the spraying begins.

Since honey bees do not nest in vineyards, locating nearby hives and asking the beekeeper to move them is the most effective means to reduce or eliminate honey bee visitation.

REFERENCES

Cervo, R., F. Zacchi, and S. Turillazzi. 2000. *Polistes dominulus* (Hymenoptera, Vespidea) invading North America: Some hypotheses for its rapid spread. Insectes Sociaux 47:155–157.

Ebling, W. 1975. Urban entomology. Berkeley: University of California Division of Agricultural Science.

Watanabe, M. E. 1994. Pollination worries rise as honey bees decline. Science 265:1170.

YELLOWJACKET AND HONEY BEE

Adult

Lepidoptera
Caterpillars

62 LARVAE FOUND IN GRAPE CLUSTERS

Larry J. Bettiga, Lucia G. Varela, and Walter J. Bentley

Although Lepidoptera (moth) larvae are the most common insect pest found in grape clusters, Coleoptera (beetle) and Diptera (fly) larvae can also be found. The following is a pictorial comparison of the more common fully grown larvae found in grape clusters. For more information on a given insect, refer to the appropriate section of this book.

Figure 62.1 Omnivorous leafroller larvae are cream to light green with a light to dark brown head capsule and prothoracic shield. The prothoracic shield may have a dark border on the outer edge. The abdomen has white oval pinacula at the base of the body hairs. *Photo*: J. K. Clark.

Figure 62.2 Orange tortrix larvae are yellow to straw colored, with a tan head capsule and prothoracic shield. The abdomen has less-distinct whitish round pinacula, in contrast to omnivorous leafroller larvae. *Photo*: J. K. Clark.

Figure 62.3 With a yellow-brown head, pale to medium green body, and whitish round pinacula, the light brown apple moth larva is difficult to distinguish from orange tortrix. *Photo*: J. K. Clark.

Figure 62.4 European grapevine moth larva, showing the prothoracic shield with a darker brown to black border. It also possesses white round pinacula on the dorsal abdominal segments. Mature larvae are dark maroon to purple. When fully grown they are half the size of omnivorous leafroller. *Photo*: J. K. Clark.

Figure 62.5 Grape leaffolder larva shows three dark sclerotized markings on the side of the thorax above the second pair of legs. *Photo*: J. K. Clark.

Figure 62.6 Western avocado leafroller has tan markings, dark brown and white lines on the head capsule, and a dark brown border on the lateral edge of the prothoracic shield. Avocado leafroller is not a pest in grapes; it is sporadically found in clusters and is shown here to avoid misidentification. *Photo*: J. K. Clark.

Figure 62.7 Navel orangeworm shows crescent-shaped markings above the second pair of legs. Navel orangeworm is not a pest in grapes; it is shown here to avoid misidentification. *Photo*: J. K. Clark.

Figure 62.8 Driedfruit beetle larva has two small brown spinelike structures (urogomphi) on the end of the abdomen. *Photo*: J. K. Clark.

Figure 62.9 Raisin moth larva with longitudinal reddish stripes and purple pinacula. *Photo*: J. K. Clark.

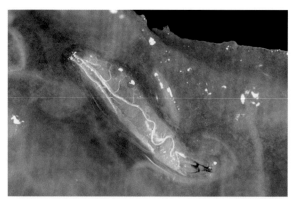

Figure 62.10 *Drosophila* spp. larva with black mouthparts in a narrow head region. No legs are present on *Drosophila* larvae. *Photo*: J. K. Clark.

Lepidoptera
Caterpillars

63 ARMYWORMS

Richard L. Coviello and Walter J. Bentley

Western yellowstriped armyworms (*Spodoptera praefica* (Grote)) (Lepidoptera: Noctuidae) and beet armyworms (*Spodoptera exigua* (Hübner)) (Lepidoptera: Noctuidae) are primarily pests of alfalfa, cotton, and vegetable row crops. They are not known to lay eggs in grapes. Their larvae feed on grape foliage in vineyards adjacent to alfalfa fields or areas having abundant broadleaf weeds. Young larvae cannot move extensive distances, but mature larvae migrate from alfalfa after it has been cut or from weedy areas that have been mowed or dried. Under heavy population pressure, larvae may move out of alfalfa before it has been mowed. Vineyards with native vegetation or legume cover crops may have endemic armyworm populations. Larvae may move into the vines and feed if the cover crop is allowed to dry.

DESCRIPTION

Mature western yellowstriped armyworm larvae are large, from 4 to 5 cm (1.5 to 2 in) long (fig. 63.1). Color can vary considerably, but they are usually flat black with a prominent yellow stripe and several fine whitish yellow stripes on each side, below which are prominent reddish stripes. A flat black spot is located on each side of the first abdominal segment (the segment behind the last pair of true legs). No other caterpillars occurring in grapes have these characteristics. Mature beet armyworms are usually green but can range from reddish to black (fig. 63.2). They have a prominent creamy yellow stripe on each side, with many fine white lines on the back between the stripes. A black spot is located on each side of the mesothoracic segment above the middle pair of true legs.

INJURY

Larvae feed on grape foliage on all parts of the vine and under heavy infestations can completely defoliate the vine. Heavy feeding usually occurs in border rows adjacent to alfalfa or weedy fields and ditch banks; however, where populations exist in cover crops within the vineyard, damage is not limited to the periphery.

SEASONAL DEVELOPMENT

Armyworms overwinter as pupae in small earthen cells just under the surface of the soil. In the warmer regions, a few adults emerge all year long, but the majority of the population emerges in late winter to early spring. Adult females lay clusters of creamy white eggs on host plant leaves. The clusters are covered with scales from the moths' body; those of beet armyworm are off-white, whereas western yellowstriped armyworm clusters

ACTUAL SIZE: WESTERN
YELLOWSTRIPED ARMYWORM

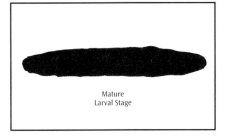

Mature
Larval Stage

Figure 63.1 Western yellowstriped armyworm (*Spodoptera praefica* (Grote)) larva. *Photo*: J. K. Clark.

are gray. Larvae hatch and feed in clusters on the terminal leaves of their host plants, skeletonizing the leaves. As they grow they disperse and feed as individuals, consuming entire leaves. Mature larvae return to the soil to pupate or occasionally pupate on the plant. There are two to three generations per year, depending on the climate.

NATURAL CONTROL

Several generalist predators, such as damsel bugs, assassin bugs, and lacewing larvae, feed on early-stage larvae. Egg parasitoids are not as effective on armyworm eggs as they are on other Lepidopterous eggs because of the scale covering over the egg cluster. Tachinid flies and Ichneumonid parasitoids such as *Hyposoter exiguae* (Viereck) can be very important in moderating larval populations. Naturally occurring *Bacillus thuringiensis* bacteria can sometimes reduce populations. In warm, wet springs, polyhedrosis viruses can infect heavy populations of armyworm larvae and almost completely eliminate them from the fields. This usually occurs, however, only under heavy worm populations and after considerable damage has been done.

MONITORING GUIDELINES

Closely observe neighboring alfalfa fields, weedy fields, and ditch banks for the presence of armyworm larvae. Look for light-colored patches in alfalfa where early-stage larvae are feeding in the tops of the plants. Sweep net samples will help determine population density and stage of growth. As larvae mature, watch for them crawling on the ground and leaving their host plants. There are no damage thresholds established for armyworm in grapes. If, when sweeping for larvae, limp, flaccid, and decaying worms are evident in the net, polyhedrosis virus has infected the population and will eliminate living worms in a few days.

MANAGEMENT GUIDELINES

Weed management on ditch banks and fallow fields can eliminate much of the armyworm threat to vineyards. Where native annuals and legumes are grown as cover crops within vineyards, careful scrutiny of the cover crops is necessary to spot egg clusters and hatching larvae before they can

reach damaging levels. Migrating western yellowstriped armyworm coming out of alfalfa fields can be sometimes managed with a steepwalled trench between the host field and the vineyard. Infestations are usually along border rows, so spraying these few rows is usually sufficient for the entire vineyard. Where populations are endemic on cover crops, spot treatments of hot spots will usually suffice. Only under very unusual situations would the entire vineyard need to be treated. *Bacillus thuringiensis* (Bt) insecticides are effective on young western yellowstriped armyworm and beet armyworm larvae and may be used on early endemic infestations. However, Bt is not effective on the large larvae migrating into vineyards from the outside. Some of the newer classes of insecticides, such as insect growth regulators and spinosads, can be effective without too much disruption of secondary pests within vineyards.

ACTUAL SIZE: BEET ARMYWORM

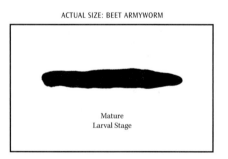

Mature
Larval Stage

Figure 63.2 Beet armyworm (*Spodoptera exigua* (Hübner)) larva. *Photo*: J. K. Clark.

64 CITRUS PEELMINER

Elizabeth E. Grafton-Cardwell and David R. Haviland

Citrus peelminer (*Marmara gulosa* Guillen and Davis) (Lepidoptera: Gracillariidae) (fig. 64.1) is a periodic pest in the Coachella and San Joaquin Valleys on susceptible cultivars of grape and other crops, including citrus, cotton, dry beans, peppers, cucurbits, and ornamentals such as willows and oleander. It moves readily from plant to plant and can maintain a population in low numbers on a wide variety of additional host plants, including nuts, stone fruits, olives, avocados, vegetables, and weeds.

DESCRIPTION

After mating, female moths deposit single eggs on stems or fruit of grapes (fig. 64.2). Females deposit an average of 50 eggs. A small yellowish white larva hatches by burrowing through the surface of the egg into the top tissue layer of the plant (fig. 64.3). As the larva grows, it creates a serpentine mine that enlarges each time the larva molts to a larger size. There are four to five sap-feeding larval instars. The last larval stage is a special form that is pink and has special mouthparts for spinning the pupal case. Just before pupation, the larva leaves the mine and seeks out a crack or crevice in which it pupates. The pupa consists of a sheet of silk adorned with 20 to 40 crystalline balls (fig. 64.4). There is no particular overwintering stage; the insect continues development throughout the year, but the length of a generation is extended during periods of cool temperature. There are seven generations per year in the San Joaquin Valley.

INJURY

Larvae form serpentine mines on the rachises and berries of grapevines. Live larvae in the fruit of table grapes can render them unacceptable for the export market. Damage to fruit is often difficult to see and is most evident on red berries (fig. 64.5). Certain cultivars, such as Redglobe, are most susceptible to damage and seem to be preferred, but the peelminer can attack the stems of any cultivar. Under heavy infestations, peelminers mine the leaves, but this is rare. Peelminer causes no economic damage to wine or raisin grapes.

MANAGEMENT GUIDELINES

Biological control is the primary means of managing this pest. Many native parasites attack peelminer to a limited extent. One eulophid wasp, *Cirrospilus coachellae*, provides some control of peelminer populations on citrus in the Coachella Valley. Two to seven parasites emerge from a single

Figure 64.1 Adult citrus peelminer (*Marmara gulosa* Guillen and Davis). A dark moth, the adult's front wings are mostly brown with tan markings. *Photo*: J. K. Clark.

ACTUAL SIZE: CITRUS LEAFMINER

Sap Feeder   Tissue Feeder   Adult

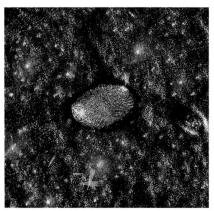

Figure 64.2 Egg of the citrus peelminer. *Photo*: E. Grafton-Cardwell.

Figure 64.3 Peelminer larvae are yellowish, except during the last instar, which is reddish. Larvae are minute, less than 5 mm (0.2 in) long at maturity. *Photo*: E. Grafton-Cardwell.

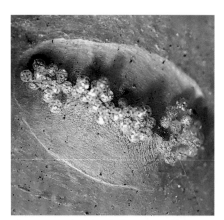

Figure 64.4 Citrus peelminer pupae form a white silk sheet covering with minute crystalline or pale balls. Larvae pupate in protected spots on fruit or in bark crevices or leaf litter. *Photo*: E. Grafton-Cardwell.

Figure 64.5 Larvae tunnel just beneath the surface of the berry. *Photo*: E. Grafton-Cardwell.

peelminer larva. The parasites pupate in the mine and can be seen through the epidermis as small, black pupae surrounded by black meconial pellets (fecal material). After the parasites emerge, several exit holes surround the remains of pupae. Long-term control of this pest will be primarily biological, as it is difficult for pesticides to reach the larvae inside the mines.

Cultivar selection and field location can aid peelminer control. Early table grape cultivars are harvested before peelminers reach damaging levels. For susceptible mid- and late-season cultivars, locate plantings away from neighboring crops such as cotton and dry beans that generate heavy densities of peelminer moths when they are dried for harvest in the late summer and fall. Planting Bt cotton or treating the cotton with insecticides reduces the population, making it less of a threat to the adjacent susceptible grape cultivar.

Frank G. Zalom, Rhonda J. Smith, and Maxwell V. Norton

Cutworms (Lepidoptera: Noctuidae), **one of** the most injurious groups of crop pests worldwide, injure grapes primarily in early spring when their feeding damages or destroys developing buds. Larvae remain in the soil under grapevines or under the bark during the day and emerge to feed after dark. Adults are night-flying moths that seek shelter during the day.

The most common species attacking grapes are the variegated cutworm (*Peridroma saucia* (Hübner)), the spotted cutworm (*Amathes c-nigrum* (L.)), and the brassy cutworm (*Orthodes rufula* (Grote)). These species can be found in coastal, foothill, and San Joaquin Valley grape-growing areas. Other cutworm species can occasionally cause damage. In vineyards these include the greasy, or black, cutworm (*Agrotis ipsilon* (Rothemburg)) and the dark-sided cutworm (*Euxoa messoria* (Harris)).

DESCRIPTION

Inconspicuously marked, cutworms are dull gray or brown caterpillars ranging from 2.5 to 5 cm (1 to 2 in) long when fully grown. The color and markings of their bodies blend well with the soil, where they are often found.

Positive identification is important in controlling cutworms because of behavioral differences in activity. Some species climb on the vines to feed, returning to the soil during the day. Others remain on the vines, under the bark, or in cracks and crevices during the day.

Figure 65.1 Variegated cutworm feeding on bud. *Photo*: J. E. Dibble.

ACTUAL SIZE: VARIEGATED CUTWORM

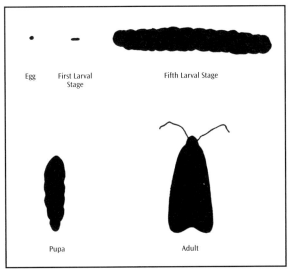

Variegated Cutworm

The adult is a grayish brown moth 2.5 cm (1 in) long, with dark or dusty mottling on the forewings and irridescent to pearly white hind wings. Wings are 4 to 5.5 cm (1.5 to 2.2 in) tip to tip. Adults are found during the day resting under foliage or shaded areas of vines and vineyard weeds, with wings folded over their backs. Eggs are small, round, flattened on top, off-white, and distinctly ribbed; they are usually deposited in massed rows on foliage, limbs, or trunks of plants in early spring. Mature larvae are about 4 to 5 cm (1.5 to 2 in) long, with smooth skin (fig. 65.1). Body color varies from pale gray to a dark, mottled brown intermixed with dull red and yellow dots. There is a row of yellow marks or spots on the top of the larva, especially on the first four abdominal segments, with the eighth abdominal segment having a black W. The spiracles are black and look like a dot on both sides of each abdominal segment. The head is light brown with a dark concave arc on each side when viewed from the front.

Spotted Cutworm

The adult is a dark gray moth about 2.5 cm (1 in) long, with light, dusty gray hind wings. The forewings have a pale, triangular area or spot on the front edge. Wings are 4 cm (1.5 in) tip to tip. Mature larvae are about 3.5 cm (1.4 in) long and are generally a dull gray-brown (fig. 65.2). The common name, spotted cutworm, comes from the row of dark or black elongated triangular markings on each side of the upper body surface of the larvae. The spiracles look like a whitish or yellowish dot on both sides of each abdominal segment. The mandible has four prominent outer teeth and one inner tooth.

Brassy Cutworm

The adult is a moth 1.8 cm (0.7 in) long, reddish or brassy to tan, with a kidney bean–shaped brown spot near the middle of each forewing. Wings are 2.5 to 3 cm (1 to 1.2 in) tip to tip. With a hand lens, hairs can be seen protruding from the compound eye area. Of the cutworms attacking grapes, this is the only one with this characteristic. The mature larvae are also reddish or brassy in appearance and are 2.5 to 3 cm (1 to 1.2 in) long.

INJURY

Cutworms have a broad host range that includes weeds and many types of crop plants, including grapes. Damage to grapevines occurs from bud swell (fig. 65.3) to when shoots are several inches long. Injured buds may fail to develop into shoots, which can cause significant yield reduction

in some cultivars. Temperature may lengthen or shorten the period of spring cutworm feeding. Grapevines can compensate for early-season damage to buds or shoots to some extent, as secondary buds may push. The fruitfulness of secondary buds varies according to cultivar. In certain cultivars, such as Ruby Cabernet, secondary buds are as fruitful as primary buds, and the only damage that occurs when buds or short shoots are destroyed is delayed maturity. Other cultivars, such as Thompson Seedless and Chardonnay, are noted for having unfruitful or significantly less fruitful secondary buds, respectively. In these varieties, destruction of primary buds can be expected to reduce the number of clusters in proportion to the number of buds destroyed.

SEASONAL DEVELOPMENT

In most California production regions, cutworms that attack grapes overwinter in vineyard soil, trash, or grass clumps as immature, quiescent larvae. In warm areas of southern California, some larvae remain active in vineyards throughout the year. When temperatures become warm in early spring (late March to early April), the larvae become active, emerging at night to feed on many kinds of plants present in vineyards. Grapevines first become susceptible to cutworm feeding at bud swell. In the north coast and Delta areas, variegated cutworm larvae normally return to the ground during the day but may also remain under the vine bark (fig. 65.4). In the San Joaquin Valley, variegated cutworm larvae do not return to the soil but move under the bark. Larvae of the spotted cutworm routinely remain

under grapevine bark during daylight hours in all production areas. These behaviors are important to consider for optimal control, since treatments target larvae.

Feeding continues for about 10 days to 2 weeks during rapid bud and shoot growth. It is at this time that most cutworm damage occurs. The mature larvae then return to the soil and hollow out cells or chambers to pupate. The pupal stage lasts 7 or more days. Moths emerge from the soil from April through mid-May. They mate and quickly lay eggs.

The variegated cutworm moth lays eggs in batches of 60 or more on leaves, stems, twigs, and branches of bushes or trees or on fences and buildings. The female of this species can deposit up to 1,000 eggs in her lifetime. Other cutworm species lay their eggs singly or in small patches on leaves or stems of grasses or other plants near the ground.

The egg stage lasts from 2 days to 2 weeks, depending on species, temperature, and other related factors. The hatching larvae feed on low-growing vegetation, but at this time grapevines have enough foliage to withstand their feeding. Moths resulting from this brood lay eggs to produce the late-summer larvae that overwinter.

Most cutworm species have one or two generations per year, but some have three or four generations, and moths may be found from spring to fall. Some cutworm species can persist with a single generation each year because while all other stages are accelerated by high temperature, the prepupal stage (the full-grown, inactive larva) is delayed by higher temperatures.

Natural Control

Natural enemies of cutworms include predaceous or parasitic insects, mammals, parasitic nematodes, pathogens, birds, and reptiles. Hymenopteran (wasp) parasites, including ichneumonids, chalcids, braconids, and sphecids, are also important in regulating populations. Predaceous beetles (often found under bark) and tachinid fly parasitoids also provide biological control.

Monitoring Guidelines

Historical records of cutworm infestation or damage for individual vineyards and areas are useful in developing monitoring strategies. Because cutworm problems are normally spotty or localized, vineyard maps drawn on a yearly basis can help determine persistently infested areas. Begin making observations of possible bud feeding by cutworms during bud swell in early spring. If previous infestations have been mapped, concentrate monitoring on those areas.

Because cutworm infestations are clumped, many sites in a vineyard must be monitored to detect the damage caused by this pest. Randomly select 20 sites within the vineyard to monitor. Check three vines at each site for buds damaged by cutworms (total 60 vines). Cutworms often feed on developing buds and succulent young shoots on one side so that shoots become weakened and fall over. The number of damaged buds that can be tolerated depends on variety. If secondary buds are highly fruitful, little yield loss will result, even when a large proportion of buds are damaged. Varieties with nonfruitful secondary buds will suffer little yield loss if less than 4% of buds are damaged. Treatment of an entire vineyard is seldom needed because cutworm distribution and their damage is normally localized; your vineyard map can help to determine appropriate areas for spot treatment.

Continue monitoring until average shoot growth has reached 15 cm (6 in). If a damaging population does not occur before this growth stage, foliar development will be sufficient to ensure production, and treatment will not be needed.

It is important to make certain that the observed damage is due to cutworms. It is best to actually see the insect feeding at night (fig. 65.5). Mark damaged vines and return to the vineyard that night to look for cutworm larvae on those vines. During the day, larvae may be found under the bark on the cordons and trunk of vines that have feeding damage. They may also be found below vines, hidden under soil clods, trash, or in clumps of weeds.

Feeding by other insects may resemble cutworm damage. Table 65.1 is a key to common insects and damage associated with buds and young shoots. The grape bud beetle

Figure 65.2 Spotted cutworm feeding on bud. *Photo*: J. K. Clark.

Figure 65.3 Cutworm damage to bud. *Photo*: J. K. Clark.

Figure 65.4 Cutworms under bark (arrows). *Photo*: J. K. Clark.

Figure 65.5 Cutworm feeding at night on a bud. *Photo*: J. K. Clark.

(*Glyptoscelis squamulata* Crotch) feeds only on buds and only at night. Click beetles, of which there are numerous species in California, generally feed on buds, shoots, and foliage. They can be easily identified because they feed on buds in full daylight. Branch and twig borer (*Melalgus confertus* (LeConte)) adults burrow into canes at the crotch or bud axil. Their damage leaves a tunnel, and the beetle or its larva is often present. Orange tortrix (*Argyrotaenia franciscana* (Walsingham)) larvae and light brown apple moth (*Epiphyas postvittana* (Walker)) larvae (in areas where it is present) may attack emerging buds or young shoots, but their feeding is generally accompanied by webbing.

MANAGEMENT GUIDELINES

Cultural Control

Cultural practices have not been demonstrated to fully control cutworms on grapes. Removing weeds in late summer or fall may be beneficial because weeds in the vineyard furnish food for cutworm larvae and shelter for the moths to lay their eggs. Plowing or disking of weeds is not recommended before bud swell in spring, because such practices can cause cutworms to move to the grapevines. Furrow and flood irrigation for passive frost protection may bring cutworm larvae to the soil surface, exposing them to adverse weather and predators, and causing significant negative impact to cutworm populations. Use of stickum at the crown of plants can block worms from reaching buds. This is most often done in organic production systems.

Chemical Control

If cultural practices, natural enemies, and climatic factors are not sufficient to hold cutworms to tolerable levels, insecticides may be needed. Unfortunately, few chemicals are highly effective.

Soil-applied insecticide baits can control some cutworms, but they are not effective on the variegated cutworm in the San Joaquin Valley or on the spotted cutworm in any location, because the cutworm does not return to the soil after nightly feeding (it stays on the vine). Hand applications of bait that adheres to upper parts of the vines are somewhat effective.

Bait impregnated with a pesticide must be fresh and properly formulated, as grape-damaging cutworms prefer loose, fluffy bait. Results are best with apple-pomace formulations rather than with hard-textured bran materials.

An insecticide spray can be used and may be easier to apply and more effective than bait applications. A delayed-dormant spray has less impact on cutworm natural enemies than treatments later in the season. A broad-spectrum insecticide used to control cutworms can be disruptive to predators of spider mites and parasites of leafhoppers. The table of relative toxicities of insecticides used in grape to natural enemies and honey bees found in the UC IPM Grape Pest Management Guidelines, www.ipm.ucdavis.edu/PMG/, is a good source for this information. A delayed-dormant barrier application containing a pyrethroid insecticide directed to the vine trunk and its soil interface can discourage cutworms emerging from the soil or that return to the soil each day from climbing onto vines and feeding on swelling buds, and there is some evidence that a hot pepper wax applied twice during this time can also repel cutworms. Check the UC IPM Grape Pest Management Guidelines, www.ipm.ucdavis.edu/PMG/, for insecticides registered to control cutworms.

Table 65.1. Key to insects and their damage associated with buds and young shoots

	If insect or vine shows	Cause/proceed to
Step 1	Insects associated with damage during daylight.	Step 2
	Insects not associated with damage during daylight.	Step 5
Step 2	Webbing present; pale green worm with dark head; location is coastal range or interior coastal valley.	orange tortrix
	Webbing not present; adult beetle; hard-bodied insect with hard front wings covering membranous hind wings.	Step 3
Step 3	Shiny, metallic blue or purple beetle, 4.5 to 5 mm (0.18 to 0.20 in) long (rare).	grapevine flea beetle
	Reddish brown, gray-brown, or black beetles, 7 to 15 mm (0.28 to 0.60 in) long.	Step 4
Step 4	Feeds on apex of buds; reddish brown females are 13 mm (0.5 in) long; grayish brown males are 10 mm (0.4 in) long; will arch body, making an audible snap if held between thumb and forefinger.	click beetle
	Burrows into canes at crotch or bud axil; beetle often entirely within feeding hole; cylindrical bodies are brown or black; females are 15 mm (0.6 in) long; males are 7 mm (0.28 in) long.	branch and twig borer (grape cane borer)
Step 5	Insects associated with damaged areas at night.	Step 6
	No insects associated with damage.	Step 11
Step 6	Adult beetle; hard body is about 6 mm (0.25 in) long and covered with light to dark gray pubescence.	grape bud beetle
	Larva; wormlike body (cutworm).	Step 7
Step 7	Row of dark brown or black, triangular, wedge-shaped markings on each side of the dorsal body surface; mandible with four prominent outer teeth and one inner tooth; spiracles white or yellowish; mature larva approximately 33 mm (1.3 in) long.	spotted cutworm
	No distinct triangular, wedge-shaped markings on dorsal body surface.	Step 8
Step 8	Reddish or brassy coloration; mature larvae 25 to 33 mm (1 to 1.3 in) long.	brassy cutworm
	Dull coloration; not reddish or brassy.	Step 9
Step 9	Light brown head with darker markings; pale gray to dark, mottled brown body coloration often intermixed with tiny, dull red and yellow dots; row of yellow marks on dorsum of abdominal segments; mature larvae 4 to 5 cm (1.5 to 2 in) long.	variegated cutworm
	Body lacking tiny red and yellow dots.	Step 10
Step 10	Pale, narrow stripe on dorsum bordered by an irregular black stripe on each side; narrow pale and dark brown stripes on sides of dorsal surface above spiracles; smooth skin; spiracles dark brown.	dark-sided cutworm
	General color above spiracles nearly uniform; skin bearing convex, rounded, distinctly isolated granules; spiracles black	greasy cutworm (black cutworm)
Step 11	Webbing associated with damaged buds or young shoots; location is coastal range or interior coastal valleys.	orange tortrix
	Webbing not present.	Step 12
Step 12	Tunnels extending into canes at crotch or bud axils.	branch and twig borer (grape cane borer)
	Feeding does not result in tunnels extending into canes.	Step 13
Step 13	Feeding on only one side of bud or young shoot, so that it becomes weakened and falls over.	cutworm
	Feeding starts at tip of bud or young shoot.	cutworm, grape bud beetle, click beetle, or grapevine flea beetle

66 EUROPEAN GRAPEVINE MOTH

Lucia G. Varela, Monica L. Cooper, and Frank G. Zalom

European grapevine moth (*Lobesia botrana* (Denis and Schiffermüller)) (Lepidoptera: Tortricidae) was first reported in the United States from Napa County vineyards in 2009. Native to Mediterranean Italy, it was first described from Austria and is now found throughout Europe, North and West Africa, the Middle East, and eastern Russia. In 2008, it was first reported in Chile and in 2010 in Argentina. It belongs to the subfamily Olethreutinae. Unlike other tortricid moths such as orange tortrix and omnivorous leafroller, European grapevine moth larvae do not roll or feed on leaves. They feed on flower parts and inside the berries. Earlier species names included *Polychrosis botrana* and *Eudemis botrana*. In Europe, common names include *eudemis* (France); *tignolleta della vite* (Italy); *bekreuzter traubenwickle* (Germany); *polilla del racimo de la vid* (Spain); and European grape berry moth and European vine moth.

Grape (*Vitis vinifera*), wild grape (*Vitis* spp.), and spurge laurel (*Daphne gnidium*) are preferred hosts. European literature includes approximately 25 host plant species other than grape. These include gooseberry (*Ribes grossularia*), blackcurrant (*Ribes nigrum*), red currant (*Ribes rubrum*), olive (*Olea europaea*), wild cherry and sweet cherry (*Prunus avium*), and a number of other domesticated and wild hosts. However, *L. botrana* is found only very rarely or accidentally on other hosts, with the exception of *D. gnidium* and *Vitis* species. In olive, only the flowers are infested, not the fruit. Significantly smaller populations have been recorded in California olive groves than in neighboring vineyards. Olive trees abutting vineyards may constitute a source of infestation by moths in the late spring.

Another species of grape berry moth, *Endopiza viteana*, is found east of the Rocky Mountains. This species is native to the eastern United States and causes damage very similar to that of *Lobesia botrana*, but the two species should not be confused. They differ in many ways, including life cycle, host range, pheromone composition, and natural enemies (the Hymenoptera parasitoids in particular). In other regions of the world, including Europe, numerous species are commonly referred to as berry and vine moths, so it is important to verify the scientific name *Lobesia botrana* when searching the literature for information on this pest.

DESCRIPTION

The adult moth is approximately 6 to 8 mm (0.25 to 0.30 in) long, with a wingspan of 11 to 13 mm (0.43 to 0.50 in), with the female being slightly larger than the male. Both males and females have similar mosaic-patterned wings. The first pair of wings (forewings) is tan-cream, mottled with brown and black markings and bluish gray bands (fig. 66.1). The second pair of wings is gray with a fringed border. At rest, the wings are held in a bell shape over the abdomen.

Unlike other common vineyard tortricids that lay eggs in overlapping masses, eggs of *L. botrana* are laid singly on flower parts (fig. 66.2A) or on berries (fig. 66.2B). The eggs are elliptical and flat, approximately 0.6 to 0.8 mm (0.02 to 0.03 in) in diameter. These lentil-shaped eggs are visible to the naked eye. Initially, eggs are iridescent creamy white, turning yellow as the embryo develops, and later developing a black spot when the head of the developing larva

is formed and visible (fig. 66.2C); a hand lens may be needed to observe color changes due to egg development. The larva emerges from the edge of the egg and leaves the translucent, iridescent chorion (outer shell) (fig. 66.2D).

The larvae are similar to those of other tortricids. There are five immature stages (instars), with sizes ranging from 1 mm (0.04 in) at emergence to approximately 12 to 15 mm (0.47 to 0.60 in) when fully grown. Upon emergence, the larva is creamy white with a black head. As it develops, the head and prothoracic shield (first segment behind the head) become tan to yellowish brown. The rear edge (closest to the body) of the prothoracic shield has a darker brown to black border (fig. 66.3). In early

stages, the body is tan to yellow-brown (fig. 66.4). In the fifth larval stage, the cuticle is transparent, so the body takes on the color of its gut contents. This can range from dark green to shades of dark pink and maroon, depending on the larval food source. White pinacula at the base of the body hairs are quite visible on mature larvae (fig. 66.5). The thoracic legs are dark brown to black. The anal comb, a toothed structure on the last abdominal segment, has five to six dark brown teeth.

A fifth-instar larva spins a grayish white silken cocoon in which it pupates. The male pupa is approximately 4 to 7 mm (0.17 to 0.28 in) long, and the female is 5 to 9 mm (0.2 to 0.3 in) long.

Figure 66.1 Female European grapevine moth (*Lobesia botrana*). *Photo*: J. K. Clark.

Figure 66.2 Eggs are laid singly on flower parts (A) and berries (B). As the embryo develops the black head is visible (C). The larva emerges from the edge of the egg and leaves the translucent, iridescent chorion attached to the flower or berry surface (D). *Photos*: J. K. Clark (A, B, D); M. L. Cooper (C).

Figure 66.3 Close-up of mid-size larva, showing head and first segment behind head. *Photo*: J. K. Clark.

Figure 66.4 Mid-sized larva. *Photo*: J. K. Clark.

Figure 66.5 As larvae mature they become darker. *Photo*: J. K. Clark.

INJURY

In early spring, *L. botrana* larvae of the first generation feed on flowers prior to and during bloom. They web individual flowers together to form "nests" (fig. 66.6) and feed on the flower cluster and inside prebloom flowers. Round holes in prebloom flowers and webbing are common signs of larval feeding. Later-generation larvae feed only on the berries. Second-generation larvae feed on green berries, starting about when berries are pea sized. Initially, a larva webs two berries together, then enters one berry where it contacts another. Often, a dark spot surrounds the point of larval entry. As berries grow, larvae hollow them out, leaving the skin and seeds. Injured berries can turn brown to purple and shrivel but remain attached to the cluster because the webbing produced by the larvae prevents injured berries from dropping to the ground. Third-generation larvae cause the greatest damage by webbing and feeding inside berries. As the berries approach maturity, larvae leave the berries to feed within bunches that become

contaminated with frass (excrement) (fig. 66.7). Feeding damage to berries after veraison exposes them to infection by *Botrytis* and other secondary fungi such as *Aspergillus*, *Alternaria*, *Rhizopus*, *Cladosporium*, and *Penicillium*. Secondary pests such as raisin moth (*Cadra figulilella*), fruit flies, and ants may also be attracted to damaged berries.

SEASONAL DEVELOPMENT

European grapevine moth generally completes two to three generations per year, although a partial or complete fourth generation may develop in warmer regions. In the Napa Valley, three generations have been observed. Pupae overwinter in diapause (a resting state) inside silken cocoons found under the bark (fig. 66.8) on the trunk, cordons, and arms, as well as in soil cracks and in hidden places on trellis posts. Adults of the first generation emerge when air temperatures exceed a threshold of 10°C (50°F) for a period of 10 to 12 days. Adult males emerge about a week before females. The first male flight may begin before budbreak

Figure 66.6 First-generation larvae web together cluster parts and feed inside these "nests." *Photo*: M. L. Cooper.

and continue for 10 to 14 weeks. Adults remain hidden during the day, emerging to fly at dusk if temperatures are above 12°C (53.5°F). Mating begins in flight. The majority of females mate only once, although they are capable of mating multiple times. Egg laying begins 1 or 2 days after mating when temperatures are above 14°C (57°F). The mated females typically lay eggs at dusk, responding to olfactory cues and taste stimuli. Eggs of the first generation are glued singly on flat surfaces on or near the flower cluster (e.g., on the bunch peduncle or on the flower bracts or calyptra). A female can lay as many as 35 eggs per day for about 6 days, with a mean of 80 to 140 eggs laid per female, depending on the generation. Adult lifespan is from 1 to 3 weeks, depending on climatic conditions.

Egg hatch depends on temperature and ranges from 10 to 15 days following oviposition when temperatures are from 17° to 20°C (62.5 to 68°F) and 6 to 7 days in summer when temperatures are from 24° to 29°C (75° to 84°F). First-generation larvae web flower parts together and feed on individual flowers and bunch stems. Like other tortricid larvae, when disturbed they wiggle and drop on a silken thread. Larval development is completed in 20 to 30 days, depending on temperature. Pupation occurs inside a webbed cocoon that may be found on the flower cluster, inside the folded border of a leaf, under the bark on cordons, or in soil cracks. Adults emerge 12 to 16 days after pupation. The adult and egg stages are considered to be the most vulnerable to environmental factors.

Female moths of the second and third flight lay eggs individually on shaded berries. A deterrent pheromone deposited during egg laying dissuades other moths from laying eggs on the same berry. A single bunch may be infested with several larvae, but usually only one larva occupies a given berry. Shortly after the larva emerges, it may enter a berry to feed.

In autumn, nights longer than 11 hours during egg or larval development and cooler temperatures initiate diapause. A diapausing pupa can withstand even the cold northern European winters. In early February, during postdiapause development and prior to adult

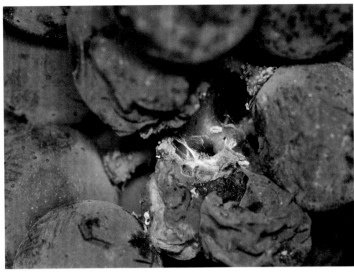

Figure 66.7 Damage at the end of the season, showing shriveled berries after they are consumed from inside, larva excrement, and webbing. *Photo*: J. K. Clark.

Figure 66.8 A webbed cocoon found under the bark is opened to show the pupa. *Photo*: J. K. Clark.

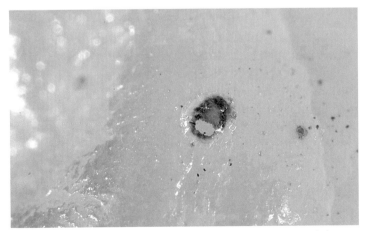

Figure 66.9 A circular hole on the European grapevine moth egg made by an emerging adult parasitic wasp. *Photo*: J. K. Clark.

emergence, pupae may die at temperatures below 8°C (46.5°F).

The lower and upper developmental thresholds are 10°C (50°F) and 30°C (86°F), respectively, although some authors report that the lower threshold is as low as 7°C (45°F). Optimal development conditions are 26° to 29°C (79° to 84°F) and 40 to 70% humidity. Some authors report that larvae die when exposed to temperatures exceeding 34°C (93°F).

Larvae feeding on flower clusters are reported to develop faster than those feeding on grape berries later in the season, and this influences generation time. In degree-days, the first generation is shorter than the summer generations. Using the 10°C (50°F) and 30°C (86°F) lower and upper developmental thresholds, eggs hatch in about 66 degree-days Celsius (DDC) or 118 degree-days Fahrenheit (DDF). Nondiapausing pupae require about 130 DDC (234 DDF) to develop. Adult females may lay eggs about 61 DDC (110 DDF) after emergence. Estimates of development time for a generation vary considerably in the literature, from 427 DDC (767 DDF) to 577 DDC (1,039 DDF) in the first generation and 482 DDC (868 DDF) to 577 DDC (1039 DDF) in later generations. While it is clear that research needs to be done in California to clarify developmental time, our preliminary estimate would be about 463 DDC (833 DDF) for the first generation and 502 DDC (904 DDF) for the second generation.

NATURAL CONTROL

Numerous grapevine moth predators and parasitoids are reported in the European literature. Among the parasitoids are four species of tachinid flies and nearly 100 species of parasitic wasps in the ichneumonid, braconid, pteromalid, and chalcid families. The parasites that are reported to cause the greatest impact are those attacking the overwintering pupa. Initial studies show the ichneumonid wasp (*Exochus* sp.) emerging from overwintering *Lobesia botrana* pupae collected in Napa Valley. Egg parasitism was also observed in Napa Valley (fig. 66.9). In Europe, the most important egg parasitoid is *Trichogramma* species.

MONITORING GUIDELINES

A sex pheromone attracting males is used to monitor male flights. Before budbreak, place red delta-style traps baited with *L. botrana* lures. As the canopy grows, move the trap so that its base touches the top of the canopy about 5 ft (1.5 m) above the ground. Set a minimum of one trap per 10 acres (4 ha); in vineyards smaller than 10 acres, set two traps. Change lures according to manufacturer's recommendations. Check traps weekly, recording the number of moths caught and removing trapped moths from the sticky trap bottom. Plot the weekly catches to determine initiation and peak of male flights in each generation. Continue monitoring with traps until the peak of the third flight.

In the spring, when trap catch numbers peak for the first time, search for eggs on 100 flower clusters, selecting 1 cluster per vine. Note the stage of the majority of the eggs found. Eggs are white when recently laid and turn yellow and later black when larvae are near emergence. A translucent egg chorion indicates that the larva has emerged. Continue monitoring eggs until at least 20% are black cap or hatched. During bloom through fruit set, search for webbing and "nests" (clumps of webbed flower parts and abscised caps). Tease apart the webbing and nests to look for feeding damage and larvae.

Begin monitoring for second- and third-generation eggs on berries 1 week after the first moths of the respective flight are caught in the traps. Inspect 100 bunches, selecting 1 per vine. Observe a cluster in direct sunlight and look for eggs laid singly on the surface of berries. Freshly laid eggs reflect direct light and appear vey shiny and white. Continue monitoring for eggs weekly until 1 week after peak trap catch. Note the timing of egg development and hatch. After egg hatch, monitor bunches for feeding damage (holes or hollow berries), webbing, and presence of larvae.

MANAGEMENT GUIDELINES

In countries where *L. botrana* is established, control measures are targeted at the second generation. This is due in part to the prolonged emergence of the first generation and because of possible reinfestation from untreated neighboring vineyards or alternate hosts. However, treatment of the first generation is recommended if populations are high or if treatments are conducted on an area-wide basis. Under present California conditions where suppression is required, control of both first and second generations may be warranted, given that this is a newly introduced pest. Insecticides are less effective after bunch closure.

Several reduced-risk insecticides are registered for use in grapes to control tortricid larvae. Refer to the UC IPM Grape Pest Management Guidelines, www.ipm.ucdavis.edu/PMG/, for materials registered for tortricid control. If the product chosen has a short residue, more than one application per generation may be needed to provide adequate control of populations. The optimal time to treat the first generation larva is prior to the beginning of bloom. The inflorescence should be fully developed with individual flowers separating but before the first flower caps fall (before 1% bloom). If eggs can be monitored, treatment should start at 20% black cap. For the second and third generations, if an insecticide is used that is ovicidal (killing eggs) and larvicidal, treat when you catch the first moth of that generation. For insecticides that are only larvicidal, monitor egg laying and determine egg hatch, targeting treatment for larva emergence.

Mating Disruption

Female moths emit a plume of sex pheromone that males follow upwind to find and mate with the female. Deploying dispensers loaded with synthetic pheromone throughout the vineyard saturates the air with pheromone, making it difficult for male moths to locate females, thereby delaying or preventing mating. Age at mating affects egg production; older females produce fewer or nonviable eggs, and fewer larvae emerge to damage bunches. Mating disruption is most effective when applied to large areas of over 10 acres (4 ha), area-wide, or to isolated blocks when populations are small. If populations are large, supplemental insecticide applications may be needed.

At present the mating disruption dispensers available are plastic twist-ties that are hand applied on the wires or canes. Mating disruption dispensers must be placed in the vineyard at the beginning of the first flight as indicated by pheromone traps. Follow the manufacturer's recommendations for dispenser rate per acre.

To monitor in a vineyard under mating disruption, place pheromone traps along the edges and in the center of the block. The edge traps give an indication of movement from outside the vineyard. The trap in the center should catch very few to no moths. If the traps in the center of the block are catching males, then mating is not being disrupted and supplemental insecticide applications may be needed. At peak trap catches, monitor for eggs and periodically sample bunches for presence of worms or damage.

References

Briere, J. F., and P. Pracros. 1998. Comparison of temperature-dependent growth models with the development of *Lobesia botrana* (Lepidoptera: Tortricidae). Environmental Entomololgy 27(1): 94–101.

Thiery, D. 2008. Les Tordeuses nuisibles à la vigne. In les Ravageurs de la vigne. Féret, Bordeaux.

67 GRAPE LEAFFOLDER

David R. Haviland and Walter J. Bentley

Grape leaffolder (*Desmia funeralis* (Hubner)) (Lepidoptera: Pyralidae) is a pest in the central and southern San Joaquin Valley. Populations fluctuate greatly. During most years unmanaged populations cause no damage, but during years of high populations a vineyard can be defoliated if not properly managed.

In the larval stage, grape leaffolder rolls and feeds on leaves, reducing their photosynthetic function. Under extreme population densities, vineyards can become defoliated and the insect feeds on the fruit. Effective control measures have resulted in little damage in recent years. The presence of curled and rolled leaves, referred to as leaf rolls, makes this insect highly visible and aids in monitoring its population.

Apparently native to the East Coast, grape leaffolder reached California in the late nineteenth century. It occurs on wild grapes from coast to coast and is especially abundant in the Southwest, Southeast, and Atlantic coastal regions north into Canada. It also ranges south to northeastern Mexico. Most, but not all, populations outside of California fold rather than roll leaves; thus, the common name grape leaffolder. Other plants recorded as hosts are evening primrose, Virginia creeper, and redbud.

Annual populations fluctuate greatly. In Tulare and Fresno Counties, heavy late-season outbreaks occurred in 1945 and 1952 and annually from 1954 through 1959. The population then remained at a low ebb until 1964, when a slow, somewhat inconsistent, upward trend began. Populations were moderate through the late 1980s, and since that time they have remained low to moderate, with heavy populations occurring only in certain localized areas.

Reasons for these fluctuations are not known, nor is it known why populations, even when low, remain in the same localized areas. For instance, the area southwest of Exeter generally associated with the Kaweah River complex, Tulare County, always has grape leaffolder in vineyards, as does the area in Fresno County along the Kings River between Centerville and Kingsburg. This is also true of the area south of Shafter in Kern County.

Figure 67.1 Grape leaffolder moth. *Photo*: F. L. Jensen.

ACTUAL SIZE: GRAPE LEAFFOLDER

Egg	First Larval Stage	Fifth Larval Stage	Pupa	Adult

DESCRIPTION

Adult moths are a distinctive black color and are about 25 mm (1 in) long (fig. 67.1). Males have one large, irregular spot on each hind wing, while females have two smaller spots partly or completely divided. Both sexes have varying amounts of white on the fringes of the wing and two white bands across the abdomen. Male antennae are elbowed; female antennae are uniformly straight. The male abdomen is pointed; that of the female is blunt.

Eggs are small, flat, iridescent, elliptical, and about 0.8 mm (0.03 in) long (fig. 67.2). They are usually laid singly on either the upper or lower surfaces of leaves, with the lower surface preferred. Many are laid against a vein, where abundant eggs may overlap. The easiest way to see them is to remove a leaf from a vine and turn it slightly in the sun so that the eggs reflect light. Both hatched and unhatched eggs glisten. Unhatched eggs are iridescent; hatched eggs look silvery. Under a hand lens, an unhatched egg appears convex; a hatched egg is concave with a torn edge where the larva has emerged.

Larvae are about 1.6 mm (0.065 in) long when hatched and 15 to 22 mm (0.60 to 0.87 in) long when fully grown (fig. 67.3). They undergo five instars before pupation. There are no characteristic marks for field identification on the first two instars. Third-instar larvae have a small black spot on each side of the body above the second pair of legs on the middle segment of the thorax. On the fourth instar there are two spots, the second being indistinct early in this stage. The fifth instar has three distinct spots on each side of the thorax and two spots near the anal end.

As the larvae feed, ingested leaf tissue shows through the translucent body wall, giving them a green color. Feeding stops at the end of each instar, the gut is voided, and the green coloration changes during molting to tan. Many people misinterpret this color as evidence of disease, parasitism, or insecticide poisoning. As the larva resumes leaf feeding, the green body color reappears. Larvae that feed on grape berries are uniformly light brownish tan instead of green (fig. 67.4).

The pupal case is brown and about 13 mm (0.5 in) long (fig. 67.5). It is found within the rolled leaves, often in the midst of black fecal pellets.

INJURY

Vine damage occurs through reduced leaf surface by rolling and larval feeding (fig. 67.6). Damage depends on population size and the time of year.

Defoliation studies show that Thompson Seedless vines tolerate about 20% leaf loss when damage occurs a month after fruit set. Greater damage can be tolerated if it occurs even later. Vine tolerance to the number of leaf rolls has not been studied in detail. Observations on the cultivar Emperor indicate that first-brood larvae (April–mid-June) usually are too low in number to cause damage. Emperor vines tolerate about 200 leaf rolls per vine in either the second (June–late July) or third brood (late August–late September) without adverse effect. Healthy Emperor vines keep growing late in the season, so the leaf surface

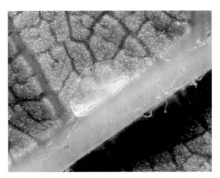

Figure 67.2 Leaffolder egg. *Photo*: J. K. Clark.

Figure 67.3 Leaffolder larva. *Photo*: J. K. Clark.

Figure 67.4 Prepupal stage. *Photo*: J. K. Clark.

Figure 67.5 Pupal stage in opened leaf envelope. *Photo*: J. K. Clark.

is partially restored from that lost due to the second brood.

Second-brood damage from moderate to high populations can defoliate as much as 50% of a vineyard, well beyond an economic level, and worms may be found in fruit (fig. 67.7). In extreme cases, larvae of the second brood can cause 100% defoliation of individual vines and result in over 50% crop loss for early-maturing table grapes. Crop losses are due to the combined effects of clusters contaminated by larvae, bunch rots due to feeding wounds, sunburn, and fruit discoloration as a result of defoliated canopies. Wine grapes with large numbers of larvae may be rejected at the winery or diverted for distilling.

The third brood develops from late August to late September. This brood develops the highest populations. Even moderate numbers of leaffolders in this generation can completely defoliate vines and infest clusters. Defoliation of primary shoots stimulates the growth of lateral buds. Lateral buds are not the primary buds that give rise to the following year's crop. It is not obvious that any crop reduction results from this damage. Studies show that a 10% reduction in crop occurs the next year when Thompson Seedless vines are 60% defoliated in early September. Yield reduction is due to smaller, not fewer, clusters. Crop reductions do not become more severe than 10%, even when vines are defoliated for 10 consecutive years.

Grape leaffolder prefers native American grape cultivars to vinifera cultivars. Shoot or sucker growth from rootstocks of American parentage is often heavily attacked.

SEASONAL DEVELOPMENT

Three broods occur per year, with a partial fourth in some areas. Moth flight periods, and the time required for each development stage, are shown in table 67.1. There may be overlapping of broods.

Figure 67.8 shows moth-trapping studies in a 4-year period. A long flight period for first-brood adults was observed with a relatively short flight period for the second brood and a slightly longer period for the third brood. Generally, more moths were trapped in the second and third broods than in the first. Brood timing may vary by up to 2 weeks from year to year and up to 10 days from vineyard to vineyard in the same year.

Adults fly primarily at night. When less abundant, only an occasional moth is seen during the day, with most remaining hidden within

Figure 67.6 Leaf rolls made by grape leaffolder (A) and close-up of grape leaffolder roll (B). *Photos*: J. K. Clark (A); F. L. Jensen (B).

Figure 67.7 Very heavy grape leaffolder damage exposes fruit. *Photo*: J. K. Clark.

the vine canopy. More abundant second- and third-brood populations result in more adults seen flying during the day. Adults live about 9 days in the field.

First-brood adults seek wind protection. Thus, they may lay their eggs on vines around barns and windbreaks or seek the densest parts of the vine. Shoots developing near the ground are frequently preferred for oviposition.

Most eggs are deposited on the second through fifth day of oviposition. The number of eggs per female has not been accurately verified. One worker reported 60 while another about 200 per female. First-brood number of eggs per leaf is usually low. Second and third broods may have numerous eggs, as many as 10 to 15 per leaf. Most eggs are fertile and hatch in 10 to 17 days in spring and 4 to 5 days in summer.

The young larvae usually feed in groups where eggs were laid. Larvae seek protection between two touching leaves, between the overlapping area at the base of the leaf, or inside leaf rolls made by the previous brood (fig. 67.9). A few larvae, especially in the first brood, feed unprotected on the leaf surface. Group feeding by young larvae never goes completely through the leaf; outer layers of epidermal leaf cells are always left. This creates a characteristic pattern of feeding injury. Thus, the presence or past occurrence of young larvae, either between leaves or in old rolls, is easily recognizable (fig. 67.10). Epidermal leaf cells are colorless, as they contain no chlorophyll. These cells dry up and turn brown in 1 to 3 days. The tissue remains intact and continues to protect the larvae. With heavy populations there may be more than 20 larvae sharing a niche between touching leaves or in old rolls.

After about 10 days of feeding (second and third broods), larvae reach the fourth instar and are ready to make pencil-sized leaf rolls. Some third-instar larvae make small leaf rolls. Larvae make leaf rolls only during darkness.

Fourth- and fifth-instar larvae eat only the free edge of the leaf inside the roll. Usually there is only one larva in a new roll; when populations are abundant there may be two larvae per roll. Shortly after a brood starts making and inhabiting leaf rolls, about half the rolls become empty because each larva exhausts its food supply inside the roll. It then vacates and rolls another leaf or pupates. Each larva makes at least two leaf rolls before completing feeding.

Disturbed larvae wriggle vigorously to escape, frequently falling to the ground. They do not usually descend on a silken strand as does omnivorous leaffolder (*Platynota stultana* (Walsingham)). Both species are sometimes found feeding together between leaves or in leaf rolls.

As the fifth-instar larva completes development, it makes a pupal envelope on the edge of a leaf. The envelope is a small section of leaf partially cut away, folded, and tightly webbed together from within. The envelope usually remains attached to the leaf in the first and second broods. The third-brood envelope often separates from the leaf and is found underneath the vine with leaves and other debris.

Inside the envelope the larva becomes shorter and broader, turns pinkish, and gradually transforms into a pupa. The pupal stage lasts from 1 to 2 weeks, except for the third-brood pupae, which overwinter. A few third-brood larvae pupate underneath the grapevine's loose bark, and some first- and second-brood larvae pupate in leaf rolls rather than in leaf envelopes.

Table 67.1. Average moth flight periods and time required for completion of various developmental stages of the grape leaffolder (Fresno)

Brood	Egg laying period	Time required			
		Eggs to hatch (days)	Larval stages (weeks)	Pupal stages	Egg to moth emergence (weeks)
first	Apr 2–May 24	10–17	3–4	10 days–2 weeks	6.5–7.5
second	Jun 15–Jul 15	4–5	2–3	7–11 days	4–5
third	Aug 3–Sep 5	4–5	3–5	overwinter	—

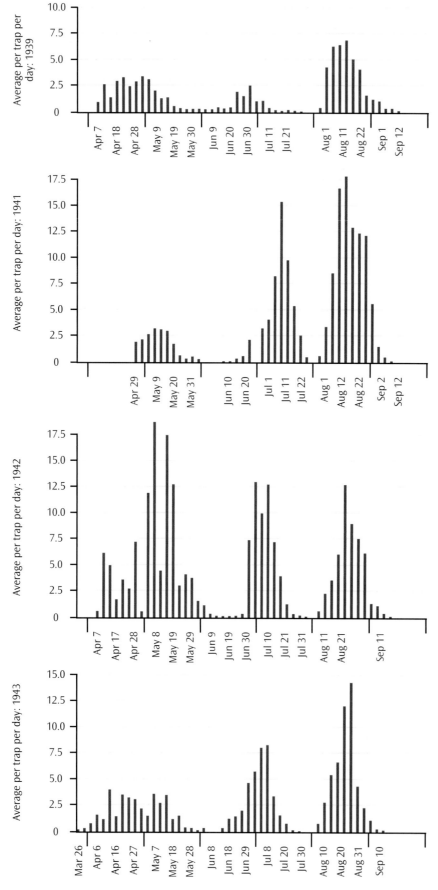

Natural Control

The most commonly observed parasite of grape leaffolder is the larval parasite *Bracon cushmani* (Muesbeck). This small wasp (Hymenoptera), about the size of the gnat but with a fat abdomen, reproduces on third-instar and older larvae (fig. 67.11). After stinging and paralyzing a larva, it lays one to several eggs on the body (fig. 67.12). Hatched wasp larvae feed externally on grape leaffolder larvae (fig. 67.13) and pupate near the consumed bodies (fig. 67.14). Parasites per host average about 8 but range from 1 to 20, depending considerably on the size of the parasitized larva. Parasitism often is in the range of 30 to 40% but can be higher. Some years these wasps may be seen flying around vines by the thousands.

Populations of *Bracon cushmani* usually increase as the summer progresses and frequently reduce the size of the second and third brood to such small numbers that little increase in the grape leaffolder population can be detected.

Two tachinid parasite flies (Diptera), *Nemorilla pyste* (Walker) and *Erynnia tortricis* (Coquillett), attack grape leaffolder. Both are larval parasites. *Nemorilla* is effective on later instars, but it appears too late in the season to regulate infestation. *Erynnia* attacks a variety of small lepidoptera. Females deposit one to several chalky or pearly white eggs on the head and thorax regions of the larvae. When it hatches the parasitic larva invades the host body, develops, and pupates within the grape leaffolder pupa, causing it to appear shorter and more blunt than normal.

Average number of moths per trap per day

Figure 67.8 Sample of average number of grape leaffolder moths taken per trap per day during 4 years of trapping with malt syrup bait traps. Numbers of males and females are about equal.

Two hymenopteran pupal parasites are occasionally collected, *Brachymeria ovata* (Say) and *Coccygomimus sanguinipes* (Cresson), but little is known of their activity or benefit. Grape leaffolder eggs attacked by *Trichogramma* species turn dark, but *Trichogramma* is not believed to be an effective parasite because of its erratic activity and the low percentage of parasitism.

General predators somewhat influence grape leaffolder populations. Many species of spiders feed on larvae; others capture adults in webs. Wasps (*Polistes* spp.) collect larvae as food for their own larvae, but these wasps are not numerous under ordinary vineyard conditions. Birds, primarily blackbirds, have been observed feeding heavily on larvae only after vineyards were essentially defoliated.

MONITORING GUIDELINES

Eggs may be hard to find, but larvae are not; their characteristic group feeding can easily be recognized at least a week before leaf rolling. Even if these signs are missed, some leaf rolls begin to appear before the bulk of the brood shows leaf-rolling activity. These first rolls appear on the upper part of the vine where they are easily seen. Monitoring leaf rolls is currently the best way to monitor grape leaffolder.

Grape leaffolder populations are not uniformly distributed in a vineyard. One area may harbor a large infestation; another may show a much smaller infestation. But the same areas in a vineyard generally tend to be infested year after year and can be watched as guides to population trends.

Moths can be monitored as a guide to general leaffolder populations or to keep track of the broods. A sex pheromone has been identified but is not available commercially for use in pheromone trapping programs. The moths themselves show some flight activity during daytime or can be seen at night around porch lights. Moths can also be caught in bait traps containing fermenting syrup or terpinyl acetate, or with black-light traps.

MANAGEMENT GUIDELINES

Deciding to Treat

In the past growers were encouraged to treat first-brood populations on the premise that this was the most effective treatment. This is now considered invalid; there does not seem to be a correlation between the past season's population and the current season's first brood or with later populations. Treatment of the first brood does not preclude the need for treating later broods. In general, each brood increases one- to five-fold over the previous brood, but there are many instances of population declines. Each brood must be inspected and judged as to its potential seriousness.

Treatment guidelines have not been developed. If population levels appear to be increasing, examine the vineyard every 2 or 3 days while larvae are making leaf rolls. If the brood continues to increase, it may require treatment. Typical populations are unevenly distributed. Decisions must be made as to whether to treat a few heavily infested spots. In wine or raisin grapes, a few defoliated vines represent little loss. Table grape growers with a similar population would probably treat because the fruit is more susceptible to damage from exposure and sunburn.

Timing Applications

Grape leaffolders are most vulnerable to insecticides while they are in their early instars prior to rolling the leaf. As with most pests, small larvae are easier to kill than large ones, and larvae that feed inside leaf rolls can be partially to fully protected from insecticides that work by contact or must be ingested. Treat immediately in an emergency situation where heavy defoliation is occurring or larvae are beginning to enter the clusters. Make sure that coverage is sufficient to penetrate the leaf rolls and the clusters.

Figure 67.9 Feeding damage of leaves tied together by leaffolder larvae. *Photo*: J. K. Clark.

Figure 67.10 Leaves pulled apart show young larvae and damage. *Photo*: J. K. Clark.

Figure 67.11 *Bracon cushmani* parasite stings grape leaffolder larva. *Photo:* J. K. Clark.

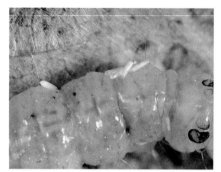

Figure 67.12 Eggs of *Bracon cushmani* laid externally on grape leaffolder larva. *Photo:* J. K. Clark.

Figure 67.13 Larvae of *Bracon cushmani* feed externally on grape leaffolder larva. *Photo:* J. K. Clark.

Figure 67.14 *Bracon cushmani* cocoons next to consumed grape leaffolder larva. *Photo:* J. K. Clark.

In typical years, first-brood larvae rarely need to be treated. If necessary, insecticides applied at bloom can be effective. For second and third broods, apply just as the brood begins to make new leaf rolls. Second-brood treatments typically fall in the period of July 5 to 15, and third-brood treatments fall in the period from August 25 into early September. Remember that there may be a few off-brood larvae, and brood times vary according to the year and the particular vineyard involved. To determine whether the leaf rolls are being made by the first larvae of the main brood, look for eggs and consider the numbers and sizes of the larvae feeding in old leaf rolls or between leaves. Optimal timing would be after almost all eggs have hatched but before any larvae enter latter parts of the third stage, when they begin to roll leaves.

The necessity for careful timing depends on the insecticide used and whether multiple pests are being targeted. For example, insecticides that must be ingested perform best when applied prior to leaf rolling. However, this timing may not be optimal from an overall insect management standpoint if other worm pests, such as omnivorous leafroller and western grapeleaf skeletonizer, also need to be controlled. Timing of insecticides is less important when using newer larvicides that target only lepidopterous larvae (worms). However, these products still work best prior to the formation of leaf rolls. The use of broad-spectrum insecticides should be reserved for later in the season so they do not disrupt biological control of mites and other grape pests.

Guidelines for the use of insecticides, including current listings of products for grape leaffolder, are available within the UC IPM Grape Pest Management Guidelines, www.ipm.ucdavis.edu/PMG/.

How to Treat

For the second and third broods, direct the insecticide to the tops of the vines because coverage is vital; treat each side of the row.

Aerial applications are satisfactory because the insecticide is deposited on top of the vines, where the larvae concentrate. Late in the brood, when most of the larvae are in leaf rolls, aerial application may not result in as good a deposit inside the leaf rolls as ground application, but it is certainly adequate for emergency treatment. Control can reduce a moderately damaging infestation by 90 to 95%. With heavy populations, reductions range from 80 to 90%. Some larvae always survive a treatment; the heavier the infestation, the more survivors.

REFERENCES

AliNiazee, M. T., and F. L. Jensen. 1973. Microbial control of the grape leaffolders with different formulations of *Bacillus thuringiensis.* Journal of Economic Entomology 66:157–158.

AliNiazee, M. T., and E. M. Stafford. 1972. Seasonal flight patterns of the omnivorous leafroller and grape leaffolder in central California vineyards as determined by blacklight traps. Environmental Entomology 1:65–68.

———. 1973. Sex pheromone of the grape leaffolder, *Desmia funeralis* (Lepidoptera:

Pyralidae): Laboratory and field evaluation. Annals of the Entomological Society of America 66:909–911.

Barnes, D. F. 1944. Notes on the life history and other factors affecting control of the grape leaf folder. Leaflet E-616. USDA, Agricultural Research Administration.

Donohoe, H. C., and G. H. Hallostian. 1937. Notes on the grape leaf folder and its parasites in the San Joaquin Valley. Journal of Economic Entomology 30:967.

Doutt, R. L., J. Nakata, and F. E. Skinner. 1969. Parasites for control of grape leaf folder. California Agriculture 23(4): 4.

Jensen, F. L. 1969. Microbial insecticides for control of grape leaffolder. California Agriculture 23(4): 5–6.

Jensen, F. L., and M. T. AliNiazee. 1972. Microbial insecticides for grape leaffolder control. California Agriculture 26(7): 5.

Stafford, E. M., F. L. Jensen, and H. Kido. 1960. Control of the grape leaf folder in California. Journal of Economic Entomology 53:531–534.

68 LIGHT BROWN APPLE MOTH

Larry J. Bettiga and Lucia G. Varela

Light brown apple moth (*Epiphyas postvittana* (Walker)) (Lepitoptera: Tortricidae) is a tortricid leafroller moth native to Australia. It is now established in New Zealand, Great Britain, Ireland, and Hawaii. It was first identified in California in Alameda County in March 2007. The first detections were in the San Francisco and Monterey Bay area counties. It has since been detected in all coastal counties from Sonoma to San Diego and in some Central Valley counties, especially around the Sacramento River Delta. It is known to feed on 250 plant species in over 50 families, with preference for plants in the aster (Asteraceae), legume (Fabaceae), knotweed (Polygonaceae), and rose (Rosaceae) families. Light brown apple moth has been reported as a pest on apple, pear, peach, apricot, citrus, persimmon, avocado, walnut, grape, kiwifruit, strawberry, caneberries, and cole crops. It may also infest oak, willow, poplar, cottonwood, alder, pine, eucalyptus, rose, camellia, jasmine, chrysanthemum, clover, plantain, and many other plants. In California it may encounter additional hosts it was not previously known to infest.

Presently in California there are two tortricid leafrollers, subfamily Tortricinae, that may appear as pests in vineyards. Orange tortrix (*Argyrotaenia franciscana*) is common in coastal vineyards; the omnivorous leafroller (*Platynota stultana*) is found in hot inland valleys but may also be present in the warmer coastal areas. Light brown apple moth may cause damage similar to that of the two leafrollers above. In its native range, it does not do well at high temperatures but does thrive in cooler areas with mild summers.

DESCRIPTION

Like other tortricids, light brown apple moth adults hold their wings flat over their abdomen and, when viewed from above, appear bell-shaped. They possess protruding mouthparts that resemble a snout, although not as pronounced when compared with omnivorous leafroller. The antennae are simple, not featherlike. The length of a resting moth is about half its wingspan. Adult size may vary during the season, with larger individuals

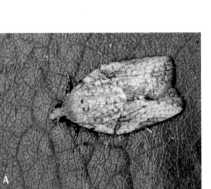

Figure 68.1 Adult light brown apple moths are light brown with dark brown markings. A male is shown in (A) and a female in (B). *Photos*: J. K. Clark.

ACTUAL SIZE: LIGHT BROWN APPLE MOTH

| Egg Mass | First Larval Stage | Fifth Larval Stage | Pupa | Adult |

present during cool, wet months and smaller individuals present during warm, dry months. The length of the forewing (the front wing—the one on top when the moth is at rest) in the male is approximately 8 mm (0.3 in), with a range of 6 to 10 mm (0.25 to 0.40 in), and in the female the length is 7 to 13 mm (0.28 to 0.50 in) (fig. 68.1).

There is a considerable variation in the coloration of the wings, especially on the males. The basal half (closest to the head) of the male forewing may be light brown to pale yellow, while the distal half (farthest from the head) is reddish brown. In strongly marked forms, the distal half of the forewing may vary from reddish brown to blackish with purplish mottling, and the basal half is sparsely speckled with black. In some males this two-tone wing coloration of the forewings may be absent. Instead, they are light brown with a slightly darker oblique marking. In the female, forewing color varies from uniform light brown, with almost no distinguishing markings or with a dark spot in the center front of the folded wings, to the typical oblique markings of the male but with less contrast between the basal and distal halves. Hind wings (back wings) of both sexes are pale brown to gray, either uniform in color or mottled with wavy dark brown markings. Males have an extension of the outer edge of the forewing, called the costal fold, that runs from the base of the wing to 40% of the length of the wing edge (fig. 68.2). This is an expanded part of the wing that folds up over the front edge of the wing as a flap. Females do not have the costal fold.

The eggs are white to light green, broadly oval, flat with a pebbled surface, and are laid slightly overlapping each other. The egg mass is covered with a greenish transparent coating (fig. 68.3). An egg mass may contain from 2 to 170 eggs but typically has 20 to 50 eggs. Egg masses are deposited on the upper surface of leaves. As the eggs develop, they change to paler yellow-green. Immediately prior to hatching, the dark head of the developing caterpillar is visible.

The newly hatched larva is pale yellow-green, 1.5 to 2 mm (0.06 to 0.08 in) long, and has a dark brown head. There are five to six larval instars, or stages. Mature larvae range from 10 to 18 mm (0.4 to 0.7 in). The head is light yellow-brown, and the prothoracic shield (segment behind the head) is light greenish brown with no dark markings (fig. 68.4). The body is medium green with a darker green central stripe that may continue to the prothoracic shield; larvae may also have darker stripes on both sides. Hairs on the body are whitish. The thoracic legs are the same color as the head but paler, and they are also unmarked. In the anal region, there is a greenish anal comb with seven teeth (a comb-shaped structure at the tail end of the larva). An overwintering larva may have a darker head and prothoracic shield.

The pupa is found in a thin-walled silken cocoon between two leaves or cluster parts webbed together. The pupa turns from green to brown as it matures. It is dark reddish brown and 10 to 15 mm (0.4 to 0.6 in) long.

Based on morphology it is difficult to distinguish light brown apple moth larvae from other tortricid species found in vineyards. DNA analysis is necessary to confirm a potential light brown apple moth identification.

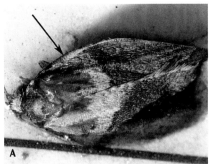

Figure 68.2 Dorsal view of trapped male with costal fold pointed out by an arrow (A) and a close-up of the costal fold (B). *Photos*: J. K. Clark.

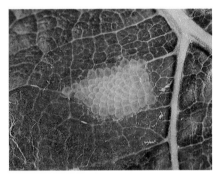

Figure 68.3 Egg mass of light brown apple moth on leaf. *Photo*: A. Weeks.

Figure 68.4 The larva of light brown apple moth is pale to medium green with a light brown head. *Photo*: J. K. Clark.

INJURY

As with other leafrollers, the primary damage is caused by larvae entering bunches and feeding along the rachis (bunch stem) and on the berries. Damage to developing and ripening bunches can increase the incidence of Botrytis and summer bunch rots.

Overwintering larvae may feed on developing buds in spring. Injured buds may fail to develop shoots or clusters. In early spring larvae can cause loss of flowers or newly set berries.

SEASONAL DEVELOPMENT

A degree-day model used for predicting light brown apple moth development indicates that there will most likely be two to three generations per year in the central and north coast areas of California and three or four generations per year in the Central Valley and southern California. In Australia, New Zealand, and the British Isles, generations overlap. Light brown apple moth does not have a winter resting stage (diapause). Cold winter temperatures slow larval development considerably. Thus, the pest overwinters as a second- to fourth-instar larva feeding on weeds and herbaceous plants, on grape buds, or on mummies on the vine and other plant material. Larvae may survive for up to 2 months in the winter without feeding.

Adult moths emerge after one to several weeks of pupation and mate soon after emergence. They stay sheltered in the foliage during the day, resting on the underside of leaves. Moths fly 2 to 3 hours after sunset and before daybreak. Females begin to lay eggs 2 to 3 days after emerging, depositing eggs at night. The majority of the eggs are laid between day 6 and 10 after emergence, but females can continue to lay eggs for 21 days. Females prefer to deposit their eggs on smooth leaf surfaces. Females usually lay a total of 120 to 500 eggs but can lay up to 1,500 eggs.

Males disperse farther than females. Moths fly short distances to find a suitable host. Most moths fly no farther than 100 m (330 ft), but some may fly as far as 600 m (2,000 ft). Adults are less likely to leave areas with high-quality hosts. Adult life span is 2 to 3 weeks, with longevity influenced by host plant and temperature.

An egg takes from 5 to more than 30 days to hatch, depending on temperature, with an average of 5 to 7 days at 28°C (82.5°F). The lower and upper developmental thresholds for light brown apple moth are 7° and 31°C (45° and 88°F), respectively. Larvae emerge from eggs after 1 to 2 weeks and spread out in search of suitable feeding sites. Early in the spring larvae are found feeding on leaves on the young shoots. Once a feeding site is found, the larva forms a silken shelter near a vein on the underside of the leaf and begins to feed. Second and later stages feed between leaves webbed together and may also feed on flower clusters. When disturbed they wriggle violently, suspend themselves from a silken thread, and drop to the ground. Larval development can take from 3 to 8 weeks, depending on temperature. Pupation is completed within the shelter made from rolled-up leaves or webbing inside clusters. The pupal stage lasts 1 to 3 weeks. Completion of the entire life cycle requires 620 degree-days C, or 1,116 degree-days F. In the summer there may be 1 or 2 generations, depending on temperature. Later-generation larvae continue to feed on leaves, but they also enter the bunch as early as bloom. They form webbing along the bunch stem and feed on developing berries.

NATURAL CONTROL

From surveys of light brown apple moth conducted on host plants in urban areas, 12 indigenous parasitoid species were reared. The most common were the egg parasitoid *Trichogramma fasciatum* (Perkins) and the larval parasitoids *Meteorus ictericus* (Nees) and *Enytus eureka* (Ashmead). Leafrollers are controlled by several predators such as lacewings, spiders, minute pirate bugs, damsel bugs, and big-eyed bugs, and by several parasitic wasps. Since predators are generalists, they will feed on light brown apple moth.

MONITORING GUIDELINES

Light brown apple moth pheromone lures are commercially available and may be used to monitor male moth flights. A degree-day model has been developed and needs to be validated under California conditions; check the UC IPM Grape Pest Management Guidelines, www.ipm.ucdavis.edu/PMG/, for updates.

MANAGEMENT GUIDELINES

Cultural control practices can reduce overwintering populations. Mow broadleaved plants before budbreak. Remove cluster mummies when pruning and place them in the row middles to be chopped.

If insecticide treatment is necessary, then time the applications by monitoring flights with pheromone traps, tracking seasonal development with a degree-day model, and field monitoring. Several reduced-risk insecticides are available for control of light brown apple moth. Spraying is most effective after eggs have hatched but before caterpillars build feeding shelters. It is important to control larvae early in the season before bunch closure. Insect growth regulators are registered for the control of leafrollers in grapevines. *Bacillus thuringiensis* and a formulation of spinosad are approved for use on organically certified grapes.

If a suspected light brown apple moth caterpillar is found, collect it and the webbed leaves or fruit where it is feeding and take the sample to the local county agricultural commissioner.

If light brown apple moth becomes more widely established in California, vineyard production costs will increase due to additional monitoring (traps and scouting) needed for this pest. Control measures may be necessary in regions where climatic conditions favor light brown apple moth and natural enemy populations are not sufficient to keep populations under control.

References

Danthanarayana, W. 1975. The bionomics, distribution and host range of the light brown apple moth, *Epiphyas postvittana* (Walk.) (Tortricidae). Australian Journal of Zoology 23:419–437.

Suckling, D. M., and E. G. Brockerhoff. 2010. Invasion biology, ecology, and management of the light brown apple moth (Tortricidae). Annual Review of Entomology 55:285–306.

Varela, L. G., M. W. Johnson, L. Strand, C. A. Wilen, and C. Pickel. 2008. Light brown apple moth's arrival in California worries commodity groups. California Agriculture 62(2): 57–61.

Varela L. G., J. T. S. Walker, P. L. Lo, and D. J. Rogers. 2010. New Zealand lessons may aid efforts to control light brown apple moth in California. California Agriculture 64(1): 6–12.

Wang, X., K. Levy, N. J. Mills, and K. M. Daane. 2012. Light brown apple moth in California: A diversity of host plants and indigenous parasitoids. Environmental Entomology 41(1): 81–90.

69 OMNIVOROUS LEAFROLLER

Richard L. Coviello and Maxwell V. Norton

Since the 1960s omnivorous leafroller (*Platynota stultana* Walsingham) (Lepidoptera: Tortricidae) has become a major pest widely distributed in California's San Joaquin and Sacramento Valley vineyards. It has also been found in some of the warmer coastal areas.

Omnivorous leafroller reduces grape yields and quality in two ways: directly by feeding on flowers and developing berries and indirectly by providing an entry site for bunch rot organisms that damage clusters. Leaf feeding is not significant.

As the name omnivorous implies, the omnivorous leafroller larva feeds and develops on many different plants; therefore, adjacent orchards, row and field crops, ornamentals, and weeds may be sources of infestation for the vineyard. Other crops attacked by omnivorous leafroller include alfalfa, apple, apricot, avocado, bush berries, celery, citrus, cotton, eggplant, lettuce, melons, peach, pepper, plum, prune, sorghum, sugar beet, strawberry, tomato, and walnut. Ornamental hosts include aster, carnation, chrysanthemum, cyclamen, eucalyptus, fuchsia, geranium, portulaca, and rose. Weed hosts include pigweed, horseweed or mare's tail, panicled willow herb, cheeseweed, California mugwort, and lambsquarters.

This tortricid moth was first described in 1884 from specimens collected from Sonora, Mexico. It was first found in California in 1913 on citrus nursery stock in Whittier. Since then it has been found on many plants, giving rise to the many common names for it such as orange web worm, orange calyx worm, orange platynota, rose leafroller, leaf tier, carnation moth, and cotton leafroller. Besides California it has been found in Arizona, Florida, Illinois, Massachusetts, Michigan, Texas, Virginia, and Washington, DC, as well as in Baja California, Sonora, and Sinaloa, Mexico. In midwestern and eastern states, omnivorous leafroller is primarily a greenhouse pest, but this may be a sibling species, the tufted apple bud moth (*P. idaeusalis* (Walker)).

Omnivorous leafroller was first found on grapes in the southern San Joaquin Valley counties of California in the 1960s. Several factors may have contributed to the problem. For example, extensive use of herbicides to control weeds in vine rows led to declining use of row plows, allowing for more omnivorous leafroller larvae to overwinter in the remaining trash, such as mummified grape clusters. In recent years, conversion to low-volume irrigation and increased use of cover crops provide for less in-season mortality (compared with flood irrigation) and additional hosts for overwintering survival and in-season reproduction. Additionally, some pesticides that control other insects, such as leafhoppers, do not control omnivorous leafroller, allowing an increase in infestation.

DESCRIPTION

The distinctive features of the moth at rest are that the wings are positioned in a bell-shaped pattern and that the snoutlike mouthparts, which are blackish gray, protrude forward from the head (fig. 69.1). Forewings are dark rusty brown with the distal half a tan color; on the resting moth, a darker band extends outward from the middle of the wings in a V-shaped pattern, separating the dark and light areas. A dark spot is located on the outer edge of the wings in the light area. Males and females look alike, except that females are larger, about 13 mm (0.5 in) long, and males are about 9.5 mm (0.38 in) long. Females also possess brown, semicircular plates (ovipositor lobes) at the end of the abdomen, in contrast to the tufted hairs at the end of the male abdomen.

The flat, elliptical, green eggs are laid on smooth surfaces such as the upper side of a leaf, on berries, or on the cane (fig. 69.2). Eggs are laid in masses, with individual eggs overlapping each other like fish scales. As larvae within the eggs develop, the eggs turn from green to greenish brown (fig. 69.3).

Newly hatched larvae are less than 1.5 mm (0.06 in) long (fig. 69.4), and mature larvae average about 13 mm (0.5 in) long. Larvae usually cast their skins (molt) five times before pupation, but some may shed six times. First-stage larvae are cream colored with light brown heads and prothoracic shields. Second and third stages have brownish black or black heads and shields (fig 69.5). The fourth stage may have either a blackish brown or black head with brown shield, or both the head and shield may be brown. Fifth and sixth stages have brown heads and shields (fig. 69.6). Mature larvae may have a darker border on the side and rear outer edge of the prothoracic shield.

Mature larvae may differ in body color from cream to brownish green or brown, with a faint stripe produced by the main blood vessel running full length on the dorsum of the body. They possess distinct, whitish, slightly convex, oval pinacula on the upper sides of the abdominal segments. Pinacula are absent on similar-appearing larvae or, if present, are round.

Larvae are generally solitary and spin a silken thread with which they weave a protective nest in the leaves (fig. 69.7A) or clusters (fig. 69.7B). When disturbed, they become active and retreat into their nests or wiggle and drop suspended on the silken thread.

Just before the pupal stage, the larvae become inactive and their bodies shorten and become translucent; they then form pupal cases inside their nest. Initially the pupae are creamy white but turn dark brown. The female pupae are more robust and longer than the male.

Figure 69.1 Omnivorous leafroller female moth. *Photo:* J. K. Clark.

Figure 69.2 Omnivorous leafroller egg mass on berry. *Photo:* J. K. Clark.

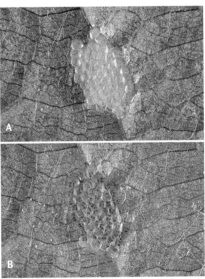

Figure 69.3 Egg mass of omnivorous leafroller on leaf (A). Omnivorous leafroller egg mass before hatching (B). *Photos:* J. K. Clark.

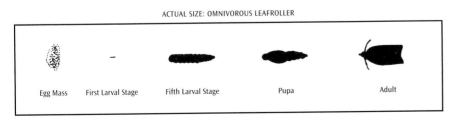

ACTUAL SIZE: OMNIVOROUS LEAFROLLER

| Egg Mass | First Larval Stage | Fifth Larval Stage | Pupa | Adult |

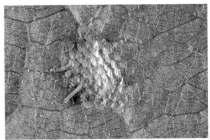

Figure 69.4 Hatching in an omnivorous leafroller egg mass. *Photo:* J. K. Clark.

Figure 69.5 Third-instar omnivorous leafroller, with dark prothoracic shield and head capsule. *Photo*: J. K. Clark.

Figure 69.6 Fifth-instar omnivorous leafroller, with brownish shield and head. *Photo*: J. K. Clark.

Figure 69.7 Omnivorous leafroller larva making leaf fold (A); omnivorous leafroller larva and nest in mature berries (B). *Photos*: J. K. Clark.

Omnivorous leafroller should not be confused with several other larval species that may be found in grape clusters (See section 62, "Larvae Found in Grape Clusters"). These include grape leaffolder (*Desmia funeralis* (Hubner)), raisin moth (*Cadra figulilella* (Gregson)), navel orangeworm (*Amyelois transitella* (Walker)), orange tortrix (*Argyrotaenia franciscana* (Walsingham)), driedfruit beetle (*Carpophilus hemipterus* (Linnaeus)), and drosophila fly (*Drosophila melanogaster* Meigen), also called the vinegar or pomace fly.

If heavy infestations of grape leaffolder develop in vineyards, larvae may invade clusters. A mature grape leaffolder larva is larger (1.5 to 2.2 cm, or 0.60 to 0.88 in, long) than the omnivorous leafroller larva and generally appears translucent, but it may have a greenish body color because of ingested leaf tissue in the gut. Raisin moth and navel orangeworm may be present in dried or decaying berries of clusters. Orange tortrix is typically found in cooler coastal regions, but in warmer coastal areas, orange tortrix and omnivorous leafroller are present, and the behavior and size of both insects are similar. Driedfruit beetle and drosophila fly are secondary invaders of clusters and are generally attracted to injured or decaying berries. Several species of nitidulid beetles may be present, but driedfruit beetle generally predominates. Drosophila larvae, about 7 mm (0.28 in) long, are white maggots that lack head capsules but have black mouthparts in the narrower head region. For more information, see section 75, "Drosphilia Flies," and section 82, "Stored Raisin Product Pests."

INJURY

Omnivorous leafroller larvae cause damage to grape clusters by feeding, which creates avenues for infection by rot-causing organisms. Larvae invade flower clusters, in which they feed and spin protective webbing in flower parts. As berries form, larvae feed on them; they may kill portions of clusters by injuring supporting stems (pedicels, branches, and rachises). However, this damage from first-generation larvae is usually not significant. As berries ripen, especially after veraison, feeding damage encourages infection by bacteria and fungi (fig. 69.8). Rotting and fermentation of ripening fruits attract secondary pests such as drosophila flies and driedfruit beetles, which further aggravate rot problems.

The amount of rot is usually related to cluster compactness. Rot in tight clusters tends to increase and spread from one adjacent berry to another. In contrast, rot does not spread as readily in loose clusters and is generally confined to a few berries. Larvae from the second and third moth flights cause the majority of berry damage by omnivorous leafroller.

Foliar injury is generally minor. Larvae may web surfaces of leaves together and live between them, or they may fold them and live in the folds. Larvae often chew holes in the leaves by feeding through the upper and lower surfaces; they may also feed only on one surface, leaving the epidermal layer of the opposite side intact so that dried-up leaf areas appear.

SEASONAL DEVELOPMENT

Omnivorous leafroller overwinters mostly as third, fourth, and fifth larval instars in mummified clusters on vines (fig. 69.9), on the ground, and on vineyard weeds. Larvae do not hibernate (diapause); they continue to develop slowly throughout the winter. Adverse weather, insect predators, and birds feeding on leftover clusters decrease overwintering populations. Very wet winters allow host material to rot and degrade before larvae can finish development. Populations are further reduced when vineyards are pruned and cultivated. In spring and early summer, larval populations are low but increase rapidly thereafter.

Females prefer to lay eggs on smooth plant surfaces, including fruit. Although egg viability is high, mortality of the first larval stage is also high because larvae have difficulty establishing themselves on vines. Newly hatched larvae may be found on the underside of leaves, where they feed and nest along leaf veins. Some are found in webbed nests at the leaf axil or in terminals of developing shoots (fig. 69.10A) or in flowers (69.10B). As larvae develop, a few remain on leaves while most invade developing clusters (fig. 69.11). If grape leaffolder infestations are also present, omnivorous leafroller larvae may often be found in abandoned leaf rolls created by grape leaffolder larvae.

During pupation, larvae become shorter, turn white, and transform into brown pupae, usually in the same nests inhabited by the larvae.

Moths are most active shortly after sunset, but if disturbed they may be seen flying during the day. Mating and egg laying take place at night. Females begin laying on the second day after mating. They lay

most eggs on the third and fourth days and may continue for 12 or 13 days. The number of eggs per egg mass may range from a few to 250. Life of the moth varies from 4 to 23 days.

The number of omnivorous leafroller generations per year varies because of differences in temperature. Generations are sometimes difficult to determine because they overlap later in the season and several developmental stages may be present at the same time. Spring moth activity characteristically begins by late February to early March with the first peak occurring in about 4 to 5 weeks. In the central San Joaquin Valley and at UC Davis, four major peaks are usually recorded using pheromone traps. Sometimes a partial fifth flight is observed. Not all flight peaks coincide with the actual peak abundance of the adults in a generation because of local variations in weather; cold temperatures lessen moth flight. Extensive research conducted in the early 1970s suggests that only three or four generations occur per year.

Laboratory observations show that developmental time from egg hatch to adult is 132 days at 12.8°C (55°F), 40 days at 18.5°C (65°F), 28 days at 24°C (75°F), 21 days at 29.4°C (85°F), and 27 days at 35°C (95°F). With addition of the preoviposition period and egg incubation time, an accumulation of approximately 700 degree-days Celsius (DDC) above 8.9°C (about 1,260 DDF above 48°F) is required for omnivorous leafroller to complete one generation. This value is very close to what has been estimated from field moth flight catches. In the San Joaquin Valley, the peak for spring flights sometimes occurs

Figure 69.8 Rotting Thompson Seedless bunch after injury by omnivorous leafroller. *Photo*: J. K. Clark.

Figure 69.9 Overwintering omnivorous leafroller larva (arrow) in mummy. *Photo*: J. K. Clark.

Figure 69.10 Early-season omnivorous leafroller nest in young shoot (A); omnivorous leafroller feeding injury in developing flowers (B). *Photos*: J. K. Clark.

Figure 69.11 Omnivorous leafroller nest in young berries (A); close-up of omnivorous leafroller larva, nest, and feeding damage to young berries (B). *Photos*: J. K. Clark.

Figure 69.12 Braconid wasp parasite of omnivorous leafroller recently emerged from white cocoon. *Photo*: J. K. Clark.

at less than 1,260 DDF, possibly because the first moths are at low numbers and hard to catch. Conversely, the peak for midsummer flights often occurs at more than 1,260 DDF, perhaps because of detrimental effects from high temperatures.

NATURAL CONTROL

The following species of wasps (fig. 69.12) and flies have been recorded as parasites of omnivorous leafroller, but they seldom account for more than 10% mortality even when omnivorous leafroller populations are high and damaging. All are internal or external larval parasites except *Trichogramma*, which is an egg parasite.

Parasitic wasps:

> *Goniozus platynotae* Ashmead, family Bethylidae
>
> *Trichogramma* sp., family Trichogrammatidae
>
> *Apanteles* sp., family Braconidae
>
> *Microgaster phthorimaeae* Muesbeck, family Braconidae
>
> *Macrocentrus ancylivorus* Rohwer, family Braconidae
>
> *Cremastus platynotae* Cushman, family Ichneumonidae
>
> *Diadegma compressus* Cresson, family Ichneumonidae
>
> *Elachertus proteoteratis* (Howard), family Eulophidae
>
> *Spilochalis* sp., family Chalcidae

Parasitic flies:

> *Erynnia tortricis* (Coquillett), family Tachinidae
>
> *Nemorilla pyste* (Walker), family Tachinidae

General insect predators and several species of spiders are found in vineyards and may influence the omnivorous leafroller population by feeding on eggs or larvae. Insect predators include green lacewing (*Chrysoperla carnea* Stephens), minute pirate bug (*Orius tristicolor* (White)), and damsel bug (*Nabis* sp.). Spiders in the family Theridiidae are also common predators. Additionally, earwigs can consume egg masses during their nocturnal forays in the canopy.

MONITORING GUIDELINES

If grapeleaf skeletonizer is also a problem, insecticide treatments directed at it usually give adequate control of omnivorous leafroller. However, where grapeleaf skeletonizer populations are not of concern and given that it may be biologically controlled, the monitoring method outlined below is the most reliable way to evaluate the omnivorous leafroller population. These populations are usually low in spring and early summer, but they may increase drastically later in the summer and cause severe rot problems. Vineyards need to be monitored throughout the season to determine whether treatments are needed and to evaluate the effectiveness of treatments.

Examination of the vineyard should include inspection of areas where infestation is suspected or where it has occurred in previous years. Grape cultivars with compact clusters should be examined carefully. Evidence of infestation includes the presence of larvae, pupae, pupal cases, and webbing produced by omnivorous leafroller larva. Occasionally, spider webs may be confused with webs produced by omnivorous leafroller, but close examination usually reveals some type of plant injury caused by larvae.

Experience has shown that the sampling method outlined below gives a reasonably good estimate of the omnivorous leafroller population in the vineyard.

1. Begin by examining the vineyard during the immediate prebloom period (first week in May). Select and mark 20 vines in approximately 20 acres (8 ha). Include vines in suspected or previously infested areas. Examining the same vines continually gives a more accurate estimate of the population trend.

2. Examine 10 clusters weekly in the center of each of the 20 vines. Do not remove the clusters. Record any evidence of omnivorous leafroller infestation, including larvae, pupae, pupal cases, webbing, and feeding damage.

3. Calculate the percentage of infested clusters by dividing the number of infested clusters by the total number of clusters examined and multiplying the result by 100. For example, if 200 clusters are examined and 10 are found to be infested, $10 \div 200 = 0.05 \times 100 = 5\%$ infested.

4. Treatment decisions should be based on weekly examinations. The period from immediately prebloom to fruit set is important for decision making because treatments are highly effective at the end of bloom. Even low population levels require treatment at this time, so they have to be determined by careful cluster examination.

Cluster infestation exceeding 10% at harvest will likely result in economic losses from excessive rot. However, economic levels of cluster infestation may vary with different vineyard situations (e.g., table grape varieties, wine grape varieties with tight clusters, vineyards with a history of rot, etc.). The acceptable infestation level must be determined by experience.

Do not rely on only one or two samples early in the season to determine the need for a treatment. Because the omnivorous leafroller population is low at that time of the year, small errors in sampling can lead to large differences in the estimated population at harvest time. Continue to sample regularly so that population estimates are constantly refined.

Maximize the accuracy of samples early in the season (immediately prebloom to fruit set) by examining at least 50 clusters under a binocular microscope. Minute larvae and nests could otherwise be overlooked. Clusters for microscopic examination should not be taken from the marked vines but from nearby vines.

This method of evaluating omnivorous leafroller infestation allows for continuous reevaluation and also helps the grower to determine the effectiveness of chemical treatments and decide whether additional ones are needed.

Monitoring Raisin Vineyards

In addition to preharvest monitoring through the season, raisin vineyards can be checked for the amount of rot on drying trays provided the total rot present is essentially induced by the omnivorous leafroller. Great care must be exercised in examining clusters for the presence of omnivorous

leafroller. Bunch rot may be extensive due to other factors such as high levels of mildew earlier in the season. The rot also obscures signs of omnivorous leafroller presence.

Procedure

As soon as the trays are laid, examine all clusters on 50 trays. Calculate the percentage of clusters with suspected omnivorous leafroller–induced rot as indicated in step 3, above. If economic losses have occurred, spray programs may have to be changed to maintain a lower percentage of loss. Examination of trays at harvest is also a good way to discover other unsuspected problems.

Monitoring Moth Populations

Because omnivorous leafroller infests many different plants, pheromone traps placed in the vineyard are not good indicators of infestation. Detailed studies have shown no correlation between trap catches using pheromone lures and harvest infestation. However, moth catches are a good indicator of flight activity and may help to pinpoint when the most intensive cluster sampling should be done. Figure 69.13 shows that in each generation, larval populations in the vines increase after the adult male moths caught in pheromone traps have peaked and declined. You may want to concentrate your cluster examination on those periods after the flight peaks when the larvae numbers are increasing.

MANAGEMENT GUIDELINES

Sanitation

After the initial appearance of omnivorous leafroller in vineyards, serious infestation usually does not occur until populations have a chance to build up over a 2- or

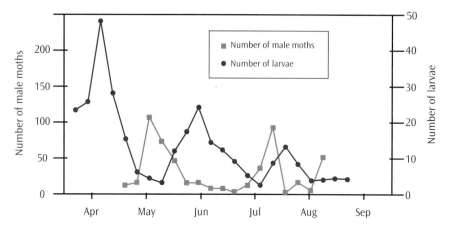

Figure 69.13 Population of omnivorous leafroller larvae in relation to adult males caught in pheromone traps.

3-year period. Proper sanitary practices during the dormant season are important in preventing this buildup. Most overwintering larvae survive in surrounding weeds and in clusters remaining on the vines or in the trash underneath them. Therefore, during pruning, remove any remaining clusters and place them in the middles of rows, where they will be disked. Vineyards with native annual cover crops present an extra challenge for omnivorous leafroller management. Larvae may be overwintering on the plants in addition to the mummified clusters and serve as a source of infestation later in the season.

Row Plowing

Along with disking, row plowing (French plowing) (fig. 69.14) buries the infested trash; this operation should be completed at least a month before new growth begins in spring. Disadvantages to row plowing are that it is slow and time consuming and that the tractor driver must be skilled to avoid damaging vines and stakes.

Burning the trash under vines with flame-throwing torches has been used, but it can be hazardous to vines and stakes. Using

insecticide sprays during the dormant period has not been effective, because spray penetration of the infested, dried-up, mummified clusters is difficult.

Early Harvest

Where infestations occur in late summer, harvesting at the earliest possible date is recommended to avoid continued buildup of the

Figure 69.14 Row plowing to bury omnivorous leafroller–infested mummies. *Photo*: J. K. Clark.

omnivorous leafroller population and subsequent loss to rot. Early harvest is particularly important if raisins are going to be made in vineyards infested with omnivorous leafroller. With moderate omnivorous leafroller populations, picking before September 1 can reduce mold and rot problems. An early-September harvest keeps more larvae from moving into the bunches, where they are apt to continue to feed and make nests on the trays.

Mating Disruption

University of California Cooperative Extension research has demonstrated the effectiveness of mating disruption as a management tool. Male moths find females by sensing the plume of sex pheromone given off by the females and following it to her. Using relatively large quantities of synthetic pheromone emitted by thousands of dispensers in a vineyard, the air becomes saturated by pheromone to the extent that males cannot follow an individual plume to a female, so the male moths are unable to find the females and mate. In the absence of mating, viable eggs are not laid and no larvae are produced to damage bunches. Mating disruption works best in large blocks or blocks that are isolated from other sources of omnivorous leafroller. It can be especially effective if a group of growers adjacent to each other use it. Mating disruption programs must be maintained for at least the first two generations of omnivorous leafroller and for the third generation in late-season varieties. Early cessation or extensive gaps in mating disruption can lead to rapid rebuilding of the pest population.

Mating disruption products are available in several types of dispensers. They may be plastic twist-ties, laminar membranes, "puffer" aerosol emitters, paraffin emulsions, or a microencapsulated sprayable material. These dispensers must be placed in the vineyard at the beginning of the flight as indicated by pheromone traps. They should be replaced according to the manufacturer's recommendations to prevent them from running out before the flight is over. If there is an untreated block adjacent to yours, it is beneficial to treat the first few rows of that adjacent block.

Pheromone traps should be placed along the edges and in the center of the block to verify that mating disruption is working and to determine whether moths are flying in from outside the vineyard. If the traps in the center of the block are catching males, there is something wrong with the mating disruption system and you need to consult your supplier immediately. During periods of unseasonably hot weather, pheromone dispensers may not have the longevity otherwise expected. Frequent checking of pheromone traps can help determine this before too large a gap in emission takes place.

Periodically sample bunches according to the UC recommendations to determine whether you have worm damage caused by other insect species such as raisin moth. Remember that omnivorous leafroller mating disruption controls only omnivorous leafroller and other species may also cause damage.

Chemical Control

In the past, spring treatments of cryolite aimed at grapeleaf skeletonizer were also effective at controlling omnivorous leafroller.

Both cryolite and *Bacillus thuringiensis* ssp. *Kurstaki* (Bt) sprays are nondisruptive, so spring treatments do not result in spider mite or other secondary pest outbreaks. In addition, spring applications have much better coverage because of less foliage and because the clusters are more exposed and open. However, cryolite use has been restricted by many wineries and in other markets, and Bt is not as effective as cryolite. Spring treatments are more effective than later sprays, and newer insecticides such as insect growth regulators are available that do not appear to provoke secondary pest outbreaks (see UC IPM Grape Pest Management Guidelines, www.ipm.ucdavis.edu/PMG/). Be aware, however, of surrounding crops, such as alfalfa, or weedy fields where omnivorous leafroller may be resident, and which can be a source of reinfestation later in the season and require additional treatments.

Treatments should be timed by using the omnivorous leafroller phenology model and degree-days rather than vine growth. Control failures have been observed in years with warm springs, when omnivorous leafroller development is early and rapid. Bloom-timed sprays in those cases are often too late for optimal control. Pheromone traps should be employed in the vineyard by mid-February to determine when moths from the overwintering generation start to fly (the biofix). Experiments have shown that the best reduction of omnivorous leafroller and its damage occurs when treatments are timed to approximately 700 to 900 DDF after the biofix. This timing seems to hold for both the first and second flights. Later in the season, because of the overlapping generations, treatments timed at 500 to 700

DDF may be more effective. Degree-day treatment timing has not been established for the insect growth regulator insecticides, but it would likely be 100 to 200 DDF earlier than with conventional insecticides. Current registered materials can be found in the UC IPM Grape Pest Management Guidelines, www.ipm.ucdavis.edu/PMG/.

REFERENCES

AliNiazee, M. T., and E. M. Stafford. 1972a. Notes on the biology, ecology and damage of *Platynota stultana* on grapes. Journal of Economic Entomology 65:1042–1044.

——. 1972b. Seasonal flight patterns of the omnivorous leafroller and grape leaffolder in central California vineyards as determined by blacklight traps. Environmental Entomology 1:65–68.

——. 1973. Management of grape pests in California vineyards. 1. Cultural and chemical control of *Platynota stultana* on grapes. Journal of Economic Entomology 66:154–157.

Lynn, C. D. 1969. Omnivorous leaf roller. California Agriculture 23(4): 16–17.

Shaw, P. B., H. Kido, D. L. Flaherty, W. W. Barnett, and H. L. Andris. 1983. Spatial distribution of infestations of *Platynota stultana* (Lepidoptera: Tortricidae) in California vineyards and a plan for sequential sampling. Environmental Entomology 12:60–65.

Shorey, H. H., C. B. Sisk, and R. G. Gerber. 1995. Disruption of pheromone communication in *Platynota stultana* (Lepidoptera: Tortricidae) in grape vineyards. Environmental Entomology 24(5): 1270–1274.

70 ORANGE TORTRIX

Larry J. Bettiga, Lucia G. Varela, and Philip A. Phillips

Orange tortrix (*Argyrotaenia franciscana* (Walsingham)) (= *Argyrotaenia citrana* (Fernald)) (Lepidoptera: Tortricidae) has been known in California since 1889, when it was found infesting orange trees, willow, and golden-rod in Los Angeles County. Since then it has been noted on many different plants, but only since 1968 has it been seen as a pest on grapes. It can also be a pest on deciduous fruit trees in the coastal districts of California, primarily apples. Orange tortrix, omnivorous leafroller, and light brown apple moth are all leafrollers belonging to the subfamiliy Tortricinae. They feed on leaves and clusters and produce webbing at their feeding sites.

In California the geographical distribution of orange tortrix ranges throughout the coastal areas and interior valleys of the coastal ranges. The high temperature and low relative humidity of the Central Valley of California tends to limit the distribution of the insect to cooler areas where the climate is under coastal influence. When spread of this pest on grape was first noted in 1968, larvae were found feeding on grape clusters and causing considerable damage in Salinas Valley vineyards in Monterey County. Since then, orange tortrix has been found on grapes in Napa, San Benito, San Luis Obispo, Santa Barbara, Santa Clara, and Sonoma Counties. Although present in most of the coastal grape-producing regions of California, it generally is more of a pest problem in the cooler areas of these regions.

Establishment of the orange tortrix in coastal vineyards may be attrib-uted to several factors: it is present in general areas where grape plantings occur; it is able to feed and develop on a wide variety of plants and read-ily adapts to grape; and it survives in trash under the vines because of the use of herbicides, whereas formerly larvae had been incorporated into the soil and destroyed by row plowing. This last factor may be the primary contributor to a buildup of this pest in vineyards. Omnivorous leafroller, a related tortricid moth, similarly developed as a pest of grapes in the hotter, inland valleys.

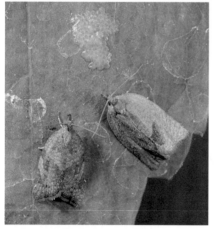

Figure 70.1 Orange tortrix moths and eggs: male (left) and female (right). *Photo*: J. K. Clark.

ACTUAL SIZE: ORANGE TORTRIX

| Egg Mass | First Larval Stage | Fifth Larval Stage | Pupa | Adult |

DESCRIPTION

The orange tortrix moth varies in size, color, and wing markings. At rest, its wings are bell shaped. The female moth is approximately 13 mm (0.5 in) long and orange-brown to buff. The female generally has V-shaped or saddle-shaped darker markings midwing when at rest. The male moth is slightly smaller than the female (fig. 70.1). The males also have distinct V-shaped markings on the center of each forewing, with a pair of crescent-shaped markings on the wing margins. Hind wings are whitish gray.

The eggs are flat, oval, and cream colored when newly laid but turn darker as the embryos develop. Eggs are deposited in masses, with each succeeding egg partly overlapping the preceding one like shingles or fish scales. The number of eggs in a mass can range from a few to more than 200. On grapevines, eggs are laid on any smooth surface such as upper leaf surfaces, stems, canes, or berries.

When first hatched, the larvae are about 2 mm (0.08 in) long. Full-grown larvae are approximately 13 mm (0.5 in) long. The head capsule and prothoracic shield adjacent to the head remain light brown throughout the five larval instars (fig. 70.2). The larvae generally have straw-colored bodies, but greenish or dark gray larvae can be found. The larvae are very active and often wiggle violently when disturbed or may drop to the ground or drop suspended on a silken thread (fig. 70.3). Orange tortrix larvae are solitary, each larva making a webbed nest among the plant parts in which it lives.

The pupae are approximately 8 to 13 mm (0.3 to 0.5 in) long. Pupation takes place in the last larval nest or location. The last-instar larva ceases feeding, constructs a silken shelter, and becomes quiescent. It then contracts slightly, and the larval skin is molted. Initially cream colored, the new pupal case turns dark brown within a few hours. Female pupae may be differentiated from male pupae as being slightly longer and more robust.

INJURY

The prime concern regarding an orange tortrix infestation is the development of grape cluster rots caused by fungi and bacteria gaining entry into the fruit through larval feeding injury. In early spring, overwintering larvae feed on swelling buds and emerging shoots (fig. 70.4). Injured buds may fail to develop shoots or clusters, which may reduce yields if damage is severe. Similar damage can be caused by cutworms and light brown apple moth, as well as by beetles such as the grape bud beetle (*Glyptoscelius squamulata* (Crotch)), click beetle, and the branch and twig borer (*Melalgus confertus* (Le Conte)). Damage by orange tortrix and light brown apple moth can often be distinguished from that of other insects by the webbing that is often associated with their feeding (see table 65.1).

The first larval generation feeds primarily on the leaves, although clusters will be fed on as they form. Larvae often web small leaves together to form protective nests in which they live and feed on foliage. They tend to concentrate in the developing whorl of leaves at the shoot tips during the first 8 weeks past budbreak. These shoot tip leaves do not open as readily because of larval webbing (fig. 70.5). This damage serves as an excellent diagnostic sign of early-season activity.

The second larval generation is found primarily in the clusters (figs. 70.6–70.8). Larvae web small clusters or portions of clusters together and feed on individual

Figure 70.2 Close-up of orange tortrix larva. *Photo*: L. J. Bettiga.

Figure 70.3 When disturbed, a larva may drop to the ground or drop suspended on a silken thread. *Photo*: L. J. Bettiga.

Figure 70.4 Orange tortrix larva feeding on developing bud; note webbing. *Photo*: J. K. Clark.

Figure 70.5 Early-spring tying of the basal leaf to form a feeding nest (A); leaf opened to expose orange tortrix larva (B, arrow). *Photos*: L. J. Bettiga.

Figure 70.6 Orange tortrix larvae in cluster. *Photo*: J. K. Clark.

berries and parts of the cluster stem, which causes cluster parts below the injury to wilt and die. Feeding by larvae opens up wounds that allow for entry and development of bunch rot organisms. In the cooler coastal regions of California, orange tortrix larvae can increase the levels of bunch rot caused by the fungus *Botrytis cinerea* (Persoon). The development and increase in Botrytis bunch rots can cause significant damage by reducing the yield and fruit quality.

In heavily infested vineyards during the dormant season, larvae may be found feeding under the bark of canes that have twisted and split during cane tying. Infestations appear to be more severe in cultivars or vines with compact clusters. Damage is observed more frequently in Chardonnay, Pinot noir, Melon, and Gewürztraminer than in other cultivars.

SEASONAL DEVELOPMENT

All developmental stages of orange tortrix can be found during the year in infested vineyards. Because of this overlap, it is often difficult to separate the generations. Investigations in coastal areas of California show that there are three generations: from late March to early May, May through July, and August to November. The use of pheromone traps to monitor male moth flights generally shows three peaks in flight activity and indicates that three generations are common (fig. 70.9).

Orange tortrix is adapted to cooler coastal regions. Laboratory observations show that the minimal development temperature is 6°C (43°F) and the optimal temperature is 25.5°C (78°F). Larvae fail to develop at temperatures above 32°C (90°F).

In spring, larval infestations occur in developing shoot tips of the vine. Small larvae are found along the veins at the leaf base, and large larvae are found nesting in webbed leaves. When the flowers and fruit clusters begin to form, larvae leave the foliage and invade the clusters; after harvest they are found on the surrounding vegetation and in clusters left on the vine.

Orange tortrix does not hibernate (diapause) and is commonly found during the winter at various larval instars in mummified clusters on the vines or on the ground. Larvae can also be found on alternate weed hosts such as mallow, curly dock, filaree, lupine, mustard (fig. 70.10) and California poppy and winter cover crops like barley.

Populations gradually decline in winter, presumably because of adverse weather, insect predators and parasites, and birds feeding on unharvested clusters. Populations increase during the spring and peak in the fall.

NATURAL CONTROL

Several parasites and predators attack orange tortrix. Examinations of larvae and pupae from vineyards in the Salinas Valley have shown an ichneumonid wasp, *Exochus nigripalpus* (Townes), to be the dominant parasite, constituting 95% of the parasites found. Three other parasites found were a braconid wasp, *Apanteles aristoteliae* (Viereck) (2%); a tachinid fly, *Nemorilla pyste* (Walker) (2%); and a chalcid wasp, *Dibrachys cavus* (Walker) (1%). All are internal parasites of orange tortrix larvae. This same complex occurs in other coastal vineyards in Santa Barbara and San Luis Obispo Counties. In the north coast the most common parasitoids are *Cotesia* species and *Apanteles aristoteliae*. Because parasitized larvae do not die until later instars or during pupation, they continue to feed and damage grapevines. Vineyards with moderate to heavy parasitization in late spring have been shown to have lower orange tortrix populations at harvest than vineyards where the level of spring parasitization is low. Selective insecticides in vineyards should be used to preserve parasite populations.

The *Exochus* wasp, a slender wasp about 6 mm (0.25 in) long, has a black head and body and yellow legs. Female wasps parasitize orange tortrix larvae by inserting an egg into the host's body cavity. The wasp larva then develops and pupates within the orange tortrix host. The adult wasp emerges from the moth pupal case. Because the moth and the wasp emerge differently, the amount of parasitism by *Exochus* can be estimated by examining orange tortrix pupal cases. Wasp emergence holes are circular; moths emerge through slits created on the sides of the pupal cases.

The *Apanteles* wasp is about 4 mm (0.17 in) long, with a black head and body and yellow legs. It also parasitizes orange tortrix by inserting an egg into the larval host's body cavity. The wasp larva then develops within and kills its larval host when it emerges to pupate. It spins a white cocoon nearby and pupates in it.

The *Nemorilla* fly parasitizes not only orange tortrix larvae but also omnivorous leafroller and grape leaffolder larvae. About the size of the common housefly, 5 to 8 mm (0.2 to 0.3 in), this fly is distinguished by a gray body with five black stripes on the thorax and reddish sides on the abdomen. The female fly deposits one to several pearly white eggs around the head and thoracic regions of the orange tortrix larva. Upon hatching, the fly larva invades and develops within the host's body. The fly then pupates in its own puparium inside the pupal case of the orange tortrix.

The chalcid wasp (*Dibrachys* spp.) is a very small, dark wasp about 2 mm (0.08 in) long. A number of these parasitic wasps may develop in and emerge from a single host. *Dibrachys* attacks many other insects and is known to parasitize other beneficial wasps.

Orange tortrix is also found on several alternate plant hosts both within and near vineyards, including coyote brush (*Baccharis pilularis* (DeCandolle)), a native shrub common to the lower mountain slopes of coastal California. The parasites *Exochus* and *Apanteles* have been reared

Figure 70.7 Orange tortrix feeding damage to berries and stem of cluster. *Photo*: J. K. Clark.

Figure 70.8 Orange tortrix nest (arrow) in ripening bunch. *Photo*: J. K. Clark.

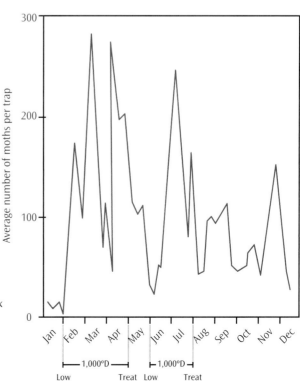

Figure 70.9 Average number of orange tortrix moths per week can be plotted on a graph showing the accumulated degree-days from the low point in late January to early February for the first generation and in June for the second generation. Allow for 1,000 ± 50 DDF to accumulate from the low point to time insecticide applications if necessary. Field monitoring should begin well ahead of the date of 1,000 DDF.

from orange tortrix and another tortricid moth, *Aristoteliae argentifera* (Busck), collected from coyote brush growing near vineyard locations. Although vineyard sites near large populations of coyote brush have had high orange tortrix parasitization rates in spring, further studies are needed to determine the degree to which coyote brush and other alternate hosts may influence biological control of orange tortrix in adjacent vineyards.

The total effect of predatory insects and spiders in reducing orange tortrix populations is not known. Spiders are commonly found in association with orange tortrix feeding sites. Some of the general predators found in vineyards are the damsel bug (*Nabis* spp.), the minute pirate bug (*Orius tristicolor* (White)), the big-eyed bug (*Geocoris* spp.), and the green lacewing (*Chrysoperla* spp.). Earwigs inhabiting the loose trunk and cordon bark by day will actively search the vine canopy at night for insect eggs, including orange tortrix egg masses.

MONITORING GUIDELINES

A management program using pheromone traps to monitor male moth flights coupled with a phenology model can be used in conjunction with larval monitoring to time insecticide applications for optimal control of orange tortrix when treatment is necessary.

Place pheromone traps in the vineyard by December. Change pheromone caps during the season as per the manufacturer's recommendation, and change the trap bottoms every 4 weeks, or less if they have become dirty or if high moth catches have reduced the adhesive quality. Record moth catches once per week during the entire season. Remember that moth counts alone are not a reliable indicator of orange tortrix infestation levels. Observations in the Salinas Valley showed that similar trap catches occurred in vineyards and in areas 2 miles away from established vineyards.

Record daily maximum and minimum temperatures to calculate the accumulation of degree-days for orange tortrix

development. The lower threshold is 6°C (43°F) and the upper threshold is 25.5°C (78°F). Degree-day calculations can be determined by using the models or reference tables available at the UC IPM website, www.ipm.ucdavis.edu. Weather monitoring equipment is available to calculate and accumulate degree-days for orange tortrix.

Low trap catches at the end of January to early February represent the beginning of the adult emergence, which will give rise to the first generation. This low trap catch signals when to begin accumulating degree-days. The degree-day accumulation started from the date of the lowest trap catch and continuing through increased catches can then be used to predict the subsequent stages of the insect's life cycle. Total degree-days Fahrenheit (DDF) for preoviposition, egg, and larval development are 950 (table 70.1). Allowing 1,000 ± 50 DDF (555 ± 28 DDC) to accumulate from the initiation of calculations enables larval development to proceed to the optimal insecticide timing in the spring. Allowing 1,000 ± 50 DDF to accumulate after the lowest trap catch in early June will indicate the timing of applications for control of the second generation. An example of a typical flight pattern from a vineyard in the Salinas Valley is shown in figure 70.9. Field monitoring of larval development should be conducted well ahead of the anticipated time when 1,000 DDF are expected. Economic thresholds for orange tortrix levels have not been established. Insecticide applications should generally be

Figure 70.10 A mustard cover crop (A), one of the hosts for orange tortrix; orange tortrix larval nest on mustard leaf (B). *Photos*: J. K. Clark.

scheduled based on larval development instead of a threshold for applying a spray. Once pupation occurs, insecticide applications are of little value.

Field monitoring should include vineyard areas where infestation is suspected or where it has occurred in previous years. Cultivars with compact clusters, such as Chardonnay, Pinot noir, Gewürztraminer, and Melon, tend to suffer more damage. Webbing on the vine indicates larval infestation and should be examined more closely for evidence of orange tortrix. In spring, larvae infest the developing shoots and later move to the clusters as they develop. A delay in the unfolding of the leaf whorl on new shoot tips is a sign of early tortrix larval activity (feeding and webbing) within those tips. Begin to monitor clusters at bloom. In infested clusters, berries may show signs of wilting because of stem injury, or feeding injury may be seen on individual berries. Examine rotted portions of clusters because orange tortrix may have injured the berry, allowing entry of rot-producing organisms.

In the dormant period, examine weeds in the vineyard as well as clusters remaining on the vines and on the ground. Weeds such as curly dock, filaree, lupine, mallow, California poppy, and mustard, as well as oats and barley grown as cover crops, are likely host plants for orange tortrix.

Management Guidelines

If orange tortrix is a problem, use the following procedures to reduce or prevent serious infestation.

Winter Cleanup

Cleanup during the dormant period should be an initial control measure. Most overwintering orange tortrix populations are larvae on weeds or in dried grape clusters on vines or on the ground. Remove clusters when pruning and place them in the row middles where disking can bury them or chop them. Row plowing or brushing can also be used to remove clusters and litter from under vines into row middles where they can be chopped or buried by disking.

Early Harvest

Observations have shown that larval populations increase in late summer and fall. Harvest as early as possible.

Insecticide Treatments

Several insecticides are registered for the control of orange tortrix on grapes. If infestation is not widespread, confine treatments to infested areas. Vine growth during the season is a factor in obtaining adequate spray coverage. Because foliar growth can impede spray penetration into the vine, coverage can become more difficult in late-season applications. Coverage of clusters also becomes more difficult as berry size increases cluster compaction. Thorough insecticide coverage is necessary, so treat each side of the row, preferably before bunch closure.

In more widely infested vineyards, include vineyard sanitation as outlined and make an early-season insecticide application between March and early May. Additional treatments may be necessary later.

Biological Control

Studies show that biological control of orange tortrix is effective and should not be disrupted. The use of more-selective pesticides is preferred to preserve parasite and predator levels, especially when other insect pest populations are under effective natural control. Developing treatment programs that leave untreated or minimally treated areas in the vineyard encourages the activity and spread of natural enemies, particularly the wasp *Exochus*.

References

Kido, H., D. L. Flaherty, C. E. Kennett, N. F. McCalley, and D. E. Bosch. 1981. Seeking the reasons for differences in orange tortrix infestations. California Agriculture 35(7): 27–28.

Kido, H., E. M. Stafford, and N. F. McCalley. 1971. Orange tortrix on grapes in Salinas Valley. California Agriculture 25(7): 10–11.

Table 70.1. Degree-days Fahrenheit (DDF) required for orange tortrix development stages

Stage	DDF required to complete stage	DDF from start of accumulation
preoviposition (female)	53	0–53
egg	243	296
larva	654	950
pupa	266	1,216
adult female	420	1,636

71 RAISIN MOTH

Walter J. Bentley, Richard L. Coviello, Stephen J. Vasquez, and David R. Haviland

Raisin moth (*Cadra figulilella* (Gregson)) was first identified in 1871 and is found throughout the world. It is considered a pest of stored raisins, infesting them on trays, in the field, or in storage. It was recognized as a pest of raisins in California in 1928. Recently, the larvae have also been found to damage fresh grapes in the field. The damage is sometimes mistaken for that of omnivorous leafroller (*Platynota stultana* Walshingham). However, raisin moth infests after veraison, when small holes appear in berries due to larval feeding. The hole looks much like the berry has been punctured with a pencil point. This hole, like damage from omnivorous leafroller, serves as a site for fungal infection, including Botrytis and sour rot.

DESCRIPTION

Raisin moth is dull gray with obscure, lighter-speckled areas on the front pair of wings (fig. 71.1). The hind wings are white, and both pairs are fringed along the margin. Raisin moth is about 10 mm (0.4 in) long, with a wingspan of 16 mm (0.63 in). Wings are folded lengthwise along the body at rest.

The egg of raisin moth is white, circular, and less than 1 mm (0.04 in) in diameter. The larva has a pinkish cast and is 12 mm (0.45 in) long at maturity, with four to six rows of purplish spots running longitudinally along the back (fig. 71.2). This gives the appearance of a series of parallel broken lines along the body. A single female can lay 350 eggs. During the winter, raisin moth is often found as larvae beneath the bark in a loose web of silk. It also can be found on the ground at the base of vines.

INJURY

Berry damage appears as a small hole in the side of the berry that can later be infected with various fruit-rotting organisms (fig. 71.3). The appearance is similar to omnivorous leafroller, but the webbing and larval nests are not present as with omnivorous leafroller. Numerous berries will be seen with holes in them (usually a single hole per berry). Damage appears after veraison.

Figure 71.1 Adult raisin moth. *Photo*: J. K. Clark.

ACTUAL SIZE: RAISIN MOTH

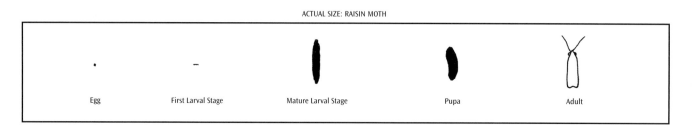

| Egg | First Larval Stage | Mature Larval Stage | Pupa | Adult |

Seasonal Development

Raisin moth is associated with drying fruit, particularly figs. In vineyards, most larvae pass the winter as grown larvae within silken webbing in the upper few inches of soil or under the rough bark of the grapevine (fig. 71.4). Approximately 80% of the larvae winter in the soil. Smaller larvae are unable to survive cold winters. Moths begin to emerge in early April, with peak emergence in May (cooler spring temperatures can delay emergence until early June). Moths live for about 15 days and are crepuscular (active at twilight). On warm evenings they begin to fly and lay eggs about half an hour after sunset, continuing flight for 3 to 4 hours. During the summer, flight ceases after 10 p.m. In the summer, a generation is completed in 45 days. There are three overlapping generations each year; in some years, a small fourth generation occurs. Figure 71.5 presents the flight activity from a raisin vineyard in Fresno County.

Spring moths actively search for drying and decaying fruit for oviposition. Besides decaying crops, fallen mulberry fruit provide a key site for oviposition. By June, larvae can be found in first-crop figs that have dropped to the ground. Later, fallen apricots, nectarines, peaches, pluots, and prunes are sites for egg laying and development. By August, ripening grapes become attractive, especially those with bunch rot, and serve as a site for egg laying. Later, raisins drying on the ground become key sites for oviposition.

It is unclear how raisin moth populations are affected by dried-on-the-vine (DOV) raisin production methods. It has been suggested that the higher moisture found in DOV raisins may make the fruit more susceptible to infestations. The movement to nontillage and drip irrigation in table and wine grape production appears to have had an impact in greater larval survival and the establishment of this insect as a pest in the vineyard.

Natural Control

Among the parasites attacking raisin moth is the wasp *Bracon hebetor* Say. This small braconid is 2 to 3 mm (0.08 to 0.13 in) long and black with yellowish markings.

Two other wasps, *Devorgilla canescens* (Gravenhorst) and *Mesostenus gracilis* Cresson, may be of importance during the late spring. All three wasps attack only larger larvae that have completed their feeding and damage, so the major control benefit is the reduction in future populations.

Bracon hebetor passes the winter mainly in the adult stage. The species is quiescent in cold weather, but on warm days it can be found actively stinging raisin moth larvae. These stung larvae become paralyzed. The adult parasite feeds on the body fluids released from the puncture created when the worm was stung. Interestingly, egg laying on the paralyzed host does not begin until spring. *Bracon hebetor* attacks multiple larvae in cocoons under grapevine bark: it is less effective at reaching larvae that have cocooned in the soil.

In stored raisins, larvae leaving fruit for pupation sites are stung. Such larvae may be found hanging from the sides of fruit boxes, often with *B. hebetor* larvae feeding on them. The parasite can be seen flying around infested dried fruit in the fall.

Figure 71.2 Raisin moth larva showing rows of purplish spots. *Photo*: J. K. Clark.

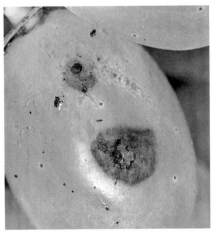

Figure 71.3 Small holes appear in berries due to raisin moth larval feeding after veraison. *Photo*: J. K. Clark.

Figure 71.4 Larvae overwinter in loosely woven cocoons under the bark of cordons and trunks or in the soil near the vine trunk. *Photo*: W. J. Bentley.

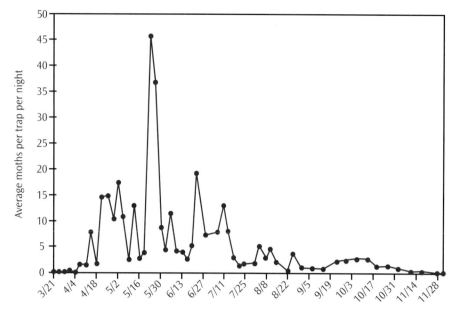

Figure 71.5 Raisin moth seasonal flight activity in a Thomson Seedless vineyard, Del Rey, California, 2000.

A microsporidia, *Nosema invadens* Kellen and Lindegren, has been reported from raisin moth larvae collected in Selma, California. The almond moth (*Cadra cautella* (Walker)) and Indian meal moth (*Plodia interpunctella* (Hubner)) are also susceptible to this pathogen.

A nuclear polyhedrosis virus, a granulosis virus, and two other baculoviruses have been isolated from raisin moth larvae in cull figs in Fresno. Raisin moth larvae have also been reported to be susceptible to a bacterium, *Rickettsiella* species, originally isolated from navel orangeworm (*Ameylois transitella* (Walker)) and to *Bacillus thuringiensis* Berliner (Bt).

MONITORING GUIDELINES

Monitoring in the vineyard is done with a synthetic pheromone placed in a sticky trap. The Indian meal moth pheromone, (z, e)-9,12-tetradecadienyl acetate, has been used to monitor raisin moth. There has been no field research in the use of this monitoring technique as an indicator of damage or on a method to time insecticide applications. Often, after veraison, grape growers examine clusters for the pinhole berry feeding and determine the need for treatment based on damage.

MANAGEMENT GUIDELINES

Currently the only guidelines for management involve the removal of unharvested clusters from vineyards in the winter. There are no chemical guidelines for managing raisin moth in vineyards. Where larval feeding has been regularly found, farmers apply *Bacillus thuringiensis* sprays during the summer.

REFERENCES

Barnes, D. F., C. K. Fisher, and G. H. Kaloostian. 1939. Flight habits of the raisin moth and other insects as indicated by the use of a rotary net. Journal of Economic Entomology 32(6): 859–863.

Burkholder, W. E., and M. Ma. 1985. Pheromones for monitoring and control of stored-product insects. Annual Review of Entomology 30:257–272.

Donohoe, H. C. 1938. The bionomics of the raisin moth, *Ephestia figulilella* Gregson. University of Minnesota PhD thesis.

Donohoe, H. C., P. Simmons, D. F. Barnes, G. H. Kaloostian, C. K. Fisher, and C. Heinrich. 1949. Biology of the raisin moth. USDA Technical Bulletin 994.

Hunter, D. K., S. J. Collier, and D. F. Hoffmann. 1973. Effectiveness of a granulosis virus of the Indian meal moth as a protectant for stored in shell nuts: Preliminary observations. Journal of Invertebrate Pathology 22:481.

Kellen, W. R., and D. F. Hoffmann. 1984. Occurrence of two baculoviruses in *Cadra figulilella* (Lepidoptera: Pyralidae). Journal of Invertebrate Pathology 43:439–440.

Kellen, W. R., and J. E. Lindegren. 1968. Biology of *Nosema plodiae* sp. n., a microsporidian pathogen of the Indian-meal moth, *Ploria interpunctella* (Hubner), (Lepidoptera: Phycitidae). Journal of Invertebrate Pathology 11:104–111.

———. 1969. Host-pathogen relationships of two previously undescribed microsporidia from the Indian-meal moth, *Ploria interpunctella* (Hubner), (Lepidoptera: Phycitidae). Journal of Invertebrate Pathology 14:328–335.

———. 1973a. New host records for *Helicosporidium parasiticum*. Journal of Invertebrate Pathology 22:296–297.

———. 1973b. *Nosema invadens* sp. n. (Microsporida: Nosematidae), a pathogen causing inflammatory response in lepidoptera. Journal of Invertebrate Pathology 21:293–300.

72 SALTMARSH CATERPILLAR

David R. Haviland

Saltmarsh caterpillar (*Estigmene acrae* (Drury)) (Lepidoptera: Arctiidae) is an occasional pest of grapes. It feeds on the foliage of a wide variety of commercial crops and weeds and generally becomes a grape problem only late in the season. Erratic outbreaks of this pest in vineyards appear to be induced, at least partially, by certain insecticides.

Saltmarsh caterpillar is primarily a pest in the hot desert valleys of southern California and Arizona, where it builds up on weeds, sugar beets, alfalfa, and cotton in late fall, when growers are not too concerned about leaf loss. Large larvae then migrate to fall vegetable crops; millions can be seen moving across roads to find new food.

Outbreaks of saltmarsh caterpillar in the San Joaquin Valley have also occurred, particularly near heavily infested sugar beet and cotton crops. Abundance of this pest began increasing since around the 1970s; however, outbreaks during the past decade have been very rare, most likely due to a reduction in sugar beet and cotton acreage, as well as a shift in pesticide chemistries to newer, more-selective products.

DESCRIPTION

Adult moths have a wingspan of 5 to 6.5 cm (2 to 2.5 in) (fig. 72.1). The female is white, except for an orange abdomen with black lateral and dorsal spots and black spots on the wings. Hind wings of males are orange rather than white.

The spherical, somewhat flattened, and finely sculptured eggs are about 0.8 mm (0.03 in) in diameter (fig. 72.2). They range from pearly white to creamy yellow. They are laid in compact groups, nearly always on the underside of leaves. A female may lay as many as 1,000 eggs, with 200 or more in each egg batch.

Figure 72.1 Saltmarsh caterpillar adult. *Photo*: J. K. Clark.

ACTUAL SIZE: SALTMARSH CATERPILLAR

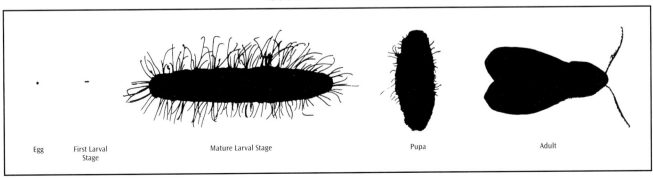

Egg   First Larval Stage   Mature Larval Stage   Pupa   Adult

On hatching, young larvae are light buff with clusters of long, dark hairs over the body. As larvae grow larger, they become more hairy; for this reason many growers call them woolly worms. Mature caterpillars are about 5 cm (2 in) long and are mottled yellow, orange, and black beneath a dense covering of long buff to black hairs (fig. 72.3).

The pupae are usually found under leaf trash on the soil and are enclosed in thin cocoons that may have larval hairs included in the silk walls.

INJURY

First- and second-instar larvae remain near an egg site and feed gregariously on the lower leaf surface, leaving the leaf veins and leaf surface intact. Damaged leaves have the appearance of fancy lacework and are easily seen when monitoring for other pests. Older larvae feed independently, eat through the leaves, and leave the foliage ragged. This injury reduces vine vigor and exposes berries to sunburn and quality loss. Severe infestation defoliates vines; end vines are the most susceptible. Some saltmarsh caterpillars pupate in bunches, making table fruit unmarketable because of their trashy appearance. This has been particularly important with exported fruit.

SEASONAL DEVELOPMENT

Saltmarsh caterpillars overwinter as fully grown larvae. Pupation occurs in early spring. Adults emerge in 10 days to 3 weeks, then mate and lay eggs, nearly always on the lower leaf surface. In warm spring weather, eggs hatch in 1 week to 10 days. Larvae develop and pupate in 4 to 5 weeks. Adults emerge in 10 days to 2 weeks, depending on the weather. A generation may be completed in about 6 weeks during warm summer temperatures. There are three to four generations per year, the fall generation being the most numerous and most destructive. Migration into vineyards from drying weed hosts or cotton generally occurs in late summer and fall.

NATURAL CONTROL

No information is available on natural control of saltmarsh caterpillar in vineyards.

MONITORING GUIDELINES

Closely observe saltmarsh caterpillar populations in adjacent fields or vineyards to determine potential movement into vineyards. In late-season harvested grapes, monitor them carefully for potential defoliation or pupation in bunches.

MANAGEMENT GUIDELINES

Problems in vineyards associated with saltmarsh caterpillar usually occur late in the season. Direct treatment at smaller larvae; they are easier to control, and this avoids problems of larger larvae pupating in bunches. Alternatively, migration to grapes can be avoided by treating larvae in their crop of origin or by maintaining a water barrier at the edge of the vineyard.

Figure 72.2 Saltmarsh caterpillar eggs, newly laid. *Photo*: J. K. Clark.

Figure 72.3 Saltmarsh caterpillars, second and fifth instars. *Photo*: J. K. Clark.

Lepidoptera
Caterpillars

73 SPHINX MOTHS

Walter J. Bentley and Larry J. Bettiga

Of the two sphinx moth species (Lepidoptera: Sphingidae) known to attack grapevines in California, achemon sphinx moth (*Eumorpha achemon* (Drury)) is the more common. The larval stage feeds ravenously, and large populations can quickly defoliate vineyards. Wild grape and Virginia creeper are also host plants for this pest. Achemon sphinx moth occurs throughout the United States but is most commonly found in the western states of Arizona, Colorado, Montana, and California. The moths fly at dusk and hide under foliage during the day. Petunias and evening primrose are common flowers that are visited.

ACTUAL SIZE: SPHINX MOTH

Figure 73.1 Achemon sphinx moth adult. *Photo*: L. J. Bettiga.

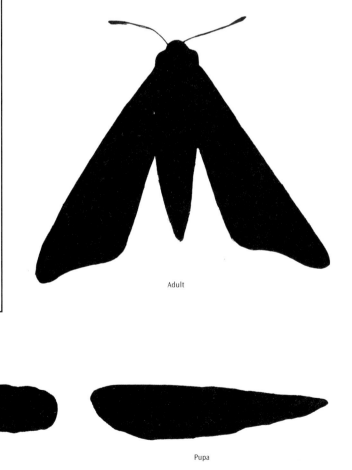

Adult

Egg

First Larval
Stage

Mature Larval
Stage

Pupa

Whitelined sphinx moth (*Hyles lineata* (Fabricius)) is closely related to achemon sphinx moth. This species is omnivorous and when abundant will consume all forms of plant life. Principal hosts include apple, pear, prune, azalea, beet, knotweed, buckwheat, collards, purslane, honeysuckle, jimsonweed, and many other range, forage, and vegetable plants. Whitelined sphinx moth occurs throughout the United States. Like achemon sphinx moth, whitelined sphinx moths fly at dusk.

Description

Achemon Sphinx Moth

About as large as a humming-bird and with similar behavior, the achemon sphinx moth (fig. 73.1) hovers outside open flowers while collecting nectar. It possesses a long, curled proboscis that extends into blossoms. Its wingspan is 7.5 to 10 cm (3 to 4 in), and it is marbled brownish gray with well-defined dark brown patch-like markings on the forewing and thorax. The hind wings are a rosy pink color with a dark brown series of spots inside a lighter brown border toward the outer edge of the wing. The pale green eggs are large and round, about 1.5 mm (0.06 in) in diameter, and are laid singly on the upper surface of older leaves. They can be easily seen with the naked eye. Newly hatched larvae are green with a black horn as long as the body at the rear end. The horn disappears with the last larval molt. The mature larvae may be either green or brown (fig. 73.2). The full-grown larva is 6 to 8 cm (2.3 to 3.2 in) long, with a yellow line along the upper body and from six to eight whitish or pale yellow oblique bars on the sides of the body extending across the spiracles.

The pupa is mahogany brown, 4.5 to 5 cm (1.8 to 2 in) long. Pupae are often found at the base of plants, just below the soil surface.

Whitelined Sphinx Moth

This moth derives its name from the broad diagonal white stripes on the wings (fig. 73.3). Moths are 6 to 9 cm (2.3 to 3.5 in) long. Larvae are about 7.5 cm (3 in) long when mature and are either bright green or black. The more common green form has a yellow head and anal horn. This color form also has a subdorsal row of pale spots that are bordered above and below with a black line. Each spiracle is enclosed within a bright spot. The black larval color form has three dorsal yellow lines and broken black lines on the sides and at the base of the legs. The head, shield, and anal horn are yellow or orange. The pupa is shiny dark brown and 3 to 3.5 cm (1.2 to 1.4 in) long.

Injury

In general, both sphinx moth species are minor pests, appearing periodically and then disappearing for long periods of time. A severe outbreak of achemon sphinx moth occurred in Arvin in the San Joaquin Valley in the early 1970s, causing substantial loss to many growers. In years of abundant populations, hundreds of larvae may be found on a single vine. A large

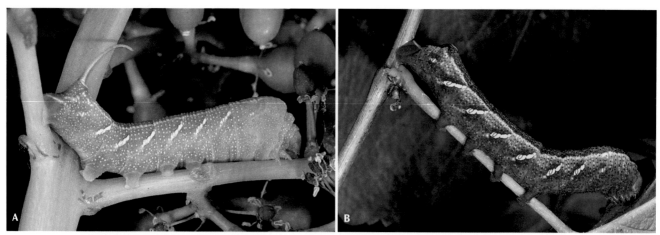

Figure 73.2 Achemon sphinx moth larva, green phase (A) and brown phase (B). *Photos*: J. K. Clark.

worm can eat nine mature grape leaves every 24 hours. When a vine has been completely defoliated, worms leave and may crawl a considerable distance to a vine with green leaves. Injury by whitelined sphinx moth larvae is similar. Both devour the interveinal areas of the leaf, leaving the short spikelike veins visible.

Mechanical harvest has created some problems with sphinx moth when they drop into harvest containers that catch the grapes. This procedure also traps the larvae with the grapes, resulting in fruit contamination. Wineries do not accept fruit with worms present. Occasionally, sphinx moth larvae severely defoliate young vines being trained to stakes.

SEASONAL DEVELOPMENT

Both species overwinter as pupae in the soil and emerge in early May in the San Joaquin Valley. They fly to the vine, where they lay eggs. Achemon sphinx eggs hatch after 6 to 9 days during the late spring and summer. Immediately after hatch, the caterpillar chews a small round hole and crawls to the lower surface of the leaf, where it continues feeding.

Caterpillars feed on grape leaves for about 25 days. They then drop to the soil, penetrate to a depth of 5 to 15 cm (2 to 6 in), and construct a smooth-walled cell in which to complete development. True first-generation moths appear in July and are more abundant than the overwintered generation. During August, they can quickly cause substantial defoliation. A generation is completed in about 55 days. During warm years and with late-harvested cultivars, a third generation may occur.

Whitelined sphinx moth development is similar. However, this species usually develops outside the vineyard, with adults flying in during the summer.

NATURAL CONTROL

Several parasitic flies (tachinids) attack sphinx moth larvae and are considered the key means of control. French plowing can aid in destroying pupae within the vineyard, but this practice is seldom used.

MONITORING GUIDELINES

There is no formal monitoring program for sphinx moths. Careful observation when sampling for mites or leafhoppers can give warning of potential problems. Whitelined sphinx moth larvae, during years of high abundance, can often be seen feeding on weeds in vineyards or bordering vineyards. The presence on weeds in June can be a good indicator of problems in vineyards in August.

MANAGEMENT GUIDELINES

If chemical control is necessary for sphinx moth, direct treatments at smaller larvae as mature larvae are more difficult to kill. *Bacillus thuringiensis* (Bt) is very effective against sphinx moth larvae.

Control of migrating larvae can be mechanical, such as by a ditch barrier with the steep side next to the vineyard. Insecticides applied to border rows are also effective and can be used in combination with the ditching.

Figure 73.3 Whitelined sphinx moth adult. *Photo*: L. J. Bettiga.

74 WESTERN GRAPELEAF SKELETONIZER

David R. Haviland, Alexander H. Purcell, and Stephen J. Vasquez

Western grapeleaf skeletonizer (*Harrisina brillians* Barnes & McDunnough) (Lepidoptera: Zygaenidae) is a defoliating pest of commercial and wild grapevines. It also feeds on ornamental hosts in the grape family such as Virginia creeper (*Parthenocissus quinquefolia*) and Boston ivy (*P. tricuspidata*) and has been rarely observed feeding on incidental hosts such as apricots, almonds, cherries, and roses.

Western grapeleaf skeletonizer appears to be native to the American Southwest, with its original range extending from central Mexico to New Mexico and Colorado. It was first found in 1941 in California, near San Diego, where it severely defoliated wild grapes (*Vitis girdiana* Munson) in canyon areas. Shortly afterward, it became a serious pest in commercial vineyards. By 1943, crop loss in some San Diego County vineyards reached 90% (the average was 40 to 60%).

After a state-imposed eradication program using cryolite dust failed, biological control was emphasized. University of California entomologists imported parasites from Mexico and Arizona. A parasitic braconid wasp, *Apanteles harrisinae* Muesbeck, and a parasitic tachinid fly, *Ametadoria misella* (Wulp), were soon established. A granulosis virus (WGLS-GV) was found infesting western grapeleaf skeletonizer larvae in rearing laboratories used for parasite production in San Diego County and in Arizona. The virus became an important biological control agent.

Beginning in 1961, western grapeleaf skeletonizer was found in the southern San Joaquin Valley (Fresno County). In spite of eradication attempts, by 1975 permanent infestations occurred in central and northern California on wild grapes, backyard grapes, and commercial vineyards. Western grapeleaf skeletonizer has spread slowly in the southern San Joaquin Valley because adults tend to remain in the area of their larval development until vines are severely defoliated. The pest has been eradicated in several commercial grape-growing areas, including the north coast.

Figure 74.1 Male and female moths copulating. Larger moth (right) is the male. *Photo*: J. K. Clark.

ACTUAL SIZE: WESTERN GRAPELEAF SKELETONIZER

| Egg | First Larval Stage | Fifth Larval Stage | Pupa | Adult |

Apanteles and *Ametadoria* parasites were collected in San Diego County and released in central and northern California. Unfortunately, they have had limited impact in the southern San Joaquin Valley's commercial grape-producing areas.

DESCRIPTION

Moths are conspicuous because of their bluish black to greenish black color (fig. 74.1) and daytime flight activity. Normal body length is about 16 mm (0.63 in), and the wingspan is about 25 to 34 mm (1 to 1.33 in). They are much smaller when food is in short supply for developing larvae.

Both sexes have comblike bristles projecting from the antennae. Male bristles, about 0.75 mm (0.029 in) long, are twice as long as those of the female, and also have fine hairs on each bristle, whereas females do not. Males have posterior tufts of hairs on the tip of the abdomen that are absent on females. The posterior end of the female's abdomen is more or less square, while the top of the male's posterior is more pointed.

Moths become active in the morning, provided air temperatures are high enough for adult flight. Optimal flight temperatures are above 22°C (71.5°F). Peak flight activity occurs about 8:00 a.m. in California, consisting mostly of males. Females fly less frequently than males but continue to fly until early afternoon. By early afternoon, most adults can be found resting within the vines. Adult flight is reduced on cloudy days.

Eggs

Capsular-shaped eggs are about 0.4 mm (0.016 in) wide and 0.6 mm (0.023 in) long (fig. 74.2). They are usually pale yellow, but some batches are whitish. All are ornamented with fine surface grooves and ridges. Eggs are laid in a single-layer cluster, without eggs touching. The average number of eggs per cluster is about 100 but can range from 7 or 8 to as many as 300 or more (fig. 74.3). All eggs in a cluster hatch at the same time (fig. 74.4).

Often there may be two or more clusters per leaf, but these are not usually laid by the same female. Females that are infected with granulosis virus lay fewer eggs per cluster, and they are more widely and irregularly spaced within the cluster than those of healthy females (fig. 74.5). The emerging larvae from these eggs become infected by chewing out of the egg, which is coated with virus.

Nearly all eggs are laid on the underside of leaves. In commercial vineyards, first-generation eggs are laid mostly on inner mature leaves under the vine canopy (fig. 74.6). Second- and third-generation eggs are almost always laid on leaves of outside shoots. This makes it easy to look for egg batches by lifting shoots and inspecting the undersides of leaves.

Larvae

The first of five instars is pale white and about 1.6 mm (0.065 in) long. These larvae line up side by side in a circular row to feed (fig. 74.7). They strip off tissue on the underside of the leaf, about the size of a half dollar or less, depending on their number. At first, feeding areas appear as white spots on the upper surface (fig. 74.8), which later turn brown as the tissues beneath the feeding areas die.

Figure 74.2 Close-up of skeletonizer eggs showing typical barrel shape *Photo*: J. K. Clark.

Figure 74.3 Typical egg mass of western grapeleaf skeletonizer on the underside of a grape leaf. *Photo*: J. K. Clark.

Figure 74.4 First-instar larvae hatching. *Photo*: J. K. Clark.

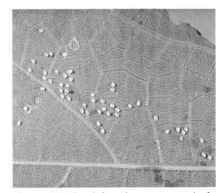

Figure 74.5 Virus-infected western grapeleaf skeletonizer females scatter their eggs. *Photo*: M. Badgley.

Figure 74.6 Typical first-generation damage on lower shaded leaves of vine. *Photo*: J. K. Clark.

Figure 74.7 First-instar larvae lining up side by side to feed. *Photo*: J. K. Clark.

Figure 74.8 Typical whitish spots caused by first-instar larvae hatching from three different egg masses. *Photo*: J. K. Clark.

The yellowish white second-instar larvae are about 3 to 5 mm (0.13 to 0.20 in) long, with black hairs on the body segments. The hairs are commonly dotted with pellets of black excrement. Late in this stage, two large, pale brown rings appear on the body.

The third instar is about 6 to 8 mm (0.25 to 0.30 in) long. This stage takes on all of the permanent body-ring colorations, consisting of two wide brown bands that mark the body into thirds: a forward portion, a middle section, and the posterior (fig. 74.9). There are five narrow brown bands: two on the forward portion, one on the middle section between the wide brown bands, and two on the posterior. Body color between bands is pale brown.

The fourth instar is about 11 mm (0.43 in) long, and the fifth instar about 16 mm (0.63 in) long just before pupation. The seven circular bands on the body become blackish purple in the fourth and fifth instar; body color between bands turns yellow (figs. 74.10–74.11).

Fully grown larvae spin silken cocoons in which to pupate (fig. 74.12). The cocoons, irregular, dirty white capsules, may be found in trash around the base of vines or under loose bark on the trunk and cordons.

INJURY

Unmanaged populations of western grapeleaf skeletonizer can completely defoliate vineyards or portions of vineyards. Early in the season, damage is usually concentrated on end vines and border rows (fig. 74.13). By the end of the second and third generations, entire vineyards can be defoliated,
with larvae feeding into November. If vines are partially or completely defoliated before harvest, fruit maturity is delayed. Heavy defoliation also causes fruit sunburn and quality loss. Defoliation after harvest reduces the photosynthetic abilities of the grapevine, which also reduces carbohydrate accumulation and storage and long-term plant health.

Young larvae in the first through early fourth instars nearly always feed on the underside of the leaf, leaving only veins and upper cuticle intact. These white, damaged portions of the leaves are easily seen from the top when monitoring (see fig. 74.8). Feeding damage from these early instars is usually limited to one or a few leaves.

Larvae in the late fourth and fifth instars abandon their gregarious behavior and become voracious feeders. They eat entire leaves, leaving behind only larger veins (fig. 74.14). It is from this feeding behavior that the term skeletonizer was derived. Defoliation of a vineyard can go from minor to very severe when larvae pass through these two instars.

Ordinarily, western grapeleaf skeletonizer does not feed on fruit. However, where population levels are high, fourth and fifth instars will feed in the clusters once they consume most of the foliage. Once fruit is exposed and damaged by feeding, it becomes vulnerable to sunburn and damage caused by bunch rot fungi.

Western grapeleaf skeletonizer can also cause harm to fieldworkers who are sensitive to contact with larvae. Large larvae, especially those in the fourth and fifth instars, have long, poisonous spines

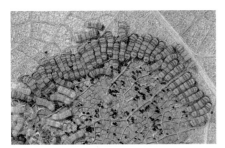

Figure 74.9 Third-instar larvae feeding side by side. *Photo*: J. K. Clark.

Figure 74.10 Larvae feed in side-by-side pattern into middle of fourth instar. *Photo*: J. K. Clark.

Figure 74.11 Fifth-instar larvae are much less gregarious. *Photo*: J. K. Clark.

(fig. 74.15). When workers brush against these spines, skin welts similar to those produced by nettles can occur. Some people have a greater reaction than others; some react to the hairs of the second and third instars. At greatest risk of coming in contact with larvae are harvest crews, and pesticide treatments for this pest may be justified to accommodate the entry of pickers into the vineyard.

Seasonal Development

Western grapeleaf skeletonizer overwinters in the pupal stage. There are normally three generations per year, with a small fourth generation of adults in early to mid-October in some years. The threshold for western grapeleaf skeletonizer development is 15.5°C (60°F) compared with 10°C (50°F) for the grapevine. This allows moth emergence, mating, and oviposition to begin after the flush of new shoots and leaves of grapevines in spring.

The female moth prefers shady areas of the vine to lay eggs and rarely oviposits on the small, tender leaves of the developing shoots. Egg laying occurs soon after mating, although it may be delayed in spring if cool weather slows egg development in the female. Adults of the first, or spring,

generation live 8 to 10 days, compared with 5 to 7 days for adults of the two summer generations in the San Joaquin Valley.

Larvae go through five instars before pupating. A small portion of the first and second generations goes into a pupal diapause. Essentially all larvae pupating in September and thereafter enter diapause. A few pupae remain in diapause for as long as 18 months. Overall population levels increase with each succeeding generation.

In cooler areas of California, such as the highland areas of San Diego County and coastal regions, first-generation adults emerge from diapausing pupae from late May through late June. Eggs of this generation hatch in an average of 12 to 16 days. Larvae evolve into second-generation adults that emerge from late July to mid-August. Second-generation eggs hatch in about 10 days. Most larvae that complete development go into diapause; a few initiate the partial third generation.

The appearance of adults and egg laying occurs first in urban areas, then in commercial vineyards, and about 2 to 3 weeks later in wild grapes.

Table 74.1 shows the sequence for the three generations in San

Figure 74.12 Skeletonizers pupating under the bark in cocoons (A); close-up of cocoons (B). *Photos*: J. K. Clark.

Figure 74.13 White, damaged leaves typical of western grapeleaf skeletonizer in the vineyard (A) and close up (B). The first to early fourth instars nearly always feed on the leaf underside, leaving veins and upper cuticle intact. *Photos*: J. K. Clark.

Figure 74.14 Fifth-instar larvae skeletonize an entire leaf, leaving only veins. *Photo*: J. K. Clark.

Figure 74.15 Close-up of western grapeleaf skeletonizer fifth-instar stinging spines. *Photo*: J. K. Clark.

Joaquin Valley commercial vineyards. In a given climatic area, adult emergence from cocoons, egg laying, and larval instars of the three generations occur over fairly distinct periods of time. However, there can be a slight overlap among the fifth-instar larvae, adults, and egg laying in the second and third generations. In spring, grapevine canopy development and western grapeleaf skeletonizer activity occur about 10 days to 2 weeks earlier in warmer Kern County.

NATURAL CONTROL

Since their importation into California, biological control organisms have caused western grapeleaf skeletonizer to go from a major grape pest to one of secondary importance. In the San Joaquin Valley, granulosis virus continues to cause significant mortality of western grapeleaf skeletonizer such that chemical controls are usually not needed. In San Diego County, western grapeleaf skeletonizer populations have been markedly reduced by the virus as well as the imported *Apanteles* and *Ametadoria* parasites.

Virus

The most effective biological control agent of western grapeleaf skeletonizer is a granulosis virus. This virus has now been spread to all grape-growing regions in California where western grapeleaf skeletonizer is found. Early in the season, the percentage of western grapeleaf skeletonizer infected by the virus tends to be low; by the end of the season, epidemics of the virus can completely decimate populations. The virus is most effective when it can spread quickly among dense populations; it is less effective when pest densities are lower and spread of the virus decreases.

Infection occurs when larvae ingest the granulosis virus. The virus attacks the midgut of the larvae. Once ingested, the virus inhibits normal feeding and digestion, and it can kill eggs, larvae, and pupae. In general, most first- and second-instar larvae that ingest virus die before pupation. Greater percentages of later instar larvae survive to pupate. Of these, some die in the pupal stage, but others become infected adults. Adult carrier males transmit the virus to healthy females during the mating process, and infected females lay about 60% fewer eggs than noninfected females. Many infected eggs do not hatch, but surviving larvae that develop from virus-contaminated eggs die during an early instar. This transmission of virus from adults to offspring is important in infecting future generations, especially in carrying the virus from the fall to the next spring generation.

Once ingested, the virus multiplies within the larval midgut, causing the larvae to reduce feeding, develop diarrhea, and wander about the vine, leaving a trail of liquid, brown diarrhetic excrement on the leaf surface. The wandering behavior promotes the spread of the virus because healthy larvae become infected when they feed on leaves contaminated by the excrement containing virions. Other insects further distribute the virus when they walk through the diarrhetic blotches.

There are four typical symptoms of infection in adults and larvae:

1. Eggs are scattered, in contrast to clustered egg batches, and the number of eggs laid is reduced (see fig. 74.5).

2. Eggs fail to hatch.

3. Larvae feed abnormally, consuming tiny patches of tissue and giving a peppered appearance to leaves (fig. 74.16), whereas healthy larvae of the first through early fourth instar feed side by side and consume entire areas of the leaf (see fig. 74.9).

4. Larval growth is abnormal, larval coloration changes, and larvae shrink, eventually dying (fig. 74.17). Many dying and dead larvae fall from leaves.

The granulosis virus remains highly infectious on leaf surfaces for many days or even weeks. Researchers have routinely made highly effective preparations of virus from western grapeleaf skeletonizer larvae collected from vines where at least some of the larvae show symptoms of viral infection (sluggish behavior, wandering, diarrhea). The collected larvae are finely pulverized in a small amount of water, which can be frozen (below –20°C, or –4°F) indefinitely or used immediately. This preparation can then be diluted in a larger quantity of water, filtered through several layers of cheesecloth, and sprayed on grapevines with active western grapeleaf skeletonizer larvae. The infective larvae resulting from these sprays can then be used to prepare additional viral sprays.

Parasites

The parasitic wasp *Apanteles harrisinae* attacks early-instar larvae (fig. 74.18) and usually deposits between three and nine eggs in a host larva. Fully grown larvae of *Apanteles* emerge from the fully grown host larva immediately after the host has spun its cocoon. The parasite cocoons are spun within the cocoon of the host, surrounding the dead caterpillar.

The parasitic fly *Ametadoria misella* prefers to lay its eggs on fourth and fifth instars during the day (fig. 74.19). Immediately after the larvae of the fly hatch from the egg, they penetrate the host. The parasite develops slowly within

Table 74.1. Development stages of western grapeleaf skeletonizer in central San Joaquin Valley commercial vineyards

Generation	Adults	Eggs	Larvae
first	late Apr to mid-May	late Apr to mid to late May	early May to late June
second	late June to early July	late June to mid-July	July to mid-Aug
third	late Aug to early Sep	late Aug to mid-Sep	Sep and Oct

Source: Data collected in Tulare County; time periods may change in warmer or cooler areas.

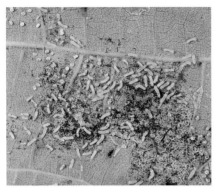

Figure 74.16 Virus-infected first instars show symptoms of disorientation and diarrhea. *Photo*: M. Badgley.

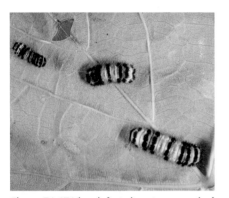

Figure 74.17 Virus-infected western grapeleaf skeletonizer larvae with the large larva beginning to shrivel, the center larva near death, and the small larva dead and attached to leaf. *Photo*: M. Badgley.

Figure 74.18 *Apanteles harrisinae*, a parasitic wasp of early instars of western grapeleaf skeletonizer. *Photo*: J. K. Clark.

the western grapeleaf skeletonizer caterpillar until the host larva transforms to the pupal stage. The parasite larva then develops rapidly, kills the host, and forms its own puparium within the host pupa. Parasitized western grapeleaf skeletonizer pupae can be identified by the presence of a respiratory siphon visible on the head of the host pupa. The parasite tends to avoid laying its eggs on western grapeleaf skeletonizer larvae infected with granulosis virus, so the simultaneous presence of both parasite and virus can greatly increase the effectiveness of biological control of western grapeleaf skeletonizer.

MONITORING GUIDELINES

Begin monitoring vineyards when overwintering pupae emerge as adults in the spring. In the San Joaquin Valley, this occurs between late April and mid-May. Monitor during the morning before 10:00. Look for shiny black adults flying near the ground between vine rows. If monitoring in the afternoon, hold the cordon wire and give the vine a good shake; at this time of the day (or all day when it is overcast), adults prefer to rest on the trunk, arms, and leaves, and shaking the vine will cause them to take flight.

First-generation eggs and small larvae are seen in late April to mid-May in the San Joaquin Valley, mostly on the mature basal leaves of the canopy. Look for small, circular, whitish spots on the upper surface of leaves, which indicate the presence of newly developing colonies on the underside of the

leaves. When found, turn the leaf over to confirm the presence of larvae. Initial samples should be taken from end vines and border rows, where western grapeleaf skeletonizer populations tend to be greatest.

As the season progresses, continue monitoring border rows for defoliation. If sampling indicates that western grapeleaf skeletonizer is becoming a problem, take additional samples within the field. Look for defoliation from aggregations of young larvae on leaves in the lower part of the canopy and for defoliation from large larvae in the upper parts of the vine. Also track the stage of development of the larvae; this will aid in determining the need for pesticides, choice of insecticide, and application timing.

Monitor vineyards just prior to harvest for the presence of large western grapeleaf skeletonizer larvae. Moderate populations of mature larvae may injure the arms and faces of pickers. After harvest, continue monitoring for defoliation until vines begin to senesce or until it appears that pest populations will not cause substantial amounts of late-season defoliation.

When monitoring eggs and larvae throughout the season, it is also important to look for symptoms of infection by granulosis virus.

While monitoring your vineyards, also pay close attention to neighboring abandoned, neglected, or mismanaged vineyards. Larval damage to vines is seen easily by driving around the perimeter of such vineyards. When leaf damage is prevalent, expect moth flights into surrounding vineyards. In an area of solidly planted vineyards, moths fly 1 to 1.5 miles (1.6 to 2.4 km) in all directions. The moth flight and egg batches laid generally decrease in relation to the distance from the source of moths. Where vineyards are scattered among other crops, moths fly 2 to 3 miles (3.2 to 4.8 km) to lay their eggs in vineyards.

Management Guidelines

Western grapeleaf skeletonizer populations are generally under good biological control throughout grape-growing regions where they are found in California. However, periodic outbreaks do occur regionally, and treatments for it are still warranted. Treatments are justified if severe defoliation has occurred or is anticipated from high western grapeleaf skeletonizer populations, or to protect field-workers from the irritating spines of large larvae primarily during harvest.

In many cases, western grapeleaf skeletonizer can be controlled by insecticides targeting other pests. Many products currently registered for control of thrips, leafhoppers, sharpshooters, omnivorous leafroller, and grape leaffolder can provide partial to complete control of western grapeleaf skeletonizer. Consult the UC IPM Grape Pest Management Guidelines, www.ipm.ucdavis.edu/PMG, for the most current information on products available.

Growers who make insecticide applications that specifically target western grapeleaf skeletonizer

usually follow one of two philosophies. The first is to control larvae in the first or early second generations. Since economic damage rarely occurs this early in the year, these treatments are made primarily to prevent late-season defoliation by removing early-season pest populations. This method is most commonly used where there is a history of western grapeleaf skeletonizer, overwintering populations are high, or there is little to no granulosis virus present. One advantage of this approach is that it prevents damage throughout the entire season. It is also easier to get good control early in the season since the leaf canopy is smaller and all larvae tend to be in the same stage at the same time. Some disadvantages are that small vineyards sprayed early in the season can become reinfested by adults from neighboring fields, and that chemical control may have done nothing more than kill larvae that would have otherwise naturally died from infection by granulosis virus.

The second philosophy is to delay treatment as long as possible. This method allows you to determine the actual need to spray based on defoliation and the amount of granulosis virus present. This method has become a viable option due to the registration of newer, reduced-risk insecticides that can quickly kill all larval stages of western grapeleaf skeletonizer. Insecticides and costs associated with them can often be avoided by relying on control by granulosis virus. Disadvantages to this method are that there must be a tolerance for some defoliation and

Figure 74.19 *Ametadoria misella*, a parasitic fly, ready to attack fifth instar (A); detail of *A. misella* (B). *Photos*: J. K. Clark.

pest populations must be watched closely, especially when larvae enter the fourth and fifth larval instars.

When making insecticide applications, it is important to consider the pesticide chemistry and biology of the pest. Insecticides that target early instars should be applied with good coverage on the underside of the leaves. Prior to mid- and late-season applications, make sure developing larvae are not missed by cutting shoots of vigorous varieties to 1 ft (30 cm) above the ground. Otherwise, when a chemical is applied, take care to treat these canes.

REFERENCES

Clausen, C. P. 1961. Biological control of western grape leaf skeletonizer (*Harrisina brillians* B. and McD.) in California. Hilgardia 31:613–637.

Curtis, C. E., P. J. Landolt, R. R. Heath, and R. Murphy. 1989. Attraction of grapeleaf skeletonizer males (Lepidoptera: Zygaenidae) to S-(+)-2-butyl-(Z)-tetradecenote. Journal of Economic Entomology 82:454–457.

Lange, W. H. 1944. The western grapeleaf skeletonizer, *Harrisina brillians*, in California. California Department of Agriculture Bulletin 32:98–104.

Smith, O. J., K. M. Hughes, P. H. Dunn, and I. M. Hall. 1956. A granulosis virus disease of the western grapeleaf skeletonizer and its transmission. Canadian Entomologist 88:507–515.

Stern, V. M., D. L. Flaherty, and W. L. Peacock. 1980. Control of the grapeleaf skeletonizer. California Agriculture 34(5): 17–19.

———. 1983. Control of western grape leaf skeletonizer (Lepidoptera: Zygaenidae), a new grape pest in the San Joaquin Valley, California. Journal of Economic Entomology 76:192–195.

75 DROSOPHILA FLIES

Larry J. Bettiga and Walter J. Bentley

Figure 75.1 Drosophila fly adult (A) and pupa (B). *Photos*: J. K. Clark.

ACTUAL SIZE: VINEGAR FLY

Adult

Although various species of *Drosophila* (Diptera: Drosophilidae) are commonly referred to as vinegar flies or pomace flies, the names are especially applicable to *D. melanogaster* Meigen and *D. simulans* Sturtevant, as these two species are difficult to separate. During harvest in vineyards and orchards, seven species of *Drosophila* can be found, of which more than 95% are *D. melanogaster* and *D. simulans*. In 2008 the spotted winged drosophila (*D. suzukii* (Matsumura)) was identified in California and has since been found along the Pacific Coast states. It has rapidly spread to other fruit-producing regions of the United States and Canada and has been reported in California infesting soft-skinned fruits such as strawberry, cherry, raspberry, blackberry, and blueberry. The term drosophila fly applies to all species of the genus found in vineyards.

DESCRIPTION

Adult drosophila flies have yellow to light brown bodies and red eyes (fig. 75.1); they are well known because of their attraction to all kinds of fermenting fruits. They are about 2.5 mm (0.1 in) long and are often seen hovering above garbage cans, culled fruit, and vegetable dumps. The eggs have two small protuberances. The larvae are a typical maggot shape and are about 3 to 7 mm (0.13 to 0.28 in) long. Adult spotted winged drosophila males have a dark spot on the front edge near the tip of each forewing (figs. 75.2–75.3). Adult spotted winged drosophila females appear similar to other *Drosophila* species fly females, with the exception that the spotted winged drosophila females have a serrated ovipositor (fig. 75.4). Certain *Drosophila* species have relatively large ovipositors, but only spotted winged drosophila has obvious serrations. This serrated ovipositor is a difficult characteristic to observe in the field with a hand lens and is best seen with the use of a dissecting microscope.

INJURY

As grape berries ripen, stems may separate from berries, especially when clusters are tight. This exposes the fleshy part of the fruit, which is an attractive spot for drosophila flies to lay eggs. Hatching larvae then feed on the berries. Adult drosophila flies are also attracted to fermenting bunches, and as they fly about, they carry bunch rot pathogens from infected bunches to previously uninfested clusters. Their greatest damage to the vineyard occurs from this secondary spread of bunch rot.

Figure 75.2 Spotted winged drosophila adult male (A) and female (B). Note the dark spots near the tips of the wings. *Photos*: M. Hauser.

In addition to being attracted to wounded or fermenting fruit, the ability of spotted winged drosophila females to lay eggs inside sound, ripening fruit makes this fly a more serious pest than other *Drosophila* species. The potential for damage in California is unknown; the insect has been reported on grape in Oregon. Higher population abundance may be observed in the cooler coastal areas and where the production of susceptible soft-skinned fruits such as cherry, raspberry, blueberry, and strawberry is more common.

Seasonal Development

Few drosophila flies survive winter when fully exposed outdoors. They may survive and reproduce in masses of fermenting material where the inner temperature of the mass is favorable. They also survive indoors wherever fruit is stored.

Drosophila melanogaster has a life cycle of 7 to 8 days at 29.5°C (85°F) and lays a maximum of 26 eggs per day, or 500 to 700 eggs in a 25- to 30-day life span. The minimum temperature for flight is 12.8°C (55°F) and the maximum is 38°C (100°F). Temperatures above 40.5°C (105°F) kill adults in a few

minutes. Adults find their food by odor and thus fly upwind, although air movement faster than 11 km/h (7 mph) restricts flight activity. Both adults and larvae prefer to feed on yeast.

Populations build during the growing season on culls and waste of several fruit and vegetable crops grown in areas near vineyards. This buildup is slowed by hot weather, but if a sudden cool spell or a light rain occurs during harvest, huge populations develop quickly.

The life cycle of spotted winged drosophila in California is not yet well understood. Like other drosophila flies, multiple generations and rapid population increases can be expected under optimal temperatures, and there may be as many as 10 generations per year. One generation requires 188 degree-days C (338 degree-days F), with a lower threshold limit of 8.8°C (48°F) based on research from Japan. In coastal California, adult flies are active and can be captured throughout most of the year. Spotted winged drosophila are most active at temperatures of 20°C (68°). Temperatures above 30° (86°F) reduce activity and egg laying.

Figure 75.4 Large serrated ovipositor of the adult female spotted winged drosophila (*D. suzukii*) (left) compared with *D. simulans* (right). *Photos*: M. Hauser.

Figure 75.3 Close-up of the wing of a male spotted winged drosophila. *Photo*: M. Hauser.

Natural control

Natural controls are not applicable for managing drosophila flies.

Monitoring Guidelines

No monitoring guidelines have been developed for *D. melanogaster* or *D. simulans*. A commercial bucket-style trap or a 1-liter (1 qt) plastic container with a screen covering the top can be used to monitor for spotted winged drosophila activity. Using a hardware cloth with 3/16-inch (4.8 mm) holes limits the number of large moths, flies, and bees captured in the traps. Attach a pheromone wing trap top (or other cover) to prevent rain and irrigation water from getting into the trap. Bait the traps with 2.5 cm (1 in) of pure apple cider vinegar with one drop of clear, unscented dish soap. Place traps about 0.9 to 1.5 m (3 to 5 ft) above the ground attached to the trellis in a shaded area in the canopy. Monitor for activity from veraison until harvest. Count only flies with spots on the tip of the wings (male spotted winged drosophila). Magnification will aid in the identification of flies. Replace the vinegar weekly. Do not dump the spent bait in the vineyard. An alternative bait solution is a mixture of 355 ml (12 fl oz) of water with 70 g (2.5 oz) of baker's yeast (e.g., Fleischmann's) and 20 ml (4 tsp) of sugar. Allow the solution to ferment for a day or so, then transfer the liquid to the trap.

Management Guidelines

Managing fertilizer and irrigation applications and the use of gibberellins (for cultivars as allowed by the label) may reduce the number of tight bunches and the incidence of bunch rot. Canopy management through leaf removal also reduces bunch rot and minimizes further damage by drosophila flies.

Chemical control of drosophila fly may reduce the amount of rotting bunches from 10 to 12% (by weight) compared with untreated vines. Treatment should be started when bunches start to show rot and become attractive to drosophila flies.

Postharvest applications of an insecticide can effectively reduce flies on and around fruit in the field, in packinghouses, and in storage and processing plants. See the UC IPM Grape Pest Management Guidelines, www.ipm.ucdavis.edu/PMG/, for more information.

Spotted Winged Drosophila

No management program has yet been determined for spotted winged drosophila. If this insect becomes an economic pest, research will need to focus on determining when the insect is present and preventing the flies from laying eggs. Reducing breeding sites by sanitation of fruit remaining after harvest is critical for all susceptible crops. An area-wide approach to reducing fly populations in an infested area has been key to successful management of other fruit-injuring flies.

76 CITRUS FLAT MITE (FALSE SPIDER MITE)

Lucia G. Varela, Walter J. Bentley, and Larry J. Bettiga

In 1984, populations of *Brevipalpus lewisi* McGregor (Acari: Tenuipalpidae), commonly called citrus flat mite or false spider mite, were observed for the first time damaging *Vitis vinifera* L. cultivars in California. The occurrence of this mite in grape is likely related to the reduction in sulfur use due to the introduction of the first triazole fungicide for powdery mildew control in 1982. Citrus flat mite is found in arid areas. This same species is considered a pest in pomegranate and pistachio and a minor pest in citrus, where it is easily controlled with sulfur. Damaging populations also occur on American grape cultivars (*Vitis labrusca* L.), which are resistant to mildew and do not require sulfur treatments.

Figure 76.1 Citrus flat mite adults. *Photo*: J. K. Clark.

DESCRIPTION

Citrus flat mites are tiny, less than 0.5 mm (0.02 in) long, flat, oblong, and wider at the anterior end (fig. 76.1). The two anterior pairs of legs extend forward, and the two posterior extend back. Color ranges from salmon reddish to red-brown.

INJURY

Damage on the foliage of vinifera cultivars resembles a russeting similar to that of light Pacific mite injury. On vinifera cultivars (e.g., Cardinal) and American cultivars (Niabell and Early Niabell), flat mite causes dehydration and blackening of the rachis and pedicels of clusters (fig. 76.2), which the market finds objectionable.

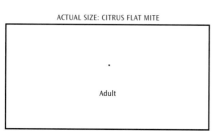

ACTUAL SIZE: CITRUS FLAT MITE

Adult

SEASONAL DEVELOPMENT

Early in the season citrus flat mite is found at the base of grape canes. Later it is present on all green tissue, including the clusters. Citrus flat mite is a warm-season pest, with populations increasing in June and peaking in late July and August.

NATURAL CONTROL

Predaceous mites (Phytoseiidae) have been observed in association with flat mites, but no studies have been done on their effectiveness.

MONITORING GUIDELINES

Studies have not been made.

MANAGEMENT GUIDELINES

Because growers generally include sulfur in their powdery mildew control program, flat mite is not considered a pest on vinifera cultivars. Control on American cultivars, which are more resistant to powdery mildew and more sensitive to sulfur burn under hot weather conditions, may require treatment with an acaricide if necessary.

Figure 76.2 Citrus flat mite feeding damage on rachis. *Photo*: F. L. Jensen.

77 GRAPE ERINEUM MITE

Lucia G. Varela, Walter J. Bentley, and Larry J. Bettiga

Grape erineum mite (*Colomerus vitis* (Pagenstecher)) (Acari: Eriophy-idae) potentially affects grapevines wherever they are grown, particularly in vineyards where sulfur is not used to control powdery mildew. Based on behavior and the type of injury, this mite species has three strains: the well-known and widely distributed erineum strain, the bud strain, and the leaf-curl strain. Molecular studies conducted in Australia in 2003 indicate that the erineum and bud strains are two distinct but closely related species. It is reasonable to suspect that in California the different strains might also be closely related different species. However, since molecular studies have not been conducted on California populations, we will refer to them as three strains: erineum, bud, and leaf-curl.

DESCRIPTION

An eriophyid mite has two pairs of legs; they can be seen with a 14× hand lens but are best observed with a dissecting microscope. The adult is light yellowish white and 0.2 mm (0.008 in) long (fig. 77.1). It has an elongated body with a broader anterior end and a tapered posterior. Colonies of 2 to 10 or more live among cast-off skins and their oval, whitish eggs. There are two nymphal stages; the first is smaller than the adult, and the second is the same size as the adult but lacks external genitalia. The eggs are oval and translucent or white.

INJURY

Erineum Strain

The most common sign is the occurrence of erinea, which are swellings or hemispherical galls that form on grapevine leaves as a result of mite feeding (fig. 77.2). Erinea are formed only in developing leaves; mites do not produce new erinea on fully expanded leaves. On the underside of the leaves, beneath the swellings, are densely lined, felty masses of over-sized leaf hairs in which mite populations develop (fig. 77.3). These hairs are whitish at first, then turn yellow and finally reddish brown. On the upper surface of the leaves, the patches manifest as blisterlike pink or reddish swellings. These swellings soon turn green; later in the season they become yellow, and in August they turn brown. Generally, the erineum strain gives rise to patchy infestations on a few vines or on a few rows of plants. High infestations may result in most leaves being galled; leaves may partially expand and then die, or they may expand to full size, mature early, and fall earlier than uninfested leaves.

Figure 77.1 Grape erineum mites. *Photo*: J. K. Clark.

ACTUAL SIZE: GRAPE ERINEUM MITE

Can be seen with a 14× hand lens or with a dissecting microscope.

Figure 77.2 Grape leaf showing erineum mite damage. *Photo*: L. J. Bettiga.

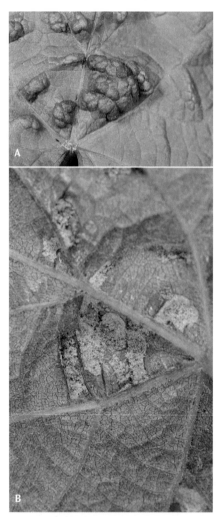

Figure 77.3 Close-up of the upper surface of a grape leaf shows erinea (A) and the underside of galls with overgrown hairs (B). *Photos*: L. J. Bettiga.

Bud Mite Strain

The bud strain does not produce erinea, confining its activity instead within buds. It generally feeds on the outer leaf primordia of the developing latent bud, where it produces blisterlike growth. It may penetrate the bud and feed on the shoot primordia, producing a nondiagnostic pattern of abnormal growth, including scarification of bark, flattened canes, and short, zigzagging internodes (fig. 77.4). In addition, the apex of all growing points within the dormant bud may be killed, so no shoots emerge at budbreak. Several lateral shoots may arise simultaneously on a shoot when the primary growing point is killed (fig. 77.5), resulting in a bushy clump of shoots sometimes called witches'-broom. No relation has been found between the number of infested buds and yield losses.

Leaf-Curl Strain

Feeding results in downward curling of leaves, ranging from a slight curl to severe curling into a ball. Affected leaves develop in summer and may be accompanied by shoot stunting, with increased lateral shoot growth, scarring of the shoots, and necrosis of the leaf underside. Like the bud strain, it does not induce typical erinea.

SEASONAL DEVELOPMENT

Erineum Strain

This form overwinters under outer leaf primordia of latent buds and moves to unfurling leaves after budbreak. It associates in small groups to feed on lower leaf surfaces; the result is the production of masses of enlarged leaf hairs inside a blisterlike area on the leaf (the erineum). Patches form in 10 to 30 days, depending on the rate of leaf development. It can take 2 to 3 weeks under favorable condition for an egg to develop into an adult, which allows for several generations per year. As the population increases, some move to apical leaves and form new erinea. From mid-August to leaf drop, the mites move from the erinea back to the overwintering site underneath the leaf primordia of latent buds.

Bud Mite Strain

The bud strain also overwinters under the leaf primordia, mostly as adult females, and their numbers decline gradually during winter. As the buds swell, the mites feed and lay small groups of eggs. When the latent buds start to grow, the primary bud begins to elongate. The outer leaf primordia of the latent bud remain at the base of the developing shoot, while the inner leaf primordia are carried out with the elongating shoot on the node to which they are attached. Thus, the mites and eggs on the outer leaf primordia remain at the base of the shoot, and those on the inner leaf primordia are carried farther out on the shoot. The number of nodes with leaf primordia bearing mites and eggs depends on how deeply mites penetrate the latent bud prior to budbreak. From May to November, mites can migrate by crawling from bud to bud, but this type of movement is less than the movement caused by elongation of the shoot.

As the shoot develops, latent buds are formed at nodes in the first leaf axil of the summer lateral (see section 2, "Important Structures and Features of Grapevines").

In late April and early May, the majority of the bud mite population on the new growth is found outside the developing latent buds in crevices beneath the prophyll at the base of the summer lateral. With the formation of the buds, the mites move into the newly formed bud tissues. After May, mites are found inside the developing bud, feeding and laying eggs on the smooth inner surfaces of the leaf primordia. During summer, as populations increase, mites penetrate deep into the buds, and more buds along the length of the shoot become infested. Depending on the population level, mites can be observed to have penetrated to the flower cluster primordia as early as July. Infestation of buds on a cane is not uniform, with mites being more prevalent in basal buds. The greatest numbers of mites are found in fall. Damage to the latent buds takes place in late summer or early fall when the mites feed on the cluster primordia and the apical meristem. The severity of symptoms the following spring depends on the location of the feeding damage within the latent bud.

Leaf-Curl Strain

Seasonal development of the leaf-curl strain has not been studied, but it is assumed to be similar to that of the erineum strain.

Natural Control

The western predatory mite (*Galendromus* (*Metaseiulus*) *occidentalis* (Nesbitt)) has been observed to be a voracious predator on eriophyid mites. However, its predatory activities are somewhat limited, as are those of species of predatory insects such as predaceous thrips. This may be because their larger size inhibits their movement through the mass of hairs in the erineum and their ability to penetrate deeply into the latent buds. The western predatory mite overwinters under the bark or within the latent buds and is especially effective on eriophyid populations in early spring, when they are exposed by expanding shoots. Its numbers commonly relate more to the number of other mite species that are its prey than to the number of erineum mites.

Monitoring Guidelines

Little or no economic loss occurs from the occasional evidence of erineum strain in mature vineyards. However, it has been observed to cause major stress on young vines by injuring young leaves and causing early drop of heavily infested mature leaves. The characteristic symptoms of erinea in spring are red swellings on leaf surfaces, below which is the felty mass of hairs in which mites may be seen with a hand lens.

Other conditions may cause symptoms similar to those caused by bud mites. An example is a temporary early-season boron deficiency in which necrotic spotting and uniform crinkling of leaves occur. Bud mite feeding is best identified under a dissecting microscope by the presence of blisters, along with mites or cast skins on the inner surface of the outer leaf primordia, in contrast to the smooth inner surface of uninfested leaf primordia. In vineyards with histories of bud mite damage, dissect buds during the dormant season and look for mites on the leaf primordia.

Figure 77.4 Short internodes, zigzag shoot growth, and scarification of the shoot due to grape erineum mite feeding on the developing bud. *Photo*: R. J. Smith.

Figure 77.5 Lateral shoot growth caused by grape erineum mite feeding and killing apical buds. *Photo*: R. J. Smith.

The leaf-curl strain is best seen by examining the underside of infested rolled leaves with a dissecting microscope.

MANAGEMENT GUIDELINES

When sulfur is applied to control powdery mildew, erineum and leaf-curl forms are seldom seen. With the use of fungicides other than sulfur to control powdery mildew, there may be increased occurrence of erineum mite. At present, early treatments of sulfur apparently hold erineum mites under control. Other acaricides and some insecticides used for other mites and insects may help reduce erineum mite populations.

The bud mite strain rarely causes commercial losses. Shoot symptoms observed after budbreak are caused by damage that occurred in the developing latent buds during the previous season. The most susceptible time for control is in early spring, when bud mite populations are most exposed. However, this timing may prevent damage only in the following season; the current year's damage has already occurred. The confirmation that a damaging population of bud mite exists should be made to determine whether treatment is necessary.

REFERENCES

Baker, E. W., T. Kono, J. W. Amrine Jr., M. D. Delfinado-Baker, and T. N. Stasny. 1996. Eriophyoid mites of the United States. Bloomfield, MI: Indira Publishing House.

Carew, M. E., M. A. D. Goodisman, and A. A. Hoffmann. 2004. Species status and population genetic structure of grapevine eriophyoid mites. Entomologia Experimentalis et Applicata. 111(2): 87–96.

Kido, H., and E. M. Stafford. 1955. The biology of the grape bud mite *Eriophyes vitis* (PGST). Hilgardia 24:119–142.

Lindquist, E. E., M. W. Sabelis, and J. Bruin, eds. 1996. Eriophyoid mites: Their biology, natural enemies and control. World Crop Pests 6. Amsterdam: Elsevier.

Stafford, E. M., and H. Kido. 1952. Grape bud mite studies. California Agriculture 6(4): 4.

78 GRAPE RUST MITE

Acari
Mites

Thomas M. Perring and Lucia G. Varela

Grape rust mite (*Calepitrimerus vitis* (Nalepa)) (Acari: Eriophyidae) is rarely a pest of grapes in California. However, it occurs in the Pacific Northwest and various wine-growing regions of Europe (particularly Spain), South Africa, and Australia, periodically resulting in economic damage.

DESCRIPTION

This mite is in the family Eriophyidae, a group characterized by being small and having two pairs of forward-projecting legs. The grape rust mite is light amber and 0.15 mm (0.006 in) long; a 14× hand lens is needed to see it. The body is elongated, with a broader anterior end and a tapered posterior. It has a vagrant life style, meaning that it freely roams the leaves and young shoots during the growing season and seeks protection in the buds during the winter months. There are two female forms: the overwintering form, called the deutogyne, and the summer form, called the protogyne. These forms can be very distinct in appearance, often being confused as two distinct species. There is a single male form. The other developmental forms are the egg and two nymphal stages. The first nymph is smaller than the adult. The second nymph is the size of the adult but lacks external genitalia.

INJURY

Grape rust mites damage the plant by feeding on buds, leaves, and flowers, causing various types of damage to the developing plant structures. Damage begins in the new buds, when deutogynes feed on the buds, causing scarification and necrosis on the inside of the primordia tissues. Heavy infestations may kill the growing point or the entire bud. Budbreak may be delayed. This symptom is often called restricted spring growth syndrome in Australian vineyards. Shoots may have shortened internodes (short shoot syndrome) with zigzag growth. Basal leaves may be distorted as they unfold.

Subsequent feeding by protogynes on young leaves causes severe leaf rolling and premature leaf drop. On more mature leaves, feeding on the surface of leaves of white grape varieties causes a yellowing or bronzing (fig. 78.1); on dark grape varieties, the injured leaves become "tanned" in some varieties and brilliant red in others. Mite feeding on flower clusters results in deformed, small clusters that have delayed development.

SEASONAL DEVELOPMENT

Deutogynes overwinter inside the latent bud among the hair masses lining the underside of outer leaf primordia, around the growing tips, and under bark crevices at

Figure 78.1 Leaf bronzing caused by grape rust mite feeding on Pinot noir. *Photo:* V. A. Walton, Oregon State University.

403

the insertion point between the canes and 2-year-old wood. When buds start to swell, deutogynes feed on them and lay eggs. At the basal area of the new shoot, they go through two nymphal stages and become protogynes and males. After budbreak in spring, the mites move to new leaves; as more shoot elongation takes place, they advance to keep up with the shoots. Eggs, larvae, nymphs, adult protogynes, and males may be found on both upper and lower surfaces of the leaf; on the upper surface they tend to cluster along the main veins. Grape flowers and clusters also are infested. In June, part of the population migrates into newly developing buds, where they increase in numbers throughout the summer. In late summer the deutogynes appear and move toward the overwintering sites, with a large proportion of the population residing in the first three basal buds of each shoot. Development from nymph to adult requires 6 days. Protogynes live about a month. The number of generations varies from 5 to 12, depending on temperatures.

Natural Control

Rust mites generally are held in check by myriad natural enemies. There are several predatory mites in the family Phytoseiidae that prey on grape rust mite. In addition, mites in the families Stigmaeidae and Tydeidae and various generalist predators (thrips, cecidomyiids, and minute pirate bugs) prey on grape rust mites.

Monitoring Guidelines

Rust mite is rarely a pest in most grape-growing regions of North America. The mite can be particularly problematic during hot, dry summers, while rain has been shown to wash mites off infested vines. While no detailed monitoring guidelines have been developed, growers would be wise to periodically check new buds in the spring for signs of necrosis on the outer leaf primordia. Likewise, growers should check any deformed shoots and flowers and bronzed leaves for mite infestation. A 14× or 20× hand lens is necessary to see grape rust mites. Inspect dormant buds in areas of the vineyard where bronzing due to rust mites was observed. In areas that have frequent damage by rust mite, double-sided adhesive traps hung in the canopy have been shown to be an efficient monitoring tool for detecting the presence of the mite.

Management Guidelines

Rust mite is rarely a pest in California vineyards. Grape rust mite generally is effectively controlled by sulfur programs for powdery mildew. If an acaricide treatment is warranted, the best treatment timing is when shoots are 5 to 10 cm (2 to 4 in) long. Studies have also shown that grape rust mite is easily spread throughout vineyards by adhering to the clothes and hands of workers. Growers should be aware of this to prevent movement of mites from vineyard to vineyard and from infested to noninfested blocks within the same vineyard.

References

Baker, E. W., T. Kono, J. W. Amrine, Jr. M. D. Delfinado-Baker, and T. N. Stasny. 1996. Eriophyoid mites of the United States. Bloomfield, MI: Indira.

Bernard, M. B., P. Horne, and A. A. Hoffmann. 2005. Eriophyoid mite damage in *Vitis vinifera* (grapevine) in Australia: *Calepitrimerus vitis* and *Colomerus vitis* (Acari: Eriophyidae) as the common cause of the widespread "restricted spring growth" syndrome. Experimental and Applied Acarology 35:83–109.

Duffner, K., G. Schruft, and R. Guggenheim. 2001. Passive dispersal of the grape rust mite *Calepitrimerus vitis* Nalepa 1905 (Acari, Eriophyoidea) in vineyards. Journal of Pest Science 74:1–6.

Lindquist, E. W., M. W. Sabelis, and J. Bruin, eds. 1996. Eriophyoid mites: Their biology, natural enemies and control. World Crop Pests 6. Amsterdam: Elsevier.

Perez-Moreno, I., M. Lourdes, and M. L. Moraza-Zorrilla. 1998. Population dynamics and hibernation shelters of *Calepitrimerus vitis* in vineyards of Rioja, Spain, with a description of a new eriopyhid extraction technique (Acari: Eriophyidae). Experimental and Applied Acarology 22:215–226.

Siqueira, P. R. E., A. D. Grutzmacher, M. Botton, and R. A. G. Kohn. 2011. Populational fluctuation of the grape rust mite in commercial vineyard in Candiota, Rio Grande do Sul State, with different sampling methods. Cincia Rural 41:1489–1495.

Walton, V., A. Dreves, D. Gent, D. James, R. Martin, U. Chambers, and P. Skinkis. 2007. Relationship between rust mites *Calepitrimerus vitis* (Nalepa), bud mites *Colomerus vitis* (Pagenstesher) (Acari: Eriophyidae), and short shoot syndrome in Oregon vineyards. International Journal of Acarology 33:307–318.

79 SPIDER MITES

Frank G. Zalom, Walter J. Bentley, Lucia G. Varela, Larry J. Bettiga, and David R. Haviland

Spider mites (Acari: *Tetranychidae*) can be a serious pest of grapes. Weather, irrigation practices, dust, and the use of disruptive synthetic organic insecticides are among the reasons this group of mites reaches pest status. Altering vineyard cultural practices to reduce spider mite activity is key to managing them. The judicious use of miticides can help reduce potentially damaging mite infestation in grapes.

Two spider mite species that commonly infest grapes in California are the Pacific spider mite (*Tetranychus pacificus* McGregor) and the Willamette spider mite (*Eotetranychus willamettei* (McGregor)). Pacific spider mite is considered the more damaging species statewide (fig. 79.1). However, Willamette mite is more often the species of concern in the coastal valleys and the Sierra Nevada foothills, and occasionally in the northern interior near Lodi and the Delta. Willamette mite had been considered the primary pest species in the warmer wine grape production areas of Monterey and San Luis Obispo Counties, but widespread mite outbreaks occurring since 2005 led to the identification of Pacific mite as a major problem. The twospotted spider mite (*Tetranychus urticae* Koch) is only occasionally found on grapes in California. Pacific and twospotted mites have a broad host range, while Willamette mites feed on cultivated and wild grapes and relatively few other plant species.

Information about spider mite distribution and abundance has come primarily from research conducted in Fresno, Kern, and Tulare Counties in the southern San Joaquin Valley, and more recently from the Lodi area as well. Spider mite problems have become increasingly common in coastal valleys and foothill areas, with their population densities continuing to increase well into September (Pacific mite) and late August (Willamette mite). Spider mites are not considered to be important grape pests in southern California's desert areas.

The distribution and abundance of Pacific and Willamette mite are changing because of pesticide use, irrigation practices, and large-scale planting of wine cultivars in areas of California where they have not been previously planted. Insecticide and fungicide use patterns

Figure 79.1 Pacific mite outbreak spot in Thompson Seedless vineyard. *Photo*: J. K. Clark.

have changed dramatically since the year 2000. The increased use of synthetic fungicides and the decreased use of sulfur have reduced the disruption of predator mite species and may allow for greater levels of natural control. Alternatively, the water management practices used to enhance wine grape quality may favor the development of Pacific mite in many areas. The increased prevalence of pests requiring insecticide application such as vine mealybug and glassy-winged sharpshooter may also reduce predator survival. These changes have affected Pacific spider mite in particular, possibly increasing its pest status in some areas. Environmental conditions, irrigation practices, and soil type also strongly influence mite abundance by increasing vine stress. For example, in western Fresno and Tulare Counties (Caruthers and Kerman areas) soils are generally alkaline and light in texture, contributing to hot, dry, dusty vineyard conditions. This favors Pacific mite. In eastern Fresno and Tulare Counties, where heavier soils and generally cooler temperatures

prevail, vineyards are more humid and less dusty, and Willamette mite is the dominant species. Soil type may influence grapevine physiology, which in turn affects spider mite nutrition and so the predominance of one species over another.

DESCRIPTION

Egg Stage

Both Pacific and Willamette mites deposit spherical, translucent eggs singly on the underside of leaves, particularly along the midrib and veins. Eggs are found on upper leaf surfaces when populations are abundant. Pacific mite also lays eggs in its webbing. The Pacific mite egg is slightly larger (but this is difficult to evaluate without the aid of a microscope), and when first laid it is slightly amber compared with the Willamette egg. With incubation, the eggs of both species become opaque; the embryo's reddish eyespots become distinctly visible shortly before the larva hatches. The Willamette mite egg has a fine papilla (hair) that tapers at the top (fig. 79.2); no papilla is found on the Pacific or twospotted spider mite egg.

Larval Stage

The newly hatched, translucent larva has six legs. Dark "food spots" form soon after feeding on the dorsum (back) of Pacific mite and on each side of Willamette mite.

Protonymph Stage

In this eight-legged stage, food spots become more apparent in Pacific mite; they are less conspicuous in Willamette mite.

Deutonymph Stage

Male mites are similar in appearance to adult females but smaller. Deutonymph males of both species can be distinguished, however the distinction is not as clear-cut as in the adult stage. Food spots become conspicuous in Willamette mite.

Adult Stage

Upon emergence from the deutonymph stage, adult Pacific mite females are 0.5 mm (0.02 in) long and are almost devoid of food spots, but as feeding begins, the spots become more distinct, although the pattern varies. Usually two large, diffuse spots appear forward and two smaller spots appear in the rear, a pattern less evident early in the season. The

Figure 79.2 Willamette mite egg shows hair-like papilla (arrow). *Photo*: J. K. Clark.

Figure 79.3 Spotting pattern of Pacific, Willamette, and twospotted mite females.

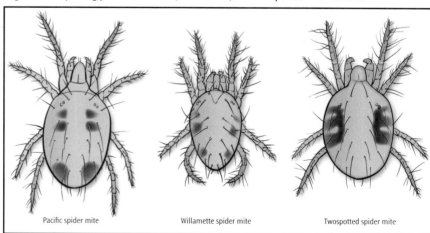

Pacific spider mite   Willamette spider mite   Twospotted spider mite

rear spots are diagnostic for field identification to dispel confusion with twospotted spider mite (fig. 79.3). Adult Pacific spider mite females vary from slightly amber to greenish or reddish (fig. 79.4A); later in the season and at high densities, they become reddish, a coloration not to be confused with the deep orange of resting state (diapausing) females.

Adult Willamette mite females are 0.5 mm (0.02 in) long and are usually pale yellow with small black dots along the sides of the body behind the eyes (fig. 79.4B). Sometimes as many as four distinctly visible spots occur on each side.

Adult males of both species are easily recognized by their pointed abdomen and smaller size (about one-half the size of the mature female). Males aggressively attend deutonymph females, chasing off other males in order to mate with females when they emerge (fig. 79.5). A hand lens and practice are necessary to distinguish the two species. Mixed populations of both species may occur. Microscopic examination of adult male genitalia is required for positive species confirmation, although relatively few adult males may be present at certain times during the season.

Identification Procedure
Proper spider mite identification requires a stereo dissecting microscope and a compound microscope. If these are available, the following procedure should be used to prepare specimens. Remove a single adult male from the leaf and place it in a small drop of mounting medium, such as Hoyer's solution, on a glass microscope slide. Place a cover slip on top of the mounting

material. The mite must be manipulated onto its side to examine the aedeagus (copulatory organ). This is accomplished by viewing the specimen under a stereo microscope and carefully moving the cover slip so that the mite specimen rolls onto its side. Lining up the small red eyes before pressing down on the cover slip facilitates proper lateral orientation. Press the cover slip down gently to make the aedeagus protrude. It is best to remove live males directly from the leaf for mounting, because those that have been in alcohol are more difficult to position and eye color is lost in alcohol-stored specimens. For species identification, set the compound microscope objective power to 45×. Using figure 79.6 and with proper mounting and examination of the aedeagus, Willamette, Pacific, and twospotted spider mite males are easily distinguished.

INJURY

Feeding by small colonies of either species produces small yellow spots on upper leaf surfaces (fig. 79.7). Yellowing of an entire leaf characterizes high densities of Willamette mite (fig. 79.8); a bronze discoloration is produced by high densities of Pacific mite. Later, especially in hot weather, leaves infested with Pacific mite turn dry, brown, and become brittle (fig. 79.9). The leaves may also be wrapped in webbing (fig. 79.10).

On rare occasions large numbers of overwintering Willamette mites may cause damage to young shoots in spring, but this is usually spotty and vines outgrow the injury without noticeable loss. Large populations of overwintering Pacific mite found at budbreak can cause

Figure 79.4 Pacific mite female (A); Willamette mite female (B). *Photos*: J. K. Clark.

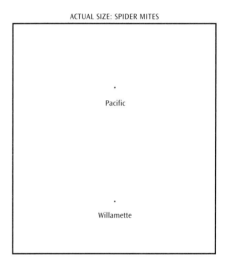

ACTUAL SIZE: SPIDER MITES

Pacific

Willamette

Figure 79.5 Willamette mite male waits to mate with female as soon as she molts to the adult stage. *Photo*: J. K. Clark.

Figure 79.6 Male Willamette spider mite and reproductive structures of the three Tetranychid species.

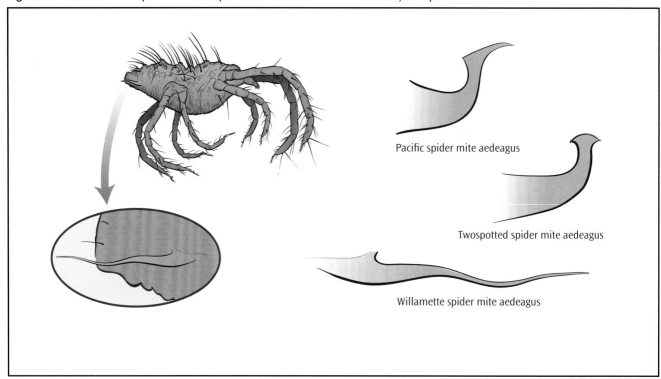

Pacific spider mite aedeagus

Twospotted spider mite aedeagus

Willamette spider mite aedeagus

more severe vine injury. Distortion of shoot tips also characterizes Pacific mite injury. In the coastal areas, Willamette mite feeding causes a reddish coloration on dark cultivars such as Pinot noir (fig. 79.11A) and a yellowish coloration on light cultivars such as Chardonnay (fig. 79.11B).

Willamette mite sometimes produces economic damage to grapevines in the southern and central San Joaquin Valley and periodically requires control. It is more common for infestations to become economically important in the northern San Joaquin Valley and in foothill, coastal, and northern California vineyards. Peak Willamette mite infestations of 50 mites per leaf have been shown to reduce the sugar content in

Zinfandel grapes during the first year of infestation. Yield, berry size, and fruit cluster abundance may be significantly reduced the following year. Willamette mite levels of less than 30 per leaf did not result in reduced productivity or quality. Moderate populations that persist throughout summer can open vine canopies, resulting in sunburned fruit. High populations of Willamette mite may cause amber berries in white table grape cultivars, such as Thompson Seedless, as a result of cluster exposure to sunlight. Vigorous cultivars with dense canopies seldom require treatment with a miticide. Less-vigorous cultivars with more-limited canopies are more susceptible to Willamette mite damage. Growers should attempt to balance the benefits of

Willamette mite as an alternate prey for predaceous mites with potential economic losses.

SEASONAL DEVELOPMENT

Pacific and Willamette mites overwinter as mature females under grapevine bark. This resting state (diapause) is induced by a combination of short day length and lower temperatures during early fall and is enhanced by mature foliage. Observations indicate that Willamette mite requires shorter day length to induce diapause, as it actively reproduces later in fall than does Pacific mite.

Diapause is also induced in Pacific mite by the foliar injury resulting from excessive mite feeding. It is not uncommon to find mature females in diapause under the bark of injured vines during summer. Whether these early-diapausing females remain under the bark and overwinter is unknown. Diapausing Pacific mites exhibit a glistening, deep orange color and lack food spots (fig. 79.12). These females differ from those that become reddish as foliage quality declines. Diapausing Willamette mite females are a glistening lemon-yellow color and also lack food spots. The effect of feeding injury on the induction of diapause of Willamette mite is not known.

Overwintering females of both species move to tender young foliage when grape buds break in spring (fig. 79.13). Willamette mite is more active during cooler temperatures and tends to build to higher densities earlier than do Pacific mites. Both species produce many generations each year. During favorable periods females can lay more than eight eggs daily; about two-thirds develop into egg-laying females in 10 days or less (fig. 78.14). This results in rapid population increases.

NATURAL CONTROL

Predaceous Mites on Grapes
An important predatory mite found in many California vineyards is the western predatory mite (*Galendromous* (*Metaseiulus*) *occidentalis* (Nesbitt)) (Acari: Phytoseiidae). With abundant prey and favorable temperature, it has a capacity for rapid population increase. This capacity is limited by predator-prey distribution patterns in the vineyard, availability of alternate prey or food for the predator, and viticulture practices that affect spider mite population levels or cause predator mortality.

Figure 79.7 Typical yellowing damage from spider mites on a vine in a San Joaquin Valley vineyard. *Photo*: J. K. Clark.

Figure 79.8 Close-up of typical Willamette mite yellowing damage. *Photo*: J. K. Clark.

Figure 79.9 Typical Pacific mite leaf burn on top of grapevine. *Photo*: J. K. Clark.

Figure 79.10 Close-up of Pacific mite webbing. *Photo*: J. K. Clark.

Figure 79.11 Willamette mite feeding damage on coastal wine grapes: reddish discoloration (A) on dark cultivars such as Pinot noir and yellowish discoloration (B) on Chardonnay. *Photos*: J. K. Clark.

Figure 79.12 Diapausing form of Pacific mite female. Note the lack of spotting. *Photo*: J. K. Clark.

Figure 79.13 Typical early Pacific mite colonization injury in a leaf fold. *Photo*: J. K. Clark.

Figure 79.14 Willamette mite female and an egg she has laid. *Photo*: J. K. Clark.

Figure 79.15 *Galendromus occidentalis* attacks spider mite egg. *Photo*: J. K. Clark.

Figure 79.16 *Galendromus occidentalis* egg. *Photo*: J. K. Clark.

The timing and amount of sulfur use may significantly affect spider mite populations. *G. occidentalis* is raised commercially in California insectaries and can be purchased for augmentative release. Adult females of some strains are reportedly tolerant of sulfur application, but further research is needed to determine possible side effects of sulfur on these predators.

Surveys of predaceous mites have shown that many predatory mite species inhabit vineyards. The dominant species vary from region to region, and *G. occidentalis* is not always the most common species. In the Napa and Sonoma growing regions, *Typhlodromus pyri* Scheuten dominates, but *Euseius quetzali* McMurtry and *G. occidentalis* are also common. In Mendocino and Lake Counties, *G. occidentalis* dominates. In the San Joaquin Valley, *G. occidentalis* and *E. quetzali* or *E. tularensis* Congdon are most common. Studies in San Joaquin Valley vineyards in which sterol-inhibiting fungicides were substituted for sulfur to control powdery mildew showed that *E. tularensis* became a dominant predaceous mite and effectively controlled Willamette mite. *Euseius stipulatus* (Athias-Henriot), a common predaceous mite on avocado and citrus, can also be found in central coast vineyards. *Neoseiulus fallacis* (Garman) is common at times in Lodi. *Metaseiulus mcgregori* (Chant) has been observed attacking Willamette mite in Arvin and Lodi vineyards, but its effectiveness has not been studied. *Neoseiulus* (*Amblyseius*) *californicus* (McGregor) has been observed preying on Willamette mite in central coast vineyards.

Like *G. occidentalis*, *N. fallacies* and *N. californicus* are raised commercially in insectaries and are available for augmentative release.

Description
Predator mites are easily distinguished from spider mites using a good hand lens and paying attention to their behavior. Adult females are narrowly oval, and most species are slightly larger than an adult female spider mite (fig. 79.15). Color varies with what they have fed on, but most are shiny white to slightly yellow or reddish. Predator mites tend to move much more quickly than spider mites as they search leaves for prey. The different species of predatory mites look alike to the naked eye. To distinguish among species of predatory mite, specimens need to be slide mounted and keyed using a phase-contrast compound microscope.

Eggs of predaceous mites are more elliptical than the spherical eggs of spider mites and perhaps three to four times larger. Freshly laid eggs are clear; they gradually turn milky and opaque before hatching (fig. 79.16).

There are four postemergence stages; the first is a six-legged larva, and the remaining three are eight legged. In order of development, the four stages are termed larva, protonymph, deutonymph, and adult.

Development
Predatory mite females are usually found along leaf veins or wedged in vein angles, where they prefer to lay their eggs in a loose grouping. Eggs are also laid in the webbing of Pacific mite colonies. After hatching, the predator larva wanders awkwardly in search of food; after

feeding, it becomes more active. The larval stage attacks all stages of prey but prefers spider mite eggs. Before molting to the protonymph stage, it passes through a short resting period.

The protonymph moves quickly while searching for prey, successfully attacking all stages of prey, although it may not consume an entire adult spider mite. More than one predator is sometimes seen feeding on the same prey. The protonymph stops moving and feeding for a short time before molting to the deutonymph stage. The deutonymph is similar to the protonymph in habits and activity.

Unlike the protonymph and deutonymph, the adult female is less active, particularly *G. occidentalis*, spending considerable time in protected angles of leaf veins. The male adult, which resembles the nymphal stages, often attends the female deutonymph while she is inactive and ready to molt. Mating occurs soon after the adult female emerges. With sufficient prey available and favorable conditions, a predatory mite is capable of developing from egg to egg-laying female in 5 days.

Galendromous occidentalis, the most common predator in the San Joaquin Valley, overwinters primarily under the buds of grapevines as mated, adult females (fig. 79.17). As with spider mites, diapause for overwintering survival is induced by short day lengths and cool temperatures in fall. Prey must be available for these predators in fall; without food, reproduction stops, and the predator population is unable to enter into the diapause-inducing stages. This life history will differ with other predatory mites.

The diapausing female of *G. occidentalis* mates but lays no eggs and only occasionally feeds. She remains inactive until cooler weather induces migration to the overwintering site under bud scales. There she remains until the following spring. In spring the emerging female searches expanding foliage for prey and begins laying eggs, the number depending on availability of prey. When a well-distributed population of predators successfully overwinters in a vineyard, spider mites are generally controlled, unless subsequent pesticide treatments disrupt predation.

Alternate prey

Galendromous occidentalis feeds primarily on spider mites. Many of the other predatory mites commonly found in vineyards, such as *Typhlodromus, Neoseiulus, Amblyseius, and Euseius* species, have a wider host range that includes other small arthropods, other mite species, and even plant pollen or leaf sap in addition to spider mites. Eriophyid, tydeid, and possibly tarsonemid mites help to support and maintain predator populations, especially in fall when spider mites are scarce. Tydeid mites are particularly important in this respect (fig. 79.18). When abundant, they indirectly influence later predation of Pacific and Willamette mites. Tydeid mites are not pests of grapes; they feed primarily on pollen and to some extent on fungi. Their secondary feeding on leaf tissue produces no discernible injury. They are difficult to see on the leaf without a microscope; the stages (adults, immatures, and eggs) are about one-third the size of equivalent spider mite stages. Characteristically these tiny mites

move as fast backward as forward. Their quiescent (molting) stages are found by searching along leaf veins and between vein angles. Their small, oval-shaped, stalked eggs are usually laid on leaf hairs (fig. 79.19). They also eat their own eggs.

Two species of tydeids have been reported in commercial vineyards in the San Joaquin Valley: *Homeopronematus anconai* (Baker), which occurs in all the grape-growing regions of the San Joaquin Valley, and *Pronematus ubiquitus* (McGregor), about which little is known in California vineyards. A different tydeid, *Triophtydeus* species, has been found on grapes in the north coast; little is known about its role as an alternate prey for predatory mites.

Figure 79.17 *Galendromus occidentalis* is pear shaped immediately before laying an egg. *Photo*: J. K. Clark.

Figure 79.18 Tydeid mite. *Photo*: J. K. Clark.

Figure 79.19 Tydeid mite egg attached to leaf hair. *Photo*: J. K. Clark.

Figure 79.20 Adult sixspotted thrips feeding on a mite. *Photo*: J. K. Clark.

Figure 79.21 Immature sixspotted thrips attacking Pacific mite. *Photo*: J. K. Clark.

Figure 79.22 *Orius* spp. (minute pirate bug) nymph feeding on a mite. *Photo*: J. K. Clark.

In contrast to Pacific mite, tydeid mite populations persist on foliage late into fall. In Thompson Seedless vineyards in the Caruthers area of Fresno County, they were found to be the main source of food for predators in fall. Tydeid mites are found overwintering under bud scales, presumably in the diapause state. *G. occidentalis* occasionally has been observed to prey on tydeids under buds during winter.

Vineyards in eastern Fresno and Tulare Counties appear to present more favorable conditions for tydeid mites than do vineyards on the western side, particularly under weedy conditions.

Tydeid mites are rare in vineyards where insecticides are applied. The resulting lack of tydeids can reduce fall predator populations and cause Pacific mite populations to flare. Where vineyards are not treated with insecticides, sufficient numbers of tydeid prey are present to maintain predator populations. Attempts to develop methods for increasing tydeid mite abundance have not been successful, but cover crops that produce wind-blown pollen show promise. (Cover cropping and other cultural practices related to mite management are discussed below.)

Willamette mites affect grapes less severely than do Pacific mites in the central San Joaquin Valley. They also act as an alternate prey for predatory mites. Twospotted mites may be found in vineyards along the San Joaquin Valley's eastern side and occasionally in the north coast, and they occasionally provide an important alternate prey for predaceous mites on grapevines and ground cover. They seldom damage grapes. Weedy vineyards are most likely to harbor twospotted mites.

Other Predators

Predatory insects and spiders are generally not effective as natural enemies of spider mites. They appear too late in the season, often after spider mite densities have reached damaging levels, or they increase too slowly to halt rapid spider mite buildup. However, do not discount their contribution to natural control. An exception is sixspotted thrips (*Scolothrips sexmaculatus* (Pergande)) (fig. 79.20), which destroys Pacific mite, impeding its spread. In this manner, sixspotted thrips often aids in control of pest mites. Sixspotted thrips are unpredictable predators of spider mites. Under favorable conditions, such as high spider mite densities, sixspotted thrips are capable of reproducing very quickly (fig. 79.21). They require large numbers of spider mites per individual to reproduce. Given their great reproductive potential and voracious appetite, they may rapidly arrest the increase of Pacific spider mites. Studies show that when 30 to 50% of the leaves have one or more sixspotted thrips, Pacific spider mite populations will be controlled within 1 week (see "Management Guidelines," below).

Because sixspotted thrips do not overwinter in vineyards, they must recolonize every year. This may partially explain their later-season and erratic appearance. Sixspotted thrips prefer webbing species of spider mites, such as twospotted and Pacific. Willamette, which produces little webbing, is not preferred.

The benefit provided by other predators (lacewings, spiders, minute pirate bugs, nabid bugs, ladybird beetles, etc.) in vineyards is not well known (fig. 79.22). Individually, they appear to exert little control; collectively, they could be important. For example, observations in vineyards and studies in the laboratory reveal that western flower thrips (*Frankliniella occidentalis* (Pergande)) feeds on Pacific mite eggs and under certain conditions may actually affect the pest's population growth, particularly early in the season. Unfortunately, western flower thrips is thought of only as a pest of agricultural crops, including certain table grape cultivars. While maintaining these generalists in a vineyard is obviously beneficial, growers should not rely on them for spider mite suppression.

Induced Plant Responses

A study has shown that low densities of Willamette mites present on leaves early in the season results in lower Pacific mite population densities later. This is not the case when Willamette mite is not present on leaves earlier. Although the mechanism for this is not fully understood, it is believed that the Willamette mite feeding stimulates the grapevine to produce natural chemical products to protect itself from injury. Such plant responses occur in many plant species. Early-season Willamette releases to induce plant response should not be attempted in vineyards that experience chronic Willamette mite pressure.

MONITORING GUIDELINES

Willamette and Pacific mite populations can be effectively monitored at the same time as leafhopper counts are made, but monitoring can also be conducted independent of that for leaf-hoppers. It is useful to consider characteristics of Willamette and Pacific mite biology and feeding when evaluating their population abundance.

Willamette and Pacific mites colonize primarily on the under-surface of the leaf, usually along midribs and veins. Willamette mites tend to disperse more over the leaf surface; Pacific mites produce more webbing and tend to aggregate. Both species prefer leaf folds and depressions.

Pacific mites generally prefer parts of grapevines most exposed to the sun. Willamette mites prefer less exposed, shady areas. This is conspicuous on grapevines cultured on arbors, where Pacific mite is found on the upper, exposed foliage and Willamette mite is found on the lower, shady foliage.

Abundant populations of Pacific mite may produce profuse webbing and cause an apparent burning of vertical shoot tips on the tops of vines. Old leaves are also burned or scorched in appearance, but this injury must be distinguished from sunburn or sulfur burn. Abundant Willamette mite damage is characterized by yellowish foliage. Usually, no burn occurs unless vines are weak. Willamette mites show little preference for vertical shoot tips on the tops of vines.

Pacific mite damage in vineyards is often spotty and tends to occur in weaker areas. Willamette mites generally prefer healthy, vigorously growing vines, but this could be more of a seasonal factor, since Willamette mites also tend to increase earlier in the season than do Pacific mites. Mixed populations of both species may occur. The damage potential of mixed populations is judged on the number of Pacific mites present.

A monitoring tool called presence-absence sampling for spider mites and predaceous mites has been developed for grapes. This method of sampling does not require counting all mites on leaves, which is time consuming. Rather, presence-absence sampling is more efficient because only the presence or absence of mites is recorded. If followed correctly, this method is easy to use and reliable. It takes into account the relationship between the average number of mites per leaf and the proportion of leaves with mites. The procedure outlined here was developed for Thompson Seedless raisin vineyards in the San Joaquin Valley. It allows for monitoring Pacific mite damage levels and mite predator effectiveness. The same method can be used for Willamette mite or mixed populations by adjusting the sampling procedures outlined below.

Two important components of population monitoring are defined, Pacific mite injury levels and predator-prey distribution ratios using presence-absence sampling. These, used in conjunction with viticulture practices (moisture stress management, dust control, etc.), form the basis for management decisions.

Sampling Procedures

Peak levels of Willamette mite often occur earlier in the summer than those of Pacific mite, although moderate to high densities may be present until harvest in the Sierra foothill and coastal areas. Where mixed-species populations occur, it is not unusual for Willamette mite to continue to build until high temperatures occur, after which the Pacific mite population increases, rapidly supplanting the Willamette mite population.

Sampling for Pacific and Willamette mites should begin in the middle of May. High mite densities can appear as early as the first week of June. Sampling should continue every week until the middle of June, then more often if populations are increasing rapidly. Peak levels of Pacific mite typically occur from mid-July until late August. In the San Joaquin Valley, Pacific mite is usually not a problem by the end of August, but it may persist into the fall on the central coast.

To sample mites, it is best to divide the vineyard into more than one sampling area, as weak areas and vines along dusty roadways may need to be managed differently than other areas. Within each area, randomly select 15 vines to sample. Do not select vines that are very different from each other. From each vine, choose three leaves (fig. 79.23), one from the middle of each of three shoots. Sample one leaf from a shoot that originates at the wire level and is oriented upright and away from the canopy (item 1 in fig. 79.23) and a second leaf from a shoot that originates at or about where the canes meet the wire (item 2 in fig. 79.23). This type of shoot is oriented downward at an angle on the outside of the canopy and is fully exposed to sunlight. The third leaf should be selected from a shoot that is oriented downward within the vine canopy and is continuously shaded (item 3 in fig. 79.23). All sampling should be done on the south side of vines in east-west plantings and on the west side on north-south plantings. Selected leaves should be examined for the presence or absence of Pacific mite,

Figure 79.23 Shoots used for selecting leaves to determine the presence or absence of Pacific and predator mites. (1) Shoot that originates at the wire level and is oriented upright and away from the canopy. (2) Shoot that originates at or about where the canes meet the wire. This type of shoot is oriented downward at an angle on the outside of the canopy and is fully exposed to sunlight. (3) Shoot that is oriented downward within the vine canopy and is continuously shaded.

Willamette mite, and predaceous mites. Using a 10× hand lens, examine only the lower surface of leaves. Begin examination where main veins branch. Predatory mites are often found resting in vein angles, especially when spider mite numbers are low. Search carefully along veins and in leaf areas that are depressed or cupped. Examine for all stages of Pacific mite, Willamette mite, and predaceous mites. Also keep a tally of the number of leaves with sixspotted thrips, if they are present.

For Pacific mite, keep a running tally for each sampling date of the number of leaves with one or more Pacific mites and those with predaceous mites. Divide the number of leaves with at least one Pacific mite by the total number of leaves sampled (45) to calculate the proportion or percentage of leaves infested by Pacific mite. Forms for such monitoring can be found in the UC IPM Grape Pest Management Guidelines, www.ipm.ucdavis.edu/PMG/.

For Willamette mite, record the number of leaves with active stages of Willamette mites present and also record the number of leaves that have a predator mite or not (presence or absence). Divide the number of leaves with at least one Willamette mite by the total number of leaves sampled (45) to calculate the proportion of leaves infested by Willamette mite; then total the number of Willamette mites from all leaves and divide by the total number of leaves sampled (45) to calculate average number of Willamette mites per leaf. Leaves may be collected in the field and returned for counting using a mite-brushing machine or other device if so desired. Remember to label samples clearly and accurately

and keep them cool (in an ice chest) during transport and before counting.

Defining Pacific Mite Injury Levels

Evaluations of Pacific mite damage levels are based on the above tallies and on observations of whether the problem is general or confined to small spots in the vineyard. View the entire vineyard from the top of a pickup truck or an irrigation standpipe. Outbreaks of Pacific mite frequently occur and may be observed from heights. Look for large, dull, discolored areas and especially any burning on tops of vines. These areas can then be categorized as follows.

- **Light:** An occasional colony is found on vines, with no bronzing or burning of the foliage. Less than 50% of leaves infested.

- **Moderate:** Colonies are numerous, with foliage showing little or no burn but some bronzing. From 50 to 65% of leaves infested.

- **Heavy:** High egg production is visible in the colonies, as is considerable bronzing of foliage and some leaf and shoot tip burning on the tops of the vines. Webbing on shoot tips is obvious. From 65 to 75% of leaves infested.

- **Very heavy:** Very large populations are observed, as well as considerable vineyard damage, extensive webbing, and severe burning of shoots. More than 75% of leaves infested.

The risk of injury at these levels varies somewhat by cultivar; those with less-vigorous vegetative

growth such as Zinfandel tend to be particularly sensitive to damage by spider mites as opposed to cultivars with vigorous vegetative growth such as Thompson Seedless.

Willamette Mite Injury Levels

Willamette mite is considered far less damaging than Pacific mite. In vineyards where they occur each year, Willamette mites must exceed 30 mites per leaf, on average, before any economic losses are detected. Use the average number of Willamette mites per leaf estimated by the sampling method previously described to determine the need for a management action.

Defining Predator-Prey Distribution Ratios

Table 79.1 shows how monitoring predator-prey distribution ratios of Pacific and predator mites was used to delay treatment to take advantage of a potentially effective predator population and maximize the control provided by miticides. Column 2 (number of prey per leaf) shows a typically increasing spider mite population in early summer. On May 22, 23 leaves out of 30 were recorded to have one or more pest mites (column 4); only 2 leaves had one or more predators (column 3), but the damage in this vigorous vineyard was judged tolerable. Subsequent monitoring showed that even though the pest mite population continued to increase (column 2), the leaf distribution gap between predator mite and pest mite populations (columns 3 and 4) narrowed substantially. Put another way, the predator to prey distribution ratio (column 5) also increased rapidly. The ratio is found by dividing column 3 by column 4.

Considerable research with both Willamette and Pacific mite

Table 79.1. Influence of predator-prey distribution ratios on the biological control of Pacific spider mites on Thompson Seedless grapes, Peterson Vineyard, Poplar, Tulare County, 1967

Date	Number of prey per leaf	30 leaves sampled; number with predators	30 leaves sampled; number with prey	Predator-prey distribution ratio
May 22	64	2	23	1:11.5
Jun 1	98	3	26	1:8.7
Jun 7	114	8	27	1:3.4
Jun 13	123	10	29	1:2.9
Jun 19	121	13	30	1:2.3
Jun 26	154	19	30	1:1.6
Jul 3	128	24	30	1:1.2
Jul 10	44	25	25	1:1
Jul 17	17	21	21	1:1
Jul 26	13	18	20	1:1.1
Aug 1	5	12	12	1:1

summer populations has shown that when the predator to prey distribution ratio is greater than 1:2, spider mite populations will predictably decrease, regardless of the number of pest mites per leaf. The table shows that the prey population (column 2) decreased rapidly after a ratio greater than 1:2 was achieved on June 26. Predaceous mites are considered

- **rare** if the ratio is less than 1:30 (little or no predation). Predaceous mites may go undetected in vineyards with heavy pesticide treatments or where mite populations are so small that predators have not increased to detectable numbers.

- **occasional** when the ratio is between 1:30 and 1:10 (not yet effective).

- **frequent** when the ratio is 1:10 to 1:2 (becoming or are effective).

- **numerous** when greater than 1:2 (highly effective).

Remember that the proportion of leaves with predators or prey is only one component of the information necessary to determine need for treatment. Decisions weigh heavily on assessing vineyard vigor, moisture stress, other pests, time of harvest, and so on, as discussed below.

MANAGEMENT GUIDELINES

Managing spider mites in vineyards is best done by integrating cultural practices with biological and chemical control.

Cultural Practices

Spider mite outbreaks frequently occur where vines are dusty, of low vigor, or water stressed. Many growers regularly control dust along heavily traveled roads and vineyard avenues using sand, water, or environmentally acceptable surface sealants. This reduces the amount of dust on fruit and also helps deter spider mite populations (fig. 79.24). All growers in areas prone to spider mite problems are encouraged to follow this practice.

Table grape growers also use summer cover crops or noncultivation to control dust, improve water infiltration, and help reduce heat damage to fruit. In surface-irrigated vineyards, row middles are cultivated and permanent furrows are established in mid-April, following the frost period. Furrows are used throughout the summer. The weeds that grow, primarily grasses, are mowed as necessary, usually three or four times. The grass cover does increase water requirements to some extent. Both table and wine grape growers using summer cover crops report fewer mite problems.

Raisin growers traditionally begin cultivating before budbreak and continue until the rows are terraced for raisin drying. Evidence shows this practice increases the incidence of spider mites. It is advisable for raisin growers experiencing mite problems to delay disking until early July, allowing summer grass to grow. This helps reduce mite populations while allowing ample time for grass to decompose before terracing.

Another recommended floor management program is no-till or to delay turning under a fall-winter cover crop until early June. Plants used for cover crops should be selected based on the site and what the production expectations for the cover are in the vineyard (see section 85, "Vineyard Floor Management"). The resident vegetation from no-till or cover crops is mowed to 3 to 4 in (7.5 to 10 cm) just before vine budbreak for frost protection in mid-March and early April. After frost danger has passed, the cover crops are allowed to grow, flower, and mature seeds (if reseeding is desired) before mowing or disking. The use of a no-till system will result in less dust being produced within the vineyard. A fall-winter cover crop may also harbor twospotted mite, which serves as an alternate prey for predaceous mites. Delaying disking or mowing of the cover crop allows predator populations, if present, to increase and then move to grapevines.

Pacific mite outbreaks frequently recur year after year in areas of a vineyard that have weak growth or are stressed. These outbreaks often result from sand streaks, shallow soils, compacted soils, poor water penetration or distribution, nematodes, phylloxera, or any combination of factors. Correcting these cultural or irrigation problems can restore vine vigor and fruit production and reduce Pacific mite activity.

Proper irrigation scheduling and water application alleviates water stress. To accomplish this may require touch-up grading, altering furrow arrangements, improving drip system uniformity, adding gypsum when low-salt water is used for irrigation, and summer cover cropping to improve water penetration. Keep vines healthy and vigorous by avoiding stress from overcropping, nutrient deficiencies, and severe irrigation deficits.

Irrigation greatly influences spider mite abundance and predator effectiveness. Dry vines permit rapid spider mite buildup. In areas of low rainfall such as the central and southern San Joaquin Valley or in dry winters elsewhere, it is advisable to irrigate during dormancy or late fall to ensure that the entire root zone is at field capacity before the irrigation season begins. During the irrigation season, the timing of irrigations and the amount of water applied must be accurately determined for each vineyard and soil type.

Finally, studies show that spider mites may be kept under control in Thompson Seedless raisin vineyards and in north coast wine grape vineyards with overhead sprinkler irrigation. The mites are suppressed by the washing and drowning action of sprinkler-applied water and by higher humidity and lower temperatures. For example, in the west Fresno County area, where Pacific mites are a severe problem, it is necessary to sprinkle approximately every 10 days for 12 hours during late June and July to keep mites in check. Also, sprinkling should be discontinued in Thompson Seedless vineyards by the end

of July or early August to prevent berry cracking. Normally, this should present no problem since raisin growers do not irrigate later than July. Fortunately, predatory mites are not adversely affected by overhead sprinkling.

Although permanent sprinklers are expensive, the initial cost of installing sprinklers becomes less prohibitive when such factors as reduced labor costs and improved water management and irrigation efficiency are considered. Some growers with vineyards on sandy soil have reported significant increases in yields where overhead sprinklers have been installed. Spider mite problems can be reduced by sprinklers, but they should be used cautiously to avoid bunch rot in the month prior to harvest.

Obviously, none of these suggestions guarantees protection against spider mites. However, these practices, along with use of selective pesticides, can help reduce problems.

Figure 79.24 Dust contributes to spider mite problems in vineyards. *Photo*: J. K. Clark.

Evaluating Other Vineyard Pests

In the past, treatment of leaf-hoppers with broad-spectrum insecticides such as carbaryl aggravated spider mite problems. Whenever insecticide sprays are applied for vineyard insect pests, it is good practice to base chemical control decisions on established guidelines rather than on the calendar or preventive treatments to minimize the number of treatments applied. Also, choose the most selective insecticide available to protect natural enemies. For leafhoppers, treating the first brood is more disruptive than treating summer broods. Delaying treatments gives mite predators and parasitoids of leafhoppers an opportunity to increase without giving any advantage to spider mites. If grape leafhopper populations can be tolerated until summer broods and spider mites are present at appreciable levels, treatment may then include a miticide for spider mite control. Many of the recently registered insecticides for leafhoppers and other insects are not as disruptive as the organophosphate and carbamate insecticides previously used (see the UC IPM Grape Pest Management Guidelines, www.ipm.ucdavis.edu/PMG/). However, thorough studies of their side effects on predators or physiological effects that might favor spider mite development are often lacking. Vigilance of unintended impacts on spider mites is warranted whenever introducing a new chemical into the vineyard.

Evaluating and Treating Various Pacific Mite Situations

For spot infestations, if there is no evidence of spread and the infested area is small, omit treatment. This allows predators (e.g., sixspotted thrips) to increase or spread. If the infested area (or areas) is relatively large but constitute only a small part of the vineyard, use spot treatments provided predators are rare or occasional (as defined above) and leaves are beginning to burn. However, if predators are common, hold off treatment until damage is obvious and the predators cannot prevent excessive damage. Use the most selective miticide available when predators are present and consider its residual action against predators.

For general infestations, if Pacific mite populations are light and predaceous mites are rare or occasional, treatments can be delayed until weaker vines show light bronzing but not burning. If vines are vigorous, allow some bronzing of foliage. A little leaf burn is permissible, but do not allow heavy burn or webbing on shoot tips. Delaying treatment is necessary to increase predator numbers and improve their distribution on vines. Remember that well-distributed predator populations and high predator-prey distribution ratios can effectively prevent resurgence of Pacific mites after treatments with selective miticides.

If Pacific mite populations are moderate or heavy with predators rare or occasional, immediate treatment with an effective miticide is necessary. Delay treatment and re-evaluate in a few days if the vineyard is vigorous and amply supplied with moisture. Apply a spray before excessive webbing or burning occurs.

If Pacific mite populations are moderate to heavy with predaceous mites frequent to numerous, carefully evaluate population trends. Is the spider mite population decreasing, stable, or increasing? Is the predator-prey distribution ratio increasing or improving? Inspect the vineyard frequently (twice a week or more). Remember that both predaceous mites and spider mites have enormous capacities to increase their populations. Irrigate to avoid moisture stress. Do not cultivate or create dust. Let natural cover grow. Delay treatment unless it is obvious that damage is too great and predators are not yet effective. If vines are vigorous they will tolerate bronzing and some burning. Again, delaying treatment makes maximum use of predators. All studies have shown that treatments are much more effective if predator populations are conserved.

Table 79.2 summarizes treatment decisions that are based on various injury levels and predator to prey ratios for Thompson Seedless raisin grapes. These guidelines assume frequent monitoring, good viticulture practices such as avoiding moisture stress and dusty conditions, and the use of selective treatments. Injury levels for less vigorous cultivars will be lower. If more than 30% of the leaves have sixspotted thrips within a mite infestation, miticide applications may not be necessary.

Chemical Control

Before the year 2000, miticide options were rather limited, and many products had extended pre-harvest intervals or worker re-entry intervals that often dictated when they had to be applied. Because of this, it was not unusual for the applications to be made preventatively based on vineyard history

Table 79.2. Treatment guidelines for various combinations of Pacific mite injury levels and predator-prey distribution ratios in Thompson Seedless raisin vineyards*

Pacific mite injury levels (percent of leaves infested)*	Predator-prey distribution ratios			
	Rare (< 1:30)	Occasional (1:30–1:10)	Frequent (1:10–1:2)	Numerous (> 1:2)
light (< 50%)	Delay treatment to increase predators.	Delay treatment.	Treatment not likely necessary.	Treatment not necessary.
moderate (50–65%)	Treat if population is increasing rapidly.	May delay treatment to increase predation.	Treatment may not be needed if the predator-prey distribution ratio is increasing rapidly.	Treatment not needed.
heavy (65–75%)	Treat immediately.	May delay treatment a few days to take advantage of increasing predation.	Treatment may not be needed if predators are becoming numerous.	Treatment not needed if damage is not increasing.
very heavy (> 75%)	Treat immediately.	Treat immediately.	Treat immediately unless predator-prey distribution ratio is increasing rapidly; carefully evaluate damage.	Treatment may not be necessary if population is dropping because of very high (greater than 1:1) predator-prey distribution ratios; carefully evaluate damage.

Note:
* Thompson Seedless vines are very vigorous and tolerate more mite feeding than less vigorous cultivars. Consequently, injury levels would be lower for other cultivars, but predator-prey ratios and comments are applicable to all cultivars.

rather than being based on IPM monitoring and action levels. More recently, a number of new products with unique modes of action have been registered that provide flexibility for growers to consider factors such as preharvest intervals, conservation of beneficials, and resistance management. Temperature and plant status appear to adversely affect some products seasonally, and oils and adjuvants may improve efficacy in some cases. For example, the residual activity of products that penetrate leaf surfaces may not be as long when leaves harden off, but penetrants may improve this activity. Stylet oil, neem oil, and low rates of horticultural mineral oil can be effective in controlling moderate levels of spider mites with little lasting impact on predators. However, because there is no residual activity from these chemicals, they may need to be reapplied based on careful monitoring. A side benefit of stylet oil, in particular, is providing moderate control of powdery mildew and leafhoppers. Although there is little phytotoxicity of oils to grape leaves, caution must be taken as berry bloom may be affected, limiting the usefulness of this practice for table grapes after fruit has formed.

The mechanisms responsible for observed mite outbreaks following applications of certain insecticides and fungicides are not always apparent or straightforward. Older products such as carbaryl were known to increase spider mite reproduction in addition to killing mite predators, resulting in outbreaks. Several studies have reported greater spider mite densities associated with sulfur applications and have attributed such outbreaks to effects on mite predators, yet other research suggests that adult mortality from sulfur is relatively low in at least some strains of *G. occidentalis*.

Predaceous mites and other mite predators on grapes are tolerant of a number of commonly used pesticides. A table of relative toxicities of insecticides and miticides used in grape to natural enemies and honey bees found in the UC IPM Grape Pest Management Guidelines, www.ipm.ucdavis.edu/PMG/, is a good source for this information. Pest managers should be continually cognizant of the effect of treatments on beneficials as well as on the pest they are attempting to control. Experience is just as important as experimentation in seeking out this important aspect of pest management. Remember that pesticide tolerance is difficult to evaluate since some new products do not kill adults and active stages directly but rather affect eggs or immature stages, resulting in side effects that are not immediately apparent. Observations or actual population monitoring after treatment can pay dividends for making future decisions.

Resistance Management

When multiple pesticide applications are required for spider mite management in a growing season, it is recommended that miticides with different modes of action be used to prevent the development of resistance. It may also be beneficial to rotate from one mode of action to another from season to season.

REFERENCES

Calvert, D. J., and C. B. Huffaker. 1974. Predator (*Metaseiulus occidentalis*)-prey (*Pronematus spp.*) interactions under sulfur and cattail pollen applications in a noncommercial vineyard. Entomophaga 19:361–369.

English-Loeb, G. M., D. L. Flaherty, L. T. Wilson, W. W. Barnett, G. M. Leavitt, and W. H. Settle. 1986. Pest management changes affect spider mites in vineyards. California Agriculture 40(3): 28–30.

Flaherty, D. L. 1969. Ecosystem trophic complexity and Willamette mite, *Eotetranychus willamettei* Ewing (Acarina: Tetranychidae), densities. Ecology 50:911–916.

Flaherty, D. L., and M. A. Hoy. 1971. Biological control of Pacific mites and Willamette mites in San Joaquin Valley vineyards: Part III. Role of tydeid mites. Researches on Popular Ecology 8:80–96.

Flaherty, D. L., and C. B. Huffaker. 1970. Biological control of Pacific mites and Willamette mites in San Joaquin Valley vineyards. I. Role of *Metaseiulus occidentalis*. II. Influence of dispersion patterns of *Metaseiulus occidentalis*. Hilgardia 40:267–330.

Flaherty, D. L., C. L. Lynn, F. L. Jensen, and D. A. Luvisi. 1969. Ecology and integrated control of spider mites in San Joaquin vineyards. California Agriculture 23(4): 11.

Frazier, N. W., and L. M. Smith. 1946. The Willamette mite on grapes. Hilgardia 17:191–195.

Fukushima, C., and E. M. Stafford. 1969. Effects of road dust on spider mites. California Agriculture 23(4): 10.

Gilstrap, F. E., and E. R. Oatman. 1976. The bionomics of *Scolothrips sexmaculatus* (Pergande) (Thysanoptera: Thripidae), an insect predator of spider mites. Hilgardia 44:27–59.

Gonzalez, D., B. R. Patterson, T. F. Leigh, and L. T. Wilson. 1982. Mites: A primary food source for two predators in San Joaquin Valley cotton. California Agriculture 36(2): 18–20.

Hanna, R., L. T. Wilson, F. G. Zalom, and D. L. Flaherty. 1997. Effects of predation and competition on population dynamics of *Tetranychus pacificus* on grapevines. Journal of Applied Ecology 34:878–888.

Hanna, R., F. G. Zalom, and L. T. Wilson. 1997. 'Thompson Seedless' grapevine vigor and abundance of Pacific spider mite (*Tetranychus pacificus* McGregor) (Acari, Tetranychidae). Journal of Applied Entomology 121:878–88.

Hanna, R., F. G. Zalom, L. T. Wilson, and G. M. Leavitt. 1997. Sulfur can suppress mite predators in vineyards. California Agriculture 51(1): 19–21.

Hoy, M. A. 1975. Effect of temperature and photoperiod on the induction of diapause in the mite *Metaseiulus occidentalis*. Journal of Insect Physiology 21:605–611.

———. 2011. Integrated mite management in California almonds. In M. A. Hoy, Agricultural acarology: Introduction to integrated mite management. Chapter 17. Boca Raton, FL: CRC Press. 247–255.

Hoy, M. A., and D. L. Flaherty. 1970. Photoperiodic induction of diapause in a predaceous mite, *Metaseiulus occidentalis*. Annals of the Entomological Society of America. 63:960–963.

———. 1975. Diapause induction and duration in vineyard collected *Metaseiulus occidentalis*. Environmental Entomology 4:262–264.

Hoy, M. A., and K. A. Standow. 1982. Inheritance of resistance to sulfur in the spider mite predator *Metaseiulus occidentalis*. Entomologia Experimentalis et Applicata 31:316–323.

Hoy, M. A., D. L. Flaherty, W.

Peacock, and D. Culver. 1979. Vineyard and laboratory evaluations of methomyl, dimethoate, and permethrin for a grape pest management program in the San Joaquin Valley of California. Journal of Economic Entomology 72:250–255.

Jeppson, L. R., H. H. Keifer, and E. W. Baker. 1975. Mites injurious to economic plants. Berkeley: University of California Press.

Karban, R., and F. G. Zalom. 1998. Success of mite-fighting tactics evaluated. California Agriculture 52(6): 21–24.

Karban, R., G. English-Loeb, and D. Hougen-Eitzman. 1997. Mite vaccinations for sustainable management of spider mites in vineyards. Ecological Applications 7:183–193.

Kinn, D. N., and R. L. Doutt. 1972a. Initial survey of arthropods found in north coast vineyards of California. Environmental Entomology 1:508–513.

———. 1972b. Natural control of spider mites on wine grape varieties in northern California. Environmental Entomology 1:513–518.

Knop, N. F., and M. A. Hoy. 1983a. Biology of a tydeid mite, *Homeopronematus anconai* (n. comb.) (Acari: Tydeidae), important in San Joaquin Valley vineyards. Hilgardia 51:1–30.

———. 1983b. Factors limiting the utility of *Homeopronematus anconai* (Acari: Tydeidae) in integrated pest management in San Joaquin Valley vineyards. Journal of Economic Entomology 76:1181–1186.

Laing, J. E., D. L. Calvert, and C. B. Huffaker. 1972. Preliminary studies of effects of *Tetranychus pacificus* on yield and quality of grapes in the San Joaquin Valley, California. Environmental Entomology 1:658–663.

Pritchard, A. E., and E. W. Baker. 1955. A revision of the spider mite, family Tetranychidae. Memoirs, vol. 2. San Francisco: Pacific Coast Entomological Society.

Saenz de Cabazon Irigaray, F. J., and F. G. Zalom. 2007. Selectivity of miticide exposure on *Galendromus occidentalis* reproductive potential. Biocontrol Science and Technology 17(5): 541–546.

Saenz de Cabazon Irigaray, F. J., F. G. Zalom, and P. B. Thompson. 2007. Residual toxicity of miticides to *Galendromus occidentalis* and *Phytoseiulus persimilis* reproductive potential. Biological Control 40:153–159.

Schruft, G. A. 1972. Les tydéidés (Acari) sur vigne. European and Meditteranean Plant Protection Organization Bulletin 3:51–55.

———. 1986. Grape. In W. Heele and M. W. Sabelis, eds., Spider mites: Their biology, natural enemies and control. Amsterdam: Elsevier. 359–366.

Schuster, R. O., and A. E. Pritchard. 1963. Phytoseiid mites of California. Hilgardia 34:191–285.

Schwartz, A. 1987. Seasonal occurrence of a predaceous mite *Amblyseius addoensis* Van der Merwe & Ryke (Acari: Phytoseiidae) on table grapes. South African Journal of Enology and Viticulture 8:78–79.

Stafford, E. M., J. E. Dibble, C. D. Lynn, and W. B. Hewitt. 1968. Effects of oil sprays for controlling Pacific mite on grapevines. California Agriculture 22(5): 2–3.

Stavrinides, M. C., P. Van Nieuwenhuyse, T. Van Leeuwen, and N. C. Mills. 2010. Development of acaricide resistance in Pacific spider mite (*Tetranychus pacificus*) from California vineyards. Experimental and Applied Acarology 50:243–254.

Tanigoshi, L. K., S. C. Hoyt, and B. A. Croft. 1983. Basic biological and management components for mite pests and their natural enemies. In B. A. Croft and S. A. Hoyt, eds., Integrated management of insect pests of pome and stone fruits. New York: Wiley Interscience. 153–202.

Wilson, L. T., M. A. Hoy, F. G. Zalom, and J. M. Smilanick. 1984. Sampling mites in almonds: 1. Within-tree distribution and clumping pattern of mites with comments on predator-prey interactions. Hilgardia 51:1–13.

Wilson, L. T., J. M. Smilanick, M. P. Hoffmann, D. L. Flaherty, and S. M. Ruiz. 1988. Leaf nitrogen and position in relation to population parameters of Pacific spider mite, *Tetranychus pacificus* (Acari: Tetranychidae) on grapes. Environmental Entomology 17:964–968.

Zalom, F. G., M. A. Hoy, L. I. Wilson, and W. W. Barnett. 1984. Sampling mites in almonds: II. Presence-absence sequential sampling for *Tetranychus* mite species. Hilgardia 52:14–24.

80 BLACK WIDOW SPIDER

Kent M. Daane, Pedro Hernandez, Glenn Yokota, Jennifer M. Hashim, and Andrew Lawson

The black widow spider (*Latrodectus hesperus* Chamberlin & Ivie) does not damage the grape cluster or feed on grape leaves or canes, but it is an unwanted spider. It is not a true pest of grapes but can, at times, be found in clusters. Although this is quite rare, it creates concerns with consumers.

Spiders commonly called widows are represented by at least 30 species that are spread throughout the world. Of these, three black widow species are known to be established in the United States: western black widow (*Latrodectus hesperus*), southern black widow (*Latrodectus mactans* (Fabricius)), and the northern black widow (*Latrodectus variolus* (Walckenaer)). Closely related species are the brown widow (*Latrodectus geometricus* (C.L. Koch)), which is found in California and throughout Africa, and the red-legged widow (*L. bishopi* (Kaston)), which is limited to Florida. Of these, *L. hesperus* is the only black widow native to the western United States and is the primary species found in California vineyards. Like other black widow species, *L. hesperus* is known to be associated with human habitat in its native region and is often found in or around gardens, houses, barns, equipment, debris, and, although not as commonly, in agricultural systems.

DESCRIPTION

Spiders have two body parts: the smaller cephalothorax containing the mouthparts, brain, eyes, and legs; and the larger abdomen, containing the guts, heart, silk glands, and reproductive organs (fig. 80.1). Adult black widows are medium-sized spiders, with a body about 13 mm (0.5 in) long and the full length (body and legs) about 4 cm (1.5 in) long. The adult female is densely covered with microscopic hairs but appears smooth, shiny, and black to the naked eye (fig. 80.2A). On the underside of the adult female's large, bulbous abdomen is a red marking, forming the characteristic hourglass. The shape and color of the hourglass varies between black widow species. At the far end of the abdomen, a red spot is often present just above the spinnerets; as the name implies, the silk thread used to make webs is extruded from the spinnerets.

Figure 80.1 A ventral view of the adult female black widow spider body. The spider is composed of two body parts. The cephalothorax has the feeding parts (chelicerae, or jaws and fangs, and pedipalps, or feelers) and four pairs of legs (each composed of seven segments: coxa, trochanter, femur, patella, tibia, metatarsus, tarus, and claw). The large, rounded abdomen has the red hourglass marking, and the spinnerets, which are short, fingerlike organs with which the spider spins silk.

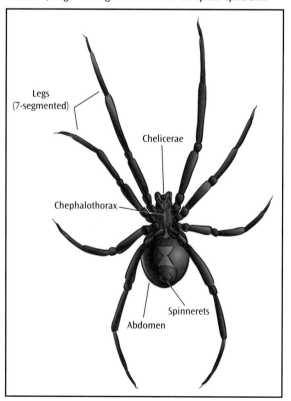

Legs
(7-segmented)

Chelicerae

Chephalothorax

Spinnerets

Abdomen

The egg sac of *L. hesperus* is tan with a paperlike appearance, about 13 mm (0.5 in) in diameter, and spherical to pear shaped. Inside each egg sac are small, pale yellow eggs about 0.8 mm (0.03 in) long. The number of eggs deposited in each egg sac is variable, with studies in San Joaquin Valley vineyards finding an average of 255 eggs per egg sac. Newly hatched spiderlings, the first-instar stage, chew small holes in the egg sac, emerge, and immediately begin to produce fine, delicate webbing. Spiderlings look nothing like the adult female. They are small, about 1.3 mm (0.05 in)

long and can be pale yellow, light brown, or gray, with black spots and stripes (fig. 80.2D).

As the female black widow matures, she will change color patterns through each of the seven or eight instars (fig. 80.2C). Young spiders are pale yellowish to a light brown with a pattern of white and brown bands on the dorsal side; the hourglass mark is not red at this stage and is either a less-apparent white or may be completely missing. With each molt, the black pigmentation increases. For this reason, there is considerable variability in appearance among

immature spiders, with some stages having vivid color patterns of red, yellow, and brown on the top of the abdomen. These markings become smaller and darker as the spider nears the adult stage; by the sixth or seventh instar, the female will attain the characteristic shiny black appearance.

The adult male appears much smaller than the female, primarily because its abdomen is slender and positioned lower, in line with the cephalothorax (fig. 80.2B). Males are not covered in black pigmentation as are the females; instead they are brightly colored, displaying yellow or red spots and white bands on the back. Males often resemble the colorful fourth- or fifth-instar females, but they can be distinguished by the smaller abdomen and larger knoblike appendages in front of the cephalothorax, called pedipalps, used for feeling.

INJURY

As mentioned, the black widow spider causes no damage to the grapevine or fruit, so it is not a direct pest of the vine, but it is unwanted. All spiders have venom to subdue their prey. The venom of most species does not affect humans, but the venom of female black widow species is a neurotoxin that can affect mammals. However, the female black widow spider is cryptic in nature and seldom bites larger animals; even when disturbed it attempts to escape rather than bite the aggressor. Biting occurs only when the spider is accidentally squeezed or pressed against the skin. Typically, only the larger black widows have large and strong enough mouthparts to pierce human skin.

Figure 80.2 The adult female black widow spider, about 4 cm (1.5 in) long, is quite recognizable, with her red hourglass marking seen from above. Immature females and males can have very different markings and colorful patterns. *Photo*: P. Hernandez.

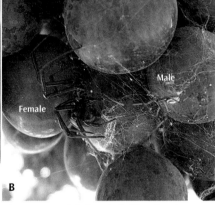

Figure 80.2 Adult female (left) and male (right), about 1.9 cm (0.75 in) long. *Photo*: K. M. Daane.

Figure 80.2 Immature female, about 2.5 cm (1 in) long. *Photo*: K. M. Daane.

Figure 80.2 Spiderling, about 1.3 mm (0.05 in) long. *Photo*: K. M. Daane.

General symptoms are abdominal pain, vomiting, cramping, sweating, fever, headache, chest tightness, and increased blood pressure. First aid treatment involves cleaning the wound and calming the victim. Antivenom is available to treat black widow bites but is prescribed only to patients who show an extreme reaction to the venom. The venom of the male black widow spider is not known to be toxic to humans.

While black widow spiders have long been known to inhabit vineyards, they are primarily a concern for table grape growers. These isolated populations may result in spiders being found in grape clusters and, although clusters are inspected several times before they are packed, some spiders have gone undetected. The movement of any black widow spider from the vineyard to the marketplace is a concern to the table grape industry. The consumer's perception of the black widow as a dangerous spider has resulted in a zero tolerance of black widow spiders in grape clusters. In response, vineyard managers, commodity organizations, and university personnel have taken actions to reduce the incidence of black widow spiders. As a result of these efforts, black widow finds in table grape clusters have been markedly reduced, although vigilant programs are needed to monitor spider abundance and apply proper treatments when needed.

SEASONAL DEVELOPMENT

Adult female black widow spiders can be long-lived, up to 1.5 years, depending on temperature and food supplies. They produce multiple (5 to 20) egg sacs throughout their life. Each egg sac has about 255 eggs, but up to 1,000 eggs per sac can be found; a single female can produce over 5,000 eggs during her lifetime. The interval between productions of each egg sac is variable and can be as short as a few days or as long as a year. During warm temperatures in spring and summer, eggs begin to hatch from 10 to 20 days after the egg sac is deposited. In each egg sac about 90% of the eggs will develop. After the spiders hatch, they fill the egg sac and undergo the first molt after 3 days. They make a hole in the egg sac through which they exit. Their predatory behavior is immediately evident, as black widows are cannibalistic and their first prey is most commonly siblings. For that reason, spiderlings soon disperse after hatching by ballooning, a process in which spiders raise their abdomen and spin a strand of silken web until the air catches that line and carries them to a new location.

Black widows deposit egg sacs mostly during the warmer months. Field studies in San Joaquin Valley table grape vineyards indicated that adult spiders were found throughout the year but were most abundant in the late summer and fall. Adult females produced egg sacs from April through September. Spiderlings were most common from May through October, typically peaking in the months of May and June. Unfortunately, the largest number of black widow spiders, particularly the larger immature and adult stages, was during the grape harvest months from August to November, when late-stage females (sixth instar to adult) comprised more than 90% of the spiders found. The large percentage of female spiders may be simply because they are large and easily found during the search, or because the female, when hungry, will attack males and reduce their numbers. The proportion of egg sacs and spiderlings decreased sharply from September through November. These results suggest that in preparation for the overwintering period, spiders develop to the more hardy adult stage, which can survive long periods of starvation. Details of these samples, collected from four San Joaquin Valley table grape vineyards and averaged over 2 years, show spider numbers and age structure (fig. 80.3).

Development from egg to adult requires at least 4 months during warm months, although this development time can be greatly extended in colder climates, as when the spider overwinters as an immature. Females go through six to eight molts to reach the adult stage; males reach maturity much faster than females, molting only five times. Adult males also live for a relatively short time, about 3 to 4 months during the warmer summer temperatures.

Location in the Vineyard

Black widow spiders prefer dark and sheltered sites to build their webs. In nature, females construct webs in hollow logs, rodent holes, under loose bark and stones, and in shrubs. Urban and agricultural environments provide artificial habitats where spiders are able to thrive. In urban environments, black widows can be found in pipes, sewers, meter boxes, park benches, under tables, in the darkened corners of basement and garage structures, and other protected sites (fig. 80.4). In agricultural systems, the preferred site is often not on the crop but in farm structures, such as the barn, wood piles, irrigation pump housings, cement irrigation pipe stands, debris on the vineyard or orchard floor, and in the milk cartons or plastic housings used to protect newly planted vines or trees.

Site preference of black widow spiders on the vine was studied in four San Joaquin Valley vineyards (fig. 80.5). The preferred nesting site depended on vineyard cultural practices (such as the type of vine stake used), vine age, and vine cultivar. In general, black widow spiders and their webs are most commonly found on the vine trunk, especially near the base and cordon (fig. 80.6). Most spiders nest in protected areas, such as the small space between the trunk and vine stake or trellis system or crevices in the cordon. The female black widow is not aggressive and avoids contact with animals that are not potential prey. She is primarily nocturnal and spends the majority of

her daylight hours inside the protected habitat created by the web. Spiders are rarely found in grape clusters or on grape leaves.

Spiderling Dispersion in the Vineyard

Spiderlings from egg sacs placed on a single vine show a rapid reduction in numbers as well as a rapid dispersal away from the inoculated vine. Rarely were more than two spiders found on any vine, even though about 255 spiderlings (from each egg sac) were initially used to inoculate the center vine. These results suggest that the spiders disperse in order to avoid cannibalism and to set up individual territories.

NATURAL CONTROLS

Black widow spiders, like most arthropods, have natural enemies that prey on them and reduce their population density. Among the most important natural enemies of black widows may be other spiders, including other black widows; young spiderlings prey on each other. For more information on common spiders present in vineyards, see section 35, "Variegated Grape Leafhopper." Specialized predators include wasps such as the yellow-legged mud dauber (*Sceliphron caementarium* (Drury)) (Sphecidae) and the blue mud dauber (*Chalybion californicum* (Saussure)). These wasps are predators that capture and paralyze prey, most commonly spiders, to provision their developing larvae (fig. 80.7). They are named for the mud cells or nests

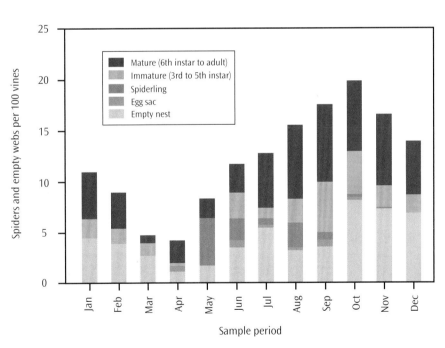

Figure 80.3 Season counts of black widow spiders (including active webbing) and empty nests (webbing but no spider found) per 100 vines (i.e., percentage of vine infestation) during the season. The data were collected from vineyards with elevated levels of spiders.

that they build and stock with prey. The female places one egg into each mud chamber, and the developing larva feeds on the captured spider. A relatively large amount of energy is spent on each offspring, and each cell is often provisioned with multiple spiders. More generalist black widow predators include preying mantids, lacewings, and, in some regions, mantispids.

There are only a few parasitoids of black widow spiders. A fly that acts as a parasitoid predator is *Pseudogaurax signata* Loew (Chloropidae); the adult lays her eggs in the spider egg sac, and the fly larvae hatch and feed on the black widow eggs. A parasitic wasp is the egg parasitoid *Baeus latrodecti* Dozier (Scelionidae). In studies of black widow spiders in San Joaquin Valley vineyards, spider egg sac parasitism levels were as high as 40% in August to September surveys. To date, there are no known attempts to manipulate biological control agents of black widow spiders in vineyards, and the impact of natural controls should currently be considered incidental, given the low tolerance for black widows in table grape clusters.

CULTURAL CONTROLS

Most spider species are commonly seen not as pests but as valuable natural enemies of agricultural pests; therefore, few control measures have been established for spiders in agricultural systems. In residential areas, sanitation and habitat management have proven to be effective black widow spider controls. Sanitation involves finding and destroying black widow spiders and their webs and egg sacs. No sanitation programs have been studied in vineyards, although common sense suggests that, because the black widow web is very evident, finding and crushing black widow spiders and their egg sacs should reduce the vineyard population.

Figure 80.5 Sampling for the cryptic black widow spider can be difficult. A more efficient sampling method than looking for the spider itself is to look for the spider web. The black widow spider webbing is quite strong, irregular in shape, and most commonly constructed between the trunk and trellis system, cordon, or ground. *Photo:* K. M. Daane.

Figure 80.4 Structures found in the vineyard that form protected, dark shelters are a preferred habitat for black widow spiders. Look for webbing, for example, at the base of the vine trunk (A), in irrigation pipe stands (B), in shelters for newly planted vines (C), and in protected areas of the trellis system (D). *Photos:* K. M. Daane.

Vineyard Management

Habitat management involves reducing the number of preferred nesting sites for black widow spiders, as well as the amount of available food. Habitat management for black widow spiders may be more difficult than for other arthropod pests. The structure of the vine and trellis system, as well as nearby farm equipment and buildings, often provide excellent sites for black widow spiders. Spiderlings balloon into the vineyard from nearby structures, even after the vineyard has been treated. What can be done, however, is to become aware of the nesting sites in order to pay additional attention to black widow spider populations in the more susceptible vineyard blocks. In an experimental Thomson Seedless block, two different trellis systems (Y-trellis, or gable with an overhead canopy, and standard T-trellis) were established and black widow adults inoculated evenly throughout the block. After a few months, more spiders developed nests on vines using the Y-trellis than the standard T-trellis. Many of the overhead canopy systems that are used to provide greater yields and better-quality fruit also create a more shaded understory and protected sites on the gable trellis system, both of which are preferred by black widow spiders. Other preferred sites in the experimental vineyard were vines with trellis stakes, milk cartons used to protect nursery replants, and cement stands for irrigation valves.

The type and placement of the trellis stake is also important. Vine stakes that abutted the vine trunk, touching to within 2.5 cm (1 in), had more black widows than stakes placed at least 10 cm (4 in) from the vines. Metal C-shaped or curved stakes also created an excellent nesting site when the stake curve abutted the vine, creating a hollow tube

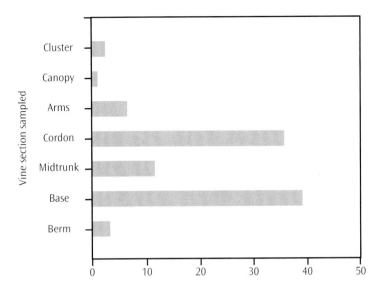

Figure 80.6 Percentage of black widow spider population found on different parts of the vine. The data are averaged across the entire season and were collected in four table grape vineyards in the San Joaquin Valley.

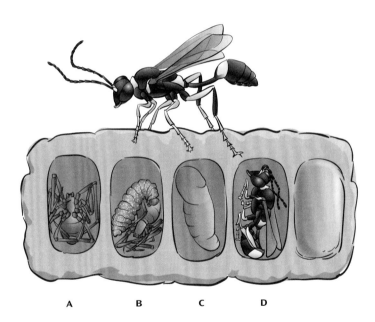

Figure 80.7 Life history of a mud dauber (family Sphecidae) wasp that captures and paralyzes spiders and places them in mud cells, much like the hive of a honey bee. An egg is placed in the provisioned cell (A), and the wasp's larva hatches and feeds on the spiders (B). The wasp pupates inside the cell (C) and emerges as an adult (D), with the pupal case removed to view developed the adult wasp in the cell.

in which the spiders could nest and find shelter from insecticides and most predators. Black widows inhabit vines without a stake, typically at the base in the leaf debris, or in the cracks and crevices on the older vine trunk.

Cultivars

Late-maturing table grape cultivars have harvest dates later in the season, when black widow spider populations are peaking, providing more opportunity for spiders to enter the cluster. While no studies have been conducted, we assume that cultivars with loose clusters are more readily inhabited by large black widow females than are tight clusters. Similar to vineyards with an overhead trellis system, cultivars with dense growth or those grafted to vigorous rootstocks create a more shaded understory. This may have two effects. First, the shaded understory provides a preferred habitat for black widow spiders. Second, when no light reaches the vineyard floor, ground vegetation dies toward summer's end and the insect prey that it supports may disappear or move upward into the vine canopy, drawing the black widow spiders nearer to the cluster in order to find food.

MONITORING GUIDELINES

Sampling methods for black widow spiders developed for research purposes can be adapted for commercial use. Vineyard managers may want to alter the program described below to make it faster and more efficient at covering a larger area (fig. 80.8).

To accurately sample for black widows, a minimum of 1,000 vines per block should be checked. This can be done quickly if you look for the web rather than the spider. The black widow web is composed of strong silk threads matted together in a disorganized structure. Count the number of webs on 1,000 vines per block (10 to 40 ac, or 4 to 16 ha) each month. This is easier than it sounds. Simply walk about 10 vine rows per block and look for webs. Look first at the base of the trunk because that is where most webs start. In winter and spring, webs are most easily seen on sunny days, especially in the morning when light reflects off the web and its collected moisture (dewdrops). Favorite hiding spots are trellis systems, trellis stakes (especially those close to the trunk), cracks in the vine, cement pipes for irrigation valves, and on the ground in clumps of leaves away from the trunk and usually on the berm. Because the black widow is not aggressive and will hide, if a web is seen use a pencil or stick to pull back the web and look for the spider.

If webs are found, mark some of the vines (50 to 100 per block) and return to those vines at night. If the nest has a live black widow, the spider will be out from its hiding spot and exposed. Another method to determine spider presence is to destroy the web and then return the next morning to see if it has been rebuilt. Typically the spider will be positioned upside down on the web, about 5 cm (2 in)

from the vine trunk or vine stake. Divide the number of black widow spiders found by the number of webs marked and multiply by 100 to get the percentage of webs infested with a live spider. Note that the small spiderlings make small, delicate webs that are difficult to find and will not be easily discovered with this sampling program.

MANAGEMENT GUIDELINES

Wine and Raisin Grape Tolerance

Currently, it is not recommended that wine or raisin grapes be treated for black widow spiders, as the processing involved in these grapes eliminates the risk of any black widows entering the marketplace.

Figure 80.8 Field crews are often the first to find black widow spider populations. Work with the harvest crews to identify black widow spider webbing and other indications that harvested grapes may be more vulnerable in specific blocks. *Photo*: L. J. Bettiga.

Table Grape Tolerance

As a general rule, tolerance for black widow spiders in table grape clusters is set at zero. However, most vineyards have some level of black widow spiders that are near or on the vines but do not make it into the harvested grape cluster. Four table grape vineyards that reported black widow spider problems were surveyed throughout the season. Average black widow spider density ranged from about 4 to 20% of the vines with webbing with or without a live spider and about 2 to 10% of the webs with live spiders (see fig. 80.3). The lowest densities were in March and April, typically after a pesticide application, and the highest densities were in August and September, during harvest. Each of these vineyards was properly treated with appropriate pesticides, and levels of spider webs and live spiders dropped to less than 5% of the vines with webbing during the harvest period. These ranges provide vineyard managers with some indication of spider counts in other vineyards. Currently, a suggested threshold is 5% of vines with black widow webs with or without a live spider as a control threshold. Remember to check a number of webs during the day (using a stick) or at night (looking for an occupied web) to be sure that the webs are made by black widow spiders rather than by beneficial spider species. Also remember that the suggested sampling program uses a rapid search of many vines that will miss the small, delicate webs made by spiderlings.

Chemical Control

Applying pesticides is another means of controlling spiders. The primary concern with all pesticides is proper coverage. Most of the effective pesticides for black widow spider control work best when the material directly contacts the spider. This is often difficult to achieve because the spiders are very cryptic during the daylight hours, hiding inside their nest, where they are often protected from direct contact. After the application is made, the spiders may not contact much of the pesticide material as they walk on the treated web, because they are touching the web or vine with only the tips of their legs. Unlike other vineyard pests, the black widow spider is not feeding on the vine, so there may be little contact with plant material.

Tests with registered pesticides found that contact materials (e.g., organophosphate, pyrethroid) provided the most effective control. Although only one insecticide was tested in each of these classes, it is likely that other insecticides would provide similar control. Each of these insecticides has some limitations on their use (e.g., preharvest intervals and potential problems with exacerbating spider mites), and current registration, restrictions, and application guidelines should be checked before any pesticide is applied. See the UC IPM Grape Pest Management Guidelines, www.ipm.ucdavis.edu/PMG/, for treatment options. Other pesticides commonly used for grape pests such as neonicotinoids,

miticides, and insect growth regulators had little impact on black widow spiders. The results suggest that the general movement toward new pesticides for mite, leafhopper, and mealybug control, which are less effective against black widows, may have allowed greater survival of black widow populations. Alternatively, the new pesticides may have changed the food web or natural enemy guild in such a manner as to favor black widows.

In tests where direct and residual control was compared, all of the effective insecticides (organophosphate, carbamate, and pyrethroid) killed black widow spiders when sprayed directly on the spiders. Only insecticide materials that have a longer residual period reduced black widow survival when the spiders were exposed to treated bark. Therefore, complete coverage of the vine to get material into the protected nesting areas, catching the black widow when it is exposed, is important to improve spider mortality. When spray rigs move through vineyard blocks, the spiders likely retreat into their protected nests (e.g., in bark crevices), where the applied pesticide often does not directly contact them. For this reason, the residual effectiveness of pesticides applied on the vine trunk is probably more important for control.

Black widow diurnal pattern

Recent studies indicate that black widows are quite active at night, even on cold winter days. Activity of black widow spiders was monitored on their web every 1 to 2 hours over a 24-hour period. The black widow spiders always come out at night, typically starting after dusk and remaining until just before sunrise. Figure 80.9 shows two sample dates, a warm September period and a very cold January period. Important to note is that the black widow spiders (mature and adult females) came out of their nest on a very cold January night, below than 0°C (32°F), which included rain from midnight to 3 a.m. Observers noted that the spiders moved slowly and were not as quickly agitated or as cryptic as spiders found during daytime searches. While not yet proven, insecticide application during this period of exposure, especially on cold mornings, might provide better coverage of spiders, resulting in better control.

Insecticide impact

If insecticide treatments are needed, mark some of the vines that have black widow webbing, confirm that spiders are present, and use a stick to destroy some of the web structure the day of or before treatment. Return to the marked vines 3 to 5 days after treatment. If the treatment was effective, there should be no new webbing: the female black widow will quickly rebuild her web if it is disturbed, often not leaving her nest site. During the winter or prolonged cold periods, it may take longer for the spider to rebuild its web, while in warm weather the web is often rebuilt in 1 day.

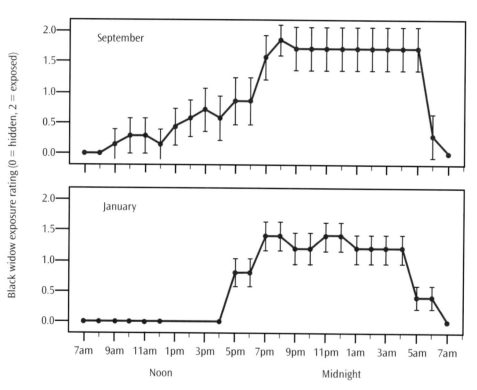

Figure 80.9 Black widow spider activity over a 24-hour period, where 0 indicates that the spider is hidden deep inside her web, 1 indicates that the spider is partially exposed, and 2 indicates that the spider is fully exposed out on her web.

81 BROWN GARDEN SNAIL

Larry J. Bettiga and Mark Battany

The brown garden snail, or European brown snail, (*Cornu aspersum* (Müller)) (= *Cantareus asperses* (Müller) and formerly *Helix aspersa*) is now found throughout the West Coast of North America, having been introduced into California from France in the 1850s to be cultivated as the edible escargot.

DESCRIPTION

The adult snail is about 2.5 cm (1 in) in diameter, and the body is about 5 cm (2 in) when fully extended. The color of the shell is grayish yellow and brown, with the brown pigment usually visible as five interrupted bands, and the body is light to dark gray (fig. 81.1). There can be variations of this pattern and shades of coloration. Snails move by gliding along on a muscular "foot." This muscle constantly secretes mucus, which later dries to form a silvery slime trail.

INJURY

The snails feed on a range of plant hosts and on dead and decaying vegetation. They can cause significant damage to grapevines by feeding on the newly emerging shoots in the spring. Damage can be separated from insect feeding by the presence of slime trails (fig. 81.2). Snails chew smooth-edged, irregular holes when feeding on leaves (fig. 81.3). High populations that hibernate on the trellis or vines can become a contaminant in machine-harvested wine grapes.

SEASONAL DEVELOPMENT

Snails are seminocturnal, being most active at night and in the early morning when conditions are damp. During cloudy, humid periods they can be active in the daylight. In mild coastal climates the younger snails can be active most of the year, while the mature snails hibernate in surface soil and on the vines or trellis during the winter. Although snails are hermaphroditic (contain both male and female organs), mating with another snail is usually required to successfully reproduce. Oviposition usually takes place 3 to 6 days after fertilization. All adults can lay eggs up to five times each season, depending on local climate and available moisture. Masses of opaque white spherical eggs about 3 mm (0.13 in) long are laid in shallow depressions dug in the soil and then covered. The average number of eggs per nest is 86. After hatching it can take approximately 2 years for a snail to reach maturity. They prefer moist conditions,

Figure 81.1 Adult brown garden snail. *Photo*: L. J. Bettiga.

and populations are highest in wet springs or in vineyards under frequent sprinkler irrigation. During hot, dry periods snails seal themselves off with a parchmentlike membrane and often attach themselves to trunks, cordons, or stakes and become dormant.

NATURAL CONTROL

The decollate snail (*Rumina decollata*) has been used successfully in southern California citrus orchards as a predator of the brown garden snail and can provide effective biological control. The decollate snail can feed only on the smaller, immature brown snails, not on the larger, mature snails. The

Figure 81.2. Slime trails (arrow) left by snails can be used to distinguish damage from other chewing pests such as cutworms. *Photo*: L. J. Bettiga.

Figure 81.3 Snail feeding damage (A), with chewing damage (B) that is similar to damage by chewing insects. *Photos*: L. J. Bettiga.

decollate snail cannot be released in California outside of Fresno, Imperial, Kern, Los Angeles, Madera, Orange, Riverside, Santa Barbara, San Bernardino, San Diego, Ventura, and Tulare Counties, due to the potential for damaging native mollusk species. Snail baits also kill predatory decollate snails.

Several natural enemies, such as carabid beetles, frogs and toads, rodents, and birds such as ducks and geese, eat snails. Most of these predators are not effective in providing adequate control of high populations of snails.

MONITORING GUIDELINES

No information on monitoring guidelines is available, but vineyards should be inspected for the presence of snails. Inspect the vineyard for active snails in the early morning, especially after rain or where the vines were recently irrigated. Also check for snails under leaf debris. Scattering metaldehyde bait over a small area in the evening and counting the number of dead snails the next day will help quantify the snail pressure. One can also place trap boards and count the number of snails resting under the boards during the day.

MANAGEMENT GUIDELINES

Cultural Control
Snails find shelter in weeds, cover crops, plant residues, wooden posts, stakes, under stones, and so on. Removing any unnecessary sources of shelter, such as by the timely mowing of cover crops, removal of leaf litter, improved weed control, and incorporation of residues into the soil, helps reduce snail populations. Surrounding areas such as access roads and ditches may also need attention, as they can be sources of snail movement into adjacent vineyards.

Chemical Control
Baits can be used to control snail populations. Bait acceptance is greatest under wet conditions when snails are actively feeding on the soil surface. Spread bait evenly on the ground beneath the vines. Once snails have moved up on the vines, they are more difficult to control since baits will not attract them back to the soil surface. Foliar applications of pesticides are registered for nonbearing vines in nurseries only.

Part 5

Stored Raisin Product Pests

Muscat of Alexandria

82 STORED RAISIN PRODUCT PESTS

Judy A. Johnson, Matthew W. Fidelibus, and Stephen J. Vasquez

In California, most raisin grapes are dried in vineyards, although heated air tunnel dryers are used to dehydrate a relatively small proportion of the grapes for specialty products such as golden raisins. Grapes may be dried in vineyards on paper trays placed on the ground between the vine rows, or on the vine, by severing the fruit-bearing canes. The dried-on-the-vine (DOV) method usually takes longer to dry the grapes, but it allows mechanized harvesting of the raisins and reduces labor. After drying, raisins are usually stored in large wooden bins, often in large stacks covered with paper (Sisal Kraft) or polyethylene sheeting.

Insect pests of raisins can be separated into two categories: insects that feed on drying raisins and those that feed on stored raisins. Most of the insects that feed on drying raisins do not continue to feed on them when drying is complete; however, they are often of primary concern to growers because infested product may be downgraded or rejected when received by the packinghouse. Driedfruit beetle and raisin moth are the major species that consume drying raisins. Pests that feed on stored raisins are of concern because they may infest the product at any time during storage, and their populations are capable of continual increase. Controlling them often involves expensive commodity treatments and, more important, they are the insects most likely to be discovered by consumers. The two most important storage pests are Indianmeal moth and sawtoothed grain beetle. Many other miscellaneous pests are occasionally found in raisins; a good general reference for identification of these is *Insects on Dried Fruits* (USDA Agricultural Handbook 464, 1975, www.ars. usda.gov/is/np/insectsdriedfruits/insectsdriedfruits.pdf).

DRIEDFRUIT BEETLE

Driedfruit beetle (*Carpophilus hemipterus* (L.)) (Coleoptera: Nitidulidae) is a sap beetle whose larvae feed on senescent vegetation and on ripe and overripe fruit throughout the world. In California, it is a pest of grapes and stone fruit, figs, dates, melons, and citrus, migrating from crop to crop as the fruit become attractive. Adult beetles are attracted to volatiles from fermenting fruit. When feeding on grapes, they are especially attracted to clusters with bunch rot. The nutritional requirements of developing larvae depend on the presence of living yeast in fruit with a moisture content of at least 30%. Populations of driedfruit beetle generally increase through the season.

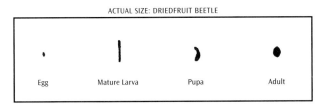

ACTUAL SIZE: DRIEDFRUIT BEETLE

Egg   Mature Larva   Pupa   Adult

Normally, sound raisins are not consumed, although damaged grapes drying on trays attract the beetles, which may feed on damaged and undamaged berries. Fruit with high moisture content are attractive to them, and periods of high humidity at harvest generally lead to greater damage of berries. Properly dried and stored raisins are generally not attacked.

Other sap beetle species found in raisins and other fruit include the pineapple beetle (*Urophorus humeralis* (Fabricius)), Freeman sap beetle (*C. freemani* Dobson), confused sap beetle (*C. mutilatus* Erichson), and yellow-brown sap beetle (*Haptoncus luteolus* Erichson). Their damage is similar to that caused by driedfruit beetle.

DESCRIPTION

Adults are dark brown with lighter brown or amber spots on their wing covers (fig. 82.1). They are about 3 mm (0.13 in) long, oval shaped, and robust. Their wing covers are short, leaving the tip of the abdomen exposed. Legs and antennae are reddish or amber colored, and their antennae are knobbed at the tips.

The newly hatched larva (fig. 82.2) is yellowish and translucent but soon becomes creamy white with brownish ends. It has a pair of pointed, spinelike projections (urogomphi) on the end of the abdomen. Fully grown, it is sparsely haired and about 6 mm (0.25 in) long. The pupa is pale yellow until nearly mature, when it darkens and becomes somewhat spiny (fig. 82.3). No cocoon is formed.

INJURY

Larvae feed directly on the flesh of raisins, and this, together with deposits of excreta and cast skins, materially reduces the quality of dried fruit. Larvae are usually found feeding on the underside of berries laid on drying trays. In the vineyard, adults carry yeast and mold spores on their bodies and help spread bunch rot by inoculating damaged fruit.

SEASONAL DEVELOPMENT

Each female scatters about 1,000 eggs over the raisins. Eggs hatch in 1 to 5 days (2 days is average). Larvae feed actively as they move through their food. The larval period varies with temperature, lasting 11 days at 28°C (82.5°F). No feeding or development takes place below 4°C (39°F).

Fully grown larvae enter the soil and make earthen cells in which they pupate; at 32°C (90°F) the pupal period is about 8 days. Mating takes place soon after adults emerge from the soil, and eggs are laid from 1 to 8 days thereafter. Egg laying may start as early as 3 days after adults have emerged.

Driedfruit beetles are strong fliers; marked beetles have been collected 2.5 miles (4 km) from the point of release after 4 days. Flights occur only in daylight at temperatures above 18°C (64.5°F). The greatest flight activity takes place at temperatures from 28° to 38°C (82.5° to 100°F) near midday.

In warm weather, there may be a generation every 3 weeks. There are several overlapping broods each year, the number of generations depending on temperature. Because of low temperature, larvae entering soil in autumn may not emerge as adults until spring. Adults may overwinter inside of fruit and duff (decaying vegetation) on the soil surface in mild winters.

NATURAL CONTROL

Pathogens are abundant in sap beetle populations. In one survey at locations in the continental United States, Mexico, and Hawaii, more

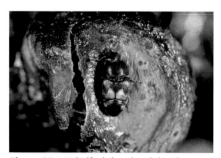

Figure 82.1 Driedfruit beetle adult. *Photo*: J. K. Clark.

Figure 82.2 Driedfruit beetle larva. *Photo*: J. K. Clark.

Figure 82.3 Driedfruit beetle pupae. *Photo*: J. K. Clark.

than 85% of the 118 sap beetle accessions examined contained at least one pathogen. Pathogens found in driedfruit beetles include the protozoans *Mattesia* sp., *Helicosporidium* sp., *Nosema* sp., *Ophryocystis* sp., and a cephaline eugregarine, as well as a sphaerulariid nematode (fig. 82.4). A fungus, *Beauveria bassiana*, which infects nitidulids in nature, may have potential as a biocontrol agent based on its performance in laboratory tests. *Cerchysiela* (*Zeteticontus*) *utitis* Noyes (Hymenoptera: Encrytidae), a solitary internal parasitic wasp, was evaluated for control of driedfruit beetle and pineapple beetle larvae in Hawaii. This parasite has been found in several central California locations, including raisin packing plants.

MONITORING GUIDELINES

Although USDA inspectors visually monitor insect infestations of raisins distributed to packinghouses, the grape grower who has observed bunch rot and decides to make raisins should monitor the raisins for insects. Previous research has shown that as many as 40 different insect species were attracted to trays containing grapes with bunch rot. In the same study, researchers noted that more than 20,000 driedfruit beetle adults were attracted

to one tray that had clusters with bunch rot. Growers should visually monitor their raisin crop beginning at harvest and fumigate for beetles if necessary (see "Commodity Treatments" at the end of this section). Monitoring should be done immediately after grapes are laid on trays, when raisins are being boxed, and after 30 to 45 days of storage.

MANAGEMENT GUIDELINES

Control of driedfruit beetle is accomplished primarily in the packinghouse, but if raisins are held on the farm they should be fumigated and kept under a gas-tight plastic cover (or similar material). Well-dried and stored raisins, free from rot, are much less susceptible to attack from driedfruit beetle. Chemical control of driedfruit beetle in the vineyard has not been developed.

Nitidulid beetles such as the driedfruit beetle may be trapped in great numbers using various fermenting materials, including bread dough. Recent research has also defined and synthesized aggregation pheromones, although none are yet commercially available. There has been some success in reducing nitidulid damage in tree fruit orchards through attract-and-kill systems that use combinations of aggregation pheromones and food baits.

RAISIN MOTH

Raisin moth (*Cadra figulilella* (Gregson)) (Lepidoptera: Pyralidae) is known to feed on ripening grapes and raisins, especially drying raisins and those held in farm storage before they are delivered to the packinghouse.

DESCRIPTION

Raisin moths are about 10 mm (0.4 in) long, with a wingspan of about 16 mm (0.63 in) (fig. 82.5). The forewings are light pinkish gray with indistinct markings. Raisin moths are similar in size to a number of common stored-product moths, including the Indianmeal moth, and all fold their wings around their bodies in the same manner when at rest. Raisin and Indianmeal moths are the two moths most commonly found on raisins, although three other moths are occasionally recovered from pheromone traps near stored raisins (see "Monitoring Guidelines," below). However, any light-colored moth,

Figure 82.5 Raisin moth adult. *Photo:* J. K. Clark.

Figure 82.4 Pathogens such as this nematode emerging from an infected larva are used for control of vineyard and stored product pests. *Photo:* J. K. Clark.

ACTUAL SIZE: RAISIN MOTH

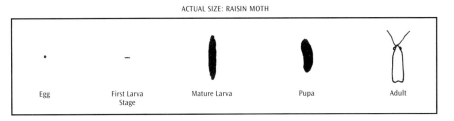

Egg · · · First Larva Stage · Mature Larva · Pupa · Adult

grayish, and with wings rounded when at rest, is usually a raisin moth.

The raisin moth egg is white and less than 1 mm (0.04 in) long (fig. 82.6). The fully grown larva is 12 mm (0.45 in) long and has four to six rows of purplish spots along its white back, giving the larva a pinkish to purple cast (fig. 82.7).

INJURY

Young larvae hatched on stored raisins feed chiefly on the raisin's raised wrinkles, but they may also bore into the interior. They do not completely consume a raisin but move about, leaving masses of excreta and webbing. During its development, one larva can damage about 20 raisins of average size (such as Thompson Seedless) or 9 larger raisins (such as the Muscat cultivars).

Figure 82.6 Raisin moth eggs. *Photo*: J. K. Clark.

Figure 82.7 Raisin moth larva. *Photo*: J. K. Clark.

SEASONAL DEVELOPMENT

The adult female generally lays her eggs on grapes drying on trays; she may also lay them on raisins in storage, but rarely are moths trapped within storage buildings. Fully grown larvae leave the raisins to search for suitable places to pupate. Any tight, dry, dark place, such as under boards, paper, or stones, or in the soil is suitable for pupation. Raisin moths overwinter as fully grown larvae in diapause, a nonfeeding state similar to hibernation, in cocoons in the upper few inches of soil near the vine trunks or under the rough bark of the grapevines. The moths usually begin to emerge in April, with peak emergence in May (mild weather can delay this until early June). On warm evenings they begin to fly and lay eggs about half an hour after sunset, continuing flight for 3 or 4 hours. Each female lays about 350 eggs. The moths live for about 15 days. In summer, a generation is completed in 45 days. There are three overlapping generations each year; in some years, a small fourth generation occurs.

The new spring moths fly in search of drying fruit, and wasted mulberry fruit on the ground is among the first available to them. By June, they are infesting first-crop figs on the ground and soon after are laying eggs in fallen apricots, nectarines, peaches, prunes, and peach-pit piles. By August, ripening grapes on the vine, especially those showing bunch rot or a few prematurely raisined berries, become attractive to the egg-laying moths. Some vineyards, however, have a high incidence of raisin moth larvae attacking undamaged grape clusters. Later, raisin moths begin laying eggs on raisins drying on trays.

NATURAL CONTROL

Among the parasites attacking raisin moth and other moth larvae that infest stored raisins, the most important is the parasitic wasp *Habrobracon hebetor* (Say). This braconid species is 2 to 3 mm (0.08 to 0.13 in) long and is black with yellowish markings. Female *H. hebetor* stings and paralyses a host larva before laying eggs on the immobilized host. *H. hebetor* attacks primarily mature larvae that have completed their feeding and damage, so the major control benefit is a reduction in future populations. However, *H. hebetor* often kill far more larvae than they parasitize. Also, they have been shown to attack diapausing larvae on warm winter days and thus may be valuable in reducing overwintering populations. Two ichneumonids, *Venturia canescens* (Gravenhorst) and *Mesostenus gracilis* Cresson, may be of importance, usually in May. *Venturia canescens* is an internal parasite of larvae, usually preferring full-grown larvae. *Mesostenus gracilis* is an external parasite of cocooned larvae and pupae. A chalcid parasite, *Psilochalcis brevialata* Grissel & Johnson, was found attacking pupae of raisin moth and Indianmeal moth in a culled fig warehouse. Several species of *Goniozus* have also been known to attack raisin moth.

Habrobracon hebetor passes the winter chiefly in the adult stage. The species is quiescent in cold weather, but on warm days it is active, stinging and paralyzing raisin moth larvae. The adult feeds on the juices issuing from the puncture wound. Egg laying on the paralyzed host does not begin until spring. *H. hebetor* attacks considerable numbers of host larvae in cocoons under grapevine bark; it is less able to reach larvae that have cocooned in the soil.

In storage, fully grown raisin moth larvae that leave the fruit in search of pupation quarters in spring are also parasitized in considerable numbers. Such larvae may be found hanging from the sides of bins, often with *H. hebetor* larvae feeding on them. Large numbers of the parasites can be seen flying about stored bins of raisins in fall.

A microsporidian, *Nosema invadens* Kellen and Lindegren, has been reported from raisin moth larvae collected from Selma, California (Fresno County). The almond moth and Indianmeal moth are also susceptible to this pathogen. Sporozoan pathogens found in Fresno colony–reared raisin moth larvae include *Mattesia* sp. and *Gregarina* sp., both protozoans.

A nuclear polyhedrosis virus, a granulosis virus, and two other baculoviruses have been isolated from raisin moth larvae in cull figs in Fresno. Raisin moth larvae are also susceptible to a bacterium, *Rickettsiella* sp., originally isolated from the navel orangeworm (*Amyelois transitella* (Walker)) and *Bacillus thuringiensis* Berliner (Bt) (see "Natural Control" in "Indianmeal Moth," below).

Monitoring Guidelines

Customarily, raisins are cleaned by running the product over a motorized shaker to remove sand, insects, and other foreign materials. At this point, insect infestations may be detected. Fumigation should immediately follow detection. Artificial sex pheromones are being used to attract raisin moth and Indianmeal moth males to sticky traps. These pheromones have been evaluated for their insect-monitoring potential in nut and dried fruit storage, processing plants, and orchards, and they are commercially available. Primarily marketed as an Indianmeal moth pheromone, five different species of stored-product moths are attracted to the same commercial pheromone. In addition to raisin moth and Indianmeal moth, almond moth (*Cadra cautella* (Walker)), tobacco moth (*Ephestia elutella* (Hübner)), and Mediterranean flour moth (*Anagasta kuehniella* (Zeller)) may be recovered in traps baited with commercial lures. Although these last three rarely feed on raisins, they may occasionally be found on traps near stored raisins. Figure 82.8 shows how to distinguish between these species.

Management Guidelines

Raisin moths can be controlled by sanitary cultural practices as well as by fumigation (see "Commodity Treatments" at the end of this section). For example, raisin moth lays its eggs at night on drying raisins, but high temperatures the next day kill eggs laid in unshaded sites. By rolling paper raisin trays as late as possible in the day, after the hot morning sun has killed eggs laid the previous evening, and before 7 p.m. so that the moths will not have a chance to lay more eggs, growers may reduce infestation. To protect raisins from reinfestation, use biscuit rolls rather than cigarette rolls because of their tightly closed ends. Rolls should be dumped in bins in the vineyard or immediately after being brought to the farmyard. Covering the bins with shade cloth will help prevent infestation.

The reduced labor cost associated with dried-on-the-vine (DOV) methods of raisin production has resulted in a growing number of DOV vineyards. These methods leave drying raisins exposed to insect attack for longer periods of time and may not produce temperatures high enough to kill developing raisin moths. Also, DOV methods do not provide a mechanical barrier to reinfestation as do biscuit-rolled raisin trays. Growers should be aware that because insect incidence may be higher in DOV raisins, more attention to monitoring may be required.

Motor-driven raisin cleaners can effectively remove infestation from Zante Currant and Thompson Seedless raisins. About 90% of the eggs and worms can be removed if the screen is properly operated. The most economical procedure is to run the raisins from the paper trays over the cleaner into storage bins without intervening storage or extra handling. The machine is less thorough with Muscat raisins, which do not readily shatter and tend to retain their compact, cluster form.

Although on-farm storage time for boxed raisins is influenced by market conditions, prompt delivery to buyers is essential to prevent further infestation during warm temperatures. Well-dried raisins are not as attractive to raisin moth, and reinfestation of raisins in the packinghouses is negligible.

Figure 82.8 Common storage moths attracted to commercially available Indianmeal moth pheromone lures. The structure of the valves is the best method to distinguish the species, but a dissecting scope is normally needed to view these properly. The valves are paired structures associated with the male genitalia found at the tip of the abdomen. *Photos:* USDA Agricultural Research Service; *illustrations:* UC IPM.

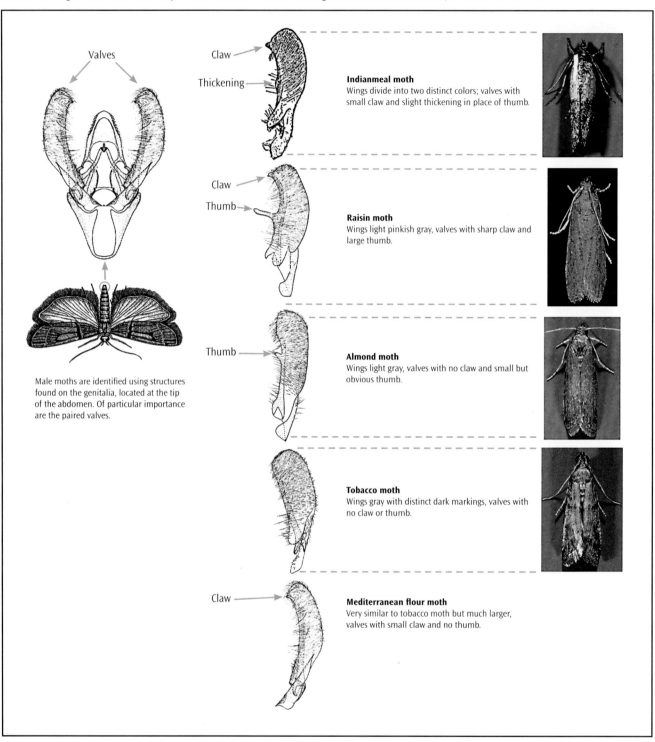

Valves

Male moths are identified using structures found on the genitalia, located at the tip of the abdomen. Of particular importance are the paired valves.

Claw
Thickening

Indianmeal moth
Wings divide into two distinct colors; valves with small claw and slight thickening in place of thumb.

Claw
Thumb

Raisin moth
Wings light pinkish gray, valves with sharp claw and large thumb.

Thumb

Almond moth
Wings light gray, valves with no claw and small but obvious thumb.

Tobacco moth
Wings gray with distinct dark markings, valves with no claw or thumb.

Claw

Mediterranean flour moth
Very similar to tobacco moth but much larger, valves with small claw and no thumb.

Figure 82.9 Indianmeal moth adult. *Photo:* J. K. Clark.

ACTUAL SIZE: INDIANMEAL MOTH

| Egg | First Larva Stage | Mature Larva | Pupa | Adult |

Because drying mulberry fruit is the first available food for the worms in early summer, dropped fruit under such trees should be raked out into the sunlight. If the fruit is spread thinly, the heat will kill worms and eggs. This practice and planting a nonfruiting cultivar of mulberry in the farmyard will reduce the localized intensity of raisin moths. Raisin moth is also known to develop on maturing fresh grapes and may be responsible for relatively high levels of bunch rot.

INDIANMEAL MOTH

Indianmeal moth (*Plodia interpunctella* (Hübner)) (Lepidoptera: Pyralidae) is found worldwide and is a serious pest of raisins and other dried fruit, nuts, grains, and cereal products. The Indianmeal moth is not as widespread in the field as is the raisin moth, but many consider it to be the world's number one storage pest. In the San Joaquin Valley, there are many host crops, particularly stored tree nuts, as well as processed and pet foods. Moths may lay eggs on raisins in the field and in storage. Field infestations are not as common as infestations in storage, but most crops stored more than 30 to 60 days become infested.

Young, first-instar larvae can enter crevices as small as 0.13 mm (0.005 in), infesting commodities in containers thought to be insect-proof.

DESCRIPTION

Adult Indianmeal moths vary in size, but generally they are about 10 mm (0.4 in) long (fig. 82.9). The outer tip of the forewings is coppery brown with darker markings; the base of the forewings is gray. The underlying hindwings are whitish gray. Indianmeal moth can easily be distinguished from other stored product moths, which are more uniformly colored. Of moths found on raisins, any moth with forewings that show a distinct color contrast and that appear clipped at an angle on the tip is most likely to be Indianmeal moth.

Seen under magnification when first laid, the eggs are less than 1 mm (0.04 in) long and are whitish and pearlescent. They turn an opaque white as they mature. They are deposited singly or in groups on the raisin surface. Newly emerged larvae, about 1 mm (0.04 in) long, immediately start feeding on the raisin. Fully grown, they are about 13 mm (0.5 in) long and may be white, light yellow, pink, or greenish, although a white or cream color is most common (fig.

82.10). The head area is dark brown. The larva's body is sparsely covered by hairs (setae).

As the larva crawls, it leaves a very fine, almost invisible white silk thread as a trail marker. Heavy infestations may be detected by the appearance of a sheet of silk on the surface of stored bulk raisins. Larvae pupate when mature. Pupae change from light brown to dark brown as they mature, usually within a silken cocoon (fig. 82.11).

INJURY

Indianmeal moth infestations usually lower raisin quality; they seldom reduce quantity. Normal handling and cleaning usually deter rejection by the purchaser or seizure or condemnation by federal inspectors. Infested raisins are contaminated by excrement, cast skins, webbing, cocoons, and living or dead larvae. Infestations that occur after the raisins have been shipped from the packaging plant may curtail marketability.

SEASONAL DEVELOPMENT

In warehouses, moths normally fly between 4:30 p.m. and 11:30 p.m. (peak flight at 9:30 p.m.) to mate and to deposit eggs. Under reduced artificial lighting, moths may also fly during the daytime.

The number of eggs laid by female Indianmeal moth varies considerably and is usually highest on grain and nut products. On dried fruit, females usually lay an average of 170 eggs, which take 2 to 4 days to hatch in summer and as long as 22 days in cooler weather. In hot weather, larvae can complete development in 21 days, but in unheated buildings during cooler periods development may take 5 to 7 months. Under ideal conditions, this insect's life cycle is less than 30 days.

Indianmeal moths pass the winter as fully grown larvae in silk cocoons constructed in cracks, under boards, between sheets of paper, and in other dark, preferably dry places. In the San Joaquin Valley, these larvae enter diapause, a nonfeeding cold-tolerant state similar to hibernation, but in the Coachella Valley partly grown, nondiapausing larvae can survive winter and will feed during warm days. Diapausing larvae pupate in spring. The pupal stage may last 4 to 9 days.

Adult moths live from 2 to 3 days in hot summer weather to 30 days in cool spring or fall weather. In the Fresno area, they produce four generations a year. Larvae of a partial fifth generation survive the winter and produce adults in spring. Brood overlap is common.

NATURAL CONTROL

All of the parasites known to attack the raisin moth also attack Indianmeal moth (see "Natural Control" under "Raisin Moth," above). The braconid wasp *Habrobracon hebetor* may be abundant on Indianmeal moth, which is much more tolerant of this parasite than is raisin moth. Several pathogens of Indianmeal moth larvae have been observed in California. Two microsporidians, *Nosema plodiae* Kellen & Lindegren and *Nosema heterosporum* Kellen & Lindegren, have been described. A protozoan, *Mattesia* sp., and a granulosis virus have been observed in both laboratory and field isolates in Fresno. The granulosis virus is an effective biological control agent for Indianmeal moth on stored raisins, and a commercial preparation of that virus is now available. The bacterium *Bacillus thuringiensis* Berliner (Bt) is also commonly observed in laboratory cultures of this insect and is registered for control of Indianmeal moth and almond moth on stored grains and soybeans.

MONITORING GUIDELINES

Indianmeal moth eventually finds access to any stored raisins. Storage of raisins in stacks on a ranch calls for a fumigation schedule similar to that used by packers. The commercially available sex pheromones already mentioned for use with raisin moth are also useful for monitoring Indianmeal moth.

MANAGEMENT GUIDELINES

This and other pests of stored raisins are controlled primarily in the packinghouse. However, growers holding raisins on the farm usually cover them with plastic or other gas-tight material and then fumigate them (see "Commodity Treatments" at the end of this section). As raisins are removed from storage, they undergo several processing steps before being packaged for sale. Each step in processing—sorting, cleaning, stemming, etc.—progressively reduces an infestation. Raisins with significant insect feeding damage are lighter and are automatically blown out during processing. Sanitation of storage facilities, processing plants, bins, and warehouses is required to reduce severe infestations. Railroad cars, trucks, and other shipping containers

Figure 82.10 Indianmeal moth larva. *Photo*: J. K. Clark.

Figure 82.11 Indianmeal moth larva spinning its cocoon (A); close-up of cocoon (B). *Photos*: J. K. Clark.

should be thoroughly inspected, and cleaned, and other control methods should be applied if necessary before raisins are loaded. As food processing methods improve, infestations will become less common.

SAWTOOTHED GRAIN BEETLE

Sawtoothed grain beetle (*Oryzaephilus surinamensis* (L.)) (Coleoptera: Cucujidae) is a cosmopolitan pest that feeds on practically any stored dried food. Both larvae and adults attack those commodities. Sawtoothed grain beetle infests all cereals (rice, wheat, maize, barley, and pastas such as macaroni), bread, flour, nuts, copra, starch, drugs, tobacco, and dried fruit. Raisins are one of its preferred foods. In raisins stored for a year or more, this insect can become abundant. It crawls rapidly, even on vertical surfaces, but it has not been observed to fly. Newly hatched larvae can pass through extremely narrow crevices in search of food.

DESCRIPTION

The adult beetle is about 3 mm (0.13 in) long and is narrow and flat (fig. 82.12). It is brown and has six toothlike projections along each side of the body in front of the wings. A look-alike beetle found in the San Joaquin Valley is the merchant grain beetle (*O. mercator* (Fauvel)). The merchant grain beetle has larger eyes than the temple region behind the head, and the head is rectangular. The sawtoothed grain beetle has smaller eyes and a more triangular head (fig. 82.13). Unlike sawtoothed grain beetles, merchant grain beetles are capable of

flight, so proper identification may assist in determining management practices.

The eggs of the sawtoothed grain beetle are white, elongate to oval, and less than 1 mm (0.04 in) long; they are not readily visible to the unaided eye. The larvae are yellowish white and when fully grown are about 3 mm (0.13 in) long (fig. 82.14). Pupae are white or yellowish white and are found in or near larval food. The larva usually makes a cocoon for protection before pupation. The cocoon consists of fine particles of food cemented together by the larva.

INJURY

This beetle attacks all parts of the raisin, feeding as much in the deep folds as on the raised wrinkles. Unlike Indianmeal and raisin moths, it does not deposit webbing. The excreta are yellowish pellets, more elongate than those of the raisin and Indianmeal moth larvae,

and they are similar in size and shape to the beetle's eggs.

SEASONAL DEVELOPMENT

Development from egg to adult requires 27 days in summer. Females begin to lay eggs about 5 days after pupal emergence. From 6 to 10 eggs are laid each day, singly or in small clusters, until they total from 45 to 285 eggs. They are laid in crevices formed by tight folds in the raisin skin. The hatch takes from 3 to 5 days in midsummer and from 8 to 17 days in spring and fall. In summer, the larvae develop in about 2 weeks, but in spring they feed and grow for 4 to 7 weeks. During larval development, they molt two to four times. Under certain conditions, larvae are cannibalistic, and some entomologists believe Indianmeal moth populations may be suppressed by large populations of sawtoothed grain beetle. Pupal period is 6 to 9 days in summer.

Figure 82.12 Sawtoothed grain beetle adults (A); close-up of thorax of an adult (B). *Photos*: J. K. Clark.

ACTUAL SIZE: SAWTOOTHED GRAIN BEETLE

Egg	First Larval Stage	Mature Larval Stage	Pupa	Adult

Sawtoothed grain beetles are long-lived. Some have been recorded as having lived for more than 3 years. Optimal survival temperatures are between 30° and 35°C (86° and 95°F). There are normally five to six generations each year; but in warm buildings, breeding and development occur throughout the year. Thus, infestation may spread during storage. In California's Coachella Valley, adults and larvae remain active outdoors throughout the year in dropped fruit in date groves.

NATURAL CONTROL

A parasitic wasp, *Cephalonomia tarsalis* (Ashmead) (Hymenoptera: Bethylidae), has been found to reduce sawtoothed grain beetle populations by attacking the larvae. However, this wasp will not economically control an infestation.

MONITORING GUIDELINES

Screening an occasional sample or composite sample from many bins will usually confirm the presence of any insects and the need for fumigation.

MANAGEMENT GUIDELINES

Control of this pest (and other pests of stored raisins) takes place primarily in the packinghouse. Growers who cover and make sweatbox stacks or bins on the ranch should have fumigation programs (see "Commodity Treatments," below). As raisins are removed from storage, they undergo several processing steps before being packaged for sale. Most processors subject raisins to shaker screens, sorter-blowers, cleaners, washers, rifflers, and stemmers. By the time the raisins are packaged for consumer sales, immature, damaged, lightweight, or otherwise undesirable fruit has been removed.

COMMODITY TREATMENTS

Although commodity treatment of raisins for live insect disinfestation is normally done at the packinghouse, there may be the need to treat farm-stored product. The most common treatment method is chemical fumigation with phosphine. Stacks of raisins may be covered with plastic and a fumigant carefully applied. Raisin processors often store raisins in large bin stacks covered with reinforced paper laminate. When properly built, these covered stacks are gas tight, and fumigants may be easily introduced. The cover also provides an effective barrier against reinfestation by insects. The first fumigation should be done when the stack is completed, and the stack should be fumigated again periodically when storage exceeds 60 to 90 days, or when the covering of the stack is compromised in any way.

Because organic producers are unable to use chemical fumigants to control stored raisins of driedfruit beetles and other insects, alternative methods must be used. Mechanically dehydrating organically grown raisins at high temperatures can avoid infestation by insects that normally attack sun-dried raisins. Many organic dried fruit and nut processors freeze the product for at least 2 weeks at −18°C (0°F). Covered raisin stacks may be treated with controlled atmospheres, either low oxygen or high carbon dioxide. Refrigerated storage of clean product can prevent reinfestation.

Figure 82.13 Anterior comparison of sawtoothed (A) and merchant grain (B) beetles. *Photos*: USDA Agricultural Research Service.

Figure 82.14 Sawtoothed grain beetle larvae. *Photo*: J. K. Clark.

References

Burks, C. S., J. A. Johnson, D. E. Maier, and J. W. Heaps. 2000. Temperature. In B. Subramanyam and D. Hagstrum, eds., Alternatives to pesticides in stored-product IPM. Boston: Kluwer Academic Publishers. 73–104.

Curtis, C. E., and J. D. Clark. 1974. Comparative biologies of *Oryzaephilus surinamensis* and *O. mercator* (Coleoptera: Cucujidae) on dried fruits and nuts. U.S. Department of Agriculture Bulletin 1488.

James, D. G., B. Vogele, R. J. Faulder, R. J. Bartelt, and C. J. Moore. 2001. Pheromone-mediated mass trapping and population diversion as strategies for suppressing *Carpophilus* spp. (Coleoptera: Nitidulidae) in Australian stone fruit orchards. Agricultural and Forest Entomology 3:41–47.

Johnson, J. A., P. V. Vail, D. G. Brandl, J. S. Tebbets, and K. A. Valero. 2002. Integration of non-chemical treatments for control of postharvest pyralid moths (Lepidoptera: Pyralidae) in almonds and raisins. Journal of Economic Entomology 95:190–199.

Johnson, J. A., K. A. Valero, M. M. Hannel, and R. F. Gill. 2000. Seasonal occurrence of postharvest dried fruit insects and their parasitoids in a culled fig warehouse. Journal of Economic Entomology 93:1380–1390.

Lindegren, J. E., and G. T. Okumura. 1973. Pathogens from economically important nitidulid beetles. USDA ARS W-9.

Phillips, T. W., P. M. Cogan, and H. Y. Fadamiro. 2000. Pheromones. In B. Subramanyam and D. Hagstrum, eds., Alternatives to pesticides in stored-product IPM. Boston: Kluwer Academic Publishers. 273–302.

Simmons, P., and H. D. Nelson. 1975. Insects on dried fruits. USDA Agriculture Handbook 464.

Soderstrom, E. L., P. D. Gardner, J. L. Baritelle, K. N. De Lozano, and D. Brandl. 1984. Economic cost evaluation of a generated low-oxygen atmosphere as an alternative fumigant in the bulk storage of raisins. Journal of Economic Entomology 77:457–461.

Stored-grain insects. 1986. USDA Agriculture Handbook 500.

Part 6

Nematodes

Merlot

83 NEMATODES

Michael V. McKenry and Larry J. Bettiga

Nematodes are microscopic, multicellular, nonsegmented roundworms commonly present in soil. They are adapted by the structure of their mouthparts to derive nutrients from soil microorganisms such as bacteria, fungi, or mesofauna, including other nematodes or plant roots.

Nematode communities are rarely comprised of a single species, and both parasites and nonparasites of grape occur in vineyard soils. A typical vineyard soil contains nematodes feeding on grape roots, on other organisms associated with grape roots, on other biological components of soil, and on other plants growing in the vineyard. Within the soil, they live and move in the water that lines soil pore spaces.

A plant-parasitic nematode life cycle consists of an egg, four gradually enlarging juvenile stages, and an adult stage. Completion of each juvenile stage is followed by the molting of the cuticle (external covering). For most species the first molt is inside the egg, so it is usually the second-stage juvenile that is the infective stage. Juveniles are typically vermiform, with a long, thin cylindrical shape; adults may have a variety of shapes (fig. 83.1). The length of a nematode life cycle is primarily influenced by the environmental temperature, moisture, and the quality of available food sources.

Plant-parasitic nematodes may reduce root efficiency. Penetration and movement through root tissues result in physical injury to cells and subsequent cell necrosis. In addition to the interruption of uptake and flow through the root system, feeding wounds can allow for infection by opportunistic soil microbes such as fungi and bacteria that cause plant damage or disease once provided an entry route into the plant. Certain nematodes, such as dagger nematodes, can also vector viruses into the root with a single feeding. In addition, ring nematodes can disrupt the plant defense mechanisms of the upper portion of plants. Vine damage may eventually become apparent as reduced vigor and yield with slight yellowing of leaves (fig. 83.2). Vine death seldom occurs unless there are other stresses on the plant. The aboveground symptoms associated with nematode damage are commonly indistinguishable from those of other root-restricting agents.

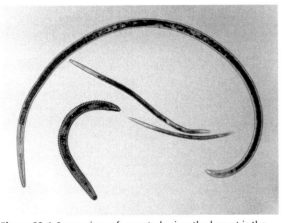

Figure 83.1 Comparison of nematode size: the largest is the dagger nematode (*Xiphinema americanum*); the short, fatter one with conspicuous rings is the ring nematode (*Mesocriconema xenoplax*); the long, thin nematode with darker contents is the root lesion nematode (*Pratylenchus vulnus*); and the smallest nematode is the root knot nematode (*Meloidogyne* spp.). *Photo*: S. Kaku.

Roots of nematode-infected vines are unable to meet aboveground demands for nutrients and water, especially during peak demand periods, and are the first to show a nitrogen or water deficiency. Depending on the nematode tolerance of a grape cultivar or rootstock, regulating cropping loads with extensive pruning can minimize vine stress. Nematode damage and symptomology are nonspecific compared with most aboveground pest situations.

Because aboveground vine symptomology is lacking and nematodes are microscopic in size, laboratory analyses are necessary to determine population levels and to identify species. Good analyses depend on proper sampling and extraction techniques. It is of primary importance to get an accurate analysis of the species present and population levels to make appropriate nematode management decisions.

Research studies of soil fumigation, nematode taxonomy, rootstock characteristics, and soil-borne viruses have enhanced the understanding of the belowground

environment in vineyards, especially the nematode components. Preplant fumigants, when properly applied, profoundly affect nematode populations. However, fumigation must be carried out in a correct manner or populations can recolonize quickly. Nematode population reduction is an objective of both preplant and postplant nematicide applications.

Fumigants for controlling nematode populations have a dramatic effect on the total microflora and fauna of soil. While they can provide amazing benefits to growers when properly applied, they can work to growers' disadvantage if they do not reduce populations of nematodes. The effects of fumigation on most soil fungi are relatively short-lived.

This section contains descriptions of the most commonly found nematodes damaging to grapes in California vineyards. Occurrence of nematode species can vary both within and between production regions. Included are data on population dynamics, geographic distribution, symptomology, and injury. Information is not provided

on nematodes that are not parasitic on grapes, even though they may feed on weeds or other plants growing in the vineyard.

ROOT KNOT NEMATODES

Root knot nematodes found in California vineyards include *Meloidogyne incognita, M. javanica, M. arenaria, M. hapla,* and *M. chitwoodi.* These species can complete 8 to 9 generations per year in the San Joaquin Valley, with 500 to 1,500 eggs produced per female. In coastal areas, because of lower soil temperatures, one can expect 4 to 6 generations. In the Coachella Valley, a dozen generations may occur annually. In many vineyards, the presence of two or more species is common. The resistance of some rootstocks may vary depending on the species and pathotype of root knot nematode present. In addition, nematode feeding on rootstocks with inadequate resistance mechanisms, such as 1613C, Harmony, Ramsey, and Freedom, can result in development of resistance-breaking pathotypes. These pathotypes commonly exhibit greater virulence and may occur among any of the above-listed

Figure 83.2 Aerial photo (A) shows weak spots in vineyard caused by nematodes. Photo (B), taken from the top of a pickup truck, shows stunted vines that may have been affected by nematodes. *Photos:* M. V. McKenry.

species. *Meloidogyne incognita, M. javanica,* and *M. arenaria* are most prevalent south of the Soledad, Livermore, and Lodi areas.

Most prevalent in cooler regions north of San Francisco, the northern root knot nematode (*M. hapla*) is the dominant species of root knot nematode in north coast vineyards. *M. hapla* can also be found in southern California vineyards, perhaps being more active there during winter months. Root knot nematodes are less prevalent in north coast valleys, although high populations can occur where previous cropping history has included root knot–sensitive crops. Relatively high population levels (perhaps five times those of *M. incognita*) are required for vine damage, and gall size is notably smaller with this nematode species.

Description

Root knot nematodes are sedentary endoparasites that live most of their life cycle inside the root of vines or other susceptible plants growing in the vineyard (fig. 83.3). Second-stage juveniles hatch from eggs and move through moist soil to contact roots. Vertical distances of 30 cm (12 in) in sandy loam soil can reportedly be traversed in 3 days by 5% of the population. Juveniles are attracted to roots and usually penetrate and enter just behind the root tip. Once inside the root, they establish themselves in the conducting tissues and begin feeding; after 2 weeks of warm summer temperatures, the females mature into egg-laying adults. Their development stimulates a cellular change in the plant in the immediate vicinity of the feeding

site, inducing giant cells to develop. This change results in formation of the familiar knot, or gall, seen on the root surface. Internally, the gall disrupts conducting tissues. Also, cracking of the roots by gall growth can allow opportunistic bacteria and fungi to infect root tissues.

A single gall may be inhabited by one or numerous adult females. The number of females living in a single gall influences its size. Galls on infected grape roots are typically 3 mm (0.13 in) in diameter but can be larger where there has been a multiple attack. However, they are seldom larger than 13 mm (0.5 in) in diameter, even on older roots. Root knot nematode confirmation requires examination of the gall for the presence of adult females. The adult female is a sedentary, pearl-colored stage, which, if dissected from the gall, is barely visible to the unaided eye. The life span of root knot nematode in grape presumably is from 1 to several months, with greatest longevity but least activity occurring during winter.

On susceptible roots, a single gall can be inhabited by successive females for many years; thus, 5-year-old roots of *Vitis vinifera* cultivars commonly exhibit galls. By contrast, rootstocks such as Teleki 5C, SO4, and RS-3 possess resistance mechanisms that ensure that galls are not maintained on roots older than 4 to 6 months.

Root knot nematode males, while sometimes present in low numbers, do not feed and are not a direct concern to the grape grower. They are not required for reproduction.

The egg population reaches highest numbers in September,

when soils of many vineyards are driest. Presumably, dry soils reduce egg hatch but not egg production. As many as 1,500 eggs may be produced by a single adult female in a Thompson Seedless root. Second-stage juveniles in soil are generally two to five times more numerous during fall and winter than in spring and summer.

Soil surveys indicate that the preponderance of the population is located 15 to 90 cm (6 to 36 in) beneath the vine row, depending on soil conditions and tillage practices, but wheel traffic and its effect on soil compaction and root distribution minimize this nematode's development in the vineyard drive row.

Root knot nematode is best adapted to coarse-textured soils, including sand, loamy sand, and sandy loam. It exhibits a wide host range, including the roots of many broadleaf weeds, grasses, and cover crops present in vineyards.

Injury

Root knot nematodes interfere with plant growth and nutrient uptake. Cell enlargement within each gall forms a nutrient sink from which the feeding nematodes withdraw vine nutrients as they develop. They further disrupt the orderly uptake of water and nutrients by their physical presence in root tissues. Damage is increased if plants are stressed. Young vines can be severely stunted when planted in sites with high levels of root knot nematodes; this stunting is a result of excessive feeding by nematodes on the developing root system of own-rooted or rootstock vines that are not tolerant of nematode feeding.

Figure 83.3 The life cycle of a sedentary endoparasite root knot nematode. (A) Egg stage. (B) First-stage juvenile within an egg. (C) Second-stage juvenile emerges from the egg. The second-stage juvenile must penetrate the root to feed. (D) Once inside the root, the second stage enlarges. (E) Third-stage male and female. (F) Fourth-stage male and female. (G) Adult stages. The vermiform male does not feed. The saccate female remains sedentary, producing eggs in a gelatinous matrix that usually develops external to the root surface. Other nematode species have slightly different life cycles. Root lesion nematode, a migratory endoparasite, remains vermiform in the adult stages, and either the second, third, fourth, or adult stages may penetrate or vacate a root. Stubby root nematode, ring nematode, needle nematode, and dagger nematode have life cycles similar to the root lesion nematode, except that they feed only at the root surface and do not enter roots.

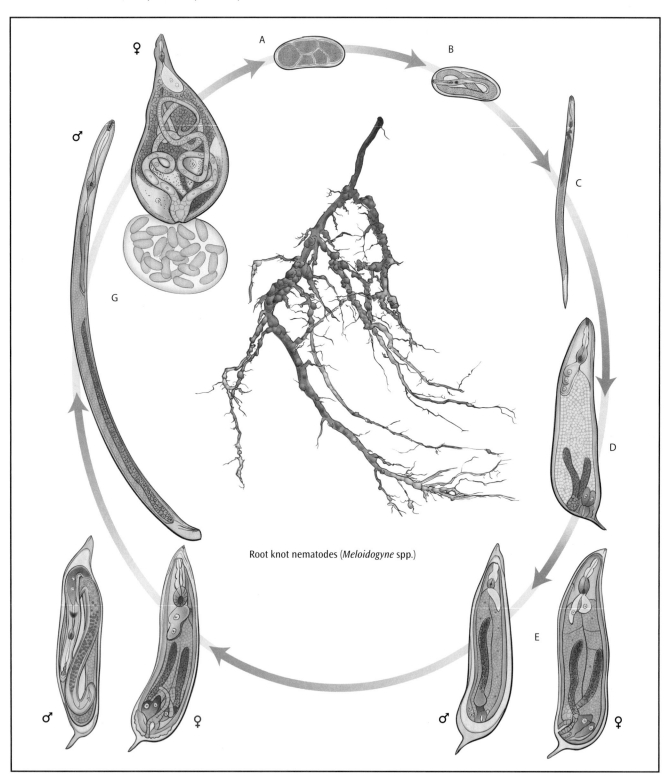

Root knot nematodes (*Meloidogyne* spp.)

DAGGER NEMATODES

XIPHINEMA AMERICANUM

Xiphinema americanum, the most common species of dagger nematode, is an external parasite generally known for its large size and its lengthy root-penetrating spear that allows it to feed deep in root tissues. It prefers young roots of woody plants but will reproduce and feed on diverse plants, including sudangrass, strawberry, and alfalfa. The designation *X. americanum* actually refers to a grouping of nematodes common throughout the United States but displaying slight diversity from one population to the next. Attempts by researchers to separate these populations on the basis of nematode morphology or with molecular techniques have not been successful.

DESCRIPTION

Juvenile stages are most evident during the early months of spring. Population levels are approximately twice as high in winter as in summer. In vineyards with moderate wheel traffic, 85% of the vineyard population resides within the surface 45 cm (18 in) soil zone directly beneath the vine row. It is reported that the life expectancy for this pest may reach 4 years. Numbers of this species are reduced in zones where there is frequent tillage or in zones of the soil profile where the oxygen content is lower.

Except for the Coachella Valley, this nematode may be found in vineyards throughout California. It is conspicuously absent, however, in certain vineyards. Preference for a particular soil texture is not apparent.

INJURY

Weak vines in a high-yielding vineyard have been shown to yield correspondingly less as the population of this nematode increases. However, the poorest-performing vines are typically also associated with other soil pests, including root knot nematode.

This nematode feeds near the root tip but does not cause an enlarged gall there. *Xiphinema americanum* is the specific vector of tomato ringspot virus, which causes yellow vein virus disease in grape.

XIPHINEMA INDEX

Xiphinema index is most widely known because of its association with grapevine fanleaf virus (GFLV). However, this ectoparasite, even when not carrying the virus, damages root tips. As its population levels increase, one can observe greater frequency of galls at root tips. These galls are typically small and may be hooked, just as they are when fed on by phylloxera. In some settings, such as when feeding on roots of the wine grape cultivar Rubired, or on AXR#1 and 1103P rootstocks, high populations can thicken and lengthen root tips to about the size of an elongated grape berry.

DESCRIPTION

Xiphinema index is a relatively large nematode and occasionally reaches higher population levels than *X. americanum.* Both commonly occur in the same vineyards; however, there are numerous regions in California where *X. index* is not found. Isolated vineyards in Madera, Fresno, Tulare, and Kern Counties support this nematode, and GFLV is sometimes associated with it. *Xiphinema index* is prevalent and problematic in the north coast, central coast, Bakersfield, and Lodi-Livermore areas. Total acreage infested by it probably does not exceed 10%, with perhaps 5% of California acreage infected with GFLV. The distribution pattern indicates that *X. index* is a more recent arrival in California, and its distribution is associated with planting of infested nursery stock, particularly prior to the 1960s.

INJURY

Xiphinema index is associated with yield reductions, which can become even more extensive when GFLV is also present. Once a field becomes infested with the virus and the nematode, the only effective control is to remove and avoid replanting grapes for at least 10 years. Development of resistance to *X. index* combined with tolerance to GFLV may provide viable options for replanting infested sites, but there will still be a need for preplant fumigation or a 10-year wait in order to reduce population levels of the virus and the nematode and thus to conserve both these useful resistance mechanisms.

The feeding of the nematode causes swelling of the root tip, not unlike the damage caused by phylloxera. Grapevine fanleaf virus exhibits a variety of characteristic shoot and leaf symptoms. These symptoms can depend on rootstock choice and the presence or absence of viroids commonly present in most *Vitis* species. See section 24, "Grapevine Virus Diseases," for more details on GFLV.

ROOT LESION NEMATODE

Root lesion nematode (*Pratylenchus* spp.) is a common name for a group that includes more than 35 species. *Pratylenchus vulnus* is the most important of this genus on grapevines, although population densities are characteristically low. *Pratylenchus vulnus* can be found throughout California but is not uniformly distributed. If the land to be planted has a history of perennial crops such as walnut, cherry, apple, or stone fruit, one should suspect the presence of *P. vulnus*. *Pratylenchus penetrans* is occasionally found in vineyards located in cooler areas and at higher elevations, primarily in sites that have a past cropping history of apples.

Other root lesion species frequently achieve high levels in grassy vineyards; these species, however, are not considered to parasitize grape roots. Species are differentiated by their host range and morphological and anatomical proportions. If present, it is important to have the species identified to determine the potential for vine damage.

Description

Root lesion nematodes are migratory root endoparasites that can feed on the surface or inside grape roots. Females lay eggs singly inside the root and in the soil. After hatching, all developmental stages may feed on roots or move through the soil to find other feeding sites. Their migration in and out of and through root tissues results in root dysfunction and allows for invasion of opportunistic bacteria and fungi. Unlike many other nematode species, root lesion nematodes can survive as adults, eggs, or juveniles without food for many years; 5% of the population may still be present and active 5 years after the previous crop has been killed with systemic herbicides and the land maintained free of weeds.

Injury

Feeding by root lesion nematodes restricts the flow of nutrients within larger roots and may kill smaller roots. Feeder roots are most susceptible, and a lack of feeder roots as well as major structural roots is one symptom of an infestation. Young vines planted in untreated soil infested with *P. vulnus* from a previous perennial crop may have severely restricted root development. In young vines, top growth is noticeably restricted, and vine recovery seldom occurs. Among older vines, damage caused by this nematode has been shown to be high.

Dark-colored lesions on the root surface are sometimes found, but this symptom is unreliable as a diagnostic tool.

CITRUS NEMATODE

The citrus nematode (*Tylenchulus semipenetrans*) has a narrow host range. In California agriculture, it is limited to citrus, persimmon, olive, and grape. While only one species is involved, there are at least five different races, based on their feeding preferences.

Populations of citrus nematode develop to high numbers in vineyards. This nematode favors loam-type soils, including loam, sandy loams, and clay loams. On shallow soils, citrus nematode achieves high population levels in the drive row as well as in the berm area.

Citrus nematode is most prevalent along the San Joaquin Valley's eastern side, including areas east of Porterville, Delano, Tulare, and Fresno. It is present in vineyards with no history of citrus. More recently it has appeared as damaging in the Napa Valley, perhaps a result of bringing in contaminated citrus or olive specimen trees.

Description

Citrus nematode is semi-endoparasitic. After hatching from eggs in the soil, juveniles migrate to roots and feed on the outer cell layers, primarily behind the root tips.

As young adults, the females become sedentary, and except for its embedded neck region, its body is extended out from the root. The exposed posterior end of the female swells as the reproductive organs develop. Eggs are laid in a gelatinous matrix in the soil. Root samples taken from soils with high populations frequently have soil particles clinging to the root surface, even after a vigorous shaking. This is because of soil embedded in the exposed egg matrix. This "dirty root" symptom is not a reliable diagnostic tool, but where nematode analyses have verified its presence, it can help determine the extent of field infestations.

Injury

Citrus nematode reduces vine vigor and yield. The best evidence of field damage has come when growers have had improved plant response after using a nematicide in vineyards where it was the predominant species.

RING NEMATODE

Of the various ring nematodes, *Mesocriconema xenoplax* is the most common species present in perennial crops. (The genus name has been frequently modified for this nematode; however, the species name has remained unchanged.) The fatter size of the adult of this nematode renders it almost immobile within individual soil pore spaces. It develops to high populations only within soils of high porosity, including sands and well-structured clay loam soils. Fine, sandy loam soils have a smaller pore size, which can limit population development.

It can be difficult to reliably estimate the population of this nematode because wide variations in soil sampling can result in wide variations in population densities. To get more uniform estimates, soil sampling several days after an irrigation or rain is suggested.

Ring nematodes appear throughout California soils. High populations have been found in coastal vineyards in a range of soil types. Rootstocks 420A and 101-14 do not host populations of *M. xenoplax* when grown in the coastal valleys of Oregon and in Mendocino and Santa Barbara Counties, but these rootstocks do host *M. xenoplax* when grown in the warmer inland valleys. It does appear that there are slight genetic differences between nematode populations from the inland and coastal valleys. Coastal populations transported to the Central Valley and evaluated in a 5-year microplot trial can overcome the resistance mechanisms in these two rootstocks in 3 years. By contrast, the ring nematode resistance mechanisms selected in RS-3 rootstock can remain useful in the Central Valley if population levels at planting time are not excessive.

Members of the genus *Hemicriconemoides* are commonly present in north coast vineyards, where

the damage it causes has not been distinguished from that caused by *M. xenoplax*. Until pathogenesis associated with the latter genus receives greater research attention, these two ring nematode genera are considered similar.

DESCRIPTION

Ring nematodes are sedentary ectoparasites. They are among the most easily identified plant-parasitic nematodes because of the distinct cuticular ring ornamentations around the body.

INJURY

Data from deciduous trees indicate extensive root pruning as a result of ring nematode feeding on smallest feeder roots. Reduced water and nutrient uptake eventually leads to stress on the entire plant, but perhaps more importantly, on young feeder roots that produce plant hormones critical to plant regulation and disease defense mechanisms. Based on yield improvements following nematicide tests, this nematode deserves greater attention as a parasite of grape roots. It can cause general aboveground lack of vigor and reduced yields. Damage associated with high ring nematode infestations occasionally includes the presence of inactive fruit and leaf buds, particularly where scions of low vigor are involved and nematode counts are in excess of 1,000 per kg (per 2.2 lb) of soil. New shoots can eventually become short and spindly.

SPIRAL NEMATODE

Several different nematode groups are given the common name of spiral nematode. The spiral nematode of concern in grape vineyards

is *Helicotylenchus pseudorobustus*. This nematode can be endoparasitic as well as ectoparasitic. On woody perennials, it may penetrate half a body length into roots. High population levels are possible. It is rarely found in California vineyards but usually reaches highest populations and causes greatest concern in silty soil textures. High population levels have been associated with weakened vines; damage symptoms are nonspecific.

SHEATH NEMATODE

There are numerous species of *Hemicycliophora* that can be widespread in riparian locations such as the north coast and also along desert riverbeds of southern California and in cranberry bogs of the eastern United States. This nematode was named for the presence of an extra cuticle that loosely surrounds the adult nematode body. The best-known species in agricultural settings is *H. arenaria*. Feeding by this nematode has been shown to result in the formation of galls at the root terminus of citrus, but its host range is much broader, including tomato, celery, and grape, where much less information is available. It is commonly found in riparian vineyard settings in association with *M. xenoplax* and *Hemicriconemoides* species, where credit for any apparent vine damage is usually implied to be the result of *M. xenoplax*.

NEEDLE NEMATODE

A long-bodied nematode similar in appearance to *Xiphinema*, the ectoparasite *Longidorus africanus* also attacks and reproduces on numerous annual crops. In vineyards, it is found exclusively in the Coachella Valley. Root damage is believed to be similar to that caused by *X. americanum*, except that terminal root galls can be apparent at high population levels.

STUBBY ROOT NEMATODE

The feeding habit and feeding apparatus of stubby root nematode (*Paratrichodorus minor*) differ somewhat from those of other nematodes. This nematode occurs in relatively low numbers on a wide variety of perennials and annuals throughout California.

DESCRIPTION

The egg stage apparently has some resistance to adverse conditions, including nematicides; the other stages, however, seem susceptible to chilling or soil disruption. This migratory ectoparasite feeds on the epidermal cells near the root tip. The first juvenile stage hatches from the egg and infects roots.

INJURY

No injury or disease symptoms are known, as this nematode seldom occurs in the absence of other nematode species except just after soil fumigation.

PIN NEMATODE

The pin nematode (*Paratylenchus hamatus*) is commonly found in vineyards. It prefers the roots of woody plants and exhibits great preference for Nemaguard peach, with a relatively moderate preference for grape roots. Pin nematode can build to relatively high population levels. This species is as prevalent at the 90 cm (3 ft) depth as at the 30 cm (1 ft) depth.

DESCRIPTION

Pin nematode, a migratory ectoparasite, is one of the smallest of the plant nematodes. It has a long stylet that allows feeding deeper into the epidermis. It feeds at or just behind the root tip. Fourth-stage juveniles are a resistant stage capable of withstanding adverse environmental conditions.

INJURY

This very common nematode in a weed-free vineyard can build to high population levels without causing apparent vine damage or reduction in yield or quality of grapes. In fact, one study indicated that *P. hamatus* populations tended to be higher among the highest-yield vines.

MONITORING GUIDELINES

VINEYARD SAMPLING

Preplant
If a proposed vineyard site has had a perennial crop in the past 5 years or it has recently lain fallow, it is important to take soil samples down to the 90 cm (3 ft) level. Samples should be from areas of the field where agronomic differences of any kind have been noted. These include different cropping histories, soil textures, soil depths, yield differences, or different management. A single composite sample should include soil from up to 10 subsamples taken from each identifiably different area.

Established Vineyards
Plant-parasitic nematodes are concentrated where feeder roots are most abundant. Therefore, sample for both soil and roots in the berm area 30 to 45 cm (12 to 18 in) from the vine trunk to a depth of 60 cm (24 in). The surface 7.5 cm (3 in)

of vineyard soil may be discarded. Sample around five vines from each identifiable area. These areas might include differences in grape cultivar, soil texture, cropping history, vine vigor, or yield. For each of the five vines sampled, it is helpful to observe the incidence of root knot galling or other irregularities. Combine these five subsamples into a single sample representative of the area. Keep a record of the description or location of the area from which samples were combined to form the single composite sample.

When to Sample
Samples can be taken any time of the year. It is best to sample when soil is moist, preferably within a week after rainfall or irrigation. Samples removed during winter usually provide the highest counts of nematode species feeding on perennial crops. A typical vine may harbor none to 10 million plant-parasitic nematodes; thus, expect extreme variability in sampling results. By standardizing the sampling methods described here, however, there is greater opportunity for correctly interpreting the results.

Number of Samples
The number of composite samples taken may be decided on the basis of cropping history, soil textural differences, geographic location, grape cultivar or rootstock, and the experience of the sampler. There is no set formula. A rule of thumb is to submit for analysis one sample that is representative of every 5 to 10 acres (2 to 4 ha), but exceptions to this rule are common.

Analyzing the Sample
One to two kilograms (2 to 5 lb) of soil for a sample are sufficient.

Soil should be placed in a plastic or waterproof bag and properly labeled on the outside with name, date, site or vineyard location, and the current or previous crop or cultivar, if any. Plastic bags should be kept away from direct sunlight and stored preferably at 5° to 10°C (41° to 50°F). Most importantly, avoid temperatures above 35°C (95°F) or lower than 2°C (35°F). Include grape roots where applicable.

COMMERCIAL LABORATORIES

Numerous laboratories provide nematode identification, but the extent of their services varies greatly. Some laboratories come to the vineyard to remove and care for soil samples; others receive samples by mail and return results, leaving all interpretations to the grower. Some laboratory personnel never see the vineyard but make elaborate interpretations of the problem and control strategies.

Extraction Methods

Laboratories must be capable of running several extraction methodologies. For example, *X. index, X. americanum, M. xenoplax,* and *L. africanus* are most efficiently extracted by some modification of the sugar flotation method and centrifugation. *Meloidogyne* species and *P. vulnus* are most efficiently extracted by a modified Baermann funnel and mist chamber technique. If a specific nematode problem is expected, one extraction method may be preferred. The method used should be reported to you, along with the results. Laboratories that are also able to report their efficiency of extraction are preferred; however, even research laboratories do not routinely report such values.

Interpreting Sampling Results

To assess or estimate nematode damage, one must first determine nematode population levels and what species are present. Some nematode species develop much higher population levels than others (table 83.1). This is a result of the quantity of food available and the suitability of the particular soil environment. A direct correlation between nematode numbers and plant damage should not be expected. One can determine whether nematodes in a given vineyard are at a high, medium, or low population level relative to other California vineyards from table 83.1. However, these are average figures and do not take into account differences in soil texture, time of sampling, grape cultivar, soil depth, or numerous other factors that alter population levels.

Table 83.1. Relative rating of nematode densities found in California vineyards

Nematode	Nematodes present in 1 kg (2.2 lb) of soil*					
	Low population		Medium population		High population	
	Oct–Mar†	Mar–Oct	Oct–Mar	Mar–Oct	Oct–Mar	Mar–Oct
root knot	< 75	< 25	75–500	25–200	> 500	> 200
Xiphinema americanum	< 20		20–200	20–100	> 200	> 100
Pratylenchus vulnus	< 20		20–100		> 100	
citrus	< 1,000		1,000–3,000		> 3,000	
stubby root	< 20		20–200		> 200	
ring	< 50		50–500		> 500	
pin	< 100		100–1,000		> 1,000	
Xiphinema index	< 20		20–200		> 200	
needle	< 20		20–200		> 200	
Helicotylenchus pseudorobustus	< 50		50–500		> 500	

Notes:
*Nematode numbers per 1 kg soil adjusted to 100% nematode extraction efficiency.
†Population densities of some nematode species are influenced by the date of sampling.

Population densities in table 83.1 have been adjusted to a 100% extraction efficiency. This is an important point to consider, as there are various methods of extracting nematodes from soil, and these methods are not directly comparable. For example, the combination sieving and mist extraction technique used by the University of California removes about 75% of the root knot and root lesion nematodes, 50% of the *X. americanum* and pin nematodes, and 5% of the ring nematodes. With the sugar flotation technique, one can expect about 30% extraction of root knot and root lesion nematode and 50% of the others. There are other extraction techniques, each with its own efficiency rating. Operator skill also affects the efficiency rating.

Once an area's relative nematode population level is known, how does one determine the degree of vine damage? Table 83.2 lists factors that influence the level of plant damage and that should be considered in conjunction with every submitted nematode sample.

With the population level known and a good description of the field, how does it all fit together? Table 83.3 attempts to explain damage levels; by no means complete, it is a starting place and is presented in a format that allows for future expansion and improvement.

Examples

The following examples explain how to use tables 83.1, 83.2, and 83.3.

Vineyard A is 20 acres (8 ha) of own-rooted Colombard, 8 years old, with deep, loamy sand soil, slight alkalinity, some weeds, and no phylloxera present. A June nematode sampling reveals that in 1 kg of soil, the poor area has 300 *Meloidogyne* and the good area has 150 *Meloidogyne*. From table 83.1 we see that we are dealing with a high population level. Consulting table 83.4, we see that this root knot–susceptible cultivar is receiving extensive nematode damage and that root knot galls should be plentiful even in the good area. A nematode control practice is needed in this vineyard.

Vineyard B is a young, own-rooted, weed-free Thompson Seedless planting. It is sprinkler irrigated on deep, loamy sand with no apparent soil-related problems. A June nematode sampling for a 20-acre (8 ha) block revealed the following numbers of nematodes per kg: poor area, 100 *Meloidogyne*, 120 *X. americanum*, 20 *P. vulnus*, 35 *P. minor*, and 20 *M. xenoplax*; good area, 100 *Meloidogyne*, 100 *X. americanum*, and 35 *P. minor*. Little is known about vine damage from mixed nematode populations, but we make the assumption that their impact is additive. Thompson Seedless has some tolerance to *Meloidogyne* species, and galls are commonly visible at less than one per inch or two of young root, but the soil is coarse and there is an indication that the ring nematode and root lesion nematode may be damaging the sandiest area. From this one can expect moderate vineyard damage; a nematode management practice should be tested in the poorer area.

Vineyard C is also own-rooted Thompson Seedless but more than 40 years old with 1,000 *Meloidogyne* species per kg of soil. Digging with a shovel along the sandiest vineyard berms indicates visible galls of root knot nematode commonly apparent on the youngest roots at levels of more than 4 galls per inch of root length. A pathotype of root knot nematode has gradually evolved in this vineyard (*M. incognita, M. arenaria,* or *M. javanica*) and has overcome the slight resistance mechanism of Thompson Seedless (see table 83.4). This nematode is now the major soil pest problem for this vineyard, and it would be a mistake to replant using own-rooted Thompson Seedless. Postplant nematicides may provide some help; vine responses can be dramatic, but their application will need to be budgeted annually.

Vineyard D involves replanting a vineyard along the central coast near Soledad (Monterey County). The current vineyard was planted on a phylloxera-resistant rootstock with limited nematode resistance after soil fumigation. These soils involve decomposed granite with 20% or more silt content. The relatively porous soils are irrigated by drip, support high counts of ring nematode (1,000 per kg soil), with occasional *Xiphinema index* (5 per kg soil) in one corner of the vineyard. *Meloidogyne* species is commonly present at a medium population level (250 per kg soil). Grape fanleaf virus is not present. This vineyard is receiving moderate damage from ring nematode, moderate damage from root knot nematode, and has the threat that *X. index* will become a bigger problem where the soil is most porous. Nematodes have become a major soil pest problem for the

Table 83.2. Information needed to interpret nematode damage levels from nematode sampling data*

Field Notes: Nematode Field Sampling

Sampling date _____ Number of acres per sample _____

Date of most recent irrigation or rain _____ How much water _____

Grower _____ Address _____

Field location _____

I. Vineyard situation

   A. Preplant

      (1) Replant after 4 years w/o perennial crop

      (2) Replant within 1 year of perennial crop

      (3) Following annual host crops

      (4) Following grasses or nonhosts

      (5) Nursery

   B. Postplant

      (1) First-leaf vineyard

      (2) Young vines (1 to 4 years)

      (3) Producing vineyard

      (4) Cover crop present

      (5) Virus complex present

II. Soil

   A. Texture

      (1) sand

      (2) loamy sand

      (3) sandy loam

      (4) loam

      (5) clay loam

      (6) clay

      (7) organic soil

      (8) other _____

   B. Estimated rooting depth

      (1) 24 inches

      (2) 42 inches

      (3) 60 inches

      (4) more than 60 inches

III. Irrigation

      (1) Furrow (a) short run; (b) long run (200+ yards); (c) uneven slope

      (2) Sprinkler _____

      (3) Drip lines _____

      (4) Nonirrigated _____

IV. Observable soil problems

   A. Soil physical problems

      (1) Compaction

      (2) Internal drainage poor

      (3) Soil layers present

   B. Soil chemical problems

      (1) Fertility

      (2) Alkali or alkaline

      (3) Other _____

   C. Soil biological problems

      (1) Armillaria root rot

      (2) Phylloxera

      (3) Other _____

V. Grape cultivar/rootstock _____

_____

*Circle items that serve to characterize the sample situation. Note any other conditions that may be helpful in identifying a special problem situation.

Table 83.3. Level of vine damage expected at various nematode population levels*

Field situation and nematode	Damage at population level		
	Low	Medium	High
First-leaf vineyard			
Meloidogyne spp., *P. vulnus*, *T. semipenetrans*, *X. index*	moderate	extensive	extensive
X. americanum, *M. xenoplax*	none	slight	moderate
Producing vineyard			
Meloidogyne spp.			
Susceptible grape cultivar			
Sand to sandy loam	moderate	extensive	extensive
Fine sandy loam to clay loam	slight	moderate	extensive
Less susceptible grape cultivar			
Sand to sandy loam	slight	moderate	extensive
Fine sandy loam to clay loam	none	slight	moderate
X. americanum, *M. xenoplax*, *L. africanus*	none	slight	moderate
X. index			
Grape fanleaf virus present	extensive	extensive	extensive
Grape fanleaf virus absent	slight	moderate	extensive
P. vulnus, *T. semipenetrans*	slight	moderate	extensive
P. minor, *H. pseudorobustus*	none	slight	moderate
P. hamatus	none	none	none
Preplant			
Replant, 3 years after perennials			
Meloidogyne spp., *T. semipenetrans*, *P. vulnus*, *X. index*	extensive	extensive	extensive
M. xenoplax, *X. americanum*	none	slight	moderate
Following annual crops, broadleaf annuals			
Meloidogyne spp.	slight	moderate	extensive
Nursery			
P. hamatus	none	none	slight
All other nematodes parasitic on grape	extensive	extensive	extensive

Note:
*Damage levels are estimated as follows: slight damage, less than 10% yield reduction; moderate damage, 10 to 25% yield damage; extensive damage, greater than 25% reduction.

Table 83.4. Suitability of selected grape roots following a 24-hour exposure to 500 *Meloidogyne arenaria* juveniles

Cultivar	Nematodes penetrating	Eggs laid
Ruby Cabernet	116	7,791
Carignane	82	4,385
Colombard	70	1,157
Rupestris St. George	69	3,064
Cabernet Sauvignon	63	2,677
Zinfandel	51	1,412
Barbera	44	1,776
Emperor	20	884
Perlette	14	363
Thompson Seedless	4	288
Harmony, Freedom	0	0
Ramsey	0	0
Dog Ridge	0	0

Source: Laboratory data of Ferris and Hunt 1979.

next vineyard to be replanted. If the new vineyard is not fumigated, there could be uneven slow growth due to the rejection component of the replant problem (see below), and only two rootstocks currently have tolerance to the rejection component. Poor growth in the first and second year after replanting coupled with high nematode populations will result in greater damage attributable to nematodes.

MANAGEMENT GUIDELINES FOR ESTABLISHING A VINEYARD

SITE SELECTION: THE REPLANT PROBLEM

Avoid replanting vineyards on sites that have been planted to other woody crops, particularly old vineyard sites where fumigants cannot be used. This is generally not an option for most grape production areas since many plantings in California are redevelopments of existing vineyard sites. Vines replanted within 1 to 4 years after removal of a vineyard may suffer from poor, uneven growth the first few years in nonfumigated soils. This early growth problem is called the rejection component of the replant problem and is likely caused by nonpathogenic microbes that have long received their food supply from the old root system. Incidence of the rejection component is not uniformly distributed across a vineyard, and in certain production regions, such as the north coast, the rejection component is uncommon. There is also a soil pest and disease component of the replant problem. Pest and disease problems are also unevenly distributed across the vineyard and from site to site, but the one time to protect against known pests and pathogens is prior to replanting. These two components of the replant problem can vary greatly in severity by region, site, cropping history, soil type, and rootstock choice.

Roots of *V. vinifera* are generally quite susceptible to the soil pest and disease component of the replant problem, particularly to high population levels of nematodes. Preplant soil fumigation can dramatically improve vine growth during the first few years of vineyard establishment as the rejection component is nullified. Some rootstocks are more sensitive to the rejection component of the replant problem than others. The rootstock Teleki 5C has been noted to grow poorly if replanted into sites without fumigation. Data is lacking to predict rootstock susceptibility to poor growth in replant situations. Even vigorous rootstocks such as Freedom and Harmony are substantially impacted, but their excessive vigor hides some of that impact. On the central coast, both the rejection component and soil pest component of the replant problem can be active. In the San Joaquin Valley, the intensity of both these replant components can reach a peak so that first-year vine growth may be one-seventh that of fumigated vines. One alternative to soil fumigation is a prolonged fallow period, but it requires 8 or more years for the old root system to completely die (the exact time required for root decomposition is not known).

A new strategy known as starve and switch is currently receiving evaluation as an alternative to soil fumigation. This strategy starves the old soil ecosystem by killing the vine roots, the nematodes' food source, using trunk applications of systemic herbicides followed by a full year of fallow, then at replanting time switches to a rootstock of very different parentage. At the present time, two rootstocks appear to provide tolerance to the rejection component in at least some locations, 10-17A and O39-16. However, planting time is also the best time to select a rootstock with resistance to prevailing soil pests, and of these two the resistance in O39-16 is limited to *X. index*, while 10-17A offers broad and durable nematode resistance. Unfortunately, 10-17A is intolerant of GFLV while O39-16 is tolerant. Interestingly, rootstocks such as RS-3 and RS-9 offer broad and durable nematode resistance but no relief from the rejection component. The parentage of 10-17A includes *V. simpsoni*. The parentage of O39-16 includes *V. rotundifolia*. The parentage of RS rootstocks includes *V. champinii* and *V. riparia,* which apparently are not different enough from *V. vinifera* to provide tolerance to the rejection component of the replant problem. As new grape rootstocks become available, a number of those will have parentage that includes *V. rotundifolia, V. simpsoni,* and other very different parentages. Some will have *V. arizonica, V. cinerea,* or *V. riparia,* which do not appear to be different enough. Field evaluations of each new rootstock in fumigated versus nonfumigated soil will be essential to identification of their tolerance or intolerance to the rejection component of the replant problem. Demko 10-17A rootstock was made available to the public in 2012. It is the first example of broad nematode resistance coupled with tolerance to root rejection component.

CULTURAL PRACTICES

Fallow

The length of time that nematodes can survive in a weed-free fallow soil is not definitively known. To interrupt the persistent effects of *X. index* and GFLV, avoid planting grapes for at least 10 years. Research has demonstrated that vines replanted after a 5-year fallow period had *X. index* detectable 6 months after replanting, while GFLV symptoms became apparent in the third year. Meanwhile, the first 4 years of vine growth within the fallowed area was similar to that achieved in an adjacent fumigated soil. A long fallow period only slightly increases the length of time before a new vineyard exhibits virus symptoms. During the fallow period, do not grow crops or plant covers that are hosts to the nematodes present. Until the majority of roots from the previous host crop have decomposed, they can continue to support nematode populations and viruses. A late winter painting of glyphosate hastens root decay.

Cultivar Susceptibility

Greenhouse testing has indicated that grape cultivars on their own roots differ in their susceptibility to root knot nematode. Table 83.4 indicates the relative susceptibility of 14 cultivars as a host for one root knot species, *Meloidogyne arenaria.* Data indicate that commercial cultivars, including Thompson Seedless, Perlette, Zinfandel, Barbera, and Emperor, have a degree of tolerance based on reduced ability of the nematode to penetrate these roots. These findings are supported by field observations concerning the incidence of root galling. It is apparent that the planting of root knot–tolerant cultivars should be considered in coarse soils where root knot damage is normally expected. Conversely, the highly susceptible cultivars should be avoided, as should own-rooted vines on soils or with cropping conditions that predispose them to damage by *Meloidogyne* species.

Sanitation

For noninfested sites or after preplant treatment to reduce nematodes, follow sanitation practices to prevent reintroduction of nematodes into the vineyard. Planting stock that has been certified by a regulatory agency to be free of detectable viruses spread by nematodes should be used. Although not currently required, the nursery should use hot water treatment of dormant planting stock to minimize the spread of nematodes. A 5-minute immersion in each of three water tanks—preheating at 30°C (86°F), hot water at 52.8°C (127°F), and cooling at 23°C (73.5°F)—has been shown to effectively control nematodes. Vineyard equipment should be cleaned with water to remove soil and roots that may harbor plant nematodes. Surface irrigation water and water that spills over the banks of rivers or drainages can be a source of nematodes, as can surface runoff water from infested sites. However, the dominant source of nematodes in California vineyards is the land itself. This can best be determined by knowing the history of the land and reviewing previous nematode sample reports. For more than 50 years, grapevine rootings transported across any one of California's county lines have had to be certified as nematode-free. This sanitation program continues at all commercial California nurseries today.

Rootstocks

Among *Vitis* species, there are an abundance of resistance and tolerance mechanisms useful for defending against soilborne pests. The task of researchers has been to recognize and categorize these resistance mechanisms and also to recognize their limitations at the field level. To replace soil fumigants, growers will need broad resistance against soilborne pests, durable resistance, tolerance to soil pest feeding, and tolerance to the rejection component of the replant problem. Combine these needs with the need to provide vines in balance with prevailing site and management conditions, and the entire process of rootstock selection becomes notably complex. No single rootstock has resistance to all soilborne pests. It follows that a rootstock that was appropriate for a given vineyard site but eventually built up certain soil pest species will probably not be the best rootstock for the following generation of vines planted to that same site. Choosing a rootstock is generally based on the perceived future problems. If the vineyard is in a fine-textured soil where phylloxera is damaging, there is a need for phylloxera resistance. If the soil is sandy, in a warm region, and to be planted to a grape cultivar susceptible to root knot nematode, the use of a nematode-resistant rootstock must be considered. If the soil is medium textured, there may be a need for protection against phylloxera and citrus nematode. Because there are many types of soils, soilborne pests, and climatic regions, one must look at the performance of the rootstock under a variety of soil pest pressures and consider long-term rootstock performance in various production regions and soil types.

When selecting rootstocks for a nematode-infested site, the grower must know whether the rootstock is resistant or susceptible as well as tolerant or intolerant of pest pressure. Root systems are designated resistant if pest reproduction is dramatically limited by the plant. For studies by the senior author, resistance is quantified as fewer than 0.2 endoparasitic nematodes per gram of root during a 2-year evaluation. If the pest is an ectoparasite, designation as resistant is reserved for vines supporting fewer than 2% of nematodes supported by an own-rooted vine. Moderate resistance for an endoparasitic nematode is quantified as 0.21 to 0.6 nematodes per gram of root during a 2-year evaluation, and for ectoparasitic nematodes as less than 5% of that supported by the own-rooted vine. A susceptible designation indicates 0.61 to 180 nematodes per gram of root; above that level, vines are ranked as highly susceptible. For ectoparasitic nematodes, population levels in excess of 5% of the own-rooted level are designated as susceptible.

This designation system can also be used when evaluating the host status of weeds and cover crops, but for grapes and other perennial crops a rigorous evaluation such as the one above is necessary because of the longevity of the crop and also because many nematode populations exist other than those used in the rootstock screening process. A good example of this is *M. chitwoodi*, a root knot species that buries deep within roots of Harmony, Freedom, and other rootstocks, causing visible plant damage, which can be found in soil at less than normal population levels but does not cause visible root galls. Researchers are always seeking quicker methods for evaluating plant resistance. In some cases, evaluations conducted for only 60 days or against only a few nematode species may provide accuracy, but in other cases they may not. For example, 2-year evaluations that indicate a high level of tolerance may or may not indicate the status of tolerance 20 years after planting, particularly if the tolerance is based on resistance.

Resistance mechanisms present in Ramsey, Dog Ridge, 1613C, Harmony, and Freedom are relatively short-lived and commonly consist of only a single resistance mechanism at work. These rootstocks remain as effective today as they were in the 1960s as long as the nematodes in the sites to which the rootstocks are planted have never previously experienced their hypersensitive response mechanism. As invasive organisms enter plant tissues, the most common resistance mechanism they confront is when the plant recognizes their entry and within hours kills root cortical cells in their vicinity. Pest progress is halted because they have been detected and their energy supply is limited. This mechanism is common and useful among plants, but it is also vulnerable. Three years after planting 1613C, 10 years after planting Harmony, or 14 years after planting Freedom into low population levels of *Meloidogyne* species, root knot nematode populations enter roots faster, in greater numbers, and without being detected by the plant. These juveniles possess greater virulence and can also be more damaging than native populations.

The designation of tolerant refers to rootstocks that support abundant nematode reproduction but receive little or no damage due to pest presence. Vines designated as intolerant are susceptible and highly damaged. Harmony and Freedom provide useful examples of nematode tolerance and intolerance. Their hypersensitive response mechanisms provide protection against normal root knot populations; when attacked by low population levels of any *Meloidogyne* species, the feeding process can significantly invigorate vines by 5 to 50%. However, once Harmony or Freedom pathotypes of *Meloidogyne* species become overly abundant, the damage they cause in sandy soil can reduce vine yields by half. The invigoration process gives the appearance of a tolerance mechanism at work, but once the resistance mechanism becomes useless the result is intolerance, and nematode galls can be found on old roots as well as root initials. In many situations vines deemed intolerant are also highly susceptible, but this is not always the case because fewer roots can lead to reduced nematode reproduction.

A century ago researchers seeking resistance to phylloxera noted that galls developed on young roots (nodosites) were not as harmful to the vine as those developed and maintained on older roots (tuberosites). When selecting for nematode resistance, these same mechanisms appear to be at work. As nematodes develop feeding sites among their favored habitat (youngest roots), their offspring continue to feed and reproduce on those same galls for many generations as roots lengthen and

enlarge, unless additional defense mechanisms are present in the rootstock. Consider rootstocks known for their phylloxera tolerance. When fed on by root knot nematodes, some of the rootstocks resistant or tolerant to phylloxera, such as Teleki 5C, SO4, Kober 5BB, Schwarzmann, and 101-14, limit nematode feeding to newest roots, and galls are scarce on older roots. Of 45 commercially available phylloxera- and nematode-resistant rootstocks we have examined, none could defend against the virulent pathotypes of *Meloidogyne* species. In 1988 the search began for broader and more durable resistance to *Meloidogyne* species. This effort resulted in the finding of multiple resistance mechanisms in RS-3, RS-9, 10-23B, and 10-17A rootstocks. These stocks possess hypersensitive response mechanisms in greater abundance than conventional *V. champinii* stocks but also have additional mechanisms, including the ability to dissolve adult females within developing feeding sites, limit nematode damage to nodosites, or in some other manner halt egg production. These rootstocks possess tolerance because they have several resistance mechanisms. This pyramiding of resistance mechanisms, particularly mechanisms that impact adult females, provides a source of durable resistance.

Based on the diversity of soils and soil pests in California, a limited number of nematode-resistant rootstocks are available; information about their resistance or tolerance to the various nematodes has recently increased. Table 83.5 summarizes the performance of nematode-resistant grape rootstocks when grown for 2 years in

the presence of various nematode species. UC and USDA breeding programs continue to search for rootstocks that have durable nematode resistance to multiple species. As new selections become available, they need field evaluation to determine their regional performance under different soils and production systems. They also need testing in fumigated and adjacent nonfumigated sites.

Rootstocks are an expensive investment, and continued research is needed, particularly at the level of field evaluation. Until more information is developed, nematode-resistant rootstock choice largely depends on experiences in a particular district, soil type, and fruiting cultivar. UC farm advisors may be a helpful source of information on local experience with rootstocks.

BIOLOGICAL AGENTS

No biological agents can be added to soil to effectively reduce parasitic nematode populations in a preplant situation. However, biological control is naturally abundant in many vineyards. There are many vineyards where population levels of *X. index* seldom exceed 5 per kg of soil, and others along the north coast where populations of 600 per kg soil are common. Active biocontrol appears to be a major reason for this inconsistency. Ring nematode also appears to be impacted by active biocontrol agents. If soil fumigation is ineffective, the surviving ring nematodes thrive due to reduction in biocontrol agents in the partially fumigated soil. We can also cite examples involving root knot and root lesion nematodes where a dozen biocontrol agents, including the fungus

Table 83.5. Rootstock responses to selected soilborne pests and problems

Pest or disease	Rootstocks							
	Harmony	Freedom	O39-16	RS-3	RS-9	10-17A	Borner	99R
Meloidogyne spp.	R-T	R-T	S-IT	R	R	R	S	S
virulent *Meloidogyne* spp.	HS-IT	HS-IT	S-IT	R	R	R	S	S
Pratylenchus vulnus	S	MR-T	S-IT	R	R	R	—	—
Tylenchulus semipenetrans	S	S-T	S-IT	SS	SS	SS	SS	SS
Xiphinema americanum	S	S	S	S	S	S	S	S
Xiphinema index	R	R	R	MR	R	R	MR	S
Mesocriconema xenoplax	S	S	MR	MR	S	S	MR	S
grape fanleaf virus	IT	IT	T	T	?	IT	T	—
rejection component, RP	IT	IT	T	IT	IT	T	IT	—

Key:

R = Resistant, < 0.2 nematodes/g of root or soil counts < 2% of own-rooted

MR = Moderately resistant, 0.21 to 0.6/g of root or soil counts 2 to 5% of own-rooted

SS = Slightly susceptible, 0.61 to 3.0/g of root, specifically with *T. semipenetrans*

S = Susceptible, 3.1 to 180/g of root or soil counts from 5 to 180% of own-rooted

HS = Highly susceptible, > 180/g of root or soil counts > 180% of own-rooted

T = Tolerance to pest or problem

IT = Intolerance to pest or problem

— No data

Dactylella oviparasitica, appear to work together to keep populations of these nematodes from escalating. These plantings usually follow a history of soil fumigation, a year or more of fallow, and avoidance of highly susceptible rootstocks. Another recent example involves a new species of *Pasteuria* bacteria that feeds exclusively on citrus nematode.

CHEMICAL AGENTS

Fumigants can be highly effective for nematode control when applied properly. They are especially useful in controlling endoparasitic nematodes that survive several years in old root systems of previous perennial crops. See the UC Grape Pest Management Guidelines, www.ipm. ucdavis.edu/PMG/, for pesticides available for preplant treatments. Follow the label application recommendations in all respects. Planting too soon after application (60 winter days) can result in phytotoxicity. Mycorrhizal fungi, which are symbionts and are beneficial to growth of vines, can be killed by fumigation treatments that include the use of a tarp. Vines subsequently planted in these soils may not thrive until the organisms are restored; it is quite common for these mycorrhizae to be introduced along with the new plants even after nursery fumigations.

The major limitation to effective nematode control involves movement of the pesticide to the pest. Successful fumigation requires proper soil preparation and timing rather than an increase in the rate of pesticide application. Proper land preparation also benefits the new vineyard. For example, most new vineyards are planted in replant situations. Nematode damage must be minimized for at least the first 6 months. Research has shown that under optimal site and application conditions, soil fumigations properly applied can provide 6 years of nematode relief. Growers also need to be aware that the best method for conserving vulnerable resistance mechanisms

is a quality soil fumigation prior to vineyard planting.

Most replant situations involve soils that have been subjected to considerable vehicular traffic in previous plantings, leading to soil compaction and stratification of the soil profile. These factors limit soil penetration by new roots, generally detract from vineyard

development, and also hinder good penetration by fumigants. Successful establishment of a vineyard depends on eliminating these physical and biological barriers by a complementary schedule of soil profile modification and fumigation as outlined below.

PREPLANT PREPARATION WHEN USING A FUMIGANT

Use the following guide to prepare a vineyard site following a tree or vine crop where damaging levels of nematodes are present. In sites with shallow or fine-textured soils, some of these guidelines must be modified or are not feasible. In addition, late-fall and winter activities that expose or disturb soil in hillside sites may likely result in erosion during rainfall.

Late summer/early fall, first year:

- Remove existing trees or vines and destroy residues.
- Chisel ground several times to bring roots to the surface for removal and destruction.

Fall/winter/early spring:

- Fallow or crop to small grains.

Spring/summer, second year:

- Harvest grain, if planted. Chisel ground again to maximum depth possible, at least 60 cm (24 in).
- If irrigation is required to settle ground after deep chiseling, complete by early summer.
- In coastal climates, sudangrass may be planted to remove deep soil moisture.
- Level field.

Late summer/early fall, second year:

- Apply fumigants when soil temperatures and soil moisture reach correct levels. Fumigants are most effective when soil is treated while in a drying condition. Fall fumigations are optimal, and October is usually the best month for treatment. See the UC Grape Pest Management Guidelines, www.ipm.ucdavis.edu/PMG/, for nematicides available for preplant applications.

Winter/spring, second year:

- Plant vines.

An Alternative to Soil Fumigation

A method known as starve and switch can be an alternative to soil fumigation. This method is not yet perfected, but it is a useful alternative in California locations where soil fumigants cannot be applied. Starve and switch shows promise in managing nematodes based on studies in perennial crops other than grape. The method consists of starving existing soil ecosystems by applying a systemic herbicide, then waiting 1 year before switching rootstock parentage when replanting. For grape, the systemic herbicide glyphosate has been used and has been applied in February to March, along with a spreader painted to cut vine trunks. Foliar or painted applications from June to November can kill aboveground portions of the vine, but they do not provide adequate root kill. In an effort to conserve resistance mechanisms within new rootstocks, consider applying non-fuming nematicidal agents along the berm via drippers placed at every square foot. Drip tapes of this type would need to be present prior to planting.

In the absence of fumigation, one needs to consider planting rootstocks that are resistant to prevailing soil pests but also are tolerant of the rejection component of the replant problem. Research has shown Demko 10-17A is capable of doing this in nonfumigated sites. A mixture of very small amounts of macro- and micronutrients should be applied at planting if bare-root vines are used. For replant sites where there was no fumigation, it is not recommended to apply composts or manures until vine roots become visibly established and have survived the impact of the rejection component of the replant problem (usually after 1 year). Applications of organic matter prior to that time will defeat the goal of starving the soil ecosystem.

MANAGEMENT GUIDELINES FOR ESTABLISHED VINEYARDS

Soil Amendments

The addition of soil amendments such as composted animal manures or green material, organic fertilizers, or mixtures of beneficial microbes may improve vine growth. Such amendments are complex in composition and have equally complex effects on vineyard soils. The beneficial effects of amendments may include stimulation of soil microbes that feed on nematodes; improvements in soil structure, water retention, and plant nutrition, which reduce stress on nematode-infested plants; and the production of nematicidal breakdown products. Sufficient information is not available to predict the beneficial effects of amendments for the management of a growth problem induced by nematodes. On-site testing, while leaving untreated areas for comparison, is the best method to evaluate the potential benefits of a given amendment.

Cover Crops

Cover crops may influence nematode population and species, but the specific outcome may not be certain. Certain cover crops tend to increase nematode populations; others may decrease damage to grape roots. Unfortunately, research information is limited, but there are specific situations where much is known about the outcome of planting other crops in an infested vineyard. For example, a sod cover crop may minimize buildup of root knot nematode, but new species of root lesion nematode will likely flourish. Salina strawberry clover is a winter legume that, unlike common or purple vetch, resists root knot nematode but is a host for ring nematode. It is desirable to select cover crop species that do not support nematode reproduction or may be antagonistic (table 83.6). As mentioned above, it is important to know what nematode species are present. If two or more species are present, the selection of a nonhost cover crop becomes more difficult.

Avoiding Vine Stress

Cultural practices that enhance nutrient and water uptake serve to reduce plant damage by root knot nematode. Alleviating soil compaction, increasing soil penetrability by water, improving irrigation methods, and correcting nutrient deficiencies may help (fig. 83.4), but these measures are no guarantee that nematode numbers will be reduced. Further, these cultural practices, especially nutrient application, call for greater management attention because of restricted root conditions caused by the presence of root knot nematode.

The advent of drip irrigation has generally increased population levels of some nematodes while simultaneously providing a useful method for reducing vine stress. Overall, these drip systems have provided vine improvement in the presence of limited root systems. In California, 40% of vineyards do not have nematode problems, but in the 60% of sites where nematode

Table 83.6. Host status of cover crops for common nematode species in grape

Cultivar	*Meloidogyne hapla*	*Meloidogyne incognita*	*Meloidogyne javanica*	*Meloidogyne arenaria*
barley, Columbia	host	poor host	good host	host
brome, Blando	host	nonhost	—	—
sudangrass, SS-222	poor host	good host	host	host
strawberry clover, Salina	host	poor host	poor host	nonhost
vetch, Cahaba White	good host	poor host	host trap crop	host
vetch, Nova II	probable host	probable nonhost	probable nonhost	probable nonhost

	Pratylenchus vulnus	*Mesocriconema xenoplax*	*Xiphinema americanum*	*Xiphinema index*
barley, Columbia	nonhost antagonistic	host	antagonistic	nonhost
brome, Blando	nonhost	host	good host	poor host
sudangrass, SS-222	nonhost antagonistic	antagonistic	antagonistic	nonhost
strawberry clover, Salina	probable nonhost	probable host	—	—
vetch, Cahaba White	host	host	antagonistic	nonhost
vetch, Nova II	probable nonhost	probable nonhost	—	—

Note:
—No data available.

Figure 83.4 This photograph was taken near Kingsburg (Fresno County), where root knot nematode and dagger nematode are present at moderate population levels. The beneficial effects from two separate cultural control practices are apparent. (1) The sand streak, outlined in white, crosses two separate properties and two grape cultivars. Muscat of Alexandria displays poorest growth in areas of lowest water-holding capacity (sand). Thompson Seedless exhibits a degree of tolerance to the root knot nematode and sand combination. Thus, cultivar selection can be important. (2) For grower A, the two vine rows on either side of the irrigation line above the arrow exhibit growth comparable to that obtained by grower B. Apparently this is due to leaks in the lines affecting adjacent vines. Notice also that for grower A, the vines on either end of the irrigation run are improved. This situation is not typical and again demonstrates that greater availability of water lessens the damage by root knot nematodes. *Photo*: M. V. McKenry.

feeding is substantial one should carefully consider how deficit irrigation is managed.

BIOLOGICAL AGENTS

No live biological control agents are currently known to economically reduce nematode populations, but toxins produced by biological agents are being marketed as nematicides. Even after considerable study, the field application of live organisms has not provided adequate nematode relief. There is, however, optimism that such microbes will eventually have field value. This optimism is based on the fact that many soils contain predators and parasites of nematodes that appear to contribute to some level of natural control. Practices such as cover cropping or organic amendments may increase this type of biological activity in soils.

CHEMICAL AGENTS

Nematodes are most numerous beneath the vines along the berm. Any nematicidal agents delivered by drip must be coupled with an irrigation to release, activate, and move the toxicant to its target. Placement and delivery are key components to economical treatment with nematicide. Drip systems have provided an effective and economical way to deliver toxicants to root systems. Currently, few nematicidal agents are available to California growers because of the need for short half-lives to avoid groundwater contamination and the need for chemicals with reduced VOC (volatile organic compound) emissions. As new nematicidal agents do become available, an important aspect of their use will involve timing of their application to meet the timing of the root flush. Some nematicides can interfere with normal nematode life processes such as feeding, root penetration, egg hatching, locomotion, and sensory perception at very low concentrations. Additionally, nematicidal agents are seldom effective for more than 60 days after treatment but during those 60 days can greatly alter the life cycle of the nematode thus

PART 6: NEMATODES

469

providing as much as 6 months of nematode reduction.

Most plant-parasitic nematode species, especially root knot nematodes, penetrate new root tips, thus targeting new root growth. Newly planted grapevines produce roots throughout much of the year. Vines that have been root pruned by mechanical or biological means may also have prolonged periods of root initiation. Roots in the surface 15 cm (6 in) of soil can exhibit new growth at various times of the year, but the root system of an established vine can be characterized by two growth flushes at two discrete periods of the year. The major flush begins after budbreak, with a peak in activity at bloom. For a 2-month period, new roots less than an inch long become evident across the root system. Most of these new roots are sloughed off within 2 months. By veraison there are very few discernible root initials. Then, just after harvest, if moisture is adequate, a second flush of root initiation can occur. Note that the timing of root flushes can vary depending on year and location.

Although millions of nematodes can feed on each grapevine, nematodes such as the root knot nematode become established during these two periods of root initiation, a period of about 4 months each year. It is during these two periods that nematicidal agents have been applied to disrupt successful attack by the portion of the nematode population poised for root penetration. With several treatments per year, root knot nematode can be controlled in vineyards. If

a vineyard does not have a nematode problem or has another factor responsible for reduced vigor, it will not respond to treatments.

Nematicide applications to non–drip-irrigated vineyards have also been tested. Use of a French plow furrow to apply the nematicidal agent to a moist surface followed by irrigation has provided some improvement in growth in May or immediately postharvest, but a greater number of furrow-irrigated vineyards have not responded to this treatment. Generally, treatment rates must be higher than those for drip-irrigated vineyards, and yield improvement has not been as dramatic as with chemigation treatment applied through the drip irrigation system.

In 2010 a completely new foliar-applied nematicide containing spirotetramat was registered for nematode control. Research has indicated that specific application guidelines need to be followed to attain optimal performance from this translocated nematicide.

See the UC IPM Grape Pest Management Guidelines, www.ipm.ucdavis.edu/PMG/, for nematicides available for postplant applications.

REFERENCES

Cohen, S., and T. Martin. 2009. Field fumigation. Vol. 9 in UC IPM Pesticide Application Compendium. Oakland: University of California Agriculture and Natural Resources Publication 9005, http://anrcatalog.ucdavis.edu/Items/9005.aspx. For DPR addendum (2011), see http://www.cdpr.ca.gov/docs/license/pubs/fieldfum_studyguide_addendum.pdf.

Ferris, H., and W. A. Hunt. 1979. Journal of Nematology 11(2): 168–174.

Lowe, K. M., and M. A. Walker. 2006. Genetic linkage map of the interspecific grape rootstock cross Ramsey (*Vitis champinii*) × Riparia Gloire (*Vitis riparia*). Theoretical and Applied Genetics 112:1582–1592.

McKenry, M. V., and S. A. Anwar. 2006. Nematode and grape rootstock interactions including an improved understanding of tolerance. Journal of Nematology 38(3): 312–318.

McKenry, M. V., and P. A. Roberts. 1985. Phytonematology study guide on nematodes and nematicides. Oakland: University of California Division of Agriculture and Natural Resources Publication 4045.

Téliz, D., B. B. Landa, H. F. Rapoport, F. Pérez Camacho, R. M. Jiménez-Díaz, and P. Castillo. 2007. Plant-parasitic nematodes infecting grapevine in southern Spain and susceptible reaction to root-knot nematodes of rootstocks reported as moderately resistant. Plant Disease 91:1147–1154.

Zasada, I. A., J. M. Halbrendt, N. Kokalis-Burelle, J. LaMondia, M. V. McKenry, and J. W. Noling. 2010. Managing nematodes without methyl bromide. Annual Review of Phytopathology 48:311–328.

Part 7

Vertebrates

Syrah

84 VERTEBRATES

Terrell P. Salmon, Rex E. Marsh, and Larry J. Bettiga

MAMMALS

Rodents and rabbits, as well as other small mammals and large mammals such as deer and feral pigs, are found in many California vineyards, where they cause considerable damage, especially to young vines. This damage can lower yields and can kill entire vines. It can also interfere with cultural operations such as irrigation and harvest. Vineyards should be routinely monitored to detect potentially damaging vertebrate pest populations.

Weedy ditches, fence lines, adjacent fields, pastures, and brush or trash piles are excellent harborage for rodents and rabbits. Eliminating or reducing heavy weed cover in or near the vineyard also improves your detection of certain animals.

To achieve a successful vertebrate pest control program, identify the species causing the problem; alter the habitat, if possible, to make the area less favorable to the pest; if population reduction is necessary, use the control method appropriate for the location, time of year, and other environmental conditions; and establish a monitoring system to detect reinfestation so you can decide when further control is necessary.

Baits, fumigants, traps, and other supplies to control vertebrate pests are generally available at farm supply and hardware stores, nurseries, garden shops, and sometimes from the county agricultural commissioner. To locate needed materials or to obtain information, consult a UCCE farm advisor or agricultural commissioner.

TIMING CONTROL

To some, the answer to when to control a particular pest is "whenever a population is detected." While this response is appropriate for some wildlife pests in certain situations, an effective pest management program requires monitoring for pests to determine whether population density has reached the threshold level (the level where control is economically justified). Unfortunately, threshold levels for rodent and other vertebrate pests in vineyards have not always been determined. Because damage caused by many vertebrates tends to be concentrated, the tolerable level is low; in some cases, it is zero.

The timing of a control program, as well as the methods and materials to use, depends on the pest species, how the area is managed, the availability of equipment and labor, and other factors.

LEGAL CONSTRAINTS OF CONTROL

Ground squirrels, meadow voles, and pocket gophers are classified as nongame mammals by the California Fish and Game Code. When they are found to be injuring or threatening growing crops or other property, they may be taken (e.g., trapped or shot) at any time and in any lawful manner by the owner or tenant of the premises. Jackrabbits, cottontails, and brush rabbits are classified as game mammals by the California Fish and Game Code. Those threatening or injuring growing crops or other property may be taken at any time or in any lawful manner by the owner or tenant of the premises. In California, deer are also classified as game mammals. Rarely can a permit to control deer damage to vineyards by shooting be obtained from a local game warden; however, shooting is not always successful. Deterrents such as fences, barriers, and repellents can all be used without a permit.

ENDANGERED SPECIES GUIDELINES

In some areas, vineyards are located within the range of federal- and state-listed endangered species. The species likely to be of concern when using traps or poison baits are the San Joaquin kit fox, several species of rare kangaroo rats, and, where burrow fumigants are used, the blunt-nosed leopard lizard and tiger salamander. Be aware of the ranges of these species in your area. Special guidelines apply to the use of toxic baits and fumigants for vertebrate pest control in these areas; these guidelines are described briefly in table 84.1 and drawings of bait stations are given in figures 84.1 and 84.2. Your county agricultural commissioner has the latest detailed maps that show the ranges of endangered species and the latest information on restrictions that apply to pest control activities in those areas. You also can get more information on endangered species regulations from the California

Department of Pesticide Regulation website, http://www.cdpr.ca.gov/docs/es/index.htm.

CALIFORNIA GROUND SQUIRREL

Damage to vineyards by the California ground squirrel (*Ostospermophilus beecheyi*) is often spotty, but because it lives in colonies, damage can become significant if populations are not controlled.

DESCRIPTION

A medium-sized rodent, the adult has a head and body 9 to 11 inches (23 to 28 cm) long and a somewhat bushy tail that is about as long as the body (fig. 84.3). The fur is a mottled dark and light brown or gray. Adults weigh 1 to 2.5 pounds (2.2 to 5.5 kg). Ground squirrels live in colonies of 2 to more than 20 animals. Their underground burrows have extensive interconnecting systems. When frightened, they seek cover in their burrows.

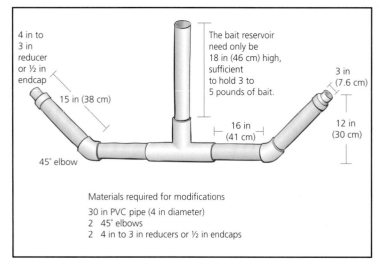

Figure 84.1 Ground squirrel bait station designed for use within the range of endangered kangaroo rats and San Joaquin kit fox.

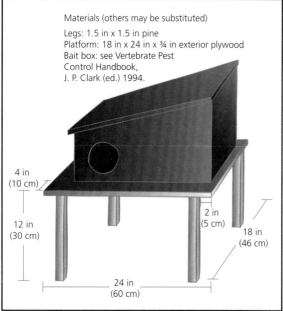

Figure 84.2 Platform design for elevating ground squirrel bait station to prevent access by kangaroo rats. This station must be constructed rigidly enough and be anchored to the ground appropriately so that it cannot be tipped easily. *Source:* UC IPM.

Table 84.1. Guidelines on the use of toxic baits and burrow fumigants within the ranges of endangered species; where more than one species occurs, the most restrictive limitations apply

Endangered species	Control	Target pest	Guidelines
all	acute poison baits	pocket gophers	No restrictions on bait placed directly in burrows by hand or by mechanical bait applicator.
blunt-nosed leopard lizard giant garter snake kangaroo rats San Joaquin kit fox	burrow fumigants	ground squirrels pocket gophers	Use must be supervised by someone trained to distinguish active burrows or dens of target species from those of nontarget species. Only active burrows of target species may be treated. Contact your county agricultural commissioner for information on training.
giant garter snake	burrow fumigants	ground squirrels pocket gophers	In addition to above restrictions, use is prohibited from October 1 through April 30 except in areas under active cultivation* or on the inner bank (water side) of water supply channels.
kangaroo rats	anticoagulant and acute poison baits (bait station)	ground squirrels	Use of toxic baits is prohibited unless used in bait stations specially designed to allow access by pest species but not by kangaroo rats OR bait stations are elevated to prevent access by kangaroo rats and designed to prevent spillage OR bait is placed in stations only during daylight hours and removed, or station entrances are closed by dusk.
	anticoagulant and acute poison baits (broadcast)	ground squirrels voles	Broadcast treatments can be made only in areas under active cultivation that are separated from native vegetation by at least 10 yards (9.1 m) of untreated crop or cultivated ground.
San Joaquin kit fox	all baiting programs listed below for these target pests	ground squirrels voles jackrabbits	Carcass removal should be part of any baiting program that may result in carcasses remaining above ground. Begin monitoring for carcasses 3 days after baiting starts and continue until at least 5 days after baiting stops. Handle carcasses carefully to avoid contact with parasites such as fleas and ticks. Bury carcasses deep enough or otherwise dispose of them so that they are inaccessible to wildlife. **Prebaiting:** Prebaiting with untreated grains such as oats or barley is recommended to make baiting more effective and shorten the time required for baiting. Do not prebait with milo or cracked corn, which are highly attractive to birds.
	anticoagulant baits (bait station)	ground squirrels	**Formulation:** Active ingredient not to exceed 0.005% in bait formulations used in bait stations. **Bait station design:** Openings not to exceed 3 inches (7.6 cm) in diameter, designed to control spillage, staked to prevent ripping, not filled beyond capacity, and never with more than 10 pounds (4.5 kg) of bait. **Bait station monitoring:** Must be monitored for signs of spillage, tampering, moisture, and depletion; monitored at least weekly after bait feeding begins; kept replenished; bait removed immediately after feeding ceases. If subsequent baiting needed, wait at least 2 weeks; this minimizes exposure of nontarget species without jeopardizing good pest control.
		jackrabbits	Self-dispensing bait stations can be used only if bait acceptance is first determined, stations are monitored and carcasses removed as described above, baiting ceases when feeding stops, and stations are used only where rabbits are active. Pelletized baits are prohibited.
	anticoagulant baits (broadcast)	ground squirrels	**Spot baiting:** Scatter handfuls of bait (about 10 handfuls per pound, or 22 handfuls per kilogram) evenly over 40 to 50 square feet (3.7 to 4.7 sq m) near active burrows or runways. Repeat every other day until feeding ceases. **Mechanical bait spreader:** apply at rate of 10 pounds per swath acre (11.3 kg per ha) through infested area. Make second application 2 or 3 days later. Pelletized baits may not be broadcast within kit fox ranges.
		ground squirrels voles	**Broadcast or spot baiting:** Active ingredient no greater than 0.01%; apply only after prebaiting with untreated bait and determining that untreated bait is taken; do not pile bait or place directly in burrows; do not reapply when significant quantities of previously applied bait remain; survey for carcasses as described above. Pelletized baits may not be broadcast or used for spot treatments within kit fox ranges.
	acute poison baits (bait station)	ground squirrels	Pelletized baits: May be used for ground squirrels only in bait stations designed to exclude the kit fox as described above.
	acute poison baits (broadcast)	ground squirrels voles	Grain baits that are not pelletized may be broadcast for ground squirrel or vole control. Follow recommendations for prebaiting and carcass removal.

Sources: Information compiled from the U.S. Environmental Protection Agency draft bulletin Protecting Endangered Species Interim Measures for Use of Pesticides, February 2000. Bulletins for each county and restrictions pertaining to specific locations can be found at the DPR website, www.cdpr.ca.gov/docs/es/index.htm, and in bulletins available from county agricultural commissioners.

Note:
*Areas under active cultivation are defined as areas that have been tilled within the previous year or that are irrigated by furrow, flood, or overlapping sprinklers.

Figure 84.3 Uncontrolled, the California ground squirrel can cause significant damage to young grapevines. *Photo*: J. K. Clark.

BIOLOGY

Ground squirrel populations often are particularly dense in areas disturbed by humans, such as along roads, ditch banks, fencerows, around buildings, and within or bordering agricultural crops. They tend to avoid thick chaparral and dense woods, as well as very moist areas, and spend much of their time in their burrows.

Active during the day, they are easily seen from spring to fall, especially in warm, sunny weather. During winter most hibernate, but some young remain active, especially where winters are mild. Most adults also aestivate (hibernate in summer) during the hottest months.

Ground squirrels breed once per year and have an average litter of eight. The young remain in the burrow about 6 weeks before they go above ground. During early spring they eat green vegetation such as grasses and forbs. When these dry, they switch to seeds, grains, and nuts. At any time of year, they can eat fruit and vegetables as well as bark from vines and trees.

INJURY

Ground squirrels gnaw vines, particularly young ones, removing bark and often girdling the trunk. They may also gnaw surface plastic irrigation pipe and may feed on vine shoots and fruit. It is their burrowing, however, that can be the most destructive.

Burrows average 4 inches (10 cm) in diameter, are 5 to 30 feet (1.5 to 9 m) or more long, and are located 2.5 to 4 feet (75 cm to 1.2 m) below the ground surface. During digging, large quantities of soil and small rock are deposited on the soil surface. The mounds and burrow openings are hazardous to machinery and interfere with harvesting. Frequent burrowing around vines can damage root systems and possibly kill plants. Burrowing beneath buildings and other vineyard structures sometimes results in their partial or complete destruction.

CONTROL METHODS

Ground squirrel damage calls for a control program of procedures suitable for the situation and time of year. Figure 84.4 depicts the activity periods of ground squirrels

Figure 84.4 Reproductive cycle and primary diet of the California ground squirrel relative to calendar months, and the best times to carry out specific types of control actions. The timing of squirrel activities varies somewhat from region to region; activities are earlier at lower elevations and more southern latitudes. Prolonged winter rains and changes in average daily temperatures also influence when activities occur. *Source:* UC IPM.

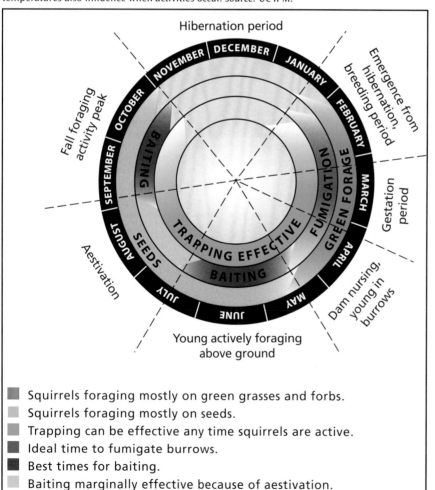

- Squirrels foraging mostly on green grasses and forbs.
- Squirrels foraging mostly on seeds.
- Trapping can be effective any time squirrels are active.
- Ideal time to fumigate burrows.
- Best times for baiting.
- Baiting marginally effective because of aestivation.

and appropriate timing for control measures. These procedures should result in acceptable reductions in populations.

Fumigation

Ground squirrels can be killed by toxic gases introduced into their burrows. Gas cartridges (smoke bombs) and aluminum phosphide are two examples (fig. 84.5). Some materials, such as aluminum phosphide, require a use permit from the county agricultural commissioner. Never fumigate burrows near or beneath buildings. Fumigation is most effective in spring or when soil moisture is high. At those times, gas is contained within the burrow system and does not diffuse into the small cracks that are often present in dry soil.

Thoroughly treat and seal all burrow entrances in the area. After 1 to 2 days, re-treat any newly opened burrows. Fumigation is not effective during hibernation or aestivation because the squirrels plug the burrow with soil. These plugs cannot be seen from the burrow entrance.

Because gases emitted from some fumigants occasionally ignite, do not use them where a fire hazard exists, such as near dry grass or other flammable material or under buildings. Follow label directions carefully and understand the hazards when using fumigants.

A relatively new fumigation device applies propane and oxygen into the burrow and ignites the gas mixture to create an explosion. This method controls squirrels by the concussion blast. The effectiveness of this method in vineyards has not been evaluated.

Toxic Baits (Rodenticides)

Baiting can be the most cost-effective method for controlling ground squirrels, especially for large populations. Bait consists of treated grain or pellets formulated with a poison registered for ground squirrel control. To be effective, the bait must be used at a time of year when ground squirrels are feeding on seeds (see fig. 84.4) and will readily accept baits. Baits are most effective in late spring or early summer. In fall months, squirrels tend to cache seeds or bait, so it may require more bait to control the population. Toxic baits to control ground squirrels are available over the counter and at many agricultural commissioner offices. Some baits may require a permit from the county agricultural commissioner. When using toxic bait to control rodents, follow label instructions carefully and use only for animals listed on the label.

Anticoagulant baits

Specific multiple-feeding anticoagulant baits are registered and commonly used to control ground squirrels because they are effective and are relatively safe to humans and pets. Anticoagulants interfere with an animal's blood-clotting mechanism, eventually leading to death. They are effective only when consumed in several feedings over 5 or more days. These features, as well as an effective antidote (vitamin K_1), make use of anticoagulant baits relatively safe around children and pets.

Anticoagulant baits can be used in bait stations, as spot treatments near burrows, or broadcast over large infested areas. Bait stations are small structures that the squirrel must enter to eat the bait. They contain sufficient bait for

Figure 84.5 Fumigation techniques: (A) Insert gas cartridge into burrow; (B) light cartridge fuse; (C) use shovel handle to push cartridge into opening; and (D) cover burrow opening with soil. *Photos*: J. K. Clark.

repeated feedings and also help prevent children and pets from reaching the bait. Follow the bait label regarding construction and placement of bait stations.

Various types of bait stations can be used; all of them are designed to let squirrels in but to exclude larger animals. One design is made of PVC pipe (fig. 84.6). To construct these stations, make the openings about 3 to 4 inches (7.5 to 10 cm) in diameter and incorporate baffles to keep the bait inside the station. Specially designed stations must be used within the ranges of the San Joaquin kit fox and endangered kangaroo rats to ensure that these species are excluded (see table 84.1 and figs. 84.1 and 84.2). Place bait stations near runways or burrows and secure them so they cannot be tipped over. If squirrels are moving into the vineyard from adjacent property, place bait stations along the perimeter of the vineyard where squirrels are invading, one station every 100 feet (30 m). Use more stations when the

number of squirrels is high. Check bait stations daily at first, then as often as needed to keep the bait replenished. If bait feeding is interrupted for more than 2 or 3 days, the bait's effectiveness is greatly decreased. Be sure to pick up any bait that is spilled and replace bait that is wet or moldy. Successful baiting usually requires 2 to 4 weeks. Continue to supply bait until feeding ceases and you observe no squirrels; then properly dispose of unused bait.

When specified on the label, anticoagulant baits can be applied as spot or broadcast treatments, which usually saves on bait compared with using bait stations. For spot baiting, scatter bait (1 lb is about 10 placements) evenly over 40 to 50 square feet (3.7 to 4.7 sq m) near active burrows and reapply according to label directions, usually every other day for three or four treatments. Scattering takes advantage of the ground squirrels' natural foraging behavior and minimizes risks to nontarget

species. Never pile the bait on the ground; this increases the hazard to livestock and certain nontarget wildlife. Broadcasting bait with a hand or mechanical seed spreader is very effective, especially when larger areas are to be treated. Research has shown broadcast baiting to be very effective while at the same time reducing secondary hazards associated with anticoagulant baits. Since squirrels poisoned with anticoagulants have some toxicant in their tissues, pick up and dispose of carcasses whenever possible to prevent poisoning of dogs or other scavengers. Burying is a good method as long as carcasses are buried deep enough to discourage scavengers. Do not handle carcasses with bare hands; use a shovel, gloves, or a plastic bag inverted over your hands.

Acute poison baits

Also available for controlling ground squirrels, acute poison baits (e.g., zinc phosphide) require only one feeding to be effective. Control is usually achieved in 1 to 3 days. They are applied by hand or by mechanical broadcaster. Place near a burrow or where squirrels are feeding. Ground squirrels are good foragers and can easily find broadcast grain. Do not pile bait as this may increase hazards to nontarget animals. As with all pesticides, follow label instructions carefully.

Consult the county agricultural commissioner, the California Department of Pesticide Regulation website, http://www.cdpr.ca.gov/docs/es/index.htm, or the latest recommendations before using poison baits in areas that are within the range of endangered species.

Figure 84.6 Four-inch plastic pipe can be used to construct a bait station for ground squirrels. The 4-inch pipe must have its entrance restricted to 3 inches when used within the range of the San Joaquin kit fox. Place baffles inside the pipe to keep bait inside the station. *Photo*: L. J. Bettiga.

Traps

Traps are practical devices for controlling ground squirrels in small areas where their numbers are low. Live-catch traps are effective, but disposing of the animal will present a problem. Because ground squirrels can carry diseases and are agricultural pests, the California Department of Fish and Wildlife prohibits their transport and release.

Several types of traps kill ground squirrels. Most work best if you place them on the ground near burrows or runways. Walnuts, almonds, oats, barley, and melon rinds are attractive baits. Place bait tied to or well behind the trigger. Bait the traps, but do not set them for several days to allow the squirrels to become accustomed to them. After they take the bait, rebait and set the traps.

A box-type squirrel trap (fig. 84.7), available commercially or constructed from a gopher box trap, kills ground squirrels quickly.

To modify a gopher trap, lengthen the trigger slot with a rat-tail file or pocketknife so the trigger can swing unhindered and the squirrel can pass beneath the swinging loop of the unset trap. Remove the back of the trap and replace it with wire mesh. This allows the animal to see the bait from both ends but prevents it from entering the trap from the back. Box traps can be placed in pairs (see fig. 84.7), in groups, or inside larger boxes. Place the traps so that nontarget animals are not likely to be caught, for example, inside a larger box with openings no larger than 3 inches (7.5 cm), which is just large enough for ground squirrels.

An all-metal tunnel or tube trap can also be used for kill-trapping ground squirrels (fig. 84.8). It is best set directly in the squirrel's trail and can be baited with grain such as oats or barley. These traps offer good protection for larger nontarget animals.

Conibear traps are most commonly placed unbaited in the burrow entrance, where squirrels are trapped as they pass through (fig. 84.9). When used in this manner, they are effective regardless of what the squirrels are feeding on. If you are using this type of trap within the range of the San Joaquin kit fox, you must place the trap in a covered box with an entrance no larger than 3 inches (7.5 cm) wide to exclude the fox, or you must spring the traps at dusk and reset them again in the morning.

Other ground squirrel traps are available. All squirrel traps have strong springs that are capable of killing similar-sized animals and can cause hand injuries if mishandled by humans. Do not place traps where they pose a hazard to children, nontarget wildlife, pets, or poultry.

Natural Control

As with all animals, natural constraints such as inadequate food and shelter, predators, disease, and bad weather can limit populations. Experience has shown, however, that in vineyard locations the point at which populations level off naturally is often too high for vineyard performance.

Ground squirrels generally prefer more-open grassy areas to feed, although they will select trees, rock outcroppings, or abandoned farm equipment under which to burrow. Removing brush piles and debris not only makes an area less desirable to them, it also makes detection of them and their burrows easier, aids in monitoring

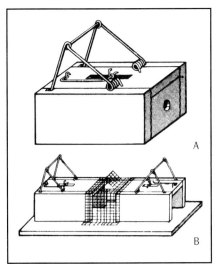

Figure 84.7 Single box-type gopher traps (A) can be used for ground squirrels. They can be used in pairs by removing the backs, connecting the two traps with wire mesh, and attaching them to a board (B). *Source:* UC IPM.

Figure 84.8 The tube- or tunnel-type trap kills animals that pass through it. *Photo:* J. K. Clark.

Figure 84.9 Conibear trap set in a burrow entrance. Secure trap with a stake. *Photo:* J. K. Clark.

populations, and improves access during control operations.

Once squirrels have been removed from an area, the remaining empty burrow systems are highly likely to be reoccupied by squirrels from adjacent areas. Tractor-drawn soil rippers may be used to destroy unoccupied burrows to a depth of 3 to 4 feet (1 to 1.2 m), reducing the number of empty burrows for reoccupation.

Many predators, including hawks, eagles, rattlesnakes, gopher snakes, and coyotes, eat ground squirrels. In most cases, predators are not able to keep populations below the level at which they become pests. Predators may prevent them from invading marginal habitats where cover is not abundant.

MONITORING GUIDELINES

Once damage has been controlled, continue to monitor for ground squirrel reinfestations. Observe areas where they may live from an isolated structure or automobile during morning hours, when squirrels are most active. They may move in from other areas and cause new damage within a short time. Ideally, maintain records on the types of control used and their success, as well as on changes in the squirrel population. Coincide monitoring with seasons of peak activity, as in early spring, early summer, and fall. Experience has shown that it is easier, less expensive, and less time consuming to control a population before it builds up and causes excessive damage.

MEADOW VOLE

Meadow voles (*Microtus* spp.) are represented by several similar species in California. Also called field or meadow mice, they are essentially a grass-loving species, feeding on stems, roots, and seeds, but they may feed on the cambium layer beneath the bark of grapevines and trees. During favorable seasons, meadow voles can cause gnawing damage severe enough to kill many vines, especially young plantings. Populations frequently develop in vineyards or on their borders and fence lines where grass, brush, and trash may accumulate or where grass or cover crops build up around vines, providing voles with ample food and shelter.

DESCRIPTION

Meadow voles are small rodents with heavy bodies, short legs and tails, and small, rounded ears (fig. 84.10). Their long, coarse, fur is blackish brown to grayish brown. Fully grown, they are 4 to 5 inches (10 to 12.5 cm) long. They are larger than a house mouse but smaller than a rat.

BIOLOGY

They are active both day and night and all year. Females bear several litters each year, with peaks of reproduction in spring and fall. Populations cycle, climaxing every 4 to 7 years and declining fairly rapidly. Peak vole populations may reach several hundred or more per acre in vineyards.

INJURY

Meadow voles damage or kill grapevines by eating through the bark to the cambium layer, completely or partially girdling the trunk from just below the soil line up to 2 to 6 inches (5 to 15 cm) above it (fig. 84.11).

Figure 84.10 California meadow vole. *Photo*: J. K. Clark.

Figure 84.11 Girdling of grapevines indicates meadow vole activity. *Photo*: W. R. Clark.

CONTROL METHODS

Preventing meadow vole damage usually requires keeping population levels low by removing or reducing vegetative cover. Removing cover also makes detection easier. When removing cover fails or is impractical, undertake a program to reduce the population. Because these animals can do severe damage and because their reproductive rate is rapid, modify the habitat or reduce the population using toxic baits before numbers explode.

Habitat Modification

In deterring meadow voles, habitat modification is particularly effective. Weeds, heavy mulch, and dense vegetative cover encourage them by providing food and protection from predators and environmental stresses. Clearing dense, grassy areas adjacent to the vineyard reduces the area from which voles invade. Weed-free strips around the vineyard can also help protect vines. The wider the cleared strip, the less apt meadow voles will be to cross in the open and become established. A minimum width of 15 feet (4.5 m) is recommended, but even that can be ineffective when numbers are high. Buffer strips are most useful around young vines.

Commercially produced trunk protectors, available for attachment around individual vines, may offer some protection. Plastic, wire, or metal barriers at least 12 inches (30 cm) high with a mesh size of ¼ inch (6 mm) or less exclude meadow voles. They rarely climb such barriers, but they may dig beneath them. To prevent digging,

bury the bottom edge 6 to 10 inches (15 to 25 cm).

Toxic Baits (Rodenticides)

When meadow voles are causing damage, the only immediately effective control is the use of toxic baits. For the safety of children, pets, and nontarget animals, carefully follow product label instructions.

Anticoagulant baits

Because anticoagulant baits are slow acting, they must be consumed over several days to be most effective. Many brands are available, but meadow voles must be listed on the product label. Regular house mouse bait is not registered for meadow voles and should not be used.

The bait must be made available for 4 to 6 consecutive days and is placed in runways or next to burrow openings for spot treatments. When spot or broadcast baiting, be sure to treat the entire infested area with bait. Be aware of any restrictions related to endangered species in the area. Follow the label instructions for application methods for the product being used.

If stated on the product label, paraffin bait blocks can be used in high-moisture areas to control meadow voles. Place them in runways and near burrow openings. Replace them as they are eaten and remove those that remain when feeding stops. Do not use bait blocks where children or pets may pick them up.

Acute poison baits

Baits such as those prepared with zinc phosphide give rapid vole control, as this acute toxicant

generally kills within 24 hours and is much less expensive than anticoagulant baits because lower rates of application are needed. Acute poisons are especially useful for broadcast application over large areas. Follow the label directions for spot and broadcast applications. These baits can induce bait shyness, a condition that results when voles eat only enough bait to make them sick. When this happens, the voles will not eat the bait again for 6 months or more. To prevent this, use the bait according to label directions and do not treat with acute poison baits more often than every 6 months. Acute poison baits act rapidly; dead voles may be found within 12 hours of baiting. Bury all dead voles or place them in plastic bags and dispose of them in the trash. Handle them only with disposable gloves or inverted plastic bags.

Traps

Because voles are often very numerous and multiply very rapidly, trapping is impractical for control. Ordinary mouse-sized snap traps are, however, sometimes used to collect specimens for identification or to determine the size of an infestation.

Natural Control

As with all animals, nature eventually places constraints on numbers, so one alternative is to wait for the voles to limit themselves. However, the natural population peak is often too high and damage occurs. Predators such as hawks and owls eat meadow voles. Barn owls can be encouraged by placing nest boxes in and around vineyards. In most cases, however, predators are unable to keep populations in vineyards below damaging levels.

MONITORING GUIDELINES

Voles mostly damage vines in winter or early spring, so during this time monthly inspection of vineyards and surrounding fields is essential for spotting vole activity and population increases, especially in heavily vegetated areas where new runways and burrows (fig. 84.12) may indicate feeding. Voles are usually found in areas marked by numerous surface runways 1 to 2 inches (2.5 to 5 cm) wide through matted grass. They are active all year, regardless of the weather, and are generally most active during the day. Brownish feces and short pieces of grass stems deposited along their runways indicate recent activity. Burrows are short and relatively shallow, have numerous round openings, and frequently contain nesting and storage chambers.

The number of runways, the amount of freshly cut vegetation, and the amount of fresh droppings found in runways indicate the relative number present. Any sign of activity in the vineyard calls for measures to prevent vine damage.

POCKET GOPHER

Pocket gophers (*Thomomys* spp.) are frequently encountered in vineyards. In California, Botta's pocket gopher (*T. bottae*) is the most common species. Active throughout the year, it can increase to high numbers and if uncontrolled can cause damage and loss of vines during the vineyard's lifetime and can also interfere with irrigation and other cultural operations.

DESCRIPTION

Stout bodied and short legged, these rodents have two pairs of prominent incisor teeth (fig. 84.13). They have small eyes and ears and their external, fur-lined cheek pouches open outside the lips on each side of the mouth and are used for carrying food and nesting materials. The head and body together measure about 6 to 8 inches (15 to 20 cm), and the scantily haired tail is less than half the body length. The color ranges from yellow-brown to gray-brown. Adults weigh about 4 ounces (113 g).

BIOLOGY

Five species of pocket gopher are found throughout California except in rocky outcrops, high mountain meadows, and some desert areas. They are most common where ample moisture and good soil encourage abundant plant growth. Named for their cheek pouches (or pockets), they feed primarily on succulent underground parts of plants, but they do pull entire plants underground. At certain times they graze on plants above ground near their burrow openings.

Pocket gophers live underground and rarely travel above ground, except when the young leave the nest after weaning to search for new homes. They are extremely territorial, so you rarely will find more than one gopher per burrow system, except when the females are with their young. A burrow system can cover several hundred square feet and consists of main tunnels and side tunnels for feeding or to push excavated soil to the surface. Main burrows are normally located 6 to 18 inches (15 to 45 cm) under the surface, but they

can be deeper. The conspicuous, fan-shaped mounds that are formed over the openings of lateral tunnels are the most obvious signs of gopher infestation (fig. 84.14). These tunnel openings are almost always closed with a soil plug, stabilizing the burrow's temperature and humidity at close to optimal conditions.

In uncultivated and unirrigated areas, pocket gophers breed after rains begin and green forage becomes plentiful. They produce one litter per year; on cultivated lands, they can breed up to three

Figure 84.12 Burrows of California meadow vole. *Photo*: J. K. Clark.

Figure 84.13 Pocket gophers damage roots and gnaw bark of grapevines. *Photo*: J. K. Clark.

Figure 84.14 Typical crescent-shaped pocket gopher mound. *Photo*: J. K. Clark.

times per year. Litters average five young. After weaning, the young are expelled from the burrow to find new territories. Pocket gophers are active all year and may reach densities of 50 or more per acre. They prefer legumes such as alfalfa and clover and other fleshy-rooted plants.

INJURY

Pocket gophers eat the below-ground portions of plants and some aboveground material. They damage grapevines when they cut roots or gnaw bark from the roots or trunk. In a relatively short time, they can completely girdle vines a few inches below the soil line, particularly damaging newly planted vineyards or young replanted stock. Pocket gophers are also known to gnaw and damage plastic irrigation pipe, and their burrows can divert irrigation water, sometimes causing extensive soil erosion.

Damage by pocket gophers may be distinguished from that of other animals because it normally occurs several inches below the soil surface. They usually remove bark tissue down to the cambium layer. In contrast, meadow voles generally start feeding from the soil level upward for several inches and often leave bits of bark attached to the wood. Gnawing marks of these animals are different and may aid

in identifying the damaging species. Because gopher damage is below ground and frequently not visible, it often goes undetected until a vine exhibits stress or dies.

CONTROL METHODS

Successful control depends on early detection and promptly applied control measures appropriate to the location and situation. Gophers in vineyards are mostly controlled with poison baits and sometimes traps. A program incorporating these methods should reduce their damage.

Successful trapping or hand-baiting depends on accurately locating the gopher's main burrow, which is usually 6 to 14 inches deep (15 to 35 cm). The crescent-shaped mounds visible above ground are connected to the burrow by lateral tunnels. Because gophers plug the lateral tunnels, trapping and baiting in them is not as successful.

Use a gopher probe to locate the main burrow (figs. 84.15–84.16). Probes are commercially available or can be constructed from a pipe, wooden dowel, or stick. The freshest mounds indicate recent gopher activity, and a small circle or depression represents the plugged lateral tunnel. This plug is generally bordered on three sides by soil, giving a crescent shape to the mound. Begin probing 8 to

12 inches (20 to 30 cm) from the mound's plug side. When the probe penetrates the gopher's burrow, it should drop suddenly about 2 inches (5 cm). Often the main burrow will be located between two mounds. To find it, you may have to probe repeatedly, but experience will improve your skill.

Toxic Baits (Rodenticides)
Commonly used pocket gopher baits are formulated with an acute poison such as strychnine (a restricted-use material requiring a permit from the county agricultural commissioner) and are generally effective with one treatment either by hand or with a mechanical applicator. Baits containing anticoagulants are also available for hand-baiting. These baits require multiple treatments or one large treatment, and their overall effectiveness has not been clearly demonstrated. All gopher bait is poisonous and should be used with caution. Since the bait is placed underground, it is generally not exposed to nontargets. However, gophers can kick bait out of their burrows, and some nontargets (e.g., dogs) can dig into gopher burrows, so caution is always necessary. Read and follow product label instructions carefully.

Hand-Baiting
Always place pocket gopher bait in the underground burrow. After

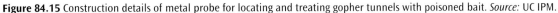

Figure 84.15 Construction details of metal probe for locating and treating gopher tunnels with poisoned bait. *Source:* UC IPM.

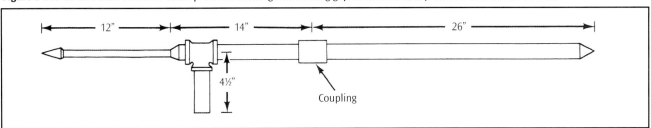

12"   14"   26"

4½"

Coupling

locating the main burrow with a probe, enlarge the opening by rotating the probe or inserting a larger rod or stick. Then place the bait carefully in the opening, taking care not to spill any on the ground surface. A funnel helps prevent spillage (fig. 84.17). Close the probe hole with sod, rock, or some other material to exclude light and prevent dirt from falling on the bait. Tamp down existing mounds so that you can distinguish new activity. This hand application method can be used for single-dose or multiple-dose baits. Reservoir-type hand probes designed to deposit single-dose baits are available. Bait application

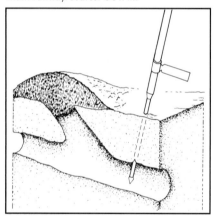

Figure 84.16 Probing to locate gophers' main runway. *Source:* UC IPM.

Figure 84.17 To probe and hand-bait for pocket gophers: (1) use probe to find gopher's main runway; (2) after you reach a noticeable give in the soil, use shaft of probe to enlarge opening and slowly pour bait into funnel, taking care not to spill any on the ground surface; (3) remove funnel and place a clod of earth over the opening to exclude light and prevent soil from falling on the bait. *Photo:* R. O'Connell.

is faster with these devices because they eliminate the need to place the bait by hand. If mound building continues for more than 2 days after treatment with acute poison bait or for 7 to 10 days with an anticoagulant bait, re-treat the burrow or use another control method.

Mechanical Baiting

Mechanical bait applicators offer a good once-over control of large areas. This tractor-drawn device constructs an artificial underground burrow and deposits poison grain bait in it at preset intervals and quantities (figs. 84.18–84.19). The artificial burrow intercepts most natural burrow systems. Gophers readily explore these artificial tunnels and consume the bait. For machine baiting, the percentage of active ingredient of toxicant is usually higher than for hand-baiting.

The machine is useful in controlling gophers in and around vineyards when the soil is neither too wet nor too dry. If it is too wet, the tractor will bog down; if it is too dry, the artificial tunnel will cave in. In nonirrigated areas, the machine should be used in late winter or early spring when natural moisture is high. Operate burrow builders down row middles and along vineyard perimeters where gophers are moving in from adjacent infested areas. When operating the machine, periodically check to see the burrows are being formed properly. If possible, wait at least 10 days before running any other equipment over treated areas. Mechanical burrow builders may not work well on rocky or sandy soils. Do not use burrow builders in areas where gophers are not present, because the constructed burrows may serve as travel ways for invading gophers.

After you use a mechanical burrow builder, follow up with a program of trapping or hand-baiting to kill any surviving or new invading gophers. Begin about 10 days after mechanical baiting if there are signs of new gopher activity. If the vineyard is free of gophers, concentrate your follow-up actions along vineyard perimeters.

Traps

Safe and effective in controlling pocket gophers, gopher traps are available in several types and brands. The most commonly used, a two-pronged pincher trap, is triggered when the gopher pushes against a flat vertical pan. The squeeze-type box trap is another popular trap.

Once the main tunnel has been located, open it with a shovel or garden trowel and set traps in pairs facing opposite directions (fig. 84.20). This placement intercepts a gopher coming from either direction. The box type is somewhat easier to set, but more excavation is required because of its large size. Box traps are useful when the diameter of the gopher's main burrow is less than 3 inches (7.5 cm) because small burrows must be enlarged to accommodate wire traps. All traps should be secured to stakes with wire. After setting them, exclude light from the burrow by covering the opening with dirt, sod, cardboard, or some other material. Fine soil can be sifted around the edges to ensure a light-tight seal. If light enters, the gopher may plug the burrow with soil, filling the traps and making them ineffective. Check traps often and reset when necessary. If no gopher is caught within 2 to 3 days, reset the traps in a different location.

Fumigation

Fumigation with smoke or gas cartridges is not effective because gophers quickly seal off their burrows when they detect smoke or gas. However, aluminum phosphide fumigation (a restricted-use material) can be effective if applied in late winter or early spring before the gopher's major breeding period when there is ample soil moisture to retain toxic gas. Follow all label instructions and safety precautions. To use aluminum phosphide, first probe to find the main burrow as with hand application of bait, then insert the number of tablets prescribed by the label into the burrow and seal the probe hole. As with other control methods, you need to keep monitoring for signs of renewed gopher activity. Re-treat the area if you find new mounds after 24 to 48 hours.

An alternative fumigation device applies propane and oxygen into the burrow and ignites the gas mixture to create an explosion. This method controls gophers by the concussion blast. It can also collapse the tunnels, which prevents other gophers from reoccupying the burrow system. The effectiveness of this method in vineyards has not been evaluated.

OTHER CONTROL METHODS

Pocket gophers can easily withstand normal irrigation, but flooding sometimes forces them out of their burrows, where they become vulnerable to predation.

No repellents available successfully protect vineyards from pocket gopher damage. The gopher plant (*Euphorbia lathyris*) has been suggested as a repellent, but no evidence exists as to its effectiveness. Frightening gophers with sounds, vibrations, or by other means has not been effective.

Predators, especially owls, eat pocket gophers, but in most cases they are unable to keep their populations below the levels that cause problems in vineyards.

Many growers feel that weed growth, especially bermudagrass and nutsedge, encourages pocket gophers. Removing these weeds may reduce gopher populations, although little information is available on its efficacy.

Figure 84.18 This mechanical bait applicator drawn by a tractor creates artificial burrows and deposits poison grain to attract one vineyard nuisance, the pocket gopher. *Photo*: W. P. Gorenzel.

Figure 84.19 Gopher machine collar wheel and shank in the ground to dig out burrows. *Photo*: J. K. Clark.

Figure 84.20 Correct placement of a gopher trap. *Source:* UC IPM.

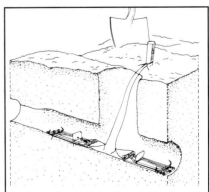

Species selection for cover crops may be a factor for increased gopher activity. Legumes are a preferred food to gophers; avoid cover crops with fleshy taproots such as legumes and consider grasses, which have fibrous root systems.

MONITORING GUIDELINES

Population buildup in a vineyard is generally gradual and can be detected by increasing numbers of gopher mounds. Fresh mounds do not necessarily indicate the number of gophers; they do indicate their presence, however, and should be used to determine their distribution throughout the vineyard. A simple vineyard map plotting this distribution from year to year is a good monitoring technique.

Even one gopher can destroy several vines, especially young vines. Economic injury and treatment levels have not been established in vineyards, so decisions about the need for control depend on grower experience and the past gopher history in the vineyard and vicinity. Because gopher numbers tend to build up if left uncontrolled, control is recommended as soon as fresh mounds are detected. If possible, gophers should be eliminated from the site before a new vineyard (or replacement stock) is planted. Gophers can move slowly but steadily from one area to another, especially if the area has old gopher tunnels. Monitor for their presence in areas adjacent to the vineyard.

RABBIT

Young grapevines are particularly susceptible to damage by rabbits. Jackrabbits (*Lepus californicus*) are the main rabbit pest, although cottontail (*Sylvilagus audubonii*) and the brush rabbit *(S. bachmani)* cause problems in some areas (fig. 84.21).

DESCRIPTION

Jackrabbits are hares, not rabbits. Hares are born fully furred with eyes open and are capable of hopping about immediately. Cottontail and brush rabbits are born blind, naked, and helpless. One other distinction between the two is that cottontails form nests beneath brush, debris, and rock piles and other enclosed places, and jackrabbits make depressions in the soil or form nests beneath brush or other vegetation. Cottontails prefer areas with good cover for protection, such as brush piles, hedges, box piles, or old buildings. Jackrabbits move more freely in the open, and they range much more widely. Jackrabbits are about the size of house cats, 17 to 22 inches (43 to 56 cm). They have short front legs, long hind legs, and large, long ears. They normally hop about, but when frightened they can outrun most dogs. Cottontail and brush rabbits are smaller and have shorter ears.

BIOLOGY

Jackrabbits breed from early February to late summer, although breeding may continue where winters are mild. Females may produce more than one litter per year, especially on irrigated land. After a gestation period of about 6 weeks, a litter (usually of three or four) is born. Larger litters are produced in spring. An adult female may produce 14 or more young per year. The breeding season for cottontails and brush rabbits begins in December and ends in June. The average litter size is usually between three and four, with up to six litters per year.

INJURY

Rabbits feed on plant stems, bark, and leaves. They damage or kill grapevines by eating through bark to the cambium layer. Rabbits chew or cut young vines from near the ground to as high as they can reach and gnaw and girdle trunks. They also chew and gnaw on plastic surface irrigation lines.

Jackrabbits and cottontail rabbits are most active from early evening to early morning throughout the year, although some are seen during the day. Their populations fluctuate and usually reach high levels every 5 to 10 years.

CONTROL METHODS

To reduce rabbit damage, physical exclusion, trapping, and poison baits are recommended.

Figure 84.21 The jackrabbit (A) and the cottontail (B) feed on young grapevines. *Photos*: D. Johnson (A); R. O'Connell (B).

Exclusion

Properly built fences can effectively bar rabbits from an area. A wire fence 30 to 36 inches (0.75 to 0.9 m) high with a mesh no larger than 1 inch (2.5 cm) and with the bottom turned outward and buried 6 inches (15 cm) in the ground excludes rabbits (fig. 84.22). Include tight-fitting gates with sills to keep rabbits from digging below the bottom rails. Keep gates closed as much as possible because rabbits can be active during the day or night. Inspect the fence regularly to make sure rabbits or other animals have not dug under it. Poultry netting supported by light stakes is adequate for rabbit exclusion, but larger animals, especially livestock, can damage it easily. Cottontail and brush rabbits usually do not jump a 2-foot (60 cm) fence. Jackrabbits ordinarily do not jump fences this high unless chased by dogs or otherwise frightened. You can discourage jumping by increasing the aboveground height to 3 feet (90 cm). Once a rabbit gets into the fenced area, it may not be able to get out.

Plastic vine sleeves can also be used to protect young vines from rabbit damage. The sleeves need to be 2.5 feet (75 cm) or higher to prevent jackrabbits from reaching the foliage by standing on their back legs.

Toxic Baits (Rodenticides)

Toxic baits are available for jackrabbit control. Bait acceptance is often difficult, so care must be taken in developing and conducting the baiting program. Multiple-dose anticoagulant baits for jackrabbit control are available from some county agricultural commissioners' offices. Follow label directions carefully. These baits must lie placed in bait stations specifically designed for rabbits, as they are not attracted to stations used for other pests. Place bait stations containing 1 to 5 pounds (0.5 to 2 kg) of bait near trails and secure them so they cannot be tipped over easily. Use as many stations as is necessary to ensure that all jackrabbits have easy access to bait, spacing them 50 to 200 feet (15 to 60 m) apart along the perimeter where the rabbits are entering the vineyard. Inspect bait stations every morning for the first several days to keep bait supplies replenished; it may take this long before jackrabbits become accustomed to feeding at the stations. Increase the amount of bait in the stations or the number of stations if all the bait is consumed in a single night. Replace bait that becomes wet or moldy. It usually takes 2 to 4 weeks or longer before results are seen with multiple-dose bait. Continue baiting until feeding ceases and you no longer observe jackrabbits. Because of the open nature of the bait station, be sure to take precautions to prevent domestic animals or wildlife from having access to the bait, such as covering bait stations when rabbits are inactive. Be sure to dispose of unused bait properly at the end of the baiting program and bury the rabbit carcasses on a regular basis. Be aware of any restrictions related to endangered species. Follow label instructions carefully.

Traps

Jackrabbits usually cannot be trapped because they are reluctant to enter a trap. Cottontail and brush rabbits can be trapped with a tunnel, box, or similar trap, although removal of cottontails from an area is usually effective only if their numbers are not large. Another simple way to trap rabbits is to construct a small corral along a rabbit-tight fence surrounding the protected area. Construct a short strip of fence at a diagonal to the main fence, funneling the rabbits through a one-way gate into the corral. Inspect the corral daily. Because rabbits can carry diseases and are considered agricultural pests, it is illegal to release them in other areas.

Figure 84.22 A deer fence can exclude rabbits and even meadow voles if half-inch wire mesh is added at the base and buried 6 inches (15 cm) underground. *Photo*: J. K. Clark.

OTHER CONTROL METHODS

Repellents can be sprayed or painted on the vine trunk. Their effectiveness depends on the desirability of the vine to the rabbit compared with other foods available. Rain and sprinkler irrigation can wash off some repellents. Read and follow label instructions carefully. Guns and dogs can effectively eliminate small numbers of rabbits, particularly in early morning or evening when rabbits are most active. Check local regulations for any restrictions on shooting. Predators, especially hawks and coyotes, eat rabbits. In most cases, however, these predators are unable to keep rabbit populations below damaging levels.

MONITORING GUIDELINES

Systematic monitoring procedures and economic injury levels have not been established for rabbits in vineyards. A tour through the vineyard in early morning, late evening, or at night to look for rabbits or evidence of feeding help alert the grower. The location of the vineyard near favorable rabbit habitat, such as rangeland or brushy areas, can greatly influence rabbit numbers in the vineyard. Rabbits do not necessarily live in the vineyard, but they can travel some distance to feed in it. Investigate trails into and out of the vineyard.

MANAGEMENT GUIDELINES

Rabbit control in and around vineyards can include shooting, exclusion, repellents, poisoning, habitat modification, and promoting natural enemies. The choice of methods depends on the nature and urgency of the problem and the cost and appropriateness. A combination of methods is often the most effective. Rabbit activity in the vineyard (especially young vineyards) should be controlled early, before a severe problem develops. After the vineyard is 3 years old or all the vines have been trained up the stake, most growers are not concerned about rabbits.

DEER

Where the habitat is favorable, deer move into vineyards and cause considerable damage. Uncontrolled, they can prevent successful viticulture. Foothill and coastal districts with woodlands that provide deer cover usually experience the heaviest damage, but some valley locations near wooded areas or stream bottoms may also suffer. Mule deer (*Odocoileus hemionus*) and blacktailed deer (*O. hemionus columbianus*) are the two subspecies common in California. California Department of Fish and Wildlife regulations limit deer control methods available to growers.

DESCRIPTION

Deer are large, 3 to 3.5 feet (0.9 to 1 m) tall at the shoulder when mature. These gray or brown animals are somewhat difficult to observe because they feed in the late evening and very early morning hours. Hoofprints in the vineyard indicate their presence. Deer hooves are split and about 2 to 3 inches (5 to 7.5 cm) long; they are pointed at the front and more rounded at the rear, unlike hooves of pigs and sheep, which are more rounded in front. Tracks of running deer show spreading of the hoof split. Deer droppings are also a good indicator of their presence (fig. 84.23).

BIOLOGY

Deer usually seek shelter in adjacent wooded or brush areas, but they may live within the vineyard. Some are permanent residents of the area; others are migratory and spend winter and spring around the vineyard and summer and fall at higher elevations.

Figure 84.23 Mule deer (A) and droppings (B). *Photos*: W. P. Gorenzel (A); J. K. Clark (B).

Injury

Deer may completely strip vines of foliage (fig. 84.24). Severe stunting of vines can result from repetitive deer browsing. Young vines may be damaged by buck deer rubbing their antlers on the trunks, arms, or cordon branches. This usually causes severe breakage or scarring.

Control Methods

Fences

Properly constructed and maintained fencing is the most effective method of excluding deer from a vineyard (fig. 84.25). Fencing is most effective when it is put in place before you plant the vineyard. Fencing must be at least 7 feet (2.1 m) high to exclude deer. On sloping terrain, an 8-foot (2.4 m) or taller fence may be necessary. Woven wire fences are used most often in California; however, electric fences and mesh fences made of polypropylene have gained some popularity in the past decade. Your choice of fence will be influenced by factors such as the potential severity and cost of deer damage, other vertebrate pests that need to be excluded, the duration over which you require protection, and the topography of the area.

Fences are sometimes constructed only along the side of the vineyard adjacent to uncultivated land where deer are usually found. While this is less expensive, it is rarely satisfactory because deer will frequently go around the ends of the fence.

Check deer fences periodically. Damaged wires, broken gates, and soil washouts beneath fences increase as fences age and become more vulnerable to breakage. Experience has shown that electric fences of the standard designs used for livestock have usually proved unsatisfactory for deer control in California. More advanced designs in electric fencing have been effective in some situations.

Repellents

To prevent damage to vines, many odor repellents have been tried, but deer usually adjust to them, especially when alternative foods are scarce. When deer populations increase, severe competition for food results, and repellents become much less effective.

Figure 84.24 Deer damage to grapevines is evident in the stripped canes. *Photo*: W. R. Clark.

Figure 84.25 Fencing (A) is the most effective way to prevent deer damage. An electric wire added to a fence (B) can improve the exclusion of pigs. *Photos*: L. J. Bettiga.

Taste repellents can sometimes be effective if applied to new foliage as it develops. This requires repeated spraying as new foliage comes on. A small backpack sprayer can be used to spray each new, unsprayed shoot tip. Some repellents tend to wash off after rain or sprinkler irrigation, making frequent reapplication necessary.

Noisemaking devices, such as propane cannons and electronic alarms, do not repel deer from most vineyards. The deer seem to adjust rapidly to them.

Shooting

In California, permits can be obtained to kill deer when they are involved in crop damage, although the Department of Fish and Wildlife is reluctant to issue these permits. Shooting is usually not a long-term solution, but it may offer relief when deer are numerous. It may be the only practical means of removing deer trapped in a fenced vineyard. Information and depredation permits should be requested from your local Fish and Wildlife office.

Habitat Management

Eliminating suitable shelter for bedding and other survival needs of deer is rarely possible. Grapevines are a favored food, especially when new foliage is developing or when the vineyard offers green, succulent feed compared with other vegetation materials available. Planting other food near the vineyard will probably not prevent damage, and may in fact result in a general increase in deer numbers in the area.

MONITORING GUIDELINES

Because severe damage can occur rapidly when deer feed in a vineyard, it is important to monitor the area for deer, especially before planting. Deer can be observed at night by using a powerful spotlight; deer tracks and pellets are easily seen during the day. If deer or their signs are present, consider control measures.

WILD PIG

The wild pig (*Sus scrofa*) can be a pest in vineyards, especially in coastal production areas that border oak woodlands and in chaparral. Domestic pigs were released in California in the late 1700s, and their free-ranging practices resulted in a feral pig population. In 1925 the European wild boar was introduced in Monterey County and has interbred with the feral population. Populations are greatest in the central and north coast areas.

DESCRIPTION

Wild pig size and conformation depend on the degree of hybridization with wild boar and the quality of their food during their development. Similar to domestic pigs, the coloring of feral pigs can be variable. Wild boars have longer legs and larger heads with longer snouts than feral pigs. The color of young boars is typically reddish brown with black longitudinal stripes. As the young develop, the stripes fade and their reddish color begins to turn brown and eventually black (fig. 84.26). Males of both the feral pig and wild boar have continuously growing tusks.

BIOLOGY

Wild pigs readily adapt to changing environmental conditions. They will modify their behavior in response to humans when it is beneficial to their survival. They feed during the day or at night, or during periods of hot weather; under hunting pressure, they remain in heavy cover during the day and feed at night.

Figure 84.26 Wild pig herd. Note the black longitudinal stripes on the young pigs. *Photo*: R. Schweitzer.

Feral pigs can begin to breed as soon as 6 months if they are on a high-quality diet and can have two litters per year. Wild boars usually do not breed until 18 months and commonly have one litter per year. The litter size depends on the sow's age, nutrition, and the time of year; litters of four to six are common.

INJURY

The rooting and wallowing activities of wild pigs can uproot young plants in newly planted vineyards. Their activities can also increase soil erosion hazard, especially when rooting activity occurs on or near stream banks. Yield loss and fruit damage can occur when low-hanging clusters are within the reach of foraging pigs.

CONTROL

Fences

Sturdy fencing can significantly reduce wild pig movement into vineyards. A deer fence with mesh wire as described above can be effective if properly constructed. The addition of an electric wire 6 to 8 inches (15 to 20 cm) above the ground can improve the exclusion of pigs (see fig. 84.25B). Pigs can root under the fence, so care must be taken to ensure a tight fit with the ground.

Shooting

In California, permits can be obtained to kill wild pigs when they are involved in crop damage. This is usually not a long-term solution, but it may offer relief when pigs are numerous. Information and depredation permits should be requested from your local Department of Fish and Wildlife office.

Traps

Trapping, especially where pig densities are high, is an effective control method. Trapping is not effective, however, during fall and winter when acorns or other preferred foods are available. Stationary corral-type and box-type traps have been used with success. These traps are permanent and should be constructed in locations where large populations of pigs are evident. A portable trap with a drop gate also is effective and may be moved as necessary. Persistence and dedication are required if a control program is to be successful. Traps must be checked daily to be reset and to replace bait when needed (fig. 84.27). When conducting a trapping program, all hunting in the area should cease before traps are set up.

BIRDS

Birds are pests in many vineyards. Their damage is generally restricted to the fruit. Initiate monitoring for injury when grapes begin to ripen and change color. Early detection is essential for successful management of bird problems.

As in rodent control, clean cultural practices may deter bird problems. Many birds (e.g., house finch, sparrow, California quail, and dove) are attracted to vineyards by available nesting and loafing habitats in the form of weedy ditches, hedgerows, windbreaks, and brush or trash piles. Seed-eating birds such as the house finch enter vineyards to feed on weed seeds and may later eat ripening grapes.

Several factors must be considered before initiating control.

Species identification is critical. Most bird species are protected by state or federal laws, and special permits are required to control them. In addition, different species require different management techniques. If birds are drawn to the vineyard by the surrounding habitat, consider altering the habitat, but keep in mind that such altering may result in other kinds of pests and management problems. Initiate a bird management program compatible with your agricultural practices. Continue to monitor bird populations and, if necessary, alter the management program as conditions change. Using more than one technique is generally most effective.

Bird control materials are not as readily available as are those for rodent control. Management of bird problems can rely on exclusion, frightening, and trapping strategies. Assistance in selecting control practices can be obtained from local UCCE farm advisors, agricultural commissioners, and pest control advisers experienced in bird control.

Figure 84.27 Trapping to reduce the pig population near a vineyard. *Photo*: L. J. Bettiga.

HOUSE FINCH

One of the most serious bird pests in California vineyards is the house finch (*Carpodacus mexicanus*). Because vineyards surrounding habitat are usually attractive to house finches, few vineyards escape at least some damage.

DESCRIPTION

The house finch is about the size of a house sparrow and has a heavy bill. Adult males are brownish with a bright red breast and forehead. Careful observation will reveal a red stripe over the eye and rump.

Figure 84.28 Female (A) and male (B) house finch. *Photos*: J. K. Clark.

Figure 84.29 Grapes pecked by house finches. *Photo*: W. R. Clark.

The backs of females are graybrown, and their underparts are streaked a dusky color (fig. 84.28).

BIOLOGY

Primarily a seed-eating bird, the house finch can be found throughout California. The female builds a shallow nest of any material available in a variety of sheltered places. Nesting begins as early as March in warm areas but may be delayed as late as July in colder areas. Two broods are often raised from the same nest.

Pairs are well scattered during nesting. As the young are fledged, they form feeding flocks, often joined by a few adults. By mid-August these flocks comprise most of the young birds of the area. Unlike many bird species, house finch flocks tend to stay in a relatively local region with only minor drift, as they follow a succession of ripening fruit or maturing seed. Between August and December, movements tend to be wider, until the flock settles into a winter habitat that offers adequate food and shelter.

LEGAL STATUS

The house finch is classified as a migratory bird in the Code of Federal Regulations. In California, lethal control must be done under the general supervision of the county agricultural commissioner. Contact the agricultural commissioner for more information about this permit process.

INJURY

House finches peck berries and tear them open (fig. 84.29). Secondary damage can occur when juice of the damaged berries leaks onto the bunch, causing a buildup of secondary organisms and bunch rot. Significant economic loss can result. Even small, local flocks can do considerable damage.

MONITORING GUIDELINES

Watching for bird movement in the vineyard, especially during early morning, is a good monitoring technique. Observations should be made where house finches may congregate before entering the vineyard to feed, such as along rivers, in windbreaks and weedy areas, and on power lines. The number that can be tolerated in a vineyard depends on the crop's market; grapes going to the winery can tolerate higher damage levels than can table grapes for the fresh market.

CONTROL METHODS

Lethal control can be carried out under the general supervision of the county agricultural commissioner. Contact the agricultural commissioner for authorization. The commissioner can help evaluate a problem and initiate a management program. Integrate several methods to obtain the most effective control.

Habitat Modification

Eliminate nesting and loafing areas by removing large brush piles, stacks of irrigation pipe, piles of boxes, and so on. Without nesting and loafing sites, these birds will spend less time in the area.

Frightening Devices

At best, gas cannons, shell crackers, electronic noisemaking devices, kites, balloons, flags, and foil strips have given only short-term results. Be mindful that noisemakers can disturb neighbors, sometimes leading to complaints about the control operation.

Shooting

Costly and time consuming, shooting requires great effort to achieve a noticeable impact on a bird population. House finches are not generally repelled from areas by gunshots, so reduced damage will only occur when considerable numbers are killed.

Traps

Well-planned trapping is effective; use modified Australian crow traps or cotton trailers converted into traps (fig. 84.30). Because the house finch is small, cover the trap with aviary wire or hardware cloth with a mesh size no greater than 0.5 inch (1.3 cm). Place 5 to 10 live birds in the trap as decoys. Decoy birds can be captured by placing a small amount of seed on the trap opening and in trays hung within the trap below the opening. Decoy traps work only if the birds in the traps remain healthy, so ample food, water, and cover are essential. Canary grass seed, rape seed, and mixtures of seeds sold for bird feeders are excellent bait and can serve as food for decoy and captured birds. Supply water using watering devices available at hardware and poultry supply stores.

Careful trap placement ensures success. Normal house finch entrances into the vineyard and locations highly visible to the birds are usually the best trapping areas. Flyways, loafing areas, and heavily damaged areas are excellent trapping sites. A properly located and baited trap should attract house finches within a week; if not, move it to another location.

Because the house finch is a protected species, trapping must be done under the general supervision of the county agricultural commissioner. Dispose of birds according to policy set by the agricultural commissioner.

Falconry

Another method used to control bird pests in vineyards is falconry. Although expensive, it does appear to work well and may be a viable alternative for high-value wine grapes.

Exclusion

On small vineyards or with high-value crops, house finches can be excluded by draping netting over vines with ripening berries (fig. 84.31). Extend the netting to the ground along the rows and tie it off at the ends to eliminate potential points of entry. Some growers have used a simple structure to suspend lightweight netting over a small vineyard. Tractor-mounted rollers can facilitate installation and removal of netting draped directly over vines.

STARLING

A frequent pest in California vineyards, the starling (*Sturnus vulgaris*) can cause extensive damage to ripening and mature grapes in late summer and fall.

DESCRIPTION

The starling, about the size and color of a blackbird, can be distinguished by its pointed bill about 1 inch (2.5 cm) long, which is bright yellow in late winter and spring, and by a speckled appearance because of the buff-colored feather tips on its breast and back. The difference between male and female starlings can be seen on only close observation.

Figure 84.30 Bird trap to lure birds away from vineyards. *Photo*: J. K. Clark.

Figure 84.31 Netted rows of grapevines. *Photo*: L. J. Bettiga.

BIOLOGY

This bird, introduced into the eastern United States in the late 1800s, reached California in the 1940s. Approximately 60% of its annual diet comprises insects. A hole-nesting bird, the starling can nest in a variety of locations, often competing successfully with native birds for nesting sites. Nesting usually begins in March, and pairs of starlings often rear two broods in a season. Breeding occurs throughout California, mostly in oak-studded foothills and near tree-lined rivers. As breeding progresses and the young are fledged, starlings begin to form large, gregarious flocks.

The two components to the California starling population, resident starlings and migrant starlings, overwinter here but migrate north in spring to breed in Oregon, Washington, and Idaho. Resident flocks are particularly threatening to early-maturing grapes; both resident and migrant starlings damage late-season grapes.

LEGAL STATUS

Starlings are not protected by federal or state laws, but local ordinances occasionally regulate their control.

INJURY

Starlings pluck and eat whole berries (fig. 84.32); they cause additional damage when they grasp and puncture lower berries with their feet. Equipped with a high metabolism, they digest grapes rapidly. Starlings are generally selective, feeding on only the ripest grapes, thereby considerably threatening varieties that mature earlier than most other grapes. However, starlings readily eat grapes that have 12% soluble solids, well below optimal maturity for most grapes.

MONITORING GUIDELINES

Carefully monitor vineyard populations, particularly as grapes reach maturity. Large flocks can easily be seen entering the vineyards, often after sunrise. Starlings have a voracious appetite for grapes, so even small flocks can do extensive damage.

CONTROL METHODS

Local UCCE farm advisors, the county agricultural commissioner, or pest control advisers with bird control experience can usually assist in evaluating problems and initiating management programs. Integrating several techniques may be necessary to achieve even moderate levels of starling control.

Habitat Modification

Starlings fly up to 60 miles (95 km) to reach a suitable source of food, so habitat modification usually brings little relief. In some cases, removing trees used for loafing reduces problems.

Cultural Techniques

Some vineyard operators believe that dense vine foliage protects clusters from starling damage. Table grape growers have experienced damage when they have opened up the vine to expose the clusters for better disease control, to promote fruit color, and to facilitate harvest. Thus, avoid excessive leaf pulling, shoot thinning, or shoot positioning in vineyards prone to bird damage unless these practices are deemed essential. Using greater foliage support with crossarm trellising could reduce potential starling damage.

Frightening Devices

Planning and persistence are the keys to using gas cannons, electronic alarm calls, shell crackers, visual repellents, and shooting, which are the most commonly used means for moving flocks of starlings from vineyards. Starlings are difficult to frighten once they establish a feeding pattern, so frightening devices should be in place and operating before damage occurs. Their placement is critical. Ensure that the sound projects over the top of the vines and that all areas are protected. Starlings rapidly acclimate to sounds, so the frequency at which a sound goes off and the location of the sound generator should be changed often. Be mindful that noisemakers can disturb neighbors, sometimes leading to complaints about the control operation.

Figure 84.32 The starling (A) plucks ripening grapes from their clusters, causing extensive damage (B). *Photos*: J. K. Clark.

Commonly used visual repellents such as mylar streamers and large scare-eye balloons are sometimes effective for a short period of time. Attach balloons to stakes so they are above the canopy and hang mylar streamers on stakes. Use visual repellents in combination with noisemakers to increase their effectiveness. Use one type of visual repellent with each type of noisemaker and switch to a different visual repellent when you switch noisemakers.

The most effective bird frightening program uses as many different kinds of noisemakers and visual repellents as practical. Shooting is usually used to reinforce the various frightening methods.

Shooting

Starlings learn rapidly to avoid humans with guns. Therefore, shooting alone is not practical; it is best used in conjunction with frightening devices.

Traps

Starlings are relatively easy to trap with modified Australian crow traps or cotton trailers converted into traps. These traps work best with live decoy birds inside and a desirable food placed in the trap and on the entrance board. The greatest trap success can be obtained by providing ample food, water, and shelter to keep the decoy birds healthy. Poultry pellets are excellent for maintaining the birds, and any variety of watering systems can be used.

Trapping can relieve damage by resident starlings, but it is usually ineffective with larger migrant flocks later in the season. Traps are most effective when situated in flyways. If a trap with live decoy birds does not catch starlings within 7 days, relocate it.

Exclusion

Use netting to exclude starlings from grapes on small areas. The netting must extend to the ground and be tied off at the ends of the rows to prevent starlings from getting under. Some growers have used a simple structure to suspend lightweight netting over a small vineyard.

Roost Control

At night, starlings group in communal roosts. Roost control is not generally practical, but if the roosting area is under your control, harassing the birds or modifying the roost by thinning or removing the vegetation in it can sometimes provide relief.

AMERICAN ROBIN

American robins (*Turdus migratorius*) reportedly damage maturing grapes throughout California and the Pacific states. They become pests in vineyards when their migration patterns bring them into areas where grapes are maturing.

Description

About 8 to 10 inches (20 to 25 cm) tall, the American robin has a dark brown head and tail and a gray-brown back. Most distinctive are its brick-red breast feathers and yellow, pointed bill.

Biology

The American robin is migratory, breeding in the northern portions of its range in spring and moving south during winter. Breeding in spring throughout California, robins produce two or three young in shallow nests of sticks and mud built in trees. Often seen foraging in turf areas, they feed primarily on insects and worms. Their other major foods are wild and cultivated berries, including grapes.

Legal Status

American robins are considered migratory nongame birds under federal regulation. A depredation permit issued by the U.S. Fish and Wildlife Service is required when lethal control measures are used.

Injury

Like the starling, the robin plucks the entire berry from a bunch of grapes. Substantial damage can result to vineyards when migratory flocks of robins move in near harvest.

Monitoring Guidelines

American robins are relatively easy to spot and identify. The numbers of migrants in California vary greatly from year to year, so vineyards where damage occurred in previous years may not be damaged subsequently. Look for robins feeding in and around vineyards in early morning or late afternoon. Look for birds when grapes near maturity.

Control Methods

American robins can substantially damage grapes, but little effort has been put into developing control measures because robins are not found in vineyards as regularly as other pest birds.

Habitat Management
Habitat management is of little use since the American robin is migratory, moving into vineyards regardless of the surrounding habitat.

Cultural Techniques

Cultural management to increase vine canopy may provide some relief from robin damage, but no effort has been made to quantify the effects.

Frightening Devices

Efforts to control robins with frightening devices are reportedly unsuccessful. American robin flocks appear unaffected by such devices.

Shooting

Firing shots to frighten or disperse robins is not successful. Shooting to reduce numbers of robins in a vineyard requires a federal depredation permit and is of little use in dealing with a migratory bird like the robin.

Exclusion

Protecting a limited acreage of grapes with netting can control American robins. As with other bird control, netting must reach the ground on both sides of the grapevine and be tied down at the end of each row to prevent birds from entering and feeding on berries. Some growers have used a simple structure to suspend lightweight netting over a small vineyard.

WHITE-CROWNED SPARROW

The white-crowned sparrow (*Zonotrichia leucophrys*) occasionally damages grapes (fig. 84.33). Distinguished by its gray breast and prominent white streaks on the head, it causes damage similar to that caused by the house finch, but its damage is seldom as extensive and is usually confined to parts of the vineyard near rivers or brush areas. Keeping brush piles and weeds to a minimum often helps reduce damage. The white-crowned sparrow is classified as a migratory bird under federal regulations. In California, lethal control must be done under the general supervision of the county agricultural commissioner. Contact the agricultural commissioner for more information about this permit process.

Figure 84.33 White-crowned sparrow. *Photo*: J. P. Clark.

DOVE AND PHEASANT

Both of these are game birds and are regulated as hunted species. The mourning dove (*Zenaida macroura*) often nests in vineyards. A seed eater, this bird is seldom a vineyard pest. The ring-necked pheasant (*Phasianus colchicus*) may be found in vineyards. It prefers brushy areas and can usually be kept out of vineyards by keeping weeds and brush to a minimum.

OTHER BIRDS

Other birds occasionally damage vineyards, and most are protected under federal or state laws. California quail, western bluebird, cedar waxwing, mockingbird, wild turkey, and scrub jay are sometimes found in vineyards, and care should be taken to identify them and determine whether they are potential grape pests. Often they visit the vineyard for the cover and nesting sites found in the lush foliage. Farm advisors, the county agricultural commissioner, or agricultural pest control advisers with bird control experience can help determine the laws and regulations that must be followed and can assist in obtaining state or federal permits necessary to prevent birds from damaging vineyards.

Part 8

Vegetation Managemen

Pinot noir

85 VINEYARD FLOOR MANAGEMENT

Glenn A. McGourty, Kurt J. Hembree, Chuck A. Ingels, and Anil Shrestha

Vineyard floors can be managed in many ways to control vegetation and weeds, including tillage, herbicides, mowing, and grazing. Choices are made based on cost, effects on pests, weed and disease management programs, appearance, protection of the soil, reducing frost risk, effects of practices on vine growth, and ease of a particular farming system.

Nearly all vineyard managers control vegetation and weeds beneath the vine row with tillage, herbicides, mowing, or a combination of these methods. This reduces competition from weeds with the vines for water and nutrients; prevents weeds from growing into the canopy, which might interfere with spraying, canopy management, and harvesting; and prevents habitat for damaging rodents such as voles and gophers. It also gives the vineyard a cleaner look. This may be important if you are receiving visitors and aesthetics are an issue in creating a positive impression of a well-maintained facility.

Row middles can be mowed, tilled, or sprayed with herbicides to manage vegetation and weeds. Statewide, there is an increasing trend to reduce tillage and simply mow the row middles.

Young vineyards are often managed by removing all competing vegetation and weeds during the growing season for the first 2 or 3 years while vines are being established. This approach can also help control troublesome perennial weeds and rodents that might be more of a problem in a no-till (only mowed) vineyard floor program.

Environmental issues can also influence management choices, as tilled vineyards can potentially affect off-site air and water quality from dust and erosion. Many California vineyards now grow cover crops to address potential problems and improve environmental conditions. Planting and managing cover crops for beneficial insects and pollinators is also an objective for some vineyard managers as a way to reduce pesticide use and increase biodiversity in their farming system. (While grapes do not require insect pollination, many cover crops do, especially self-reseeding clovers and other forbs). With cover crops and reduced tillage, there is also the potential to sequester carbon by building soil organic matter to help offset increased carbon dioxide levels in the atmosphere. Additionally, Ground Water Protection Areas (GWPAs) are defined throughout the state to help prevent potential groundwater contamination from herbicides, including simazine and diuron.

The use of cover crops has greatly increased in California during the past decade, and growers have many choices for their vineyard floor management systems. Generally, growers plant cover crops that are compatible with vineyards, low growing for easy management without excessive tillage, and needing fewer multiple mowing passes.

THE IMPORTANCE OF COVER CROPS

A cover crop is a tool to help grape growers manage vineyard soils in several ways:

- Protect the soil from erosion. The foliage of cover crops reduces the velocity of raindrops before they hit the soil surface, preventing soil from splashing. This prevents slaking of soil aggregates (fig. 85.1) and sealing of the soil surface (when this occurs, runoff increases, along with soil erosion). The roots of the cover crops bind soil particles together, improving soil structure and water penetration, while preventing the soil particles from moving.

- Competition with weeds. Some cover crops provide weed suppression by competing strongly with winter annual weeds. The residue left after mowing winter annual cover crops may also reduce the emergence of summer annual weeds (such as lambsquarters and puncturevine) and reduce weed growth (especially compared with bare tilled soil). Perennial grasses planted in fertile vineyard sites are known to discourage annual and perennial weeds, including prickly lettuce, puncturevine, field bindweed, nutsedge, and many others. Growers have used this strategy to reduce tractor passes required for tilling or mowing unwanted and unsightly weeds.

- Regulate vine growth. Cover crops can invigorate vines (augmenting soil nitrogen from nitrogen-fixing legumes) or devigorate vines (root competition with the vines from non-legumes for nutrients and water).

- Improve soil fertility. Besides increasing soil nitrogen, decomposing cover crops increase the soil organic matter and thereby increase the soil cation exchange capacity. Therefore, the ability of a soil to hold and exchange nutrients increases. Additionally, nutrients are often chelated into organic complexes, and under certain conditions they are more readily exchanged from these substrates than from inorganic clay minerals.

- Improve soil structure, water infiltration, and water-holding capacity. Initially, cover crop roots help aggregate soils as fine roots penetrate the soil profile, especially the roots of grasses. Cover crops with large taproots help create macropores when the plants die and leave voids from the decomposing roots. These macropores greatly assist the movement of air and water into the soil profile.

Figure 85.1 Erosion caused extensive damage in this vineyard. *Photo*: J. K. Clark.

Soil organisms using the decomposing cover crops as a food source create waxes and other sticky substances that hold the fine particles into aggregates, lowering bulk density and improving soil tilth. As organic matter increases in the soil, so does the soil's ability to hold water. Physical improvement of the soil permits greater root expansion and can improve plant access to nutrients and water.

• Enhance biological diversity in the root zone. Decomposing cover crops are a food source for macro- and microorganisms. Many of these organisms assist in recycling the cover crops into the soil, improving soil physical qualities in the process. Particularly noteworthy are increases in earthworm populations, a good indicator of soil health and improved physical condition. Increased biological activity occurs in the soil after the incorporation of organic matter from cover crops. It has been clearly shown by researchers that these organisms can reduce damage from root pathogens and inhibit the growth and development of pathogens.

• Provide habitat for beneficial generalist predator and parasitoid insects and arachnids (spiders and mites). Cover crops can provide habitat and food for beneficial insects and mites. Food sources include pollen and nectar from flowers and extrafloral nectaries. Cover crops also provide habitat for beneficials and prey such as aphids, mites, caterpillars, and other creatures. Spiders are often abundant on the vineyard floor, and they may also forage in the vines themselves. Research entomologists have a difficult time understanding the dynamics of pest and prey relationships in a cover crop and its effect on grapevine canopies. Some researchers have suggested that competition between the vines and cover crops may reduce vine vigor and decrease stem and leaf water potential, making the vines less attractive to leafhoppers. Growing legume cover crops that ultimately increase the foliar nitrogen content may make the vines more attractive to insect feeding. The effect of cover crops on vine pest pressure is highly variable and difficult to predict. Many growers have reported reduced mite and leafhopper problems when they moved from a tilled to a no-till vineyard floor with cover crops. It is also possible that cover crops can be a haven for pests and diseases. Various grasses are attractive to sharpshooters that transmit Pierce's disease (see section 9, "Pierce's Disease"). Orange tortrix lives in the larval stages on numerous weeds and cover crops (see section 70, "Orange Tortrix"). False chinch bugs may infest cover crops and then move onto grapevines as the cover crop dries up in the spring. Their feeding can seriously damage small vines.

• Provide firm footing for harvest and cultural operations. When no-till sod-forming cover crops are planted, vineyard access during wet weather becomes more feasible, as the cover crops provide firmer footing. This can enable harvest, pruning, and spraying during inclement weather.

• Improve air and water quality. Water quality laws are being increasingly enforced, and vineyard water runoff must be free of silt and excess nutrients. Cover crops help prevent runoff and erosion. The filtering effects of cover crops on soil sediments can also reduce the off-site movement of sediment, soil-adsorbed nutrients (such as phosphorous), and pesticides. Nitrogen fixed by legumes is less mobile than soluble nitrogen fertilizers. Cover crops can assimilate free nutrients in the soil and stabilize them during periods of high rainfall. During the dry periods of the year, cover crops help reduce dust, improving air quality. This also helps reduce mite infestations, which thrive under dusty conditions.

Table 85.1 Annual cover crops for tilled vineyards

Scientific name	Common name	Suggested cultivars	Seeding rate, lb/ac (kg/ha)	Potential nitrogen, lb/yr (kg/yr)
Avena sativa	oats	Cayuse; Swan	60–90 (67–101)	0
Brassica spp.	mustards	many	5–12 (5.5–13.5)	0
Hordeum vulgare	barley	UC476	60–90 (67–101)	0
Phacelia spp.	phacelia	Phaci	15–30 (17–34)	0
Pisum sativum	field pea	Magnus; Miranda; Austrian Winter	20–70 (22.5–78.5)	120 (54.5)
Secale cereale	cereal rye	Merced	60–90 (67–101)	0
Trifolium alexandrinum	berseem clover	Multicut	15–20 (17–22.5)	200 (91)
Vicia benghalenis	purple vetch	purple vetch	50–60 (56–67)	150 (68)
Vicia dasycarpa	woollypod vetch	Lana vetch	50–75 (56–84)	150 (68)
Vicia faba	bell bean (fava)	Diana; many	100–190 (112–213)	100 (45.5)
Vicia sativa	common vetch	common vetch	60–75 (67–84)	150 (68)

Scientific name	Tolerant to traffic	Weed competition	Requires spring mowing	Fertility requirements	Canopy height, inches (cm)
Avena sativa	no	good–excellent	no	N, P	tall, 30–60 (75–150)
Brassica spp.	no	good–excellent	no	N, P	medium–tall, 12–60 (30–150)
Hordeum vulgare	no	good–excellent	no	N, P	tall, 30–60 (75–150)
Phacelia spp.	yes	very good	no	N, P	medium, 12–24 (30–60)
Pisum sativum	no	good–excellent	no	Ca, P, K, S	sprawling, 18–24 (45–60)
Secale cereale	no	good–excellent	no	N, P	tall, 36–72 (90–180)
Trifolium alexandrinum	yes	good–excellent	yes	Ca, P, K, S	medium, 12–24 (30–60)
Vicia benghalenis	no	good–excellent	no	Ca, P, K, S	sprawling, 18–24 (45–60)
Vicia dasycarpa	no	good–excellent	no	Ca, P, K, S	sprawling, 12–24 (30–60)
Vicia faba	no	fair–good	no	Ca, P, K, S	tall, 30–60 (75–150)
Vicia sativa	no	good–excellent	no	Ca, P, K, S	sprawling, 18–24 (45–60)

Vineyard Floor Management Systems

Choosing a vineyard floor management system depends on the relative vigor of the vineyard; water availability in the soil; viticultural objectives (increasing or decreasing vine vegetative growth); and pest (insect, mite, and weed) management objectives. For a summary of cover crop species and their uses, see tables 85.1–85.3. This subject is well covered in *Cover Cropping in Vineyards: A Grower's Handbook* (UC ANR Publication 3338). Following are discussions of several different approaches.

Annually Tilled and Seeded

The majority of growers use this system to conserve moisture in their vineyards. Winter annual cover crops are planted in the fall or germinate with fall and winter rains to form a sward (a mix of green plants) on the vineyard floor. The sward is allowed to grow until some point in time in the spring before frost is likely to damage emerging shoots. While the ground can still be easily cultivated, the plants are mowed and tilled into the soil (fig. 85.2). This operation is often timed when the cover crop is flowering, as the cover crops will decompose easily at this stage. This system is best suited for relatively flat vineyards in which soil erosion is not a serious potential hazard. Cover crop species typically used in this system include annual small grains (barley, oats, rye, triticale), winter peas, vetch, bell beans, daikon radish, Persian clover, and other annuals that establish quickly and grow well during the cool months of the year (figs. 85.3–85.4).

In upland areas prone to soil erosion where water is not available for irrigation of either the vines or the cover crop, it is highly recommended to use straw mulch pressed into the vineyard floor to minimize the loss of soil while waiting for the cover crop to start growing in the fall. It may not be necessary to cover the entire vineyard floor—often just a band of straw placed strategically over part of the vineyard most prone to erosion is adequate to prevent off-site soil movement.

This vineyard floor management system is tillage intensive, and soil is left bare during the summer. Loss of soil structure and organic matter occur if tillage is excessive. Tillage also increases dust in the vineyard, which can affect air quality and also predispose vines to attack by mites. Regardless, this system may allow for the production of high-quality fruit without irrigation or applications of concentrated fertilizers. Many people like the look of cultivated vineyard floors, and this often is the method of choice near expensive and attractive winery facilities. For vineyards that are flood irrigated, tillage may be necessary to form furrows to receive water, and then are tilled, leveled, and shaped again prior to harvest. Summer annual cover crops (plants that do not tolerate frost and grow in the warm portion of the year) are grown in some vineyards to help control dust, improve footing following irrigation, reduce reflective heat, and provide habitat, pollen, or nectar for beneficial insects. The sward may consist of summer annual weeds, including purslane, common knotweed, prostrate spurge, and other low-growing

species. If desirable weed species are not present, fast-growing summer annual grasses can be planted, including sudangrass and sorghum-sudangrass hybrids. These species usually require summer irrigation, and they must be mowed to prevent excessive competition with the vines; alternatively, this competition can control excess vine vigor. Annual buckwheat is planted to provide a summer pollen and nectar source for generalist predators and parasitoids. It can be very helpful under some situations, particularly if there are no other protective cover or food sources for beneficial insects surrounding the vineyard (fig. 85.5).

No-Till Vineyard Floor Management with Annual Species

In this system, the vineyards are tilled initially and seeded with species that will reseed themselves on an annual basis. Thereafter, the vineyards are mowed in spring and early summer, or winter annual weeds are allowed to grow (fig. 85.6). Tillage is restricted only to beneath the vines, or herbicides are applied to control weeds in a completely no-till approach. Subterranean clover, rose clover, crimson clover, red clover, berseem clover, bur medic, bolansa clover, and Persian clover are all suited for this farming system. Grasses can include Blando brome and Zorro fescue. Some growers have successfully managed cereal grasses such as barley to set seed and persist for 2 to 3 or more years before needing to reseed. The disadvantage of this is that the large amount of seed may attract increased rodent and bird activity.

If the area is sloping, it may be necessary to place straw mulch beneath the vines to keep bare soil

Table 85.2. Annual cover crops for mowed vineyards

Scientific name	Common name	Suggested cultivars	Seeding rate, lb/ac (kg/ha)	Potential nitrogen, lb/yr (kg/yr)
Bromus mollis	soft brome	Blando	10–12 (11–13.5)	0
Festuca megalura	foxtail fescue	Zorro	10–15 (11–17)	0
Lolium multiflorum	annual ryegrass	Gulf, Common	60–90 (67–101)	0
Medicago polymorpha	burclover, bur medic	Santiago, Circle Valley	15–20 (17–22.5)	30–60 (13.5–27)
Trifolium hirtum	rose clover	Hykon, Overton, Wilton	15–20 (17–22.5)	30–60 (13.5–27)
Trifolium incarnatum	crimson clover	Dixie, Flame	20–30 (22.5–34)	30–60 (13.5–27)
Trifolium subterraneum	subterranean clover	Karridale, Koala, Trikkala, Junee, Clare	20–30 (22.5–34)	30–60 (13.5–27)
various (see table 85.1)	cereal grasses	various	60–90 (67–101)	0

Scientific name	Tolerant to traffic	Weed competition	Requires spring mowing	Fertility requirements	Canopy height, inches (cm)
Bromus mollis	yes	good–excellent	no	N	low, 6–12 (15–30)
Festuca megalura	yes	good	no	N	low, 6–12 (15–30)
Lolium multiflorum	yes	excellent	no	N	low, 6–12 (15–30)
Medicago polymorpha	yes	good–excellent	yes	Ca, P, K, S	low, 6–12 (15–30)
Trifolium hirtum	yes	fair–good	yes	Ca, P, K, S	low, 6–12 (15–30)
Trifolium incarnatum	yes	good–excellent	yes	Ca, P, K, S	medium, 12–24 (30–60)
Trifolium subterraneum	yes	good–excellent	yes	Ca, P, K, S	low, 6–12 (15–30)
various (see table 85.1)	no	good–excellent	no	N, P	tall, 30–72 (75–180)

SECTION 85: VINEYARD FLOOR MANAGEMENT

504

from eroding. Rice straw applied at the rate of 3 tons per treated acre (6.7 t/ha) is a preferred method by some north coast vineyard managers.

Another no-till approach is to plant cover crop species every year that are not self-reseeding, such as peas, or to manage species such as oats, barley, rye, or vetch to prevent them from reseeding. These cover crops can be planted with a no-till drill, which is useful when tillage could cause erosion and it is desirable to keep tillage to a minimum. Usually, seeding is done just before fall rains. In spring, the cover crop is then simply mowed and left to lie on the soil surface.

Summer weeds are often discouraged by the residual material from a winter cover crop. However, there may be an increase in gophers, field mice, and voles with no-till vineyard floor management.

No-Till Vineyard Floor Management with Perennial Species
Perennial species are most commonly grown in vineyards planted on fertile sites. Many of the perennial grasses are very competitive with grapevine roots and will have a devigorating effect on the vineyard. This may be desirable if the vineyard is out of vegetative balance. Cover crops vary from being slightly competitive to very competitive. The fine fescues (hard fescue, creeping red fescue, and sheep fescue) are the least competitive, grow very short, and survive well. Some require little mowing, since they are less than 4 inches (10 cm) tall. Turf selections of perennial ryegrass and tall fescue are intermediate in their competitiveness. They also have a fairly low

stature, requiring mowing only once or twice per year. There are now glyphosate-tolerant selections of these grasses that might be useful in some situations. Finally, pasture selections of perennial ryegrass, tall fescue, and orchardgrass are the most competitive and can have a tremendous impact on the vigor of a vineyard. They should be planted on only the most vigorous sites with deep soils.

These grasses may also be grown in parts of the vineyard that are prone to erosion or in places where it is desirable to hold down dust. Seasonal waterways, vineyard roads that aren't heavily trafficked, turnaround areas, staging areas, or other places where the soil needs to be protected are potential sites for these grasses.

There is a good case for including perennial legumes in a sward of grasses, as they will supply nitrogen for the grasses. Unfortunately, they may also attract rodents such as voles and gophers that can damage grapevines. Despite this potential problem, many growers also include white clover, strawberry clover, alsike clover, and birdsfoot trefoil in their perennial mixes. These species provide not only nitrogen for the grasses but also habitat for generalist predator and parasitoid insects. Some growers have also had success by planting perennial grasses alone, and then after two or three seasons, planting annual legumes into the sward. If the annual legumes and perennial grasses are initially planted together, the annual legumes will shade the grasses out, and a poor stand of perennial grasses is likely to occur.

Finally, there are also California native grasses that can be grown

as cover crops. Commonly planted species include pine bluegrass, along with Mokulemne and Molate red fescue, as less competitive species; and California brome, meadow barley, and blue wild rye as more competitive choices. Seed for these grasses is expensive, and they are not as competitive with weeds in some cases as other introduced pasture and turf grass species used as cover crops. It is also important to let these grasses flower late in the spring, in order for them to accumulate carbohydrates in their root systems, which improves their persistence and competitiveness with weeds. Many go dormant during warm summer weather.

Using Both Tilled and No-Till Farming Systems
Some growers use different farming systems in alternate rows to moderate vigor, incorporate compost or other fertilizers, provide diverse habitat for beneficials, or for aesthetic reasons. One common system is a no-till program of self-reseeding annuals for 3 years in alternate rows, with annually planted and tilled cover crops in the other rows. After 3 years, the planting systems are switched in the alternate rows. Perennial species are also grown in this way. In most cases, this approach is used on more vigorous sites not prone to soil erosion (fig. 85.7).

Cover Crop Rotations
After some time, cover crops can develop pests and pathogens that make it difficult to reseed the same species year after year. This is one of the reasons that mixes are planted, as the effect of planting the same species annually seems less pronounced when a mixture of diverse species is grown.

Table 85.3. No-till perennial cover crops for vineyards

Scientific name	Common name	Suggested cultivars	Seeding rate, lb/ac (kg/ha)	Potential nitrogen, lb/yr (kg/yr)
Bromus carinatus	California brome*	California brome	10–20 (11–22.5)	0
Dactylis glomerata	orchardgrass*	Potomac, Palestine, Paiute	15–25 (17–28)	0
Elymus glaucus	blue wildrye*	Berkeley	10–15 (11–17)	0
Festuca arundinacea	tall fescue*	many	15–25 (17–28)	0
Festuca ovina	sheep fescue	Covar, MX86	15–25 (17–28)	0
Festuca ovina var. *duriuscula*	hard fescue*	Durar	15–25 (17–28)	0
Festuca rubra	red fescue	many	15–40 (17–45)	0
Hordeum brachyantherum	meadow barley*	meadow barley	20–30 (22.5–34)	0
Lolium perenne	perennial ryegrass*	many	40–50 (45–56)	0
Lotus corniculatus	birdsfoot trefoil	Empire, Viking	5–10 (5.5–11)	30–60 (13.5–27)
Trifolium fragiferum	strawberry clover	O'Connors Legume, Salina	5–15 (5.5–17)	30–60 (13.5–27)
Trifolium repens	white clover	New Zealand, White Dutch	5–15 (5.5–17)	30–60 (13.5–27)

Table 85.3. *Continued*

Scientific name	Tolerant to traffic	Weed competition	Requires spring mowing	Fertility requirements	Canopy height, inches (cm)
Bromus carinatus	yes	good–very good	no	N	medium–tall, 12–30 (30–75)
Dactylis glomerata	yes	good–very good	no	N	medium–tall, 24–48 (60–120)
Elymus glaucus	yes	good–very good	no	N	medium–tall, 24–48 (60–120)
Festuca arundinacea	yes	very good–excellent	no	N	low–medium, 6–18 (15–45)
Festuca ovina	yes	fair–good	no	N	very low, 3–6 (7.5–15)
Festuca ovina var. *duriuscula*	yes	good–very good	no	N	very low, 3–6 (7.5–15)
Festuca rubra	yes	good–very good	no	N	low, 6–12 (15–30)
Hordeum brachyantherum	yes	fair–good	no	N	medium, 8–28 (20–70)
Lolium perenne	yes	very good–excellent	no	N	medium–tall, 12–30 (30–75)
Lotus corniculatus	yes	good–very good	yes	Ca, P, K, S	medium, 12–24 (30–60)
Trifolium fragiferum	yes	fair–good	yes	Ca, P, K, S	low, 3–12 (7.5–30)
Trifolium repens	yes	fair–good	yes	Ca, P, K, S	low, 6–12 (15–30)

Note:

*Recommended for vigorous sites only.

Figure 85.2 Complete tillage by cultivation with spring teeth in the row middles and spring blades in vine rows during summer. *Photo*: L. P. Christensen.

Figure 85.3 Herbicide-treated rows with a no-till winter cover crop of barley. *Photo*: L. J. Bettiga.

Figure 85.4 A mixed sward of annual legumes and small grains. *Photo*: G. McGourty.

Figure 85.5 Sorghum-sudangrass is a tall-growing summer annual that is occasionally grown to add organic matter, reduce sunburn damage, or slow winds. *Photo*: L. J. Bettiga.

Figure 85.6 Mowing a no-till vineyard that has used resident vegetation as a cover in the row middles in spring. *Photo*: C. L. Elmore.

Some growers plant completely different species from year to year, such as mustards or radishes one season, followed by legumes, which are then followed by annual grains. Other growers take the approach of mixing all three together simultaneously, increasing the likelihood that at least one of the species will perform well under that particular season's growing conditions of temperature and rainfall.

Because some leguminous cover crops are hosts to nematodes that can damage grapevine roots, they may increase nematode populations in the vineyard. Field experience is not clear, but if nematodes are a concern, cover crops that are nonhost species for the nematodes present should be selected. This can include many annual grasses. Cahaba white vetch is planted in sandy soils as a winter legume that will not host the major root knot nematode species or ring nematode. However, this cover crop is susceptible to soilborne disease if planted in two or more consecutive seasons. For more information, see section 83, "Nematodes."

Grazing

Some growers allow sheep to graze the vineyard floor during the winter when there is no foliage on the vines. Sheep can be very effective at maintaining a well-groomed sward, and when managed properly, they can minimize winter weeds while assisting with cover crop growth (particularly clovers, since their grazing may actually remove competing weeds). Grazing works best in vineyards that are securely fenced from predators and then cross-fenced with portable electric fencing so that sheep can

be carefully managed and stocked to uniformly graze vegetation on the vineyard floor. Normally, sheep are removed from the vineyard before budbreak. Organic and biodynamic growers report that it is much easier to control weeds with tillage after the sheep have grazed their vineyards in the spring. Sheep also can control vegetation when it may be difficult to use tractors to mow due to wet soil conditions. Soil compaction is a concern and must be considered when developing a grazing program. Normally, under controlled grazing with electric fencing, sheep do not stay in the same area for long periods of time, so soil compaction is minimized.

Most vineyard owners work with sheep producers to bring in the animals, as opposed to having their own flock of sheep. However, some vineyard owners also raise sheep as part of their farming enterprise, and they integrate grazing in the vineyards and other pasture areas. Some have even designed their trellises so that the grapevine foliage is above the reach of the grazing sheep, and they can use sheep for vineyard floor management at any time.

Experimentation with aversion training suggests that sheep can be conditioned to not eat grapevine foliage. During training, sheep are first fed grapevine leaves and shoots, which they readily eat. Then they are given a dose of lithium chloride, which makes them very uncomfortable. They associate this discomfort with eating grapevines and are then conditioned to avoid eating the foliage. Training can be done fairly quickly, is not harmful to the long-term health of

the sheep, and is long lasting. In the future, it may be possible to use aversion-trained sheep much longer into the growing season to control vineyard floor vegetation.

VINEYARD FLOOR MANAGEMENT PRACTICES IN CALIFORNIA

North Coast and the Northern Foothill Regions

Vineyards in the north coast are planted on a wide range of geological landforms and soil types. Many are planted along valley floors that have deep, fertile alluvial soils. These sites are prone to frost. Usually, weeds are controlled under the vines with herbicides or cultivated with mechanical devices. Row middles are often farmed no-till and planted to annual or perennial cover crops.

Other vineyards are planted on sloping alluvial fans, hillsides, and ridge tops. These sites are less prone to frost damage and may have rocky, shallow soils. Some vineyards are contour planted or developed on highly engineered terraces to mitigate potential erosion problems (fig. 85.8). Vineyards on sloping soils are usually managed without tillage: self-reseeding annual cover crops are planted and mowed. Many winter annual weeds, such as annual bluegrass, annual fine fescue, chickweed, filaree, corn spurry, and scarlet pimpernel, are suitable volunteer cover crops. They set seed early and are managed by mowing when prunings are shredded in late winter. Herbicides are often applied to control weeds beneath the vines. Other practices include straw mulching on exposed soil; seeding roadways and headlands; and providing armored water conveyances, including drop inlets and buried drain pipe, rocked and grass surface waterways, and small holding ponds to slow water and allow sediment to drop out.

Tillage is used in vineyards that are dry farmed or with little water for irrigation. Great care must be taken to prevent soil erosion, including planting winter annual cover crops, straw mulching, straw wattles, and other practices that prevent surface water from moving until cover crops are large enough to protect the vineyard floor.

Central Coast

Most central coast vineyards are planted on rolling hillsides and bench lands. Soils vary greatly from sandy loams to silty clays with rocks and cobbles. No-till is widely practiced, using small grains, self-reseeding annual cover crops (especially Blando brome), and annual winter weeds, which germinate and grow well under low-rainfall conditions. Weeds are controlled beneath vines with

herbicides or tillage. In more fertile bottomland sites, perennial cover crops can be planted to reduce vine vigor and provide firm footing. Some vineyards also plant sorghum-sudangrass hybrids in every other row in the early spring and allow them to grow tall to serve as windbreaks. These are planted in tilled soil in rows perpendicular to prevailing winds.

Southern California

In San Diego, Riverside, and San Bernardino Counties, many vineyards are planted in soils low in organic matter and nitrogen. Many sites are planted on slopes with highly erosive soils. No-till farming is widely practiced. Self-reseeding annual covers that germinate well under low-rainfall conditions are preferred, including bur clover, subterranean clover, barrel medics, Zorro fescue, and Blando brome. Weeds are usually sprayed with herbicides beneath the vine row.

San Joaquin and Sacramento Valleys

This region has very diverse soils, irrigation methods, and vineyard products. In the San Joaquin Valley, soils tend to be light- to medium-textured and low in organic matter. Certain clay and clay loam soils tend to surface seal and have low rates of water infiltration. Although most Central Valley growers use resident vegetation, planted cover crops can be valuable because they improve water penetration and help reduce leaching of nitrogen fertilizers more than does resident vegetation. Green manure cover crops that include legume and grain mixes are favored. Tillage is common in many vineyards to help form furrows for flood irrigation and to form tilted beds for sun-drying raisins.

Other vineyards use a mow-only approach, especially in some of the upland benches with rolling hills in the Sacramento Valley. Here, growers rely on winter annual weeds or self-reseeding winter annual cover crops such as bur clover, barrel medic, Blando brome, and Zorro fescue.

Some growers are using California native grasses in more-fertile sites. These plants provide good footing in wet weather for pruning, spraying, and other vineyard operations. Many of the species go dormant during the summer and do not compete with vines for water and fertilizer. These covers begin to grow again in the fall with rain and cool weather. Some growers limit these covers to every other row due to excessive competition with the vines when planted in sites with lower vigor potential.

Figure 85.7 Cover crops can be planted in alternate middles to reduce the risk of frost damage, reduce costs, and facilitate vineyard operations. *Photo*: C. Ingels.

REFERENCES

Ingels, C. A., R. Bugg, G. McGourty, and P. Christensen, eds. 1998. Cover cropping in vineyards: A grower's handbook. Oakland: University of California Division of Agriculture and Natural Resources Publication 3338.

Ingels, C. A., K. M. Scow, D. A. Whisson, and R. E. Drenovsky. 2005. Effects of cover crops on grapevines, yield, juice composition, soil microbial ecology and gopher activity. American Journal of Enology and Viticulture 56:19–29.

McGourty, G. 1994. Cover crops for north coast vineyards. Practical Winery and Vineyard 15(3): 1–6.

———. 2005. Cover cropping systems for organically farmed vineyards. Practical Winery & Vineyard 26(5): 22–28.

McGourty, G., and J. Reganold. 2004. Managing vineyard soil organic matter with cover crops. Proceedings of the Soil Environment and Vine Nutrition Symposium, June 29–30, San Diego. Davis, CA: American Society for Enology and Viticulture. 145–151.

Smith, R., L. Bettiga, M. Cahn, K. Baumgartner, L. Jackson, and T. Bensen. 2008. Vineyard floor management affects soil, plant nutrition, and grape yield and quality. California Agriculture 62(4): 184–190.

Tourte, L., R. Smith, L. Bettiga, T. Bensen, J. Smith, and D. Salm. 2008. Post-emergence herbicides are cost effective for vineyard floor management on the central coast. California Agriculture 62(1): 19–23.

Figure 85.8 Mulched terraces to reduce erosion on steep hillside vineyard in Napa Valley. *Photo*: C. L. Elmore.

86 WEED MANAGEMENT

Kurt J. Hembree, W. Thomas Lanini, Joseph M. DiTomaso, and Ronald N. Vargas

Weed management plays an important role in the successful production of grapes in California's diverse vineyard-growing regions. Controlling weeds in vineyards enhances the establishment of newly planted vines and improves the growth and yield of established vines. Weeds compete with grapevines for water, soil nutrients, and sometimes sunlight. Weed competition is most severe during the first 3 years after planting, when vine root growth is limited, but heavy stands of annual and perennial weeds can reduce growth and yield in well-established vineyards. Vineyards with dense weed growth often require additional water and fertilizer to maintain production.

Some weeds may interfere with cultural and harvest operations, while others provide a good habitat for field mice, voles, and other rodents that can girdle and kill young vines. Gophers are common in no-till vineyards where perennial clovers and field bindweed can be a problem. Gophers feed on the roots and weaken or kill young vines. Other pests, including insects, pathogens, and birds, can cause economic damage when weed control is not maintained. Dry weeds can become a fire hazard.

Weed management decisions and methods are based on several factors, such as economics, scale of production, terrain, soil type, irrigation method, potential for groundwater contamination, permit requirements, and grower philosophy. Growers have many cultural, mechanical, and chemical management tools available to achieve their objectives. The specific tools and methods may vary from year to year and from vineyard to vineyard. Weeds are commonly controlled either chemically or mechanically in a strip 0.6 to 1.5 m (2 to 5 ft) wide in the vine row. The area between vine rows may be chemically treated, mechanically mowed, tilled, or planted to a cover crop. Alternatively, mulches, subsurface irrigation, and flamers can also control weeds in vineyards. Often, several weed management techniques are used in a vineyard, depending on weed species, age of vines, soil conditions, and grower preference.

SOIL CHARACTERISTICS

Soil characteristics such as texture and organic matter influence which weed species are present, the number and timing of cultivations required, and the activity and residual effects of herbicides. Annual species such as puncturevine, crabgrass, horseweed, hairy fleabane, and *Panicum* species or perennials like johnsongrass, nutsedge, and bermudagrass are more prevalent on light-textured soil, while perennials such as curly dock, field bindweed, and dallisgrass are more common on heavier-textured soils. While less preemergent herbicide is required for weed control on sandy, light soils, residual control may be shorter than on clay or clay loam soils. Use lower rates of herbicides on sandy soils or soils low in organic matter. Clay soils are slower to dry, and hence irrigated less frequently, which makes cultivation more effective. On lighter soils, cultivation often needs to be done more frequently to be effective.

Irrigation and Rainfall

The irrigation method, amount of water applied, and pattern of rainfall affect weed growth. In addition, the frequency and timing of cultivation and the selection of chemicals and their residual activities also affect the growth of weeds. Successful cultivation of young weeds is facilitated by slightly moist soil conditions. In areas of higher late-winter and spring rainfall, excessive soil moisture can delay the use of tillage equipment for weed control. Annual broadleaves and grasses are particularly difficult to control once they develop extensive rooting systems, especially in heavier, wet soils. In-row cultivation should be done only where furrow or basin flood irrigation is practiced or where low-volume irrigation tubing is suspended off the soil surface and timed to avoid periods of excessive soil moisture.

Herbicide degradation is promoted by frequent wetting of the soil surface. Herbicide degradation is generally faster in moist, warm soils than in dry, cold soils. Degradation is also more rapid in fields with drip emitters or microsprinklers than with furrow irrigation. The first irrigation following an herbicide application is the most critical in terms of how far the herbicide is moved into the soil; subsequent irrigation is less important to the movement of the herbicide.

Loss of herbicides through leaching or runoff can occur, depending on the method and frequency of irrigation and soil type. Soil residual herbicides, such as simazine, diuron, and norflurazon, are susceptible to leaching under low-volume, frequent irrigation or following heavy rainfall events in coarse soils or where soils form large cracks. This can result in possible groundwater contamination and crop injury. These herbicides are also prone to runoff on heavier, sloping soils. Special permits are required for using these and other herbicides prone to leaching or runoff in specific Ground Water Protection Areas (GWPAs). These permits are issued by the county agricultural commissioner. Refer to "Using Herbicides in Ground Water Protection Areas," below, for detailed information.

Weed Monitoring

Scouting or monitoring for weeds is an important, but often overlooked, component of weed management. Early detection of newly introduced weeds or those that have escaped control efforts can help prevent them from becoming established, spreading, or shifting to species that are more difficult to control. Some of these problematic weeds are nutsedge, johnsongrass, field bindweed, horseweed, and hairy fleabane. Weed types and populations vary from area to area and year to year, even within a vineyard. Weed monitoring is useful for evaluating the progress of the current management program and to make adjustments to changing weed populations. Routinely scouting fields is cost effective by helping to reduce or eliminate ineffective treatments. Table 86.1 describes four criteria needed for weed monitoring.

Conduct weed surveys following each treatment to determine the best control practices for your particular situation. Pay particular attention to anywhere water accumulates in low-lying areas and around low-volume drip emitters or microsprinklers. Monitoring at least twice a year (summer and winter) will give a good indication of summer and winter annuals and perennials that are present in the field. These weed surveys should be the basis for weed management decisions that determine herbicide choice or cultivation equipment and practices. Keep written records of survey results for future reference. In addition to this manual, use *Weeds of California and other Western States* (ANR Publication 3488), or others that have color photos, to help identify local weeds. The weed susceptibility charts presented in this publication (see the UC IPM Grape Pest Management Guidelines, www.ipm.ucdavis.edu/PMG/) will help serve as a guide for herbicide selection based on weed species found on the farm.

Table 86.1. Important criteria for weed monitoring in vineyards

Criteria	Typical questions to be addressed
1. Know your farm.	Which weeds are known to be present? When are specific weeds a problem? How do soil conditions and terrain vary? Are there drainage problems in certain areas? Are weeds present on field edges, fence lines, and irrigation canals or ditches? What control methods have been successful in the past?
2. Develop a strategy.	What chemical or mechanical options are needed for the weed flora? Do you have ample equipment and labor to properly time control practices? Are you considering areas surrounding the field? Is it affordable?
3. Implement the strategy.	Does the strategy meet label and timing recommendations? Do you allow for weather and field conditions? Are you observant of equipment in operation?
4. Review the strategy.	Which weeds still persist? Did any unanticipated events affect the results? Were there any surprise successes? Were there any side effects (erosion, vine injury, etc.)? What were the costs versus the benefits?

MECHANICAL CONTROL

Mechanical cultivation uproots or buries weeds (fig. 86.1). Weed burial works best on small weeds, while larger weeds are better controlled by destroying the root-shoot connection or by slicing, cutting, or turning the soil to separate the root system from contact with the soil. In vineyards with permanent sod middles, a mower (fig. 86.2) is often used periodically to maintain low-growing plants. Where resident vegetation is allowed to grow in the middles (fig. 86.3), the area may be treated with postemergent herbicides to suppress weed growth (fig. 86.4). In this case, cultivation is limited to a strip under the vine row. The reverse might be true in systems where mulches are employed for weed suppression under the vine row and cultivation is used to control weeds and incorporate cover crops between the rows. In any case, cultivation must be kept shallow to minimize damage to vine roots and to avoid bringing more weed seeds near the surface to germinate. Adjust mechanical equipment sufficiently to avoid damaging the trunks of the vines.

Several tools or machines are available for weed cultivation or weed removal in vineyards, many of which can be used for in-row cultivation. Some types of equipment cultivates the soil deeply, while others provide shallow cultivation. The choice of machinery depends on the terrain, soil type, soil moisture, types of weeds, vine spacing, and outlay and operational costs.

Table 86.2 lists some common mechanical equipment for managing weeds on the vineyard floor. This list may not be complete, but it provides examples of many types of equipment used in vineyards.

Perennial weeds, which have established root systems, are difficult to kill with a single tillage operation. Many perennial weeds are, in a sense, like an iceberg: 80 to 90% of the plant is in the soil, 10 to 20% is emerged. Tillage removes the top, but the plant generates a new top using the underground reserves. For perennials, tillage at a depth of 7.5 to 10 cm (3 to 4 in) depletes the maximum amount of reserves and forces the weeds to use up more of the reserves.

Even the best cultivators will not eliminate all weeds, and hand-weeding is often needed. Hand-weeding alone may be effective on a small scale (fig. 86.5). In large-scale plantings of vines, where in-row tillage is desired, mechanical hoes such as the Weed Badger, Kimco, or Green Hoe may be useful. These tractor-mounted cultivators extend from the tractor and can till very close to the vine without damaging the plant. Attachment options include powered rotary tillage tools and scraper blades that can move soil away from or to the base of the vines.

Table 86.2. Mechanical equipment commonly used to control weeds in vineyards

Type of machine	Description
French or hoe plow	Heavy duty; does best in moist soil; needs soil thrown back under the vine in subsequent pass (fig. 86.6).
Clemens cultivator	Sturdy; few moving parts; slices under the weeds; can be mounted in front, mid, or rear; can handle tight spaces and is faster than some other cultivators (fig. 86.7).
Kimco cultivator	Extremely heavy duty; usually very slow; can be fit with cultivator or mower head; has some ability to adjust the angle, allowing use on slopes; the teeth can wear out rapidly.
Gearmore cultivator	Similar to the Clemens but not as heavy duty; reliable though lighter; uses a blade to slice weeds; less expensive than Clemens.
Weed Badger cultivator	Fairly heavy duty; different models vary in durability; lots of moving parts; fair reliability but slow; can be fit with cultivator or mower; works for any size weed; head can be adjusted to work on a variety of angles and slopes but may be too wide for narrow rows.
Pellenc Sunflower cultivator	Works on single and dual rows; mid or rear mount; good ability to handle slopes; works best on small and medium weeds; teeth can wear out rapidly; hard-facing is needed; fairly slow and expensive.
Bezzerides cultivator	Shallow cultivator with single rod/blade; durable; better for use on mature vines; generally used on flat land, but can be adapted for slopes; faster than most other cultivators; not good for young vines.
ID David cultivator	Versatile, with several attachments including mower, weed knife, cultivator, hoe; slow; lots of parts; good ability to adjust to different row widths, berm heights, and slopes; fairly good sensor; will handle large weeds; mounted on front or mid.
Omnas Boomerang	Cultivates with a rototiller head; its mode of articulation around vines permits close cultivation; useful for young vineyards and on small terraces; flexible to adjust to different slopes.
Spedo	Has optional attachments for undervine tillage: a weed knife, rotary hoe, and mower; offers flexibility; distributed by Gearmore; manufactured by Spedo & Figali.
Kimco in-row mower	Mows vegetation under the vines, an option for vineyards that are no-till systems.
Perfect rotary mower	Manufactured in Holland; can be initially adjusted for different row sizes; has options for mowing between the vines and arms for mowing under the vines.
propane flamer	Uses propane gas burners to produce a controlled and directed flame that passes over weeds. The intense heat sears the leaves, and the weed wilts and dies 1 to 3 days later. Needs to be used on young weeds; comes in various models; can be fitted to tractors or used in a hand-held model; moves slowly; burn permit required.

The latter, known as grape hoes, have been used for many years in vineyards. Specialty tillage equipment is expensive and may not be cost effective for small vineyards. Grow tube protection is recommended for the vines in vineyards less than 3 years old. Weed control is still necessary in these young vineyards, and some hand removal of weeds that grow up into the tubes may be necessary.

HERBICIDES

When properly used, herbicides can control most weed species found in vineyards. In most situations, tank-mix combinations or sequential applications of herbicides will be required to provide effective, economical control. Before using any herbicide, correctly identify the weeds being targeted, then read and follow product label directions carefully.

Herbicides are classified as either preemergent or postemergent according to their activities. Refer to the UC IPM Grape Pest Management Guidelines, www.ipm.ucdavis.edu/PMG/, appropriate herbicide product labels, and other resources for specific weed sensitivity to preemergent and postemergent herbicide products.

Preemergent Herbicides

Soil-applied, residual, or

Figure 86.1 Disking the vineyard middles in the early spring. *Photo*: C. L. Elmore.

Figure 86.2 Mowing the middles of a vineyard. *Photo*: J. K. Clark.

Figure 86.3 Vegetation allowed to grow between rows, then mowed, tilled, or sprayed with herbicides. *Photo*: C. L. Elmore.

Figure 86.4 Vineyard in which weeds in the middles have been chemically suppressed. *Photo*: C. L. Elmore.

Figure 86.5 Hand cultivation of the vine row. *Photo*: W. E. Bendixen.

Figure 86.6 Using a hoe plow to remove weeds in the vine row. *Photo*: C. L. Elmore.

preemergent herbicides are applied to the soil surface to control germinating weeds. These herbicides do not generally control dormant weed seeds or weeds that have emerged from the soil. If weeds are present at the time of application, add a postemergent, or foliar, herbicide to the tank for control. In most vineyards, preemergent herbicides are applied to a narrow strip 0.6 to 1.5 m (2 to 5 ft) down the center of each vine row, reducing the amount of herbicide needed to 15 to 30% of the total vineyard acreage (see fig. 86.3).

Application of preemergent herbicides must be followed by incorporation and activation by rainfall, irrigation, or mechanical means into the top 2.5 to 5 cm (1 to 2 in) of soil, where weed seeds germinate (table 86.3). If the herbicide is unevenly applied or incorporated, weed control may be reduced, and vines may be injured. Some residual herbicides (such as napropamide) degrade rapidly after they are sprayed on the soil surface if rainfall or irrigation does not follow the application within 5 to 10 days. Trifluralin is so volatile on moist soil that mechanical incorporation is required within hours of treatment. Other herbicides (such as oryzalin and simazine) can remain on the soil surface for longer periods (3 to 4 weeks) before incorporation with water without appreciable loss in persistence.

Properly applied and incorporated preemergent herbicides can persist from a few months to a year or more, depending on application rate, rate of degradation, and whether leaching or runoff occurs. Preemergent herbicides

applied to vineyards that are frequently watered with drip or microsprinkler irrigation are generally degraded faster than those in vineyards under furrow or flood irrigation. In soils that are sandy, low in organic matter or clay content, and receive heavy rainfall or frequent wetting by irrigation, some herbicides (such as simazine, diuron, and norflurazon) may leach into the vine's root zone and cause plant injury.

Postemergent Herbicides

Herbicides applied to actively growing weeds are referred to as foliar-applied or postemergent herbicides. They are classified as contact or systemic based on their mode of action.

Contact herbicides (such as paraquat or glufosinate) kill the green parts of the plant that are actually sprayed; adequate spray volume and coverage is essential for control. Time the application when weeds are small and most

susceptible to control. Refer to herbicide labels for recommended timing of weed sprays. Avoid contact with green foliage, shoots, or immature bark of the grapevine or injury may result.

Systemic, or translocated, herbicides (such as sethoxydim and glyphosate) move from one part of the plant to another. They are more effective on young, vigorously growing weeds. Because the herbicide must be moved through the plant to kill it, control is usually slow (2 weeks or more). Tank-mixing pre- and postemergent herbicides can improve control over a broader spectrum of weeds than using either alone.

Postemergent herbicides are commonly applied as strip spray treatments to control weeds that escape preemergent herbicides or in lieu of preemergent herbicides. They are applied either as a uniform treatment across the vine row or in spot applications with a hand

Figure 86.7 Mechanical weed control in the vine row with a Clemens cultivator (A). (B) shows a Clemens cultivator that has been modified by the grower for rocky soils. *Photos*: L. J. Bettiga.

wand (fig. 86.8). Shielded equipment or spray nozzles designed to reduce spray drift should be used whenever possible to prevent the spray solution from coming into contact with any green or immature part of the vine. While plastic-coated or cardboard wraps may help prevent young vines from being damaged by vertebrate pests and wind, they do not guarantee protection from herbicide sprays, especially if equipment or windy conditions do not favor uniform application at the base of the vines.

Application Equipment

Herbicide application equipment must be accurately calibrated and maintained to ensure that the proper dose of herbicide and volume of water or carrier are applied. For safe application and to minimize drift, spray equipment should be equipped with a short boom that has nozzles that are either capable of operating at low pressures (for example, XR8004VS) or designed to reduce drift (like turbo or air induction). Off-center nozzles on the end of the boom can apply chemicals (mainly preemergents) as a directed application in the vineyard row, but generally provide better soil coverage where vine rows are not grown on raised berms. Low-volume controlled-droplet applicators (fig. 86.9) are effective when using systemic postemergent herbicides, especially for perennial weeds. However, because they produce very small spray droplets (less than 100 microns in size), which are sensitive to drift, they must be monitored carefully during application. A smart sprayer can be very effective for controlling weeds that occur in patches in the field. These sprayers can reduce the amount of product applied by 50% or more compared with treating the entire vine row. Some herbicides require special application requirements, so read the label carefully and follow all recommendations. Proper sprayer cleaning following application is also important to prevent crop injury on subsequent treatments. Herbicides such as 2,4-D are active at very small quantities and can adhere to hoses and other sprayer parts, so follow label directions carefully when rinsing out spray equipment after its use.

A Word of Caution

After selecting the herbicide(s) you want to use, read and follow all label instructions carefully. This publication is not intended to replace the registered labels of herbicides used in vineyards. Limitations pertaining to the use of herbicides discussed here are subject to change. Information concerning limitations is available from regulatory officials, through agricultural chemical trade channels, and from University of California Cooperative Extension offices. Restrictions are also listed on the manufacturer's label. Observe all precautions on the label regarding use of protective clothing and equipment, handling and storage of chemicals, and protection of pets, domestic animals, wildlife, fish, and desired vegetation. A permit is required from the county agricultural commissioner for the purchase and use of restricted-use pesticides such as paraquat and 2,4-D. Additionally, a similar permit is required for using certain herbicides in specified Ground Water Protection Areas (GWPAs).

Figure 86.8 Spot spraying a contact herbicide to control summer weeds. *Photo*: L. J. Bettiga.

Figure 86.9 Low-volume shielded applicator. *Photo*: K. J. Hembree.

Table 86.3. Incorporation timing requirements of some preemergent herbicides

Common name	Trade name	Time to incorporation or activation
diuron	Karmex, Direx	within 14 days of treatment
flumioxazin	Chateau	within 28 days of treatment
indaziflam	Alion	within 21 days of treatment
isoxaben	Trellis	within 28 days of treatment
napropamide	Devrinol	within 5 days of treatment
norflurazon	Solicam	within 28 days of treatment
oryzalin	Surflan, Oryzalin, etc.	within 21 days of treatment
oxyfluorfen	Goal, etc.	within 28 days of treatment
pendimethalin	Prowl H$_2$O	within 21 days of treatment
rimsulfuron	Matrix	within 14 days of treatment
simazine	Princep, etc.	within 28 days of treatment
trifluralin	Treflan, Trilin, etc.	within 24 hours of treatment

Preemergent herbicides can persist in the soil for a relatively long time after application, and their use should be discontinued 1 to 2 years before vineyard removal. Growers should plan ahead and cultivate or use postemergent herbicides for weed control during the period preceding vineyard removal. Follow label recommendations regarding plant-back restrictions following herbicide treatment.

If it is necessary to replant vines in the field after preemergent herbicides have been applied, particularly down the vine rows, use clean, untreated soil to backfill around the new plantings. To avoid applying excessive amounts of herbicides, shut the sprayer off when stopping or turning at row ends. Always apply at a constant speed; slowing down increases the amount of herbicide applied, which increases the risk of crop injury. When cleaning clogged nozzles, catch chemicals in a pail and return to the spray tank.

Herbicide application rates included in this publication are expressed as amounts of active ingredient and are based on actual sprayed acres. A broadcast application treats 100% of the vineyard acreage; in a strip application, less than the full vineyard is treated. Therefore, adjust the application rate to only the proportion of an acre represented by the strip application.

Herbicide application rates are within the ranges recommended on the registered labels and represent those generally found to be safe and effective by UC weed scientists. However, rates may need to be adjusted for specific California grape-growing regions and conditions. Growers should consult pest control advisers or farm advisors at their county Cooperative Extension office for region-specific herbicide information.

Using Herbicides in Ground Water Protection Areas (GWPAs)

The California Department of Pesticide Regulation (DPR) produced regulations that took effect in April 2004 designating approximately 2.4 million acres (971,000 ha) across the state where groundwater is most vulnerable to pesticide contamination as Ground Water Protection Areas (GWPAs). The DPR website, http://www.cdpr.ca.gov/docs/emon/grndwtr/gwpamaps.htm, contains maps that show where GWPAs

519

are located within each county. The regulations further delineate GWPAs into two categories:

- *Leaching* GWPAs, where pesticide residues move from the soil surface downward through the soil profile with percolating water to reach groundwater. Soils in these areas are coarse, with fairly rapid infiltration rates.

- *Runoff* GWPAs, where pesticide residues are carried in runoff water to more direct routes to groundwater, such as drainage wells, poorly sealed production wells, or soil cracks, or to areas where leaching can occur. Soils in these areas may have a hardpan layer or low infiltration rates.

Seven pesticides (table 86.4) on the 6800[a] list are in regulation as groundwater contaminants. Of the seven listed, three are pre-emergent herbicides commonly applied in grapes (diuron, norflurazon, and simazine). The regulations prescribe actions by growers and others writing recommendations to help prevent these pesticides from reaching groundwater in GWPAs. If your farming site is located within a leaching or runoff GWPA and you want to use or prescribe materials on the 6800[a] list, then you must obtain a restricted-use materials permit from the county agricultural commissioner and comply with management practices specified by regulation in your restricted-use materials permit. If you are using materials in a GWPA that are not on the 6800[a] list, you do not need a restricted-use materials permit, unless otherwise required by label restrictions and local regulations.

Management guidelines for leaching GWPAs

In leaching GWPAs, materials on the 6800[a] list can be applied to grape vineyards by a permitted applicator if any one of the following three management practice options is met, as designated on the restricted-use materials permit, for 6 months following application of the herbicide.

Option 1: No irrigation water is applied for 6 months.

Option 2: No contact with downward-leaching irrigation water. Herbicides are applied to the vine row above the level of irrigation water in the furrow or basin so they have no contact with leaching irrigation water.

Option 3: Irrigation management. Manage irrigations so that the ratio of the amount of irrigation water applied divided by the net irrigation requirement is 1.33 or less (leaching fraction of no more than 33%).

Management guidelines for runoff GWPAs

In runoff GWPAs, materials on the 6800[a] list can be applied to grape vineyards by a permitted applicator if any one of the following management practice options is met, as designated on the restricted-use materials permit:

Option 1: Soil disturbance. The soil is disturbed within 7 days before herbicide application, by using a disk, rotary tiller, or other mechanical method. (Note: this restriction does not apply if the herbicide is applied as a banded treatment; see band treatment below.)

Option 2: Incorporation of the herbicide. The herbicide is incorporated on at least 90% of the area

Table 86.4. Herbicides on the 6800[a]* list in California used in Ground Water Protection Areas (GWPAs)

Herbicide common name	Herbicide trade name	Registered in grapes
atrazine	Aatrex	no
bentazon	Basagran	no
bromacil	Hyvar X, Krovar	no
diuron	Karmex, Direx	yes
norflurazon	Solicam	yes
prometron	Pramitol	no
simazine	Princep	yes

Note:
*Section *6800[a] of the California Code of Regulations.*

treated within 7 days after application by a mechanical method or by low-flow irrigation (0.25 to 1 inch, or 6 to 25 mm, of water), including chemigation if allowed by the label, provided that no runoff occurs. (Note: this restriction does not apply if the herbicide is applied as a banded treatment; see band treatment below.)

Option 3: Band treatment. The herbicide is applied as a banded treatment down the vine row, not to exceed 33% of the distance between crop rows.

Option 4: Timing of application. The pesticide is applied between April 1 and July 31.

Option 5: Retention of runoff on field. All irrigation runoff and all precipitation on and drainage through the field are retained on-site for 6 months after the application, provided that the retention area on the field does not have a percolation rate of more than 0.2 inch (5 mm) per hour.

Option 6: Retention of runoff in a holding area off the field. Channel all irrigation and runoff to a holding area off the application site, under the control of the property owner, that is designed to retain all runoff for 6 months following application. The holding area should have a percolation rate of 0.2 inches (5 mm) per hour or less.

Option 7: Runoff onto a fallow field. For 6 months after application, channel all irrigation and rainfall runoff onto an adjacent unenclosed fallow field. The fallow field should be at least 300 feet long and not irrigated for 6 months after application, with full consideration of any plant-back restrictions.

Option 8: Alternative management practices, if approved. Check with your local county agricultural commissioner for information.

Prior to Planting

Control annual and perennial weeds before planting a vineyard to reduce the competition from weeds during vineyard establishment. It is especially important to control established stands of perennial weeds before grapevines are planted in order to reduce their competition and to avoid potential injury to young vines from herbicides. Perennial weeds that can be especially troublesome include field bindweed, johnsongrass, dallisgrass, bermudagrass, and nutsedge.

Nonchemical Control

An effective method of weed control before planting vines is to cultivate, irrigate to germinate new weeds, and cultivate again to destroy seedling weeds. Frequent cultivation lowers weed seed populations in the soil, reducing weed growth. At least two cycles of cultivation, irrigation, and shallow cultivation are needed for a marked reduction in weed seedlings. This method is not usually effective on established perennial weeds.

For control of emerged perennial grasses, such as bermudagrass and johnsongrass, cultivate the soil when it is very dry. Cultivation cuts the rhizomes into small pieces so they can desiccate. The soil can then be reworked frequently using spring tooth harrows to pull new rhizomes to the surface and desiccate them as well. If the soil is irrigated or rain occurs before total control of the perennial plant is achieved, the rhizome pieces will begin to grow and the effectiveness may be reduced. By the same token, working the soil when wet can increase the population of perennial weeds, because each piece of cut rhizome can root and develop into a new plant.

Field bindweed growth can be reduced for 1 to 2 years by deep plowing or with a reclamation blade (a large V-shaped blade) to cut the roots 40 to 45 cm (16 to 18 in) deep in dry soil. Populations of nutsedge can be reduced by deep plowing with large, specialized moldboard plows (such as the Kverneland Plow) to bury the nutlets to a depth of at least 30 cm (12 in), where they can decompose. Seedlings of perennials can be controlled with repeated cultivation.

Soil solarization is a nonpesticidal method of controlling soilborne pests by placing clear plastic sheets on moist soil during periods of high ambient temperature. The plastic sheets allow the sun's radiant energy to be trapped in the soil, heating the upper levels. Solarization during the long, clear summer days can increase soil temperature to levels that kill many disease-causing organisms (pathogens), nematodes, and weed seedlings. It leaves no toxic residues and can be easily used on a small or large scale. Soil solarization also improves soil structure and increases the availability of nitrogen and other essential plant nutrients. For additional information on this technique, see *Soil Solarization* (UC ANR Publication 21377).

Herbicides

Weeds can be controlled either with preemergent or postemergent herbicides before planting. Trifluralin can be applied before planting a vineyard to provide preemergence control of annual grasses and certain annual broadleaf species. Apply the herbicide in a strip down the center where the vines will be planted and incorporate with a disk 5 to 10 cm (2 to 4 in) deep, then plant into the treated soil, but use untreated soil around roots when backfilling. Many growers prefer to use preemergent herbicides only after the vines have been planted to avoid possible exposure to herbicides that may be in the backfill soil. Postemergent herbicides generally have a short soil residual period and are safer to use before planting vines. Bordering up the field, irrigating, then treating with postemergent herbicides can be an effective method for reducing the population of annual and perennial weeds before planting.

Newly Planted Vineyards

During the first few years after planting vines, rooting is limited and weed competition can reduce vine growth by 50%, depending on the types and density of weeds present. Newly planted vine rows covered with a dense population of dead weeds or mulch can also reduce soil temperatures, delaying growth. This area can also be a

good habitat for vertebrate pests at a time when small vines are the most vulnerable to girdling. Weedy vineyards may require several more years to become economically productive than weed-free vineyards. Regardless of the method used to control weeds, care should be taken not to injure vines with chemicals or to mechanically damage the vine trunk or roots. After about the third year, the effect of competition from weeds is somewhat lessened as vines become established and shading from the vineyard canopy reduces weed growth. In older vineyards, however, weed growth can interfere with cultural practices and harvest; for example, weeds can disrupt the application pattern of water from low-volume spray emitters. Frequent cultivation near vines can injure vine roots or the base of the vine trunk. Vine trunk injuries can encourage crown gall infections.

Mechanical Control

Some growers prefer to manage weeds without herbicides for the first year or two after planting. Because vines are usually planted on a grid, mechanical methods of weed control can be practiced on terrain easily traversed by equipment. This requires cross-cultivating and using handweeding around individual vines several times during spring and summer. This technique can be effective for controlling many annual and perennial weeds before stakes, wire, and irrigation tubing are installed. When cultivating, weeds should be small and the soil moist enough to allow for tillage to flow smoothly without pulling up large clods.

Mechanical cultivators are available for use in vine rows

as well, including weed knives, spyder cultivators, and rotary tillers. Rotary tillers such as a Weed Badger, Kimco, or Clemens Hoe are most effective on loose soil that is not rocky. Hand-held mechanical flails (Weed Eaters) can be effective, but they can also injure vine trunks. Disks, tillers, or mowers can be used between the rows. Mechanical control of weeds must be done repeatedly when weeds are immature. The equipment should be set to cut shallowly to minimize damage to vine roots. As weeds mature, they are more difficult to control, may clog equipment, and produce seed. When using any mechanical equipment around vines, be careful not to injure the grapevine feeder roots or trunk.

Cover Crops

Planted cover crops can also reduce weed populations between vine rows. With cover crops, the species selected and management differ from one area of the state to another. Be sure to select a cover crop that will not compete with the vines. Some clovers can spread to vine rows and are difficult to control with herbicides labeled for vineyards, so proper cover crop selection and management are important for your particular conditions. Cultivation in preparation for planting a winter annual cover crop also reduces weed growth. To preserve surface cover, mow the cover crop to the correct height recommended for that crop. Refer to section 85, "Vineyard Floor Management," for additional information concerning cover crop selection and management.

Mulches

Organic mulches (cereal straw, green waste, composted wood

chips) or synthetic mulches of polyethylene, polypropylene, or polyester can be used around young vines to reduce or prevent weed growth. Always apply mulches when the soil surface is free of weeds. Mulches help prevent the germination and growth of weeds by blocking light at the soil surface. They create more uniform moisture conditions, which can promote young vine growth. However, in some situations, large amounts of plant-based mulches can reduce the soil temperature and reduce vine growth. Mulches may also provide a good habitat for gophers, voles, and mice and may be a source of new weed seed that came with the mulch. Mulches do not control perennial weed growth unless all light can be excluded. Some woven fabric mulches offer excellent weed control for several years, but the initial cost of purchase and installation is high.

Herbicides

Since most vineyards are planted with dormant plants, selective preemergent herbicides usually offer the most effective weed control. Although postemergent herbicides can be applied in new vineyard plantings, extreme care should be taken to prevent the spray from contacting green foliage and immature wood. Some herbicides can be applied in only a certain period before the grapes come into production, so refer to the appropriate product label before applying herbicides.

To control weeds with herbicides after grapevines are planted and before bearing, apply a preemergent herbicide (such as oryzalin, napropamide, or oxyfluorfen) to either a square or

circle around each vine at least 0.9 to 1.8 m (3 to 6 ft) across or as a directed strip-spray down the vine row. All preemergent herbicides, with the exception of trifluralin, require overhead water to move them into the soil. Trifluralin requires mechanical soil incorporation. Select an herbicide based on expected weed species, soil texture, and irrigation method. In many situations, a combination of preemergent herbicides broadens the spectrum of weed control and increases the persistence of residual activity.

Herbicides can also be applied to control weeds after they emerge. Selective postemergent herbicides available for annual grass control and suppression of perennial grasses such as johnsongrass and bermudagrass include sethoxydim, fluazifop, and clethodim. These herbicides require the addition of an adjuvant (either a nonionic surfactant or a nonphytotoxic oil). They do not control nutsedge or broadleaf weeds, and only clethodim controls annual bluegrass. Paraquat and glufosinate can control weeds near young vines protected with shields or wraps. Take care not to spray green stems. Nonselective herbicides such as glyphosate control broadleaf weeds after emergence, but they should be used only around vines with brown bark and should not be allowed to contact leaves, green shoots, or immature wood.

ESTABLISHED VINEYARDS

From a weed management viewpoint, the term established vineyard refers to a vineyard at least 3 years old. The actual amount of time it takes for a vine to reach maturity and production status depends on

the type of grape (wine, table, or raisin), rootstock, variety, growing region, and other factors. Usually, by the third year the grower has decided whether the weed management program will be mechanical (cultivation and mowing), chemical, or a combination of methods. Regardless of the method, timing of treatment is essential for optimal control.

Timing Weed Removal

Weeds should be destroyed before they produce seed, which helps deplete soil seed reserves by germination without replenishing new seeds. Table 86.5 shows the seed production of weeds commonly found infesting grape vineyards. Killing weeds early also conserves soil moisture, which is important in areas with limited water supplies. Also, destroying weed growth before budbreak enhances air movement, reducing the risk of frost damage where air movement is a factor; weeds can promote frost by preventing the soil from absorbing heat during the day and emitting radiation at night to warm the air. Winter weeds also are an excellent overwintering site for leafhoppers and thrips, as well as diseases that can damage new vine growth. Remember to apply preemergent herbicides before weeds emerge from the soil and to apply postemergent herbicides when weeds are small and actively growing. Weeds are most sensitive during this time to both mechanical and chemical weed control. Allowing a few weeds to set seed can significantly increase the seed reserves in the soil for years. For example, common purslane seed can remain viable for more than 20 years in the soil.

Mechanical Control

By the second year of most plantings, trellises, stakes, and irrigation tubing are installed, eliminating the opportunity to cross-cultivate or disk. Cultivation in established vineyards can control annual and biennial weeds and seedlings of perennial weeds. Control seedlings of field bindweed, bermudagrass, and johnsongrass before they are 3 weeks old or they may form perennial reproductive structures such as rhizomes. Cultivating for nutsedge control is not recommended, since this can increase the spread of underground nutlets throughout the field.

In-row cultivation equipment as shown in table 86.2 can also control weeds within the vine row. Equipment must be properly set and closely monitored during operation to prevent damage to vine trunks and roots. Weeds should be small and not producing seed prior to control. Mechanical methods usually require at least two operations during the season for maximum control, depending on the age and shading of the vines, type of trellis, field conditions, and grower preference. Mechanical control should not be practiced during wet conditions, as this promotes soil compaction and erosion problems. Once canes begin to drop down, potential damage limits this practice unless cane lifters or cutters are used. Even with the best equipment, hand-hoeing immediately around grapevines 3 years old or younger is normally required.

Propane flaming can control young weeds in mature vineyards. Use either a single flame directed at the base of the vine or several burners on a boom to burn the weeds between the vine rows. Flaming is effective only on young weeds, and annual broadleaf weeds are more susceptible to control than grasses or perennials. Do not use flaming around young vines, because it may damage the thin green bark. Dry vegetation may ignite and cause a fire that can girdle young vines. Flaming may also damage wooden stakes and plastic irrigation tubing.

Mulches

Organic and synthetic mulches can suppress weed growth in established vineyards, as previously discussed above in "Newly Planted Vineyards." Because organic mulches degrade, they must be replenished annually. As these mulches degrade, they become a good growth medium for weed species such as common groundsel, prickly lettuce, common sowthistle, and panicle willowherb.

Herbicides

Growers electing to use herbicides usually spray a strip down the vine row 0.6 to 1.2 m (2 to 4

Table 86.5. Weed seed production

Scientific name	Common name	Seeds/plant
Amaranthus retroflexus	redroot pigweed	117,400
Avena fatua	wild oat	250
Capsella bursa-pastoris	shepherd's purse	38,500
Chenopodium album	common lambsquarters	72,450
Conyza canadensis	horseweed	200,000
Conyza bonariensis	hairy fleabane	10,000
Digitaria sanguinalis	large crabgrass	150,000
Echinochloa crus-galli	barnyardgrass	40,000
Croton setigerus	turkey mullein	223,200
Lactuca serriola	prickly lettuce	27,900
Portulaca oleracea	common purslane	52,300
Setaria pumila	yellow foxtail	6,420
Tribulus terrestris	puncturevine	10,000

ft) wide and mechanically control weeds between rows, particularly in areas where raisin drying is practiced using paper trays on the soil or where trellis systems do not impede equipment. However, management of weeds between rows varies considerably, depending on what the grapes are grown for (raisin, wine, or table), economics, and grower preference. Some growers opt for no-till, using low rates of herbicides to manage the weeds in the middles. No-till is also practiced in some regions where perennial or annual cover crops are planted in the middles and either mowed or treated with herbicides to prevent excessive growth.

When using herbicides to control weeds, apply a preemergent herbicide or a combination of herbicides for broader weed control in the fall or winter following trimming of canes, in the spring before budbreak, or split into two applications. A postemergent herbicide should be added if weeds are present at the time of application. For the greatest safety, apply the herbicides as a directed application at the base of the vines, not at the vine, shoots, or 1- to 2-year-old wood. Many growers make repeated applications of postemergent herbicides in lieu of preemergent herbicides. Field access and timing of application to the proper weed size are important for this to be effective. Large weeds are generally not effectively controlled with postemergent herbicides and often lead to additional weed seed production. To determine which herbicides to use, consider the weed species, soil type, irrigation method, age of the vines, variety grown, label registration, and county restrictions.

Over time, you may observe a change or shift in the types of weeds present. These weeds may be annuals that are tolerant to the herbicides being applied or perennials that flourish without annual weed competition. Referring to notes obtained during field monitoring for weeds will help you adjust your selection of herbicides before difficult annual and perennial weeds become well established. Rotating herbicides or using combinations of herbicides often helps eliminate this problem. Preemergent herbicide rates should be adjusted to the lowest rate that provides effective control and matches the soil type. Always adjust the herbicide rate to match the coarsest texture of your soil if there is soil variability within the field and follow specific rate recommendations on the herbicide label.

If perennial weeds like johnsongrass, field bindweed, bermudagrass, or nutsedge become established, consider modifying the herbicide program. Currently, effective materials for these and other perennial weeds are primarily limited to postemergent compounds applied during active weed growth. Repeated spot treatment of patches of perennial weeds will be required. Herbicides such as glyphosate, sethoxydim, and 2,4-D are registered for this use. Nutsedge can be controlled with the preemergent herbicides thiazopyr (nonbearing vines) and norflurazon (vines 2 years old or more). When using postemergent herbicides, spray the nutsedge plants before they have four leaves, before new nutlets are formed.

Other Methods

Weed control in the area between vine rows is now commonly managed by mowing resident vegetation, interseeding with cover crop species, or chemical control. No-till or mowing is adaptable under drip irrigation, and its advantages include lower management cost, reduced soil residue of herbicides, reduced erosion on steep terrain, and possible insect management. Disadvantages may include increased vertebrate pests and soil insects, difficulty preparing terraces for raisin drying, increased water use, and increased frost potential due to the reduction in reradiation of heat.

Annual grasses such as Blando brome, Zorro fescue, or subterranean clovers, or fall-seeded cereal crops such as wheat, oat, cereal rye, or barley, can help suppress weed growth in vine row middles. These are seeded into a prepared seedbed between vine rows in late September through mid-November. Most plants will reseed themselves if mowed in January or early February and allowed to grow into April and May. Mowing after the seeds mature ensures seed for the next season. Keep cover crops away from young vines. Rotating cover crop species reduces the potential for buildup of disease pathogens, weeds, vertebrate pests, and insect pests. For more information on cover crops, see section 85, "Vineyard Floor Management," or consult *Covercrops for California Agriculture* (UC ANR Publication 21471) or *Cover Cropping in Vineyards: A Growers Handbook* (UC ANR Publication 3338).

Irrigation Systems

The type of irrigation system can greatly affect weed management in California vineyards. Common irrigation methods include drip (surface and subsurface), furrow, flood or basin flood, and sprinkler. The choice of cultivation, mowing, herbicide, or combinations of these is influenced by irrigation systems. Combining cultivation and complete wetting of the soil usually encourages weed seed germination, whereas drip irrigation favors summer weed growth only in or near the wetted pattern of the emitters. Irrigation tubing should be buried or suspended above the soil surface if mechanical equipment is to be used within the vine rows. The irrigation method and frequency of irrigation also influence the residual properties of preemergent herbicides and the degree or length of control. In drip-irrigated fields, preemergent herbicides must be applied before or during the rainy season. Preemergent herbicides tend to break down more rapidly under frequent drip irrigation than with other methods of irrigation. Weed management under sprinkler irrigation provides greater latitude in choosing herbicides and timing applications.

Specific herbicide properties such as solubility, volatility, half-life, and so on can influence the duration of weed control achieved under different irrigation methods. Herbicides such as simazine, diuron, and norflurazon are susceptible to leaching or runoff (possibly leading to groundwater contamination and crop injury) under certain field and irrigation conditions, so consult the label for specific recommendations when using these and other herbicides under irrigation systems.

Organic Production

Controlling weeds in organic vineyards requires the use of many techniques and strategies to achieve economic control and yield. Weeds can always be pulled or cut out, but the question is simply how much time and money a grower can spend to reduce weed pressure. The more a grower is able to reduce weed pressure (seed and perennial propagules), the more economical it will be to produce crops.

A good organic weed management plan should present a minimum risk of soil erosion, provide a "platform" for the movement of farm equipment, not adversely impact pest management or soil fertility, and minimize weed competition for water and nutrients. Vineyards that will be managed organically should be designed for nonchemical weed control practices. The following is an overview of some organically acceptable weed control practices for vineyards.

Mulches

Weed control in the vineyard can be a daunting task whether you are an organic or conventional grower. One encouraging control method is the use of organic mulches. The mulch blocks light, preventing weed seed germination and weed growth. Many materials can be used as mulches, including plastics or organic materials such as municipal yard waste, wood chips, straw, hay, sawdust, and newspaper. To be effective, mulch must block all light to the weeds; mulch materials vary in the depth necessary to accomplish this. Organic mulches must be maintained in a layer 10 cm (4 in) thick, or more. Organic mulches decompose with time; the original thickness typically reduces by 60% after 1 year.

One option is to grow cover crops in the middles and in the spring "mow-and-throw" the cuttings around the base of the vines. This works well if the mulch layer is thick. Weeds that emerge through the mulch can be controlled using an organic contact herbicide or hand-weeding. Cover crops may be planted under the vine row in some situations, but excessive competition may occur, possibly reducing grape yields.

The additional benefits of mulches are significant. Mulch conserves moisture by reducing evaporation. It also maintains a more consistent soil temperature and adds organic material to the soil as the mulch decomposes. Weed germination and growth are greatly impeded. Some grasses will survive mulching, but they will be shallow rooted and can be easily pulled out. Partially rotted straw or hay can be used as mulch, but it must come from fields that have not used pesticides or chemical fertilizers.

Herbicides Accepted in Organic Production

Several organic contact herbicide products are available for use in organic production. These include clove oil, acetic acid, citric acid products, and other plant-based materials in products such as GreenMatch EX, Matran II, All-Down, and others. For a list of products approved for organic production, consult the Organic Materials Review Institute, OMRI, http//www.omri.org. These products damage any green vegetation contacted, including the leaves and young stems of grapevines, though they are safe as sprays directed on woody stems and trunks. Because these herbicides kill only contacted tissue, good coverage is essential; adding an organically acceptable surfactant is recommended. These materials lack residual activity, so repeat applications will be needed to control new flushes of weeds.

Clove oil or cinnamon oil at concentrations of 1 to 5% may also provide some degree of control of small weeds. A surfactant is needed to assist spread of the material. In most cases, organic herbicides require a large volume of water (about 80 gal per acre, or 750 L per ha) to adequately wet the weed foliage. If these materials are applied through a smart sprayer, the amount of material and the cost could be reduced.

Organic herbicides are expensive and may not be affordable for most commercial vineyard production systems. Seek approval in advance from an organic certifier, as the use of alternative herbicides may not be approved by all agencies. Also, the efficacy of currently available materials is much less than that of synthetic herbicides.

Irrigation Management

Water management is a key tool for controlling weeds in organic vineyard operations. Drip tape buried below the soil surface can provide moisture to the vines and minimize the amount of moisture that is available to weeds on the surface. If properly managed, this technique can provide significant weed control during the nonrainy periods of the year. Possible disadvantages include the difficulty of prompt detection of any malfunction due to blockage of the outlets, damage from roots and wild animals, as well as problems of accurate placing of the line to ensure optimal irrigation.

Weeder Geese and Sheep

Geese have been used to control weeds in a large number of crops for many years. All types of geese will graze weeds. There is considerable literature citing their use in strawberries and occasional mention of usage in orchards or vineyards. Geese prefer grass species and will eat other weeds and crops only after the grasses are gone. If confined, geese will dig up and eat johnsongrass and bermudagrass rhizomes. They appear to have a particular preference for these weeds, which are especially troublesome in vineyards.

Care must be exercised when using geese to avoid placing them near any grass crops, such as corn, sorghum, and small grains, as these are their preferred food. Certain other crops might also be vulnerable, such as tomatoes when they begin to color. Geese also require drinking water, shade during hot weather, and protection from dogs. Portable fencing helps keep them in a given area and also keeps dogs and other predators out. Young geese work best, as their major interests are eating and sleeping; older geese prefer to fight and mate instead.

Under normal circumstances, sheep and goats are excellent grazers. However, they must be managed carefully to avoid damage to the vines, particularly when tender shoots are present during the spring. Use a short-statured breed of sheep, such as Babydoll Southdown, that cannot reach the vine canopy. Studies are being conducted using sheep with a trained aversion (orally administered lithium chloride) to grape leaves for spring vineyard floor management. If successful, this may provide

a way to control weeds without injuring grapevines; for more information, see "Grazing" in section 85, "Vineyard Floor Management."

Propane Flamers

Flamers can be used for weed control, with propane-fueled models being most common. Fire causes the cell sap of plants to expand, rupturing the cell walls; this process occurs in most plant tissues at about 54°C (130°F). Weeds must have less than two true leaves for greatest efficiency of the burner. Grasses are harder to kill by flaming because the growing point is below the ground. After flaming, weeds that have been killed change from a glossy to a matte finish. This occurs very rapidly in most cases. Foliage that retains a thumb print when pressure is applied between your thumb and finger has been adequately flamed. Typically, flaming can be done at 3 to 5 mph through fields, although this depends on the heat output of the unit. Repeated flaming can suppress perennial weeds such as field bindweed. Care must be taken to avoid igniting dry vegetation, which could injure the vines or start a wildfire.

The specific flaming angle, flaming pattern, and flame length vary with the manufacturer's recommendations, which range from 30° to 40° at 20 to 30 cm (8 to 12 in) above the base of the plants, with flame lengths of approximately 30 to 38 cm (12 to 15 in). Best results are obtained under windless conditions, as winds can prevent the heat from reaching the target. Early morning or evening is the best time to observe the flame for adjustment.

Weed control efficacy using flaming depends a great deal on

the weed species present and their growth stage. In general, annual broadleaf weeds with fewer than four true leaves will be most sensitive. Grasses and perennial weeds are not generally controlled but can be suppressed with several repeated applications.

Problems often associated with flaming are high energy consumption, low driving speed, and irregular weed control. Another nonchemical method is based on hot steam. High-temperature water provides a form of thermal weed control, yet eliminates the danger of flame application in arid regions where open fires present a hazard. The hot water at high pressure damages the cellular structure and kills weeds within several hours or a few days. First signs of effectiveness are a change in leaf color and plant withering. In general, steam has been shown to be less effective than flaming. Even with a temperature of 100° to 150°C (212° to 302°F), the steam was not able to control all weeds. Factors affecting the use of steam were the age of weeds, slow application speed, amount of steam applied, and cost of propane fuel. Steam weeders range in price from $9,000 to $35,000.

WEED RESISTANCE TO HERBICIDES

Weed resistance to herbicides is not a new phenomenon, but it is somewhat less common than insecticide or fungicide resistance. The first report of herbicide resistance occurred in 1960, with the discovery of triazine-resistant common groundsel (*Senecio vulgaris*). Since that time 319 weed biotypes around the world have evolved resistance to herbicides.

Weed resistance has been defined by the Weed Science Society of America as the inherited ability of a weed biotype to survive and reproduce following exposure to a dose of herbicide normally lethal to the wild type. This means that an herbicide that once killed a particular type of weed no longer kills it. This should not be confused with herbicide tolerance, which has similarly been defined as the inherited ability of a plant to withstand the specific effects of a particular herbicide. Resistance may be naturally occurring or induced by such techniques as genetic engineering; it may occur in plants by random and infrequent mutations. Through selection, where the herbicide is the selection pressure, susceptible plants are killed while herbicide-resistant plants (biotypes) survive to reproduce without competition from susceptible plants. Weed biotypes are naturally occurring plants within a given population that differ slightly in genetic makeup but cannot be distinguished visually from susceptible biotypes.

Resistance may further develop into cross- or multiple resistance. Weed biotypes that have developed resistance to one herbicide and are now also resistant to other herbicides with the same mode of action are said to have cross-resistance. An example of this is littleseed canarygrass (*Phalaris minor*), growing in the Imperial Valley of California, which has developed resistance to the lipid synthesis inhibitor herbicides sethoxydim (Poast), clethodim (Prism), and fluazifop (Fusilade). Weed biotypes that have developed resistance to two or more

chemically unrelated herbicides with different modes of action are said to have multiple resistance. An example is rigid ryegrass (*Lolium rigidum*), which has developed resistance to a number of herbicide classes including sulfonylureas, dinitroanilines, triazines, and substituted ureas.

Weed population shifts can be due either to herbicide tolerance or the development of resistance. When an herbicide does not kill the entire weed population, leaving the resistant biotype to survive and produce seed, a shift to the resistant biotype occurs. Weed shifts can also be caused by using low rates of herbicide. A 7-year, multiple-site Roundup Ready cropping system study conducted by the University of Nebraska demonstrated that when Roundup was applied at half the label rate, the weed spectrum shifted from kochia (*Kochia scoparia*) and wild proso millet (*Panicum miliaceum*) to predominately Roundup-tolerant common lambsquarters biotypes. When applied at the full label rate, no weeds developed resistance to Roundup.

Currently, 19 weed biotypes in California have evolved resistance to herbicides (table 86.6). The greatest herbicide resistance problems have occurred in aquatic weeds in rice production in the Sacramento Valley. Many of these weeds species have been selected for resistance to the sulfonylurea herbicide bensulfuron (Londax). Also, rigid ryegrass (*Lolium rigidum*) has exhibited resistance to Roundup in northern California. With the use of herbicides that lead to rapid selection for resistant weeds—pyrithiobac sodium (Staple) in cotton, rimsulfuron (Matrix) in tomatoes and orchards and vineyards, triflusulfuran (Upbeat) in sugarbeets, bensulfuron (Londax) in rice, imazethapyr (Pursuit) in alfalfa, and imazemethabenz (Assert) in wheat—it is probable that the number of cases of resistance in California will increase. In addition, the availability of Roundup Ready cotton, corn, and alfalfa may promote the sole reliance on a single herbicide that will increase the selection pressure on weeds, which can lead to resistance. Reports of poor or ineffective control of lambsquarters (*Chenopodium album*) in Roundup Ready cotton systems have already been noted. Additionally, populations of hairy fleabane were shown to have multiple resistance to both glyphosate and paraquat in 2009 in the southern San Joaquin Valley.

Several weeds commonly found in California grape vineyards that have been shown to have herbicide resistance include rigid ryegrass, horseweed, hairy fleabane, and junglerice (resistant to glyphosate). In the case of horseweed and hairy fleabane, resistance to glyphosate is enhanced with an increase in plant age. Other weeds prone to developing resistance to glyphosate in California include lambsquarters and redroot pigweed. Weeds common to grape vineyards that have developed herbicide resistance in other parts of the United States include annual bluegrass, barnyardgrass, common groundsel, field bindweed, johnsongrass, and numerous others.

Factors Leading to the Development of Herbicide Resistance

Factors that can lead to or accelerate the development of herbicide resistance include weed characteristics, herbicide characteristics, and cultural practices. Weed characteristics conducive to rapid development of resistance to a particular herbicide include annual growth habit, high seed production, relatively rapid turnover of the seed bank due to high percentage of seed germination each year (i.e., little seed dormancy), several reproductive generations per growing season, extreme susceptibility to a particular herbicide, and high growing vigor of the resistant biotype. Genetically diverse species are more likely to contain a gene that confers resistance to a particular herbicide than are weeds with little genetic diversity.

Herbicide characteristics that lead to rapid development of herbicide resistance in weed biotypes include a single site of action, broad-spectrum control, and long residual activity in the soil. In addition, herbicides that are detoxified by weeds by a common metabolic pathway (e.g., cytochrome P_{450} monooxygenase, glutathione-*S*-transferase) are more likely to develop resistance among weed species than are herbicides that do not metabolize rapidly in plants or are degraded by a less common pathway.

Cultural practices that increase the selection pressure on a weed population increase the likelihood of resistance development. Exclusive reliance on herbicides for weed control, especially the continuous or repeated use of a single herbicide or herbicides with a similar mode of action, can increase the probability of selecting for herbicide-resistant weeds.

Resistance Management

The first step to preventing herbicide resistance is early detection. Scout fields and be on the lookout for patterns that would indicate resistance. Whole fields infested with weeds or strips of weeds do not typically indicate resistance. Patterns of resistance include patches in fields, areas of dense populations with lesser population radiating out from the central patch, escapes scattered in no particular pattern throughout the field, and dead and live weeds of the same species growing side by side after an herbicide application.

Weed management strategies that discourage the evolution of herbicide resistance should include the following, with the last two not readily applicable to a vineyard cropping system:

- **rotate** herbicides with a different mode of action
- **use** the minimum number of applications of any one herbicide per season
- **use** tank mixes of different modes of action when possible
- **use** short-residual herbicides
- **do not** entirely eliminate tillage from the production system
- **use** hand-weeding to remove escape weeds, preventing them from going to seed

Table 86.6. Herbicide-resistant weeds in California

Scientific name	Common name	Situation	Herbicide classification	Year
Amaranthus palmeri	Palmer amaranth	tree and vine, roadside, cotton, alfalfa, corn	glycine (glyphosate)	2012
Ammannia auriculata	eared redstem	rice	ALS inhibitors	1997
Ammannia coccinea	redstem	rice	ALS inhibitors	2000
Avena fatua	wild oat	barley, wheat	unknown (difenzoquat)	1996
Conyza bonariensis	hairy fleabane	ditch bank, tree and vine, rights-of-way	glycine (glyphosate)	2007
Conyza bonariensis	hairy fleabane	roadside, tree and vine	glycine (glyphosate) and bipyridiliums (paraquat)	2009
Conyza canadensis	horseweed	ditch bank, tree and vine, wheat, rights-of-way	glycine (glyphosate)	2005
Cyperus difformis	smallflower umbrella sedge	rice	ALS inhibitors	1993
Digitaria ischaemum	smooth crabgrass	rice	synthetic auxins	2002
Echinochloa colona	junglerice	tree and vine, roadside, corn	glycine (glyphosate)	2008
Echinochloa crus-galli	barnyardgrass	rice	ACCase inhibitors and thiocarbamates	2000
Echinochloa oryzoides	early watergrass	rice	ACCase inhibitors and thiocarbamates	2000
Echinochloa phyllopogon	late watergrass	rice	ACCase inhibitors and thiocarbamates	1998, 2000
Lolium multiflorum	Italian ryegrass	tree, roadside	glycine (glyphosate)	2008
Lolium perenne	perennial ryegrass	rights-of-way	ALS inhibitors	1989
Lolium rigidum	rigid ryegrass	almond	glycine (glyphosate)	1998
Phalaris minor	littleseed canarygrass	onion	ACCase inhibitors	2001
Sagittaria montevidensis	California arrowhead	rice	ALS inhibitors	1993
Salsola tragus	Russian-thistle	roadside	ALS inhibitors	1994
Scirpus mucronatus	ricefield bulrush	rice	ALS inhibitors	1997
Senecio vulgaris	common groundsel	asparagus	Photosystem II inhibitors	1981

- **prevent** weed seed spread by use of clean equipment
- **use** certified planting seed for cover crops
- **avoid** reliance on the lowest label rates, especially if control is poor

If you suspect weed resistance where herbicide applications have failed to control weeds, to further confirm, check that only one weed species has escaped, the sprayer calibration, and whether weather conditions were favorable for herbicide performance. Confirm suspected resistance by respraying and report the problem to your UC Cooperative Extension farm advisor and specialist personnel.

The potential for herbicide resistance should receive serious and thoughtful attention. As weed management systems change and new herbicides and herbicide-resistant crops are introduced, resistance management must be an integral part of the production system. If selection pressure is maintained through the continuous use of the same herbicide, herbicide resistance will soon render it ineffective.

REFERENCES

Crop Data Management Systems, Inc., http://www.cdms.net.

DiTomaso, J. M., and E. A. Healy. *Weeds of California and other western states.* 2 vols. Oakland: University of California Division of Agriculture and Natural Resources Publication 3488.

Elmore, C. L., J. J. Stapleton, C. E. Bell, and J. E. DeVay. 1997. Soil solarization: A nonpesticidal method for controlling diseases, nematodes, and weeds. Oakland: University of California Division of Agriculture and Natural Resources Publication 21377.

Ingels, C. A., R. L. Bugg, G. T. McGourty, and L. P. Christensen. 1998. Cover cropping in vineyards: A grower's handbook. Oakland: Unviersity of California Division of Agriculture and Natural Resources Publication 3338.

International Survey of Herbicide-Resistant Weeds, http://www.weedscience.org/in/asp.

Miller, P. R., W. L. Graves, W. A. Williams, and B. A. Madson. 1989. Covercrops for California agriculture. Oakland: University of California Division of Agriculture and Natural Resources Publication 21471.

Prather, T., J. M. DiTomaso, and J. S. Holt. 2000. Herbicide resistance: Definition and management strategies. Oakland: University of California Division of Agriculture and Natural Resources Publication 8012. UC ANR CS website, http://anrcatalog.ucdavis.edu/Weeds/8012.aspx.

Senseman, S. A., ed. 2007. Herbicide handbook. 9th ed. Lawrence, KS: Weed Science Society of America.

Weed Science Society of America, http://www.wssa.net.

Kurt J. Hembree, Joseph M. DiTomaso, Anil Shrestha, and Richard Smith

HORSEWEED AND HAIRY FLEABANE

Horseweed (*Conyza canadensis*) and hairy fleabane (*Conyza bonariensis*) (fig. 87.1) are related summer annual broadleaves belonging to the Asteraceae (sunflower) family. They reproduce solely by seed, which typically germinate from late fall through spring, but they can germinate year-round under favorable conditions. Seeds that germinate in late summer and fall can act as biennials. Plants grow vegetatively as basal rosettes early in the season and mature and produce new seed from July through September (fig. 87.2).

Their seed is windborne and can be carried at least a quarter of a mile. It is common to find both species growing within the same vineyard. At the earliest stages of growth, both species look similar, but as they mature, their differences become apparent. Horseweed, which is considered a native species, grows as an erect plant with a single stalk as tall as 3 m (10 ft), while hairy fleabane, native to South America, produces numerous branches without a central stalk and is usually less than 1 m (3.3 ft) tall.

The competitive effect of these weeds with vine growth is not fully understood, but they can interfere with daily activities, including spraying and harvest (fig. 87.3). These weeds attract ants, which feed on mature grapes. Horseweed is also known to be a host for the glassy-winged sharpshooter, a vector for Pierce's disease. Under high populations, these weeds may increase the humidity in a vineyard, which might interfere with the drying process of dried-on-the-vine (DOV) raisins. Where paper trays are used for drying raisins on the soil surface, seeds from these plants can land in the folds of drying raisins and contaminate them.

Horseweed and hairy fleabane do not grow well in disturbed soils and can be controlled through frequent shallow cultivation within vine rows. Cultivation of young plants should be practiced when they are less than 15 cm (6 in) tall and prior to flowering. Mowing is not effective, because it stimulates lateral branching of the two species, making control with postemergent herbicides ineffective.

Both species show some tolerance to most of the soil residual herbicides used in grapes. Treatment in fall through winter with simazine, rimsulfuron, or flumioxazin provides the best residual control when applied at higher label rates. Control of emerged plants can be accomplished with well-timed foliar herbicides. Postemergent herbicides like

Figure 87.1 Young plants of horseweed (*Conyza canadensis*, left) and hairy fleabane (flaxleaf fleabane) (*Conyza bonariensis*, right). *Photo*: J. K. Clark.

Figure 87.2 Life cycle of horseweed and hairy fleabane in the southern San Joaquin Valley.

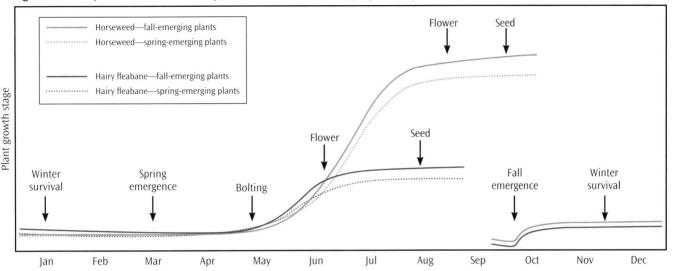

Figure 87.3 Mature horseweed can be difficult to control and can impede normal cultural operations. *Photo*: B. Fischer.

paraquat, glufosinate, glyphosate, and 2,4-D are effective materials, but they should be applied with thorough spray coverage before the plants reach the rosette stage. Since horseweed and hairy fleabane populations are resistant to glyphosate, using alternatives (such as glufosinate, paraquat, or 2,4-D) provides improved control. The addition of a surfactant and/or ammonium sulfate to the spray improves control. Unless the vine canes are trained high enough, treatment with these herbicides is limited to early in the season. A hooded spray boom should be used to prevent contact with vines and possible injury. Control these weeds along field edges, borders, fence lines, and ditches to prevent introduction of new seed into the vineyard.

TURKEY MULLEIN

Turkey mullein (*Croton setigerus* = [*Eremocarpus setigerus*]) (fig. 87.4), a low-growing native annual broadleaf, has densely hairy, pale, gray-green to yellowish green foliage. In many locations in California, this species is considered a desirable component of the natural vegetation. The seeds are an important food source for a variety of birds and small mammals. While not competitive with grapevines, turkey mullein is sometimes troublesome in dry pastures, vineyards, orchards, and other disturbed places. It attracts sparrows and finches, which feed on both the seeds of mullein and maturing grapes. The presence of these birds attracts other grape-feeding birds, such as starlings.

Turkey mullein is very sensitive to frost. Although it grows poorly in wet places, it is a problem in gravelly soils, where cultivation is difficult. When possible, cultivation can control larger populations of small plants, but large plants can clog cultivation implements.

Turkey mullein can tolerate commonly applied preemergent herbicides such as diuron, simazine, oryzalin, and napropamide. Seedlings have a long emergence period, extending from mid-March to June. Plants produce two types of seeds, mottled and uniform gray. Gray seeds develop as plants senesce and appear to germinate under drier conditions than do mottled seeds.

Turkey mullein can be controlled when very small, less than 5 cm (2 in) across, with postemergent herbicides such as glyphosate, paraquat, glufosinate, or oxyfluorfen. However, once the seedlings are larger, the numerous star-shaped hairs on their leaves prevent adequate herbicide penetration and control.

JOHNSONGRASS AND BERMUDAGRASS

Johnsongrass (*Sorghum halepense*) is cultivated for food and forage, but it has escaped cultivation and is a troublesome agricultural weed in temperate to tropical regions nearly worldwide (fig. 87.5). It is considered to be one of the ten most noxious weeds in the world. Johnsongrass can serve as an alternate host for the sorghum midge and the viruses that cause sugarcane mosaic virus, maize chlorotic dwarf virus, and corn stunt disease. Johnsongrass seed can survive for at least 6 years under field conditions,

and it has been estimated that some seed may remain viable for up to 15 years. A mature plant can produce up to 90 m (300 ft) of rhizomes in a single season. Rhizomes grow mostly in the top foot of soil, but they can grow to 1.2 m (4 ft) deep in cultivated soils. Most rhizomes only live a single year.

Bermudagrass (*Cynodon dactylon*) was introduced from the warm climates of Africa. However, numerous hybrids and cultivars have been developed, including some that tolerate cooler conditions. Because of its vigorous creeping habit, bermudagrass is a noxious weed in many situations, particularly where warm-season moisture is ample (fig. 87.6). It produces both aboveground creeping stolons and belowground rhizomes. Most rhizomes grow in the upper 5 cm (2 in) of soil, but some may extend to depths of a foot or more. Although the rhizomes can survive considerable dehydration and extended periods of drought, they cannot survive prolonged periods

of freezing temperatures. Bermudagrass also produces seed that germinate from spring through fall when temperature and moisture conditions are favorable. Some seeds survive for about 3 to 4 years under field conditions, but most germinate within 2 years. Hybrids and other *Cynodon* species seldom produce viable seed.

Johnsongrass and bermudagrass are highly competitive perennials that can colonize large areas. Once established, they are difficult to eradicate because they can easily spread from even small rhizome or stolon fragments that are dragged along by field equipment. Fragments as small as 2.5 cm (1 in) can produce new plants from depths to about 13 cm (5 in). Therefore, for eradication, it is essential to prevent the formation of new seeds and propagative structures.

Although mechanical control is common in the row middles, it is seldom effective when used alone against these well-established grasses. When tillage is conducted

Figure 87.4 Turkey mullein growing in the vineyard row in a gravelly soil. *Photo*: L. J. Bettiga.

Figure 87.5 A single johnsongrass plant can produce thousands of seeds (A); (B) shows the collar region of a johnsongrass blade. *Photos*: J. K. Clark.

Figure 87.6 Bermudagrass reproduces from seeds, rhizomes, and stolons (A). (B) shows a stalk of bermudagrass. *Photos*: J. K. Clark.

only once early in the season, it can encourage new rhizome growth and new shoots from fragmented rhizomes. However, persistent manual removal of rhizomes and stolons can suppress both john-songrass and bermudagrass from spreading. Typically, other control methods should be used in conjunction with mechanical methods, especially in the vine rows. If chemical control is used in the vine rows, accurate timing and application of the treatments are necessary. Slanting knives or sweeps that run below the soil surface can supplement chemical control in the vine row, but they are difficult to use if surface drip systems are present.

In established vineyards, one successful technique in early spring is to allow johnsongrass to grow until it is 30 to 45 cm (12 to 18 in) tall or to allow bermudagrass to reach early flowering. Directed sprays of glyphosate can then be applied to these grasses before grapevine shoots begin to trail downward. This permits maximum growth of these perennial weeds so that glyphosate will move readily into the growing points, including roots. However, avoiding direct contact or drift of glyphosate on the green vine shoots is essential. Shielded spray booms can help avoid such drifts. Also, in established vineyards, sethoxydim has successfully controlled both of these weeds. For maximum effectiveness of sethoxydim, as in spring glyphosate applications, johnsongrass must be 30 to 60 cm (1 to 2 ft) tall, and the runners of bermudagrass must be shorter than 15 cm (6 in) and actively growing when sprayed.

In nonbearing vineyards, fluazifop and clethodim have satisfactorily controlled both of these

weeds. Vineyards treated with these herbicides, however, cannot be harvested within 1 year of application. Again, for maximum effectiveness of these chemicals, the weeds should be actively growing and johnsongrass must be 30 to 60 cm (1 to 2 ft) tall and bermudagrass must have runners shorter than 15 cm (6 in) when sprayed. It is important to remember that systemic herbicides are most effective when applied to plants that are not water stressed.

In another technique, a French or hoe plow is used in the vine rows when vines are dormant to move the stolons and rhizomes toward the row middles. Any remaining stolons and rhizomes are hand-hoed from around each vine trunk. The soil and weeds are disked well to cut stolons and rhizomes into short segments, and trifluralin is applied at the maximum rate and disk incorporated. The berm is then re-established with the treated soil. Subsequent spot treatment of weed regrowth with glyphosate or a postemergent grass herbicide such as sethoxydim, fluazifop, or clethodim hastens eradication. This technique can provide 75 to 90% control the first season and, if the herbicide application is repeated the second season, eradication can be achieved.

Follow-up with a residual herbicide is required for about 5 years to prevent re-establishment of seeds present in the soil. Residual herbicides such as napropamide, trifluralin, oryzalin, diuron, flumioxazin, or norflurazon control emergence of johnsongrass from seeds. It is also important to prevent dispersal of rhizomes, stolons, and seeds by cleaning mowers and agricultural machinery after use in areas infested by bermudagrass or johnsongrass.

Weeder geese are sometimes used in established vineyards that are heavily infested with johnsongrass. These vineyard areas should be fenced to keep the geese in and dogs out. Geese must be provided with water and removed before berries begin to ripen. These requirements make geese impractical for many weeding situations, but their preference for johnsongrass (they will not eat many other weeds) has helped some growers completely eradicate this weed where other methods have failed.

FIELD BINDWEED

Field bindweed (*Convolvulus arvensis*) is native to Europe and is considered one of the most noxious weeds of agricultural fields throughout temperate regions of the world. Plants typically develop into large patches and are difficult to control. In addition, field bindweed can harbor the viruses that cause tomato spotted wilt and vaccinium false bottom.

Field bindweed is a vinelike perennial broadleaf capable of reproducing from deep underground root systems. Roots can penetrate soil to a depth of 3 m (10 ft) or more, depending on the availability of soil moisture. Most horizontal creeping roots develop in the top 60 cm (2 ft) of soil. Consequently, it is difficult to eliminate by cultivation. Field bindweed also produces seeds that are known to typically survive in the soil for 15 to 20 years, and sometimes as long as 60 years. Seeds are hard coated and can survive ingestion by birds and other animals. The impermeable seeds require scarification

or degradation of the seed coat by microbial action to imbibe water and germinate. Seeds germinate throughout the growing season, but peak germination usually occurs from midspring through early summer. Undisturbed patches can expand their radius up to 10 m (33 ft) per year, and root fragments as small as 5 cm (2 in) can generate new shoots.

Field bindweed is especially troublesome in new vineyard plantings because it is highly competitive, as it is able to grow up into new vines and shade them, slowing vine growth. In mature vineyards, vines shade field bindweed and reduce its growth and competition to some extent. In addition, the weed's root systems competitively extract soil moisture and can survive extended periods of drought and repeated cultivation. The combination of shading and herbicides can effectively reduce

field bindweed from vine rows in mature vineyards.

Cultivation to a depth of at least 10 cm (4 in) within 3 weeks after emergence can control seedlings. Frequent disking of row middles helps reduce the growth of field bindweed plants (fig. 87.7A). In vine rows, cultivation plus repeated applications of a postemergent herbicide such as glyphosate or paraquat temporarily controls bindweed. This approach is expensive, and if applied to the vine trunk, these herbicides may cause injury in the year vines are trained up the stakes, as well as the year after training. Furthermore, control is only temporary, and bindweed will re-establish itself as soon as the herbicides are discontinued.

Applying trifluralin in a subsurface blade creates an herbicide barrier that can effectively control field bindweed and does not injure

Figure 87.7 Field bindweed growing in the dry middles of a vineyard (A). (B) shows field bindweed blossoms. *Photos*: J. K. Clark.

vines. The growing tips of bindweed shoots cannot penetrate or are destroyed when they contact the herbicide layer. A weakness of this method is the tendency of bindweed to flourish at the edge of the treated area and adjacent to the stakes and trunks of vines. Also, in clay loam soils, deep cracks can develop when soil dries, permitting shoots to emerge. Trifluralin can also be mechanically incorporated into the soil surface, but this is generally less effective than the subsurface application method and does not control bindweed emerging from seed. Winter applications of oryzalin, norflurazon, simazine, or diuron, where they can be safely applied, control field bindweed emerging from seed.

Glyphosate when applied at low spray volumes (10 to 20 gal/ac) to actively growing field bindweed just as it begins to flower provides effective control (fig. 87.7B). Stems and leaf surfaces of the plant have a texture that is difficult to wet. The addition of a wetting agent to certain herbicides may make them more effective. Grapevines are sensitive to these herbicides, so avoid their contact with trailing vine shoots. Even slight spray drift or contact on one or two grapevine leaves will cause foliar injury the following spring. Use of low-pressure systems and hooded booms reduces the possibility of drift and injury.

YELLOW AND PURPLE NUTSEDGE

Yellow (*Cyperus esculentus*) and purple (*Cyperus rotundus*) nutsedge are perennials with triangular stems that generally reproduce from underground tubers or nutlets. The nutsedges are among the most noxious of

agricultural weeds in temperate to tropical regions worldwide. They often form dense colonies, can greatly reduce crop yields, and are difficult to control. In California, the nutsedges are especially problematic in crops that receive summer irrigation.

Yellow nutsedge is a widespread, highly variable native of Eurasia and North America, including California and other western states. In some countries, yellow nutsedge is cultivated for its edible, earthy, almond-flavored tubers, which are used to make a milky drink (fig. 87.8A). Purple nutsedge is native to Eurasia; unlike yellow nutsedge, its tubers taste bitter.

These weeds favor moist, light-textured soils, where they can reproduce rapidly. They are commonly found growing in the wetted areas of drip and low-volume sprinkler irrigation. In California, they are designated as facultative wetland indicator species.

Both species develop an extensive system of rhizomes, tubers, and roots. The tubers store starch and have several buds that produce new rhizomes, which develop more basal bulbs and new plants.

Only yellow nutsedge produces viable seed in California (fig. 87.8B). Seeds of yellow nutsedge and tubers of both species germinate in spring. Tubers develop to soil depths of about 30 cm (1 ft), but most are in the top 20 cm (8 in). Under favorable conditions, one plant can produce hundreds to thousands of tubers in a single season. In purple nutsedge, typically only one tuber in a chain germinates, unless the chain is severed. Tubers typically survive up to about 3 to 4 years, but under certain conditions they can remain viable for up to 10 years or more. Seed production can be high in yellow nutsedge, but viability is quite variable. In California, seed viability in yellow nutsedge

Figure 87.8 Yellow nutsedge tubers (A) and flowers (B). *Photos*: J. K. Clark.

is typically low. A single plant of either species can develop into a dense colony 3 m (10 ft) or more in diameter, and the boundary of the infestation can increase by more than 1 m (3.3 ft) per year. Yellow nutsedge is found throughout California, while purple nutsedge is found primarily south of Madera County, particularly in the desert regions of southern California. Control strategies can vary, depending on the particular species present. The easiest way to distinguish the two species is to pull plants out of the soil and observe the tubers or nutlets (table 87.1).

Nutsedges do not directly affect production in established vineyards, but they are highly competitive for water and nutrients, especially in new vineyard plantings, when root growth is limited. Gophers and other vertebrate pests have been observed to feed on yellow nutsedge tubers.

Cultivation should not be used for nutsedge control in vineyards because it spreads the plants and tubers in the field. Cultivation can worsen an infestation. However, if used, it must be repeated often enough to exhaust tuber reserves and prevent new tuber formation. Shading or solarization can help to limit populations by weakening shoots and decreasing new tuber formation, but mature tubers may not be eliminated. Although these plants look similar to grasses, they are sedges and are not controlled

with postemergent grass herbicides such as clethodim, fluazifop, or sethoxydim. There is no easy way to control these weeds in vineyards, but some effective options are available.

Planting vines into fields that do not have a history of nutsedge is the best way to avoid these weed species. Routine monitoring should be conducted well before vineyard establishment to determine whether these weeds are present. Fields with no nutsedge or a limited population of nutsedge will be easier to manage once the vineyard is planted. Repeated tillage in the summer, while the field is idle, can bring tubers to the surface so they can dehydrate. A spring-tooth harrow is usually the best tillage tool for this, while disking is often ineffective. Burying tubers more than 30 to 40 cm (12 to 16 in) deep into the soil profile with a modified moldboard plow (like the Kverneland plow) prior to planting can significantly reduce nutsedge populations, since they do not emerge from these depths.

If the population is low, repeated application of a postemergent herbicide such as glyphosate is effective as long as moisture is provided to encourage sprouting of the tubers. To help prevent the formation of new tubers, it is critical that applications be made before the nutsedge plants have 3 to 4 leaves. Postemergent herbicides do not translocate adequately

into maturing tubers, so the plants must be treated before tubers form. Treat these weeds as new emergence occurs—about every 21 to 28 days.

Certain pre- and postemergent herbicides can help manage nutsedge after grapevines are planted. Soil residual herbicides such as rimsulfuron, norflurazon, and thiazopyr can provide good suppression when the nutsedge population is low. Fields with heavy infestations usually require applications over several years. Rimsulfuron gives partial control of yellow nutsedge, and thiazopyr gives partial control of purple nutsedge. When using thiazopyr, apply a split application (fall and winter) for yellow nutsedge control. Likewise, norflurazon is effective on yellow nutsedge, but not on purple nutsedge. Follow-up treatments with postemergent herbicides are normally required to control those escaping the soil application. Glyphosate provides the best postemergent control when applied to plants with fewer than 3 to 4 leaves and at intervals of 21 to 28 days during the season. Repeated in-season treatments should be made only where adequate protection of the grapevine can be maintained during the application. Eliminating nutsedge from a field requires diligent efforts yearly, without allowing plants to produce additional tubers.

Table 87.1. Physical characteristics of mature yellow and purple nutsedge tubers

Yellow nutsedge	Purple nutsedge
small, smooth, and globe shaped	large, oblong, coarse, and scaly
light brown color	dark brown to purplish color
pleasant almond or earthy flavor	bitter flavor
formed at the end of roots or rhizomes	formed in chains along roots or rhizomes
produces 1 or 2 plants arising from apical end	produces several plants along entire surface

Part 9

Pesticide Application and Safety

Zinfandel

88 PRINCIPLES AND TECHNIQUES OF VINE SPRAYING

Larry J. Bettiga and Walter J. Bentley

To achieve pest control, a lethal dose of pesticide must be delivered to the pest. To do this the applicator must determine the proper combination of equipment and technique, including choosing the right equipment, setup, calibration, quantity of formulated product, and application rate of the finished tank mix. Success or failure is influenced by accessibility of the pest, vine canopy architecture, weather conditions, and proper chemical selection. For more detailed information on pesticide application, see *The Safe and Effective Use of Pesticides*, 2nd ed. (O'Connor-Marer 2000).

VINE SPRAYING EQUIPMENT

Ground spraying of vines is most often accomplished with one of three pieces of equipment:

- over-the-vine, high-pressure sprayers that cover two or more complete rows (fig. 88.1)

- air-carrier single-row sprayers that treat one-half of each adjacent row (fig. 88.2)

- air-carrier multiple-row sprayers that cover two or more rows (figs. 88.3–88.5)

Over-the-vine hydraulic boom units are usually used at 150 to 400 gallons of spray per acre (gpa). With nozzle and pressure adjustments, these sprayers can effectively apply as little as 50 gpa. Air-carrier sprayers are often designed for reduced-volume applications of 10 to 40 gpa. Either type of sprayer can satisfactorily deliver the pesticide if the unit is properly set up, calibrated, and operated. Over-the-vine, high-volume, high-pressure sprayers have one disadvantage: they require frequent refills, thus requiring extra manpower and equipment or much downtime. Also, the spray boom is difficult to control during operations and transportation.

Some large sprayers have their own engine: most, however, are powered by the tractor power takeoff (PTO). These sprayers usually require a minimum of 45 horsepower (hp) with 55 or higher preferred. Without sufficient energy input (tractor hp), the pump, agitator, fan, or forward travel of PTO-operated sprayers does not perform satisfactorily.

Most grape sprayers are mounted on two wheels and are towed behind the tractor. Three-point hitch or integrally mounted units are suited to smaller vineyards or to high-concentrate applications because of their smaller tank capacity. Grape harvester chassis are also used to mount sprayers for multiple-row applications.

Figure 88.1 Over-the-vine, high-pressure sprayer covering two complete rows.

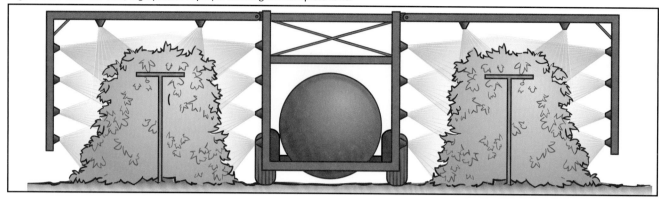

Figure 88.2 Air-carrier single-row sprayer covering one-half of each adjacent row (two half rows).

Figure 88.3 Air-carrier double-row sprayer covering four half rows.

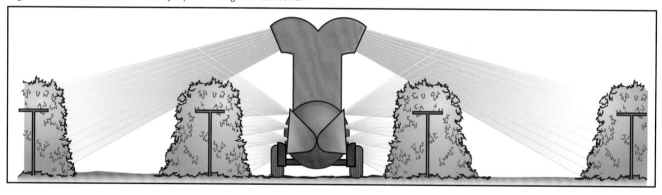

Figure 88.4 Air-carrier double-row sprayer covering two complete rows.

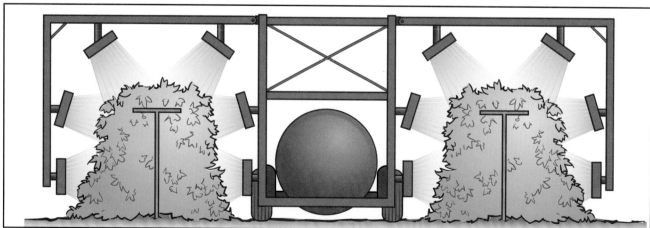

Figure 88.5 Over-the-row sprayer mounted on a grape harvester chassis for four-row applications. *Photo*: L. J. Bettiga.

Terms concerning rate concentrations used in vine spraying are defined in table 88.1, and useful metric equivalents are given in table 88.2.

Tanks

Commonly available materials used in the manufacture of spray tanks include stainless steel and polyethylene. Your choice of tank material should be based on its resistance to the chemicals to be used, structural support available on the sprayer, cost, and other factors. General advantages and disadvantages of each type of tank material are found in table 88.3.

All tanks must have a large opening for ease of filling and cleaning. The opening must have a tight-fitting, spill-proof covering or lid. If the tank contains over 50 gallons, it must have a sight gauge or other accurate means to determine the volume of liquid in the tank. Sight gauges outside the tank must have a shutoff valve to prevent loss of the tank mix if the gauge is damaged. A drain point in the bottom of the sump allows liquid to be completely drained and can be easily opened without exposing the operator. Locks for covers help prevent unauthorized use of the sprayer and may be required in some counties. Always check with the county agricultural commissioner's office for current regulations.

Agitators

During sprayer operation, continual agitation of spray material in the tank is essential. Agitators can be either mechanical, with rotating paddles (fig. 88.6), or hydraulic, with jets that continually recirculate liquid in the tank (fig. 88.7). Hydraulic agitation systems require additional pump capacity to provide continual flow to the tank and to the nozzles; insufficient pump capacity can produce inadequate turbulence for mixing chemicals uniformly, especially when wettable powders are used. Flow from a jet agitator should be in the range of 1 gallon per minute (gpm) per 30 gallons of tank capacity.

Adequate agitation can be even more difficult to obtain when using heavy compounds such as zinc or hard-to-wet materials such as sulfur. It may be necessary to mix them as a slurry and add the slurry slowly to the tank to get good mixing and suspension. It is usually best to add the chemical to the tank while the tank is agitating and is one-half to two-thirds full. Consult the material label for specific mixing instructions.

Pumps

Selecting the appropriate pump depends on the pesticide formulation to be used and the volume and pressure required for application. Water-soluble and emulsifiable concentrate pesticide formulations are less abrasive to pumps than are wettable powder or flowable and dry flowable formulations. Construction materials and type of pump also affect performance and wear. When choosing a sprayer pump, consider the following features.

Capacity. A pump must supply enough volume for all nozzles under every use condition. If the sprayer is equipped with hydraulic agitation, the pump must have additional output for recirculating material in the tank. The output capacity of a pump is given in gpm.

Table 88.1. Spray rate terminology for grapes

dilute spray	100–400 gpa
semiconcentrate	40–100 gpa
concentrate	10–40 gpa
Hi-concentrate	< 10 gpa

Table 88.2. Useful conversion factors for calibration

U.S. STANDARD MEASURE
Length
1 ft = 12 in
1 yd = 3 ft
1 mi = 5,280 ft
Area
1 sq in = 0.007 sq ft
1 sq ft = 144 sq in = 0.000023 sq ac
1 sq yd = 1,296 sq in = 9 sq ft
1 ac = 43,560 sq ft = 4,840 sq yd
Volume
1 tsp = 0.17 fl oz
1 tbs = 3 tsp
1 fl oz = 2 tbs = 6 tsp
1 cup = 8 fl oz = 16 tbs
1 pt = 2 cups = 16 fl oz
1 qt = 2 pt = 32 fl oz
1 gal = 4 qt = 8 pt = 128 fl oz = 231 cu in
Weight
1 oz = 0.0625 lb
1 lb = 16 oz
1 ton = 2,000 lb
1 gal of water = 8.34 lb

METRIC CONVERSIONS
Length
1 in = 25.4 mm = 2.54 cm
1 ft = 304.8 mm = 30.48 cm
1 yd = 914.4 mm = 91.44 cm = 0.914 m
1 mi = 1,609 m = 1.61 km
1 mm = 0.03937 in
1 cm = 0.394 in = 0.0328 ft
1 m = 39.37 in = 3.281 ft
1 km = 3,281 ft = 0.6214 mi
Area
1 sq in = 6.45 sq cm
1 sq ft = 929 sq cm
1 sq yd = 8,361 sq cm = 0.8361 sq m
1 ac = 4,050 sq m = 0.405 ha
1 sq cm = 0.155 sq in
1 sq m = 1,550 sq in = 10.76 sq ft
1 ha = 107,600 sq ft = 2.47 ac
Volume
1 fl oz = 29.5 ml = 0.0295 l
1 pt = 437 ml = 0.437 l
1 qt = 945 ml = 0.945 l
1 gal = 3785 ml = 3.785 l
1 ml = 0.033 fl oz
1 l = 33.8 fl oz = 2.112 pt
1 l = 1.057 qt = 0.264 gal
Weight
1 oz = 28.35 g
1 lb = 454 g = 0.4536 kg
1 ton = 907 kg
1 gal of water = 3.786 kg
1 g = 0.035 oz
1 kg = 35.27 oz = 2.205 lb

Source: O'Connor-Marer 2000.

Table 88.3. Pesticide tank selection guide

Advantage/disadvantage	Stainless steel	Polyethylene
rust and corrosion resistant	excellent	excellent
easily cleaned	excellent	excellent
easily repaired	yes	no
cost	high	low
acid resistance	depends on grade	good
alkali resistance	excellent	good
organic solvent resistance	excellent	fair
strength and durability	excellent	good
weight	heavy	light
absorbs pesticides	no	no
requires external reinforcement	no	yes

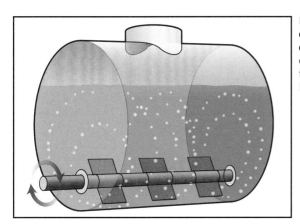

Figure 88.6 Mechanical agitation (the most common system) consists of paddles or propellers that continually stir the liquid in the spray tank.

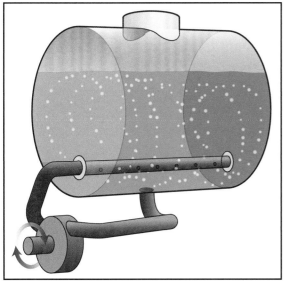

Figure 88.7 Hydraulic agitation recirculates spray material back into the spray tank via the pump, providing continual mixing of solution.

Pressure. Pumps must produce the desired capacity of spray material at a pressure suitable for the work being performed. Some high-capacity pumps are able to produce only low pressures. High-pressure pumps can often be regulated for low-pressure work as well. Pressure is measured in pounds per square inch (psi).

Resistance to corrosion and wear. The type of materials used to manufacture the pump and the pump's design dictate its ability to resist corrosion and wear. Pumps with the fewest parts coming in contact with spray chemicals are the most suitable for corrosive pesticides. Proper pump design reduces the amount of wear due to abrasion, for example, by wettable powders.

Ease of repair. An important feature of any pump is easy repair. Parts must be readily available.

Type of drive. Depending on their design, pumps require different operating speeds. PTO shafts rotate at 540 or 1,000 rpm; gasoline and diesel engines and electric motors have specific operational rpm ranges. Because each pump requires a particular horsepower to operate efficiently, consider the drive unit speed and horsepower. If a pump requires a change in rpm, a transmission or gear unit will be needed to obtain the necessary rotational speed.

Piston pump

A piston pump is a positive displacement pump in which a given amount of liquid is forced out of the pumping cylinder with every rotation of the input shaft (fig. 88.8). Often the most expensive, it is also the heaviest pump available. It is capable of high pressures, and the flow does not vary with pressure at a given input rpm. Wear-resistant cups prolong pump life when abrasives are used, and the cups can be replaced to revitalize the pump. Piston pumps are reciprocating, so they require a surge dampener or surge tank to absorb the pressure and flow pulsations. They must also be plumbed with a bypass to provide a liquid outlet if all nozzles are turned off.

Diaphragm pump

A diaphragm pump is also a positive displacement pump, but instead of using a reciprocating piston, a cam following an eccentric on the input shaft causes the diaphragm to flex and alternately draw liquid into and force liquid from the pumping chamber (fig. 88.9). Like the piston pump, it is capable of high pressures, and a bypass must also be used. Most diaphragm pumps have an internal surge chamber, but adding a larger one externally may help to smooth flow pulsations. Diaphragms of many materials can be chosen according to their resistance to chemicals used in the pump. They are easily and quickly replaced, reducing downtime when ruptured. This pump's moving parts are isolated from the liquid, making it especially suitable for use with abrasive and corrosive materials.

Centrifugal pump

Found on some equipment, centrifugal pumps have the advantage of being able to provide high volumes of spray liquid, but they provide limited high-pressure output (fig. 88.10). The pressure can be increased by coupling several pumps in sequence or stages. There is no direct contact between moving parts of the sprayer, so it can handle abrasives. It may also be deadheaded (run without a liquid output) for brief periods. It should never be run dry, as the liquid lubricates the bearings and seals. Centrifugal pumps are cheaper than piston or diaphragm pumps.

Figure 88.8 In a piston pump, the downward movement of a piston draws liquid through a one-way valve into the cylinder. When the piston moves up, liquid is forced out through another one-way valve. Some pumps consist of several pistons working opposite each other.

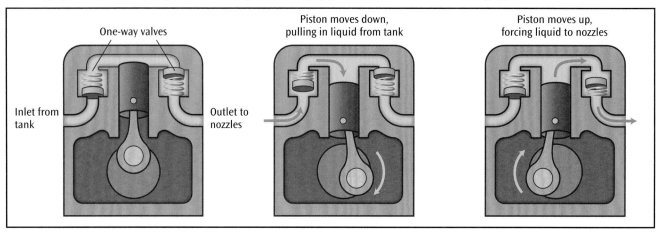

Figure 88.9 In a diaphragm pump, a flexible diaphragm is moved up and down by a cam mechanism. This oscillation moves liquid through one-way valves. Some diaphragm pumps incorporate two or three diaphragms moved by the same cam.

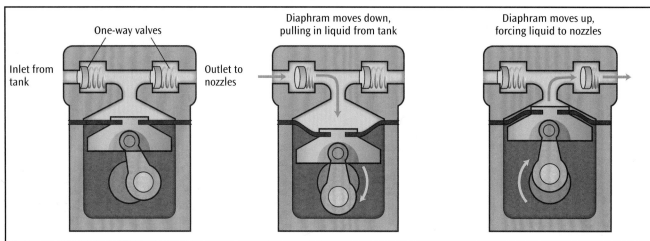

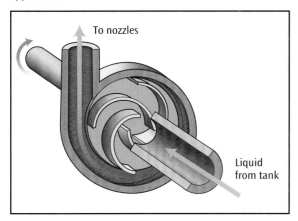

Figure 88.10 In a centrifugal pump, liquid enters the center of a vaned rotor. As the rotor spins, the liquid is moved away from the center by centrifugal force. Rotors must turn at a high rpm to build up sufficient pressure for most spray applications.

Other types of pumps

Gear pumps and flexible-impeller pumps are also available, but they are not commonly found in sprayers used for vineyard pest control.

Nozzles

Hydraulic

In a hydraulic spray system, the discharge rate (gpm) is governed by the size of the nozzle orifice and by the pressure applied. Nozzles vary in pattern, size, and material. Those on high-volume sprayers usually have larger orifices because they must dispense a greater amount of liquid per minute. Some spray units use adjustable nozzles, but these quickly lose adjustability and pattern accuracy because of corrosion and wear. Conventional sprayers commonly use nozzle tips of brass (not recommended), plastic, stainless steel, tungsten carbide, or ceramic. The latter three resist abrasion and wear best. Nozzle tip wear is greatest when wettable powders are used. The higher cost of ceramic nozzles is often justified by their longer life and the reduced need to recalibrate sprayer output due to nozzle wear from abrasive materials or high-volume sprays. Manufacturers often color-code nozzles to indicate specific spray characteristics. Behind the nozzle tip, some nozzles have a swirl plate that regulates the flow

and starts the spray in a swirling motion, creating a hollow- or solid-cone pattern. Spray droplet size is determined by nozzle type, orifice design, and operating pressure. Nozzle orientation in the airstream and velocity of air also influence droplet size in air-carrier sprayers.

Air shear

The air-shear atomization system is used in sprayers that operate at very low pressures, 14 to 35 psi. With this nozzle system, the atomization device is placed in the airstream. As the spray liquid leaves the orifice, it is sheared off into droplets by the air moving past the liquid stream. This system offers the advantage of minimal wear and reduced plugging, but it requires adequate airflow for even atomization. Instead of nozzles, some air-carrier sprayers use a simple metering orifice whose only function is to release a set amount of spray liquid into the discharge area of an air-producing fan.

Centrifugal

In a centrifugal system, the energy to produce droplets comes from liquid fed onto a rotating wheel, disc, or cone. As the speed increases, smaller droplets are produced. These rotating devices are also called controlled-droplet atomizers (CDAs) for their ability to produce droplets that are more uniform in size than produced by other nozzle types. CDAs produce low pressure and low volume, with a uniform pattern of fine droplets that are directed onto the foliage and dry quickly.

Electrostatic

In this system, as the liquid is atomized, droplets are electrically charged and carried to the target in an airstream. In principle, all the droplets have the same charge and are strongly then attracted to the surfaces of a grapevine, which have the opposite charge. Electrostatic sprayers are generally used at low volumes. When operated correctly they can increase pesticide deposition and reduce spray runoff and off-site drift.

Spray Droplets

Droplets are characterized by size, which is measured by their diameter in microns (μm). All nozzles produce a range of droplet sizes. Generally, hydraulic nozzles produce a wider range of droplet sizes than do other types of nozzles. CDA nozzles produce a narrow droplet range. Droplet size can be categorized into six size ranges in accordance with the American Society of Agricultural Engineers (ASAE) standard S572 (table 88.4). These size and color code classifications can be used to compare nozzles and are often used in manufacturer catalogs. Droplets of 100 μm or less can be more effective in penetrating canopies and reaching insect pests, but they are also the most susceptible to drift.

Filters

Screen filters, necessary on all sprayers, remove debris and sediment that enter sprayer lines and clog nozzles. A relatively coarse main screen should be located in the line before the pump, and a finer mesh screen should be attached at the base of the nozzle manifold to remove smaller particles (fig. 88.11). A finer mesh, with openings smaller than the nozzle orifice, should be located in each nozzle body. Considerable downtime is eliminated by not having to stop to clean plugged nozzles.

Spray Transport

After atomization, the liquid droplets must be transported to the target. With hydraulic sprayers, the hydraulic pressure of the liquid provides the energy to move the droplets to vines. In air-carrier sprayers, a large volume of moving air carries a small volume of spray droplets to target surfaces. The air is moved by a fan and directed toward vines by ducts.

Fans in different sprayers vary in size, shape, function, and number per sprayer. They also

Table 88.4. Droplet size category and color code standards, ASAE S572

Classification code	Color code	Approximate volume median diameter, µm
very fine	red	< 100
fine	orange	100–175
medium	yellow	175–250
coarse	blue	250–375
very coarse	green	375–450
extremely coarse	white	> 450

deliver different volumes of air. Air speed, or velocity, is measured in miles per hour (mph). Sprayer fan capacity is generally expressed in cubic feet of air per minute (cfm). As the spray rate per acre is reduced, the spray droplet size may be reduced. To get these lighter, smaller droplets to deposit on target, they must travel at a higher velocity. Therefore, low-volume sprayers need to produce high-velocity air for good deposition.

Sprayer Operation

With over-the-vine, high-volume, high-pressure sprayers, it is important that the discharge rate be

greatest from the nozzles directed at vine shoulders on nonpositioned canopies. This is where foliage is most dense and where fruit bunches need maximum protection. Better in-the-vine deposition usually results if the nozzles on one side of the vine point slightly forward in the line of travel and rearward on the opposite side. This arrangement prevents the sprays on both sides of the vine from interfering with each other and allows increased spray penetration into the canopy. It also is of value to alternate every other nozzle between a full cone and a more narrow, penetrating cone.

Figure 88.11 Sprayers contain filter screens, which are located in various parts of the system. The suction strainer is positioned between the tank and pump. The pressure strainer is located between the pump and nozzles. Nozzle strainers are located adjacent to or in the nozzle bodies.

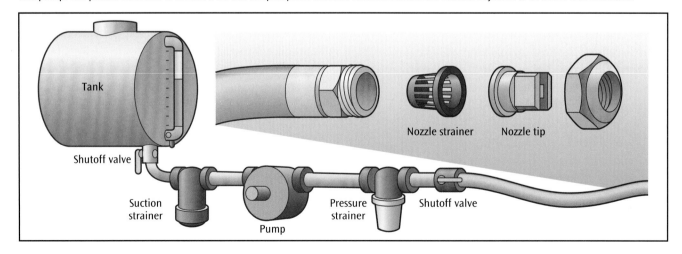

Greater spray effectiveness can be obtained if the bottom nozzle can be extended toward the vine to direct spray upward.

The speed of travel in vineyards is best limited to a maximum of 3.5 mph to allow the sprayer to deliver sufficient liquid to each vine for effective deposition on all vine surfaces. Thorough coverage of interior areas of the vines is especially important for control of such pests as omnivorous leafroller, orange tortrix, scale, mealybug, and certain disease-causing organisms. Suspected resistance to pesticides has repeatedly been shown to be due to a failure to deliver a lethal dose to the pest, primarily because the sprayer was traveling too fast. Excessive speed can also damage equipment, particularly on rough ground.

The bulk of the air and spray solution must be directed by air-carrier sprayers to the vine's shoulder area on nonpositioned canopies. This can be done with air deflectors, nozzle placement, and nozzle size. Adjustment may vary for variety, trellising methods, pruning styles, and other cultural considerations. If possible, direct the air blast 15 to 20 degrees forward or 10 degrees rearward from the line of travel. This nozzle alignment, as with high-pressure sprayers, allows the spray to enter the vine at an angle to the leaves, eliminating leaf shingling (fig. 88.12), which would otherwise block spray penetration to the inside of vines and grape bunches. The objective is to replace the air in the vine with the droplets in the airstream from the sprayer. The spray should just reach the far side of the canopy. Air volumes require change as the canopy develops. Speed of

travel for a single-row air-carrier unit should be limited to 4.5 mph. Two-row and four half-row sprayers should not exceed 3.5 mph. Generally, the more dense the vine foliage or tighter the grape cluster, the slower the travel speed must be to achieve good spray penetration.

Dusters

Dusters are mainly used to apply sulfur to control powdery mildew. Deposition requirements for this purpose usually differ from those of insecticides. Dusts have no special advantages. In fact, they are very difficult to control or direct, are more subject to wind and drift than sprays, and largely depend for effectiveness on plant wetness, leaf hairiness, and the amount of horizontal surface area of the target. Dust can be very effective, however, if the pest is susceptible to initial chemical deposit or fuming action. On the other hand, if a residual deposit is necessary for control, very little dust remains on the plant for very long. Therefore, regardless

of the type of application equipment, a dust application is usually not very successful.

Unlike certain disease-controlling applications, insect dusts must be applied to every row at a rate of 30 to 50 pounds of dust per acre. Because most dusters have inaccurate flow rate markings due to different material properties, trial-and-error methods are needed to meter each dust formulation. Dust discharges should be directed completely into vines and not straight up or over vine tops. Speed of travel depends mainly on the discharge and blowing capacity of the duster, but it should not exceed 5 to 6 mph for good penetration.

CALIBRATING VINE SPRAYERS

Calibrating a vine sprayer is relatively simple, whether it is a high-volume, low-volume, air-carrier, or herbicide boom sprayer. Often, each sprayer operation has certain knowns, and a little arithmetic and a nozzle chart provide all the factors needed for

Figure 88.12 Spray that is improperly aimed at foliage may cause leaves to push or overlap and prevent proper coverage, a condition known as shingling. Proper use of an air-carrier sprayer or oscillating boom sprayer will ruffle the foliage and improve distribution of spray droplets.

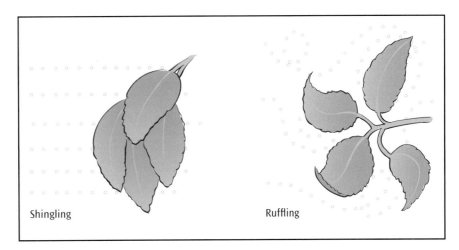

Shingling

Ruffling

proper calibration. Typically known are

(1) gpa (gallons per acre) desired

(2) psi (pounds pressure per square inch) desired

(3) mph (miles per hour) desired

(4) number of nozzles on sprayer

(5) vine row spacing

Typically unknown are

(6) gpm (gallons per minute) needed

(7) nozzle sizes and placement

(8) simple measurement for speed

Travel Speed

Travel speed must be measured under field and tractor operating conditions. Values read from engine tachometers on the tractor can have significant errors due to tire size and inflation differences and wheel slip due to soil characteristics, tractor weighting, and sprayer loads. Before doing the calculations associated with nozzle selection and placement, measure the actual travel speed.

Mark out a known distance, such as 100 or 200 feet, preferably in the vineyard to be sprayed. If that is not possible, duplicate such vineyard conditions as soil tilth, cover, and soil moisture on the marked course. Connect the tractor-sprayer combination to be used and fill to one-half to two-thirds with water. Engine operating rpm and gear selection should be that used for pesticide application.

Start from several yards before the marked course and drive the tractor just as during the application. The sprayer should be operating. Measure the time required to pass through the known distance with a stopwatch

or a watch with a second hand or digits. Perform the procedure at least two times, traveling in both directions, and average the resulting time (*T* in the calculation below). Calculate the travel speed:

Speed = (100 ft ÷ *T*) x (1 mi ÷ 5,280 ft) x 3,600 sec

or

Speed = (100 ft ÷ *T*) x 0.6815

Example: Two passes are made on a 100-foot course, one at 22 seconds, and the other at 23 seconds. Average pass = 22.5 seconds.

Speed = (100 ÷ 22.5) x 0.6815

Speed = 3 mph

You can also use vine spacing to calculate the speed in vines per minute, using the vine spacing and the fact 1 mph = 88 feet per minute:

Vines/min = (speed x 88) ÷ vine spacing

Example: Using the 3 mph in the above example with a vine spacing of 8 feet,

Vines/min = (3 x 88) ÷ 8

Vines/min = 33

An alternative to the calculations is to use table 88.5, which shows the number of vine spaces you must pass in 1 minute to obtain your desired travel speed (mph).

Application Rate and Nozzles

Examples A, B, C, and D show the calibration for different vine sprayers. See "Spray Check," below, for procedures to determine the actual flow rates of the sprayers discussed in the examples.

Example A

An over-the-vine, high-pressure boom sprayer covers two complete rows per pass (see fig. 88.1).

Known:

(1) gpa = 200. Desired application rate per acre.

(2) psi = 300. Pounds pressure per square inch at nozzle.

(3) mph = 3. Selected travel speed.

(4) number of nozzles on sprayer = 20 (10 per side).

(5) vine row spacing = 24 feet. (Although row spacing is 12 feet, to spray two rows, use a 24-foot spray swath; for a 10-foot planting, spray swath is 20 feet.)

(6) 495 (conversion factor).

Table 88.5. Travel speed relative to planting distances

Miles per hour (mph)	Number of vine spaces passed per minute		
	Planting distances		
	6 ft	7 ft	8 ft
2	30	25	22
2.5	37	31	28
3	44	38	33
3.5	51	44	39
4	59	50	44
4.5	66	57	50
5	73	63	55

Unknown:

(7) Application rate, gpm
  = (gpa x mph x row spacing) ÷ 495
  = (200 x 3 x 24) ÷ 495
  = 14,400 ÷ 495
  = 29 gpm

(8) For 20 nozzle positions you will need a discharge rate of 29 gpm.
  = 29 ÷ 20
  = 1.45 gpm/nozzle

Because vines are not uniformly thick or dense from bottom to top, it is necessary to use two or three different nozzle sizes (S = small, M = medium, L = large) to place more spray in the shoulder area (fig. 88.13). To do this, select some nozzles that discharge more and some less than 1.45 gpm. Nozzle calculations are more easily made if based on one row or one side and then duplicated for the other row or side. Accordingly, aim for a 10-nozzle arrangement and a total discharge of 14.5 gpm (10 x 1.45 gpm per nozzle) (fig. 88.14).

Nozzle charts for the type of nozzles on your sprayer (as shown in table 88.6) give the gpm discharge of different-sized tips. If you use swirl plates in your nozzles, use the nozzle chart corresponding to the swirl plate size.

For the sprayer in the above example, using a spray pressure of 300 psi, check the 300 psi column to find the gpm for each size of nozzle tip. You will need an average output per nozzle of 1.45 gpm, but because of the variations needed for proper vine coverage, you will probably want four nozzles smaller than 1.45 gpm, four nozzles approximately 1.45 gpm, and two nozzles larger than 1.45 gpm, placed as shown in figure 88.14, to provide the greatest coverage to the densest part of vine rows. Therefore, by selecting four No. 6 tips, four No. 7 tips, and two

Figure 88.13 Spray boom on one side of an over-the-vine, high-pressure boom sprayer, showing relative nozzle sizes.

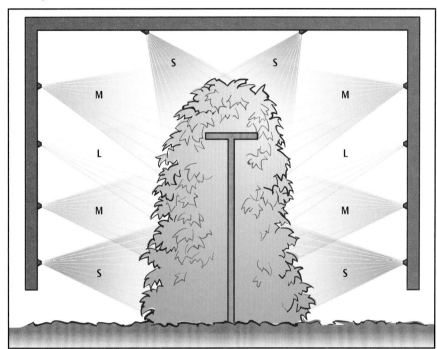

Figure 88.14 Spray boom on one side of an over-the-vine, high-pressure sprayer, showing the actual disc arrangement using a No. 25 swirl plate. This nozzle arrangement can be duplicated on the other side of the sprayer.

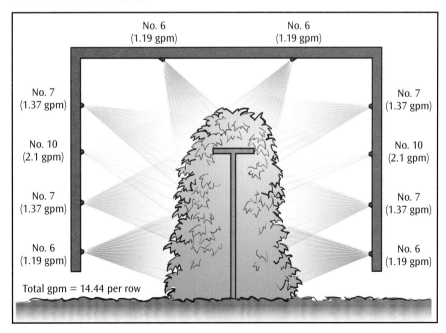

Table 88.6. Hollow-cone nozzle chart

Disc-core number	Gallons per minute (gpm)			
	40 psi	100 psi	200 psi	300 psi
4-25	0.29	0.45	0.62	0.75
5-25	0.35	0.54	0.75	0.90
6-25	0.44	0.70	0.97	1.19
7-25	0.52	0.80	1.18	1.37
8-25	0.61	0.97	1.36	1.68
10-25	0.76	1.21	1.71	2.10

No. 10 tips you can arrive at an acceptable nozzle arrangement.

4 No. 6-25 disc-core
= 4 x 1.19 = 4.76 gpm

4 No. 7-25 disc-core
= 4 x 1.37 = 5.48 gpm

2 No. 10-25 disc-core
= 2 x 2.10 = 4.20 gpm

Total gpm = 14.44

The 14.44 gpm is satisfactorily close to the 14.5 gpm desired. (Obtaining the exact nozzle gpm output is seldom possible.)

Example B

An air-carrier sprayer travels each row middle and sprays two half rows (see fig. 88.2.).

Figure 88.15 One side of an air-carrier sprayer, showing relative nozzle sizes.

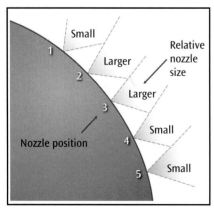

Known:

(1) gpa = 50. Desired application rate per acre.

(2) psi = 100. Pounds pressure per square inch at nozzle.

(3) mph = 3. Selected travel speed.

(4) number of nozzles = 10 nozzles on sprayer (5 per side).

(5) vine row spacing = 12-foot row (or swath).

Unknown:

(6) Application rate, gpm
= (gpa x mph x row spacing) ÷ 495
= (50 x 3 x 12) ÷ 495
= 1,800 ÷ 495
= 3.6 gpm

(7) For 10 nozzle positions you will need a discharge rate of 3.6 gpm.
3.6 ÷ 10 = 0.36 gpm/nozzle

Because vines are not uniformly thick or dense from bottom to top, it is necessary to use two or three different nozzle sizes (S = small and L = large) to place more spray into the shoulder area (fig. 88.15). To do this, select some nozzles that discharge more and some less than 0.36 gpm. For one side of the sprayer and for ease of calculation, aim for a five-nozzle arrangement. The five nozzles are required to discharge only half of the necessary 3.6 gpm, or 1.8 gpm per side.

Using a nozzle chart for the type of nozzles on your sprayer, as the following example shows in table 88.7, check the column headed by the pressure (psi) you will use to get the gpm discharge for each different-sized nozzle tip. This example uses a pressure of 100 psi. For nozzles with swirl plates, use the nozzle chart corresponding to the size of the swirl plate.

Check the 100 psi column for the gpm for each different nozzle tip. In this example you will need an average output per nozzle of 0.36 gpm, but because of the nozzle size difference for proper vine coverage you will probably want three nozzles smaller than 0.36 gpm and two nozzles larger than 0.36 gpm. By selecting three No. 3-25 disc-cores and two No. 4-25 disc-cores, you can arrive at an acceptable nozzle arrangement sufficiently close to the required 1.8 gpm discharge requirement (fig. 88.16).

3 No. 3-25 disc-core = 3 x 0.29
= 0.87 gpm

2 No. 4-25 disc-core = 2 x 0.45
= 0.90 gpm

Total gpm = 1.77

(8) Sprayers that use air-shear nozzles and are calibrated on the basis of gallons per hour (gph) would be calibrated as 3.6 gpm x 60 minutes = 216 gph. Since they use low-pressure, air-shear-type nozzles rather than conventional nozzles with different-sized orifices and cores, nozzle pressure is not important. Therefore, follow a simple calibration step of setting a valve pointer at the desired gph. Still, where adjustment of individual nozzle flow is possible, try directing the greatest flow to the densest part of vines.

Figure 88.16 One side of an air-carrier sprayer, showing nozzle size selection and placement. This nozzle arrangement can be duplicated on the other side of the sprayer.

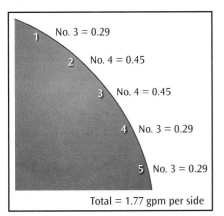

No. 3 = 0.29
No. 4 = 0.45
No. 4 = 0.45
No. 3 = 0.29
No. 3 = 0.29

Total = 1.77 gpm per side

Example C
An air-carrier sprayer travels every other row and covers four half rows per pass (see fig. 88.3.)

Known:

(1) gpa = 50. Desired application rate per acre.

(2) psi = 100. Pounds pressure per square inch at nozzle.

(3) mph = 3. Selected travel speed.

(4) number of nozzles = 14 nozzles on sprayer.

(5) vine row spacing = 24 feet. (Although row spacing is 12 feet, to cover the equivalent of two rows, use a 24-foot spray swath, 2 rows x 12 feet.)

Unknown:

(6) Application rate, gpm
= (gpa x mph x row spacing) ÷ 495
= (50 x 3 x 24) ÷ 495
= 3,600 ÷ 495
= 7.27 gpm

(7) This system employs two air heads per side (each head having its own set of nozzles), one low head for the row adjacent to the sprayer and a high head directed at the next row beyond the adjacent row (see figs. 88.3 and 88.17). In this example, you could use four nozzles on the low head and three on the high head. Therefore, for actual nozzle selection, be guided by the visual pattern shown in preceding figures and by Example B.

Sprayers that use air-shear nozzles and are calibrated on the basis of gallons per hour should be calibrated as follows:

7.27 gpm x 60 minutes = 436.2 gph

Because they use low-pressure, air-shear-type nozzles rather than conventional nozzles with different-sized orifices and cores, nozzle pressure is not important. Therefore, follow their simple calibration steps, which can consist of setting a valve pointer at the desired gph. Still, where adjustment of individual nozzle flow is possible, try to direct the greatest flow to the densest area of the vine.

Example D
Multiple-air fan (over-the-vine), two-row sprayers cover two complete rows per pass and travel every other row (see fig. 88.4). If the sprayer is an over-the-vine, two-row, air-carrier sprayer using four to six small fans per row, calculate the gpm as shown in Example A. However, because you are not dealing with high-pressure conventional nozzles, adjust the spray flow per fan so that the bulk of the spray discharge is directed at dense shoulder areas of vines. This is where the greatest leaf growth and number of fruit bunches are located. Because the fans on these sprayers have adjustable angles and there may be four to six fans per row, trial-and-error adjustments are necessary for optimal deposition.

Vineyard Floor Sprayers
Vineyard floor sprayers either cover the entire soil surface between vine rows (fig. 88.18) or treat vine row berms only (fig. 88.19). Such sprayers can be constructed simply and economically. Small pumps are satisfactory because of the low gallon-per-acre output (10 to 100 gpa) and low pressure requirements (20 to 60 psi). Booms set parallel to the ground transfer pesticides and allow proper spacing and support for the nozzles, which are usually flat-fan types. Because the target (the ground) is relatively flat and at a uniform distance from each nozzle, the same size of nozzle is used across the boom to maintain an even pattern. These nozzles should be set at a uniform distance

Table 88.7. Hollow-cone nozzle chart

Disc-core number	Gallons per minute (gpm)				
	40 psi	100 psi	150 psi	200 psi	300 psi
2-25	0.16	0.25	0.29	0.34	0.41
3-25	0.19	0.29	0.35	0.40	0.48
4-25	0.29	0.45	0.54	0.62	0.75
5-25	0.35	0.54	0.65	0.75	0.90

Figure 88.17 An example of an air-carrier sprayer that travels every other row and sprays four half rows.

Figure 88.18 Vineyard floor sprayer with complete-coverage boom.

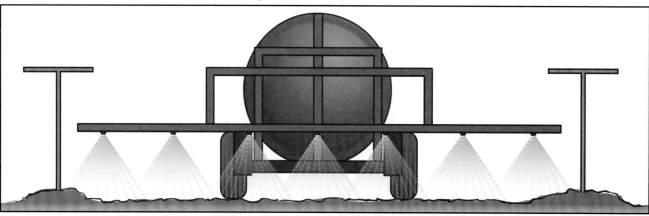

Figure 88.19 Vineyard floor sprayer for berm-only coverage.

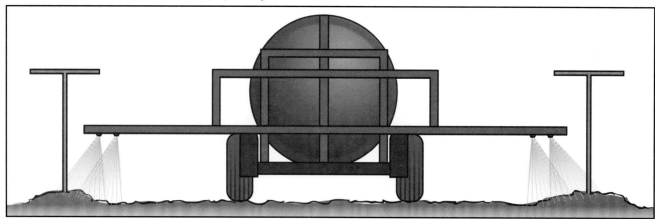

apart and height above the ground so that they properly overlap at the edges of their fan pattern. Nozzle catalogs have charts showing the proper relationship between nozzle angle, height, and spacing.

Controlled-droplet atomizer nozzles in a shielded covering can be used to apply contact herbicides at very low volumes. Even when operated correctly, these nozzles may apply reduced amounts of herbicide with an increased potential for drift.

For safety, the boom should be hinged so that it will swing away and not be damaged if it hits a vine. Hinged booms can also be folded back during transport. With a simple spring attachment, the boom can be designed to return and hold to normal position after retraction.

Calibrating boom sprayers is similar to calibrating vine sprayers. Therefore, if the psi, mph, number of nozzles, and swath width (usually the same as the boom width and/or row width) are known, the unknown factors can be accurately and quickly determined. As with vine sprays, actual output should always be checked (see "Spray Check," below). For example:

Known:

(1) gpa = 40. Desired application rate per sprayed acre.

(2) psi = 30 or 40.

(3) mph = 3.

(4) number of nozzles = 7.

(5) swath width = 11.67 feet.

Unknown:

(6) Application rate, gpm
= (gpa x mph x swath width) ÷ 495
= (40 x 3 x 11.67) ÷ 495
= 1,400 ÷ 495
= 2.8 gpm

(7) Application rate per nozzle, gpm
= application rate ÷ no. of nozzles
2.8 ÷ 7 = 0.40 gpm/nozzle

Because all nozzles can be the same size for this type of spraying, look at flat-fan nozzle charts (table 88.8), as per the following example, and read the output for 40 psi. From this chart, select the nozzle size that most closely discharges 0.40 gpm. Place seven of these nozzles on the boom, spaced as recommended at 20 inches apart and 17 to 19 inches above the ground. This would be an 80-degree fan nozzle with a flow rate of 0.40 gpm at 40 psi. If you are spraying only vine row berms (see fig. 88.19) and you wish to use two nozzles per berm, follow the same procedure. For example:

Known:

(1) gpa = 15. Desired application rate per sprayed acre. Three acres of vineyard are treated with this amount since only 4 feet of each 12 are treated.

(2) psi = 30.

(3) mph = 3.

(4) number of nozzles = 4.

(5) swath width = 4 feet.

Unknown:

(6) Application rate, gpm
= (gpa x mph x swath width) ÷ 495
= (15 x 3 x 4) ÷ 495 = 180 ÷ 495
= 0.36 gpm

(7) Application rate per nozzle, gpm
= application rate ÷ no. of nozzles
= 0.36 ÷ 4
= 0.09 gpm/nozzle

Because all four nozzles can be the same size with this type of application, look at a flat-fan nozzle chart and read down the 30 psi column. From this chart, select the nozzle that most closely discharges 0.09 gpm (No. 1s). Place four of these nozzles on the boom, two at each end for proper berm coverage. To eliminate double coverage, off-center nozzles may be more desirable at the end of the boom.

Spray Check

Finally, check your calibration.

1. Spray an area of vines with plain water to check the spray pattern, then rearrange or change nozzles as needed.

2. Determine the actual flow rate (gpa) of the sprayer.

   • For high-pressure and air-carrier sprayers where it is not possible to collect the sprayed liquid, determine the output as follows: Fill the tank to a known level with clean water; run the sprayer at the normal operating conditions for a timed period; refill the tank to its original level, measuring the amount

Table 88.8. Flat-fan nozzle chart

Nozzle tip no.	psi	psi
1	30	0.09
	40	0.10
2	30	0.17
	40	0.20
3	30	0.26
	40	0.30
4	30	0.35
	40	0.40
5	30	0.43
	40	0.50

of water used; and calculate output by dividing the measured volume of water sprayed by the time period in minutes (gpm = gallons ÷ minutes). Perform this procedure two more times and calculate an average output.

- For low-pressure vineyard floor boom sprayers, measure the timed output of each nozzle on the boom. The variation among the nozzles should not be greater than 5%, and their individual output should not exceed the manufacturer's rated output by more than 10%. If you replace any of the nozzles, recheck the flow rate of all the nozzles. Changing nozzles may affect system pressure, so readjustment may be necessary to maintain the desired pressure. Total boom output is the sum of all the nozzles (in gpm).

3. If the actual flow rate (gpa) is incorrect, check whether your original pressure reading (necessary for proper nozzle size selection) was wrong, whether your nozzle size selections were incorrect, or whether the speed of travel was too slow or too fast.

4. There are several methods for checking sprayer deposition. One method is to visually evaluate the coverage by spraying the vines with a water-soluble dye that does not injure vines

and is permissible to use on grapes. Water-soluble food coloring dyes used in the baking industry are available in different colors at food supply houses.

5. For foliage-applied materials, staple 3-by-5-inch file cards at 1-foot intervals on a 7-foot lath. Place one to three of these laths inside the vines on each side of the travel row against the support wire. Operate the calibrated sprayer past the test area and observe the spray deposit on the cards. Deposits show not only hits and misses but also the sprayer's spray droplet pattern. It is wise, however, to make an initial run outside the vine row to see how the pattern looks unobstructed. Here, you simply anchor the laths 12 feet apart (if 12 feet is the row spacing) and drive the sprayer between the two laths. After reading the results and making minor corrections, repeat the operation in the vine rows. This type of spray check is often revealing and may help visualize problems with an existing sprayer setup. You can also use water-sensitive paper, which eliminates the need for colored dye. Water-sensitive paper can underestimate the deposition of fine droplets (100 microns or less).

6. Ultraviolet tracers can also be used effectively to evaluate spray coverage in the vineyard. After spraying, check vines at night with an ultraviolet (black) light to observe

the coverage of the leaves and clusters in the outer and inner canopy.

7. All spray equipment should be double or triple rinsed after use. This involves running clean water through the entire system and nozzles, followed by a mix of rich horticultural oil and water. After the tank has been emptied, leave drain and fill holes open so that tank and lines can dry.

8. Never treat vineyards with spray equipment in which hormone-type herbicides (2,4-D) have been used; residues can build up in rubber hoses and fittings, leading to contamination and vine damage.

Calibration and the ability of the sprayer to deliver the lethal dose of the material to the target pest are strongly affected by nozzle wear and travel speed. Perform calibration as the canopy develops, when soil conditions change dramatically, or whenever the operator, tractor, tractor tires, or other factors change. A skilled person can perform a calibration in 20 to 30 minutes at little cost. A 10% error in application rates, such as traveling 1.8 mph instead of 2.0 mph, or applying a rate of 16 gpm instead of 14.5 gpm, or operating at 121 psi instead of 100 psi, can easily be corrected with calibration. The cost in chemical, additional operator time, reduced pest control, and other costs caused by improper calibration, when multiplied over hundreds of acres and several applications, far outweighs the small cost of performing a proper spray calibration.

Subsurface Spray Blades

A subsurface spray blade can apply herbicides to control field bindweed (perennial morning glory) between vine rows. This process consists of passing a straight blade 4 to 6 inches underground, parallel to the soil surface, and injecting a uniform layer of herbicide at that depth. Nozzles are spaced 4 to 5 inches apart and spray toward the trailing edge of the blade. The entire assembly is mounted on a tool bar to allow depth control. Applications with a spray blade should be made using 40 to 80 gpa of water. Calibration can be achieved by using either of the methods described for vineyard floor sprayers. Because pressure loss occurs in the lines to the blade, measure the pressure as close to the base of the blade as possible.

Variable Rate Pesticide Application

Sprayers are available that have sensors for better targeting of pesticide applications. For example, spray units with infrared optical sensors recognize plant tissue and turn individual nozzles on and off, reducing the amount of pesticide sprayed on the soil.

References

O'Connor-Marer, P. 2000. The safe and effective use of pesticides. 2nd ed. Oakland: University of California Division of Agriculture and Natural Resources Publication 3324.

89 CHEMIGATION THROUGH MICROIRRIGATION SYSTEMS

Lawrence J. Schwankl, Walter J. Bentley, and Michael V. McKenry

Chemigation is the injection of chemicals into irrigation water for delivery to the crop or field. It includes the application of fertilizers, insecticides, nematicides, herbicides, and chemicals used for irrigation system maintenance. Pesticide chemigation in vineyards is almost exclusively done through drip emitter microirrigation systems. Although there are some instances where microsprinklers are used, they are rare. The method of injection into a microirrigation system, whether a drip or microsprinkler, is the same. This section focuses on the injection of insecticides and nematicides for pest control.

INJECTION DEVICES

Growers wishing to inject pesticides should consider either a venturi device or a positive displacement pump. The choice of device depends on the flow rate, injection site design, equipment availability, and cost of the device. Figure 89.1 shows the chemical concentration levels during injection for the two devices. Both deliver a relatively constant concentration during the injection period.

Venturi Devices

Venturi devices (fig. 89.2), often referred to as mazzei injectors after the trade name for a particular brand of venturi injector, consist of a constriction in a pipe's flow area, resulting in a negative pressure, or suction, at the throat of the constriction. A venturi injector is frequently installed across a valve or other device where from 10 to 30% of the pressure is lost (fig. 89.3). This is equivalent to the pressure loss as water moves through a venturi. The inlet of the venturi injector must be at a pressure 10 to 30% higher than the outlet port in order to have flow through the venturi. Because of these significant pressure losses, the injector should be installed parallel to the pipeline so that flow through the injector can be turned off with a valve when injection is not occurring. The injection rate of a venturi device is determined by the size of the venturi and the pressure differential between inlet and outlet ports. Injection rates as high as 700 gallons per hour (gph) are possible with large venturi devices.

Venturi injectors can also be installed with a small centrifugal pump that draws water from the irrigation system, increases its pressure while moving the water through the venturi, and then returns the water and chemical back into the irrigation system (fig. 89.4).

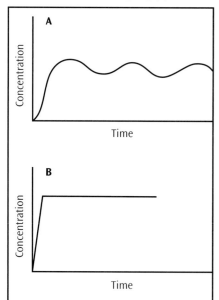

Figure 89.1 Chemical concentration levels during injection using a venturi injector (A) and positive displacement pump (B).

Figure 89.2 Venturi injection device.

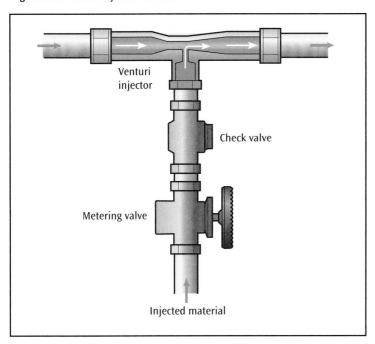

Figure 89.3 Venturi injection layout.

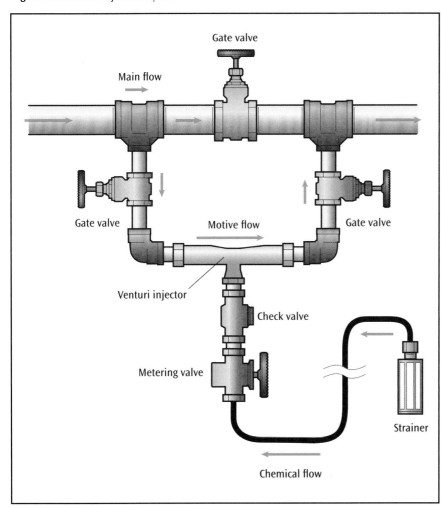

Venturi devices are inexpensive and relatively simple to operate, but they do not inject chemicals at as constant a rate as positive displacement pumps.

Positive Displacement Pumps

Positive displacement pumps are piston or diaphragm pumps that inject at precise rates. The pumps are powered by electricity (fig. 89.5), gasoline, or water. Water-driven pumps can be installed in locations that lack power. When a small amount of pesticide must be injected continually and very precisely (see fig. 89.1B), positive displacement pumps are preferable. This makes them excellent candidates for use with many of the newer pesticides that are delivered in very small amounts. Positive displacement pumps are the most expensive of the injection devices, with costs for electric pumps running $750 or more.

Injection Point

The injection point is the location where the pesticide is delivered into the irrigation system. It should be located so that the injected chemical and the irrigation water become thoroughly mixed well upstream of any branching of the flow to the site of injection. For injection of pesticides, a special flow mixing injection port that delivers the chemical into the center of the pipeline to aid mixing is often recommended. Due to concerns over chemicals being flushed out when the microirrigation system filters are backwashed, the injection point should be downstream of the filters. To ensure that no contaminants are injected into the microirrigation system, a good-quality screen or disk filter should be installed on the line between the

Figure 89.4 Venturi injection system with small pump withdrawing water from the irrigation system, pumping it through the venturi injector, and returning the water and chemical to the irrigation system. *Photo*: L. J. Schwankl.

Figure 89.5 Electrically driven positive displacement pump injector. *Photo*: L. J. Schwankl.

chemical tank and the injector. The injection point must be downstream of any backflow prevention valves for insecticides and nematicides.

The system should be allowed to fill and come up to full pressure before injection begins. Following injection, the system should continue to be operated to aid in ensuring uniform application of the chemical. This postirrigation clean water application should not be so long that it flushes the injected material from the vine's root zone. Since leaving residual chemical in the microirrigation system may encourage emitter clogging as well as interfere with future chemigation practices, flushing the lines a day or two following the chemigation is recommended.

UNIFORM CHEMIGATION

Once injection begins, the injected material does not immediately reach the emitters: there is a travel time for water and injected pesticide to move through a microirrigation system. Measurements on commercial vineyards using drip irrigation indicate that this travel time may range from 30 minutes to well over an hour, depending on the microirrigation system design. To ensure that application of any injected material is as uniform as the water applications, the following steps should be taken.

Step 1: Determine the travel time of pesticides to the farthest hydraulic point in the microirrigation system. This is a one-time determination and can be done by injecting a red dye into the system, then collecting water in a clear container and watching for the appearance of the colored dye.

Step 2: The injection period should be at least as long as it takes the injected material to reach the end of the last lateral line (determined in Step 1). A longer injection period is even better.

Step 3: Once injection is stopped, the irrigation should continue for a period of time as long as it took the injected material to reach the end of the farthest lateral (determined in Step 1). A longer postinjection irrigation period is better, but make sure, especially with injected materials that easily travel with the water, that water (and injected material) does not move below the root zone. Such overirrigation could waste the injected material and could contribute to groundwater contamination. In general, the system should be run for half an hour to one hour to clear the underground component of the system without impacting the efficacy of the pesticide.

CHEMIGATION SAFETY

Appropriate care should be exercised when handling all injection chemicals, and the safety of personnel should be of highest priority. Environmental safety associated with chemigation should also be a priority. Chemigation regulations vary from state to state. In California, chemigation safety regulations apply only to pesticides, not to fertilizers. Local regulations for pesticide application should be checked and followed. Figure 89.6 is a sample chemigation layout that has safety devices required for preventing environmental contamination when injecting pesticides. There are also numerous other approved configurations that incorporate

Figure 89.6 Typical layout of chemigation injection system.

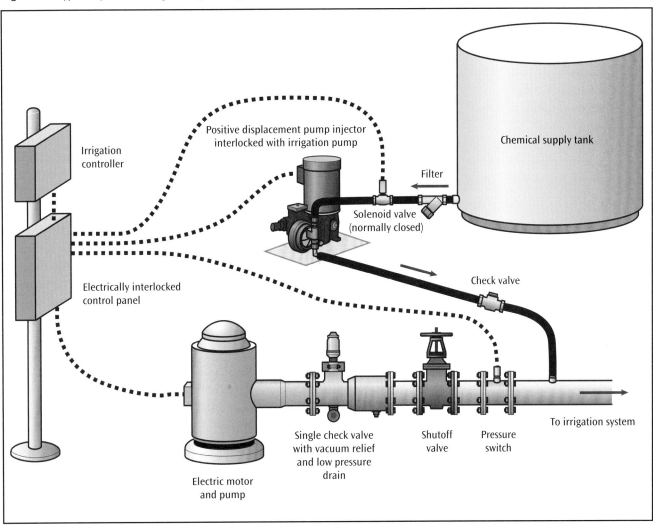

Irrigation controller

Positive displacement pump injector interlocked with irrigation pump

Chemical supply tank

Filter

Solenoid valve (normally closed)

Electrically interlocked control panel

Check valve

Electric motor and pump

Single check valve with vacuum relief and low pressure drain

Shutoff valve

Pressure switch

To irrigation system

different injectors and other safety devices. The safety devices in figure 89.6 include the following:

- A chemigation check valve, located between the water source and the injection point, prevents chemical from moving back to the water source. The check valve has a one-way, spring-loaded flap inside that allows water to pass only downstream. The chemigation check valve also has an air vent/vacuum relief valve and a low-pressure drain upstream of the

one-way flap closure (fig. 89.7). The vacuum relief valve prevents a vacuum from forming that could draw water and chemical through the closed check valve. If some water does leak past the closed check valve, it will drain out of the low-pressure drain, which is open when the irrigation system is shut down but closes when the irrigation system is pressurized. Such a valve is necessary if pesticides are to be applied in the

system. Even if there is no expectation that chemicals other than fertilizer will be injected through the irrigation system, installation of a chemigation valve is a prudent move. Backflow of fertilizer to a well or other water source can result in groundwater contamination.

- An electronic interlock between the water pump and the injector pump prevents operation of the injector if water is not being pumped.

- A check valve in the line from the injector to the irrigation system prevents water from flowing back through the injector and overflowing the chemical storage tank.

- A normally closed solenoid valve (or a normally closed hydraulically operated valve) between the chemical tank and the injector keeps chemical in the tank from flowing into the irrigation system when the system is not operating.

- A pressure switch in the irrigation system, interlocked to the pump, shuts down the irrigation and injection systems if there is a break in the pipeline or some other cause for a drop in operating pressure.

APPLYING NEMATICIDES AND INSECTICIDES WITH CHEMIGATION

Chemigation of pesticides into soil via the irrigation system requires that the materials be soluble in water. Vineyard drip emitter microirrigation systems are well suited to chemigation because they deliver water directly to the root zone. Irrigation through drip emitters

Figure 89.7 A double chemigation check valve protecting a well from backflow contamination. A double check valve is installed for safety redundancy and is required in some states. *Photo*: L. J. Schwankl.

concentrates root distribution, which results in the concentration of soil pests. This concentrated target simplifies remedial actions that enhance or protect root development and allows for maximum uptake of systemic insecticides. Although chemigation optimizes the use of the materials that are carried in the water, safety is a main concern. This is particularly true for the farmworker and the environment, including the water supply. Strictly following label instructions and regulations governing chemigation is of paramount importance. Similarly, calibration of the delivery must be done precisely.

Chemigation involves two main chemical delivery scenarios. Fertilizers are taken into plants via roots and then actively moved throughout the root system by the plant. Uniform soil delivery of nutrients throughout the wetted zone may not be a critical factor during fertigation. Similar mechanisms are at work when systemic pesticides (nematicides and insecticides) are applied to root systems for eventual movement into foliage. However, systemic agents may only be systemic within foliage directly associated with conductance tissues of specific roots. To optimize delivery to each vine, the root system must be contacted uniformly. Nematicides, and some insecticides, available today perform almost all their benefit by direct contact of the pesticide with the pest in the soil. Therefore, uniform contact with the root zone is critical with such pesticides.

Chemigation with systemic insecticides can be accomplished by relatively short-term injections (as short as an hour or two) of the chemical into the drip system. To get uniform chemigation application of the injected insecticide, follow the steps above on uniform chemigation. For currently available nematicides, minimal attention to soil condition is required at time of delivery. However, with insecticides, particularly the chloronicotinyl compounds, greater care must be taken to prevent movement of the chemical below the vine's root zone. Although the systemic chloronicotinyl insecticides are relatively water soluble, they vary in their tendency to bind to soil particles. For example, imidacloprid is quite soluble in water but does bind readily to organic matter. Field experiments have demonstrated high sorption to soil particles, and the presence of silicate clay increases soil particle sorption. This is not the case with dinotefuran, which readily moves through coarser-textured soils.

Accounting for Prevailing Soil Conditions

Contact Nematicides and Insecticides

The dominant microirrigation system in vineyards involves drip irrigation with individual 0.5 gph emitters positioned on either side of the vine trunk, but this system experiences variations in flow rate and dripper spacing. The movement of water beyond the puddle that forms below each dripper forms a three-dimensional area shaped like a cone or an onion, with the size and shape of the wetted area determined by flow rate, soil texture, length of irrigation, and presence of saturated zones remaining from the most recent irrigation. With contact nematicides and insecticides, the goal is to chemigate a pre-wetted zone at field capacity. Nematodes or phylloxera can reside as deep as the deepest root, but over the last 20 years it has been confirmed that uniform delivery throughout the surface 2.5 feet (45 cm) of the onion-shaped area can provide best pest relief. This is accomplished by pre-wetting the soil with a normal irrigation, waiting hours (course-textured soils) or days (fine-textured soils) for field capacity to be achieved throughout the onion-shaped area, then chemigating over a 4-hour period, with the first 3.5 hours receiving uniform delivery of pesticide agent followed by half an hour of water only. Then, time the next irrigation depending on the half-life, mode of action, and delivery characteristics of the pesticide. Some pesticides that are highly adsorptive to soil particles must be applied only when soil particles are well coated with moisture. Some materials possess a half-life of only a few days, so delivery must be fast and will almost always be best in soils with larger pore spaces.

Successful use of materials with a short half-life against root knot nematode has generally involved two separate treatments timed during the 8 to 10 weeks of root flush (once at bloom time and again just after harvest). Treatments to ectoparasitic nematodes may be applied at various times. Some broad-spectrum nematicides should be applied as few times as possible and not when the soil is too warm.

Systemic Insecticides and Nematicides

With systemic pesticides, knowledge of soil structure is of critical importance and will often guide the choice of pesticide used. If the pesticide is highly soluble and binds poorly to soil particles, it may be carried past the root zone before it is taken into the plant. Alternatively, the use of a product that quickly binds to soil particles may not move through fine-textured soils to the active root zone. The characteristics of the soil, the pesticide, and the chemigation system must work together to deliver the correct amount of pesticide only to the active root zone.

Recipe for Nematicide and Insecticide Treatments

1. The day before treatment, irrigate the vineyard to thoroughly moisten soil. Check emitter lines for leaks and stoppages. Check for leaky valves. Post the field every 600 feet (180 m) with danger signs as appropriate.

2. On the day of the treatment, introduce the pesticide into the system after the emitters have run for half an hour. Usually the material is delivered to the system within 3 to 3.5 hours.

3. Allow the system to run an additional half an hour to empty underground lines.

4. Do not irrigate for a few days, then resume the normal irrigation cycle.

References

Cox, C. 2001. Insecticide factsheet/ imidacloprid. Journal of Pesticide Reform 21(1): 15–21.

Hanson, B., N. O'Connell, J. Hopmans, J. Simunek, and R. Beede. 2006. Fertigation with microirrigation. Oakland: University of California Agriculture and Natural Resources Publication 21620.

Schwankl, L., and T. Prichard. 2001. Chemigation in tree and vine microirrigation systems. Oakland: University of California Agriculture and Natural Resources Publication 21599.

Pesticides play an important role in pest management in vineyards, but many chemicals are hazardous to people, wildlife, or the environment if used improperly. Improper use may also damage vines or reduce crop quality. Handlers who misuse pesticides are subject to severe fines and possible jail sentences. To perform the way they were legally and safely designed to, pesticides must be used in strict accordance with label instructions.

PESTICIDES

Pesticides are grouped according to function. For example, insecticides control insects, and herbicides control weeds (table 90.1). Plant growth regulators enhance vine growth or fruiting (although some synthetic plant growth regulators are used as herbicides). Attractants and repellents are also used for pest control. Many groups of pesticides can be used in vineyards.

Each group of pesticides may contain several chemical classes. Insecticides, for instance, include organophosphates, carbamates, organochlorines, neonicotinoids, and botanical extracts. Usually, chemicals of the same chemical class have a similar mode of action toward the target pest. They may have other similarities, such as mobility in the soil, persistence in the environment, and hazards to people or nontarget organisms.

RECOGNIZING POTENTIAL HAZARDS

Pesticides are grouped into Category I, Category II, or Category III, and by the corresponding signal words Danger, Warning, and Caution, according to their toxicity or potential for causing injury to humans (table 90.2). Different label and regulatory requirements apply to each category.

Category I Pesticides

Category I pesticides are identified by the signal word DANGER that appears on container labels (fig. 90.1). Labels may also include POISON and bear a skull and crossbones. A few drops to a teaspoonful of most pesticides in this category will probably cause death if swallowed. Spilled on the skin or splashed into the eyes, these materials can often be very dangerous. Pesticides having a lower toxicity may be included in Category I if there is an identified hazard, such as severe skin or eye irritation or a particular danger to the environment. Use of Category I pesticides in California vineyards is normally restricted, so permits are generally required

Table 90.1. Pesticide classification based on target pests and pesticide functions

Pesticide group	Pests controlled
acaricide	mites
algaecide	algae
attractant	attracts pests
bactericide	bacteria
desiccant	removes water from arthropod pests or plant foliage
fungicide	fungi
growth regulator	regulates plant or animal growth
herbicide	weeds
insecticide	insects
molluscicide	snails or slugs
nematicide	nematodes
repellent	repels animals or invertebrates
rodenticides	rodents
silvicide	trees and woody shrubs

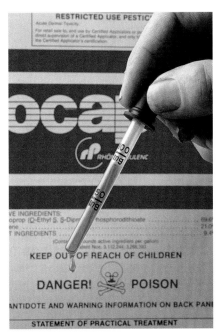

Figure 90.1 Category I pesticides are recognized by the word DANGER on the label. A few drops to a teaspoon of Category I pesticide, taken internally, would probably cause death. These pesticides have an oral LD50 (the lethal dose to kill 50% of an exposed test population) of 50 mg/kg or less and a dermal LD50 of 200 mg/kg or less. *Photo*: J. K. Clark.

from a county agricultural commissioner for their purchase and use.

Category II Pesticides

The signal word WARNING on the pesticide label identifies moderately toxic or hazardous Category II pesticides (fig. 90.2). Swallowing between 1 teaspoon to 1 ounce (6 teaspoons) of some of the chemicals in this group may be sufficient to kill an adult (for information on weights and measures, see table 88.2).

Category III Pesticides

The least toxic or hazardous, Category III pesticides are still capable of causing injury (fig. 90.3). The signal word CAUTION appears on their labels. Usually, more than 1 ounce of a pesticide in this category needs to be swallowed to cause death of an adult.

PESTICIDE HAZARDS

Improper use of or accidents involving a pesticide can injure people. With improper use, there are risks of groundwater and environmental contamination that pose dangers to people and wildlife. An accident or error in application can also result in illegal residues in crops or the soil.

Dangers to People

Breathing, swallowing, spilling, or splashing pesticides into the eyes or onto the skin may result in injury. Most poisonous chemicals injure people by interfering with biochemical and physiological functions; the nature and extent of injury depend on the toxicity of the chemical and the amount that enters the tissues. Category I pesticides are very toxic and may cause severe injury at low doses. Other pesticides are so mildly toxic that large amounts must be consumed before illness can be detected. Nevertheless, because potential

hazards exist, anyone working with pesticides should avoid exposure to their skin, lungs, digestive tract, and eyes. Treat all pesticides with respect. It is impossible to predict the ultimate effects of long-term, repeated exposures to even the least hazardous pesticides.

Groundwater Contamination

Groundwater in California is vulnerable to many types of contaminants, including pesticides. Once contamination does occur, it is difficult or impossible to contain. Because groundwater flows slowly, it may take several hundred years before contaminants are removed naturally. Protecting groundwater from pesticides and other pollutants is therefore essential.

Pesticides enter groundwater by leaching through soil and by direct entry through wells or other structures in contact with aquifers. Leaching occurs when rainwater or irrigation water percolates through the soil, dissolving water-soluble chemicals, including some pesticides (fig. 90.4). Pesticides, often incorporated into the soil or incorporated through irrigation in vineyards, can be leached out and may eventually be carried to groundwater sources.

Mixing pesticides near a well, pumping water into pesticide application equipment, or injecting pesticides into an irrigation system—if performed carelessly or improperly—are some of the ways that pesticides can contaminate groundwater. Disposing of surplus pesticides and washing contaminated equipment near a well are also likely to cause groundwater contamination. Abandoned wells that have been improperly sealed provide possible underground routes for pesticides and other contaminants. Occasionally,

Table 90.2. Pesticide toxicity categories

Hazard indicators	Toxicity category–signal word		
	I - DANGER	**II - WARNING**	**III - CAUTION**
oral LD50	up to and including 50 mg/kg	from 50 through 500 mg/kg	from 500 through 5,000 mg/kg
inhalation LC50	up to and including 0.05 mg/l	from 0.05 through 0.5 mg/l	from 0.5 through 2 mg/l
dermal LD50	up to and including 200 mg/kg	from 200 through 2,000 mg/kg	from 2,000 through 5,000 mg/kg
eye effects	corrosive (irreversible destruction of ocular tissue) or corneal involvement or irritation persisting for more than 21 days	corneal involvement or other eye irritation clearing in 8–21 days	corneal involvement or other eye irritation clearing in 7 days or less
skin effects	corrosive (tissue destruction into the dermis and/or scarring)	severe irritation at 72 hours (severe reddening of the skin or edema)	moderate irritation at 72 hours (moderate reddening of the skin)

Precautionary statements by toxicity category		
Toxicity category–signal word	**Oral, inhalation, or dermal toxicity**	**Skin and eye local effects**
I - DANGER	Fatal (poisonous) if swallowed, inhaled, or absorbed through skin. Do not breathe vapor (dust or spray mist). Do not get in eyes, on skin, or on clothing. (Front panel statement of practical treatment required.)	Corrosive, causes eye and skin damage (for skin irritation). Do not get in eyes, on skin, or on clothing. Wear goggles or face shield and chemical-resistant gloves when handling. Harmful or fatal if swallowed. (Appropriate first-aid statement required.)
II - WARNING	May be fatal if swallowed (inhaled or absorbed through the skin). Do not breathe vapors (dust or spray mist). Do not get in eyes, on skin, or on clothing. (Appropriate first-aid statement required.)	Causes eye (and skin) irritation. Do not get in eyes, on skin, or on clothing. Harmful if swallowed. (Appropriate first-aid statement required.)
III - CAUTION	Harmful if swallowed (inhaled or absorbed through the skin). Avoid breathing vapors (dust or spray mist). Avoid contact with skin (eyes or clothing). (Appropriate first-aid statement required.)	Avoid contact with skin, eyes, or clothing. In case of contact, immediately flush eyes or skin with plenty of water. Get medical attention if irritation persists.

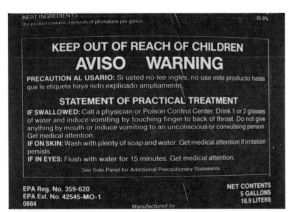

Figure 90.2 Category II pesticides are recognized by the word WARNING on the label. One teaspoon to 1 ounce of Category II pesticide, taken internally, would probably cause death. These pesticides have an oral LD50 of 50 to 500 mg/kg and a dermal LD50 of 200 to 2,000 mg/kg. *Photo*: J. K. Clark.

Figure 90.3 Category III pesticides are recognized by the word CAUTION on the label. These pesticides are the least toxic. Category III pesticides have an oral LD50 greater than 500 mg/kg and a dermal LD50 greater than 2,000 mg/kg. *Photo*: L. J. Bettiga.

Figure 90.4 Water enters aquifers by percolation through the soil. As water passes through the soil, it may dissolve some pesticides and carry them into the aquifer. This process is called leaching. Water wells located in or near vineyards may be a direct channel into groundwater.

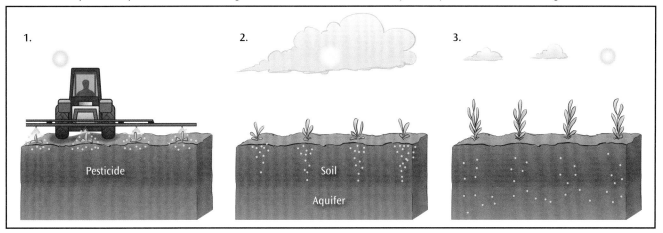

pesticide waste or runoff may enter groundwater directly through sinkholes or exposed shallow aquifers.

Preventing Groundwater Contamination

The following techniques help prevent pesticides from contaminating groundwater.

Storage. Store pesticides in enclosed areas, protected from rain. In case of fire or rupture of storage containers, be sure runoff is contained. Promptly remove contaminated soil.

Mixing and loading. Avoid spilling pesticides. If a spill occurs, clean up and dispose of wastes quickly. Remove contaminated soil. Triple-rinse empty liquid pesticide containers and dispose of them at a designated disposal site. Do not overfill spray tanks. Use a check valve on filling pipes to prevent backflow of contaminated water into water supplies.

Application. Whenever possible, select pesticides with low soil mobility or use ones that degrade rapidly. Avoid drift of pesticides out of your vineyard by using proper application techniques; try to make applications during optimal weather conditions whenever possible. In areas where high risks to

groundwater exist, reduce pesticide use by integrating chemical control with other control methods, use pesticides only when necessary, mix and apply only those amounts that will adequately control pests, and reduce the number of pesticide applications whenever possible.

Disposal. Never dump excess pesticide or pesticide mixtures onto vineyard soil or into sewers, drains, or septic systems. Unused agricultural pesticide waste must be transported to a Class I disposal site.

Cultural practices. Avoid excessive use of irrigation water after a pesticide application and prevent irrigation water runoff.

Environment and Wildlife

Wildlife may be accidentally harmed by pesticide use either directly by being poisoned or indirectly by having their food sources or habitats altered. Although a pesticide dose may not immediately cause death, the effect may weaken a nontarget animal, eventually leading to illness or death because it will be unable to get food and water or to protect itself from natural enemies. Some pesticides may influence the ability of wildlife

to reproduce. Animals feeding or nesting in an area where pesticides are used may unintentionally become poisoned by pesticides.

Fish are susceptible to several types of pesticides—even at low concentrations—that enter waterways through drift, by direct spraying, by leaching from the soil through runoff of irrigation and rainwater, through erosion of treated soil, or through accidents and illegal dumping.

If your vineyard is near a wildlife area or is a habitat for nonpest wildlife, avoid using pesticides known to be highly toxic to birds and other animals, and avoid formulations that are attractive, such as baits or pellets. Prevent runoff into waterways, lakes, or ponds. Always prevent drift when making liquid or dust applications.

Endangered Species

Federal and state laws designed to protect certain rare or vulnerable wildlife and plant species from extinction may restrict the types of pesticides that can be applied in specific locations, or they may regulate usage of some pesticides. Severe fines and imprisonment can be imposed if endangered species are harmed.

To avoid harming protected wildlife and native plants, follow pesticide label directions and precautions. Check with your county agricultural commissioner or the nearest Endangered Species Office of the U.S. Fish and Wildlife Service and local or regional offices of the California Department of Fish and Wildlife for up-to-date laws and information on the location and protection of endangered species. Before considering applying pesticides in or near native habitats, contact specialists in the Fish and Wildlife Service or Department of Fish and Wildlife to identify any endangered species that could be affected.

Pesticide Residues

In vineyards, pesticide residues remain on treated surfaces for a time. Persistence of residues is a factor of the chemical nature of the pesticide and the type of formulation. Residues are also influenced by the frequency of application and the amount used. Environmental factors may also affect residues.

Residues are necessary for controlling some grape pests because continuous exposure improves control (as with some herbicides). They can be undesirable, however, if they expose people, domestic animals, or wildlife to unsafe levels or exceed the legal tolerance (or legal limit) levels on harvested produce. Residue tolerances on food, established through laboratory and animal testing, are the amounts of pesticide considered safe to consumers—with a generous margin of safety. Tolerances are established for each pesticide, and levels depend on the pesticide's toxicity and the type of commodity. In establishing tolerance levels, the consumer's average lifetime diet is considered. State

and federal agencies analyze samples of produce to ensure that pesticide residue tolerances are not exceeded; when agricultural products are found to contain pesticide residues greater than the maximum allowable, they are usually seized and may be destroyed if residues cannot be reduced to tolerance levels. Internationally, tolerances are referred to as maximum residue levels (MRL).

Illegal residues or residues exceeding tolerances can occur on grapes if the crop accumulates pesticides from the vineyard soil, too much pesticide is applied to the vines, the pesticide used is not registered for grapes, the pesticide is applied too close to harvest, or the vineyard received pesticide drift from another area.

Pesticide Persistence

The time between application and degradation of a pesticide is known as the pesticide's persistence. Chlorinated hydrocarbon insecticides and certain classes of herbicides do not break down rapidly in the environment and are considered highly persistent. Toxic effects against insects or weeds may remain from one to several years while the pesticide is present in the soil. Pesticide persistence may be beneficial where long-term pest control is desired. A material with lengthy persistence may be more hazardous, however, and the possibility of poisoning nontarget organisms increases. Longer restricted entry intervals for workers may be required, and chances of off-site transport through water movement, soil leaching, and wind and rain erosion increase.

The persistence characteristics of certain pesticides in the soil may restrict the types of plants or crops

that can legally be grown there for a specified period. This is known as a plant-back restriction. This restriction has been established to prevent residues of some pesticides from occurring in crops for which a tolerance has not been set or to prevent phytotoxicity to sensitive plants. Under plant-back restrictions, the pesticide label specifies the crops that can be planted and the waiting period after application before the grower can plant other crops. When planting new vines in locations previously not used as a vineyard, consider their pesticide-use history.

Pesticide Safety

Using pesticides safely in vineyards avoids undesirable effects, such as groundwater contamination and excessive residues. Strictly adhere to label directions and local, state, and federal laws, and use safe techniques during mixing and application. Always store unused pesticides in a secure location and dispose of wastes in approved areas.

Training Workers

California law requires employers to provide training to all employees who handle pesticides prior to the employee handling any pesticide. This training includes proper mixing and application, handling and disposing of pesticides and pesticide wastes, using protective clothing and equipment, recognizing symptoms of pesticide poisoning, and understanding pesticide labels. The training of each employee must be recorded, and it must be updated at least once a year and prior to each time a new pesticide is to be used.

Medical Supervision

Those who apply pesticides

regularly should have periodic medical checkups. Locate a medical facility staffed with trained specialists who can treat any worker injured because of pesticide exposure. These medical specialists should be familiar with the types of pesticides used in your vineyard.

Pesticide worker safety regulations developed by California Department of Pesticide Regulation require a special blood test for employees who apply organophosphate or carbamate pesticides for any part of any 6 days within any 30-day period. Exposure is considered to begin the moment a pesticide container is opened for mixing or application and continues until the person has bathed and changed clothing after completing the application. This blood test, called red cell and plasma cholinesterase determination, establishes a baseline for measuring exposure to organophosphate and carbamate pesticides.

Other medical procedures, such as urine analysis and other blood tests, can detect poisoning resulting from exposure to classes of pesticides other than organophosphates and carbamates. Law, however, does not mandate these tests.

Understanding Pesticide Labels

Before use in California, each pesticide must be registered with the U.S. Environmental Protection Agency as well as with the California Department of Pesticide Regulation. This registration procedure is necessary to provide for the proper and safe use of pesticides and to protect people and the environment from ineffective or detrimental chemicals. To complete registration, the manufacturer must supply specific toxicology and groundwater data and a label meeting all federal and state requirements. Labels are legal documents containing important information for the user; read and understand the complete label before applying a pesticide.

On some types of pesticide packages, manufacturers attach supplemental labels that contain additional information and instructions (fig. 90.5). Before you purchase, mix, or apply any pesticide, obtain a complete set of label instructions, including supplemental labels.

When to Read the Pesticide Label

Read the pesticide label during the following times.

- **Before purchasing the pesticide.** Be certain the pesticide is registered for your intended use. Find out what protective equipment is required and make sure it can be used under current weather conditions and against the pest life stage you are trying to control.

- **Before mixing and applying the pesticide.** Understand how to mix and safely apply the material. Learn what precautions to take and what first-aid and medical treatment are necessary should exposure occur.

- **When storing pesticides.** Find out how to properly store these materials to prevent breakdown of the compounds. Understand the special precautions to prevent fire hazards.

- **Before disposing of unused pesticides and empty containers.** Learn how to prevent environmental contamination and safety hazards to people by properly disposing of unused pesticides and empty containers.

Mixing Pesticides

Techniques for mixing pesticides are the same for large and small volumes: the proper amount of pesticide must be thoroughly incorporated into a measured amount of water or other diluent. Before beginning, read the mixing directions on the labels of all pesticides you will use and decide on the proper order for adding chemicals to the spray tank. Adjuvants, if needed, are usually added before pesticides, unless label instructions give a different order.

Wear the protective clothing required for mixing and application. Check spray equipment for cracked hoses or leaks, and check filters, screens, and nozzles for cleanliness. Arrange to have a supply of clean water nearby in case of an accident.

Clean water is necessary for mixing pesticides. It should be free of sand, dirt, algae, or other foreign matter to avoid excessive wear on pumps and nozzles and clogging of filters, screens, and nozzles. Algae can also react with pesticides to reduce their effectiveness. Chemicals or organic materials in water may react unfavorably with some pesticides. For example, chlorine used in domestic water supplies to control bacteria reacts with certain pesticides, reducing their effectiveness. High levels of dissolved salts deactivate many pesticides and

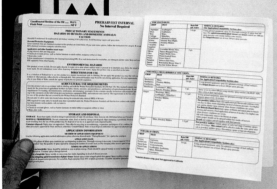

Figure 90.5 Some pesticide packages have a supplemental label that provides detailed information not found on the container's label. Before using a pesticide, make sure you have a complete set of labels. *Photos*: L. J. Bettiga.

Figure 90.6 Closed mixing systems are used for mixing liquid Category I pesticides. Closed mixing systems enable accurate measuring of pesticides, and most systems enable rinsing of empty containers. *Photo*: J. K. Clark.

may even damage sensitive foliage. If possible, check the pH of the water. Some pesticides require water at a specified pH. High pH (alkaline water) causes hydrolysis, or breakdown, of many pesticides before they can be sprayed onto the target surface. Use a buffer or acidifier if the pH is too high.

Measure pesticide amounts accurately, since faulty measuring can produce large errors in the amount of pesticide being applied. Category I liquid materials call for a closed mixing system that enables accurate and safe measuring of the pesticide going into the spray tank (fig. 90.6). The closed system requirement does not apply if you handle 1 gallon or less of Category I pesticide per day and the liquid pesticide is in an original container of 1 gallon or less. Dry formulations and Category II and III liquids do not require a closed mixing system unless the person mixing them is younger than 18 years old.

For mixing, select a location that can be decontaminated easily should an accident occur. Begin by filling the spray tank at least half full with clean water. Avoid filling the tank more than three-fourths full to allow room for the pesticide, adjuvants, and residues from triple-rinsing of containers. Start agitators if the equipment has them. When not using premeasured packets, measure and weigh chemicals in a clear, open area. Stand upwind to reduce chances of exposure. Wear an approved dust or mist respirator or cartridge respirator to prevent inhaling dust while weighing and mixing dry pesticides. Use measuring or weighing devices calibrated to the amounts you will be measuring. Protect hands and clothing with appropriate outerwear. Liquids can be easily spilled and splashed, so wear rubber gloves and a rubber apron or waterproof pants and jacket. Refer to the pesticide label for specific protective clothing and equipment needs for mixing and loading. A face shield or goggles must be worn, however, even if the requirement is not on the pesticide label (fig. 90.7). Reduce chances of spills or splashes into your face and eyes by always measuring and pouring pesticides below eye level.

Open pesticide containers carefully to prevent spilling and to make resealing easier. Cut paper containers with a sharp knife or scissors; do not tear them. Metal containers, glass and plastic bottles, and plastic pails have protective seals that must be broken before use; most of these containers can be easily resealed with screw caps.

LOADING PESTICIDES

After measuring or weighing the proper amount of pesticide, carefully pour it into the partially filled tank. Always pour with your head and arms at a level above the tank (fig. 90.8).

Rinse the measuring container and pour the rinse solution into the spray tank. While rinsing, prevent splashing. Some closed mixing systems are equipped with container-rinsing devices that pump the rinse solution into the pesticide tank. Unless rinsed automatically, liquid containers should be drained into the spray tank for 30 seconds after being emptied, then rinsed and drained three more times (triple-rinsed). After each draining, fill the container about one-fourth full of water, put the cap back on, and shake for several seconds to mix the residue with water. Pour each rinse solution into the spray tank and drain the container for 30 seconds.

Once the pesticide has been added, fill the spray tank to its final volume. Do not allow the tank to overflow during filling, and do not let the hose, pipe, or other filling device come in contact with liquid in the tank. If the tank is being filled through a top opening, allow an air space equal to at least twice the diameter of the filling pipe (fig. 90.9). This gap will prevent siphoning of the spray mixture back into the water supply. Side- or bottom-filling systems require using check valves to prevent backflow of pesticides into the water supply.

APPLICATION CONSIDERATIONS

For your personal safety and to protect others and the environment, understand the unique problems associated with pesticide application in your vineyard and develop techniques to minimize them. Safe techniques require working with the weather, controlling droplet size and deposition, being familiar with the application site and its hazards, developing special application patterns for the site to accommodate hazards and environmental conditions, and leaving buffer zones to protect sensitive areas.

Weather

Weather greatly influences vineyard pesticide applications. Temperature affects the phytotoxicity of certain pesticides, so label directions usually warn against applying these products when temperatures are above or below critical limits. Differences in air temperature are responsible for the inversion phenomenon that often influences pesticide drift (fig. 90.10). To detect a temperature inversion, observe a column of smoke rising into the air. If the smoke begins moving sideways or collects in one area a few hundred feet above the ground, an inversion condition probably exists.

Inversions occur when the air 20 to 100 or more feet above the ground is warmer than the air below it. This layer of warm air forms a cap that blocks vertical air movement. Inversion conditions are dangerous during a pesticide application because fine spray droplets and pesticide vapor can become trapped and concentrated, similar to the smoke column. Rather than dispersing into the atmosphere, the pesticide often moves as a cloud away from the treatment site.

High temperatures accelerate pesticide breakdown and volatilization. Warm temperatures associated with clear, sunny weather may increase pesticide degradation because ultraviolet light is most intense during those times.

Figure 90.7 Protective goggles are used to protect the eyes during mixing and applying pesticides. Goggles must have full side shields with specially designed vents that prevent dust or spray droplets from getting in. *Photo*: J. K. Clark.

Figure 90.8 Carefully pour pesticides: avoid splashing the material and do not allow pesticides to spill onto the outside of the tank. Rinse measuring containers and empty and triple-rinse liquid pesticide containers. Always pour the rinse solution into the spray tank. *Photo*: J. K. Clark.

Figure 90.9 When filling a spray tank from the top, be sure there is an air gap between the filler pipe and the top level of the water in the tank. This will prevent backflow of pesticide-contaminated water into the water supply. *Photo*: J. K. Clark.

Figure 90.10 These drawings illustrate normal (left) and inversion (right) conditions. A temperature inversion is a layer of warm air above cooler air closer to the ground. This warm air prevents air nearer the ground from rising, acting like a lid. *Source:* UC IPM.

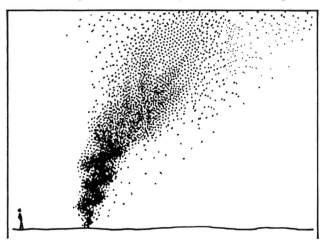 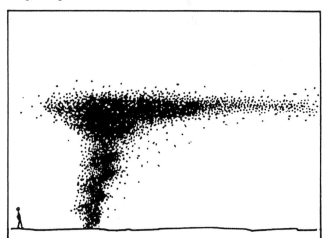

Rainfall, fog, and even heavy dew affect pesticide applications because moisture dilutes and degrades pesticides and may wash them off treated surfaces into the vineyard soil. Pesticides can be carried away from the vineyard through water movement after heavy rains. This may result in possible contamination of groundwater and surface water. Pesticide mist may remain suspended in fog and move off-site.

Wind influences pesticide drift and also affects volatility. Strong air movements are responsible for uneven pesticide deposits, although some air movement assists in getting good coverage of treated surfaces.

Droplet Size and Deposition

Spray droplet deposition is influenced by droplet size, pressure of the spray stream, force and volume of air used to distribute spray (if any), and travel speed of the application equipment. Droplet size is determined by the nozzle's size, style, and condition in combination with spray volume, spray pressure, and weather. Most types of application equipment emit a spray having a wide range of droplet sizes, although the best applications result from even, uniform-sized droplets.

Increase the uniformity of spray droplets by selecting nozzles designed for the working pressure and volume of your application equipment. Also, replace worn or defective nozzles. Application speed is critical when applying a pesticide to vines; slower speeds are usually required for large or densely leaved vines to allow proper penetration of spray droplets. For more information, see section 88, "Principles and Techniques of Vine Spraying."

Site and Environmental Hazards

Before applying a pesticide, study the vineyard's physical characteristics and its potential hazards. Check for ditches, embankments, steep slopes, electrical wires, electric fences, and other structures that can harm careless operators or equipment. Look for environmentally sensitive areas to avoid, such as lakes, streams, wildlife areas, and inhabited areas.

Application Pattern

In applying a pesticide in a vineyard, the applicator follows a pattern to evenly distribute the pesticide over an area and to avoid overlaps or gaps.

The pattern used may be dictated by the arrangement of the vine rows, but whenever possible, consider the prevailing weather, terrain configuration, pesticide being sprayed, and hazards in or near the application site. Design the pattern so that the operator need not travel through airborne spray or freshly treated areas. Shut off the spray before making turns in the vineyard.

Buffer strips are areas intentionally left untreated if the treatment area adjoins locations where organisms, people, or structures may be endangered. The size of the strip depends on the application equipment used, prevailing weather, nature of the pesticide, type of pest problem, and the vulnerability of the adjoining area. Generally, the buffer should be no less than one spray swath (fig. 90.11).

TRANSPORTING PESTICIDES

Spills resulting from vehicle accidents while transporting pesticides may cause serious exposure. Some pesticides are flammable, and if they catch fire, they are capable of emitting toxic fumes. Once pesticides are spilled on public roads, they may be blown or splashed onto people, animals, residential areas, or nearby crops, or they may be scattered by passing vehicles. During rainstorms, spilled chemicals may be washed into ditches, streams, and rivers, possibly causing injury to wildlife and contaminating surface water and groundwater. Spilled pesticides may also contaminate the vehicle, its occupants, or other cargo.

Never carry pesticides in any passenger compartment; they are most safely transported secured in the back of a truck (fig. 90.12). Never stack pesticide containers higher than the sides of the transporting vehicle. Do not allow children, adults, or animals to ride in the area where pesticides are carried, and never transport food, animal feed, or clothing in the same compartment. Do not leave pesticides unattended in a vehicle unless they are inside a locked compartment.

Pesticide Storage

Store pesticides in their original, tightly closed containers in a separate building away from people, living areas, food, animal feed, and livestock (fig. 90.13). Protect them from extremes in temperature and from becoming wet. The area must be well ventilated, well lighted, dry, and secure, with lockable doors and windows. Post signs warning that the building contains pesticides near all primary entrances.

Some pesticides do not store well for long periods; most should not be kept for longer than 2 years. Before pesticides exceed their shelf life, use them in an appropriate

application or transport them to an approved disposal site.

Pesticide Disposal

To avoid leftover pesticide mixtures, purchase and mix only enough pesticide for the job. Transport any leftover spray to a Class I disposal site or use it in another suitable location. Dumping of spray mixtures is a potential source of environmental and groundwater contamination and is illegal.

Regulations concerning the disposal of pesticide containers vary from county to county. Specific disposal information can be obtained from your regional water quality control board, the county's department of health services, and the local agricultural commissioner.

Metal, glass, and plastic containers that have been triple-rinsed at the time of use to remove traces of pesticide can either be offered to the pesticide manufacturer for recycling or transported to an approved Class II disposal site. If these containers have not been triple-rinsed, they can be taken only to a Class I disposal site. The regional water quality control board or agricultural commissioner in your area can provide information on the locations of approved disposal sites.

PERSONAL PROTECTIVE EQUIPMENT

Prevent exposure by selecting appropriate personal protective

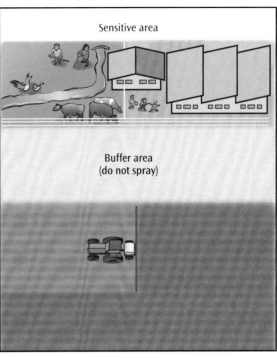

Figure 90.11 Leave untreated buffer areas when an application site adjoins locations where organisms, people, or structures might be harmed by pesticide exposure. The buffer should be no less than one spray width.

Figure 90.12 Pesticides should be transported only in the back of a truck. Containers must be secured in the cargo area and protected from moisture and damage. Do not allow children, adults, or animals to ride in the cargo area. Never transport food, animal feed, or clothing in the same compartment. *Photo*: J. K. Clark.

equipment. This includes clothing to cover your arms, legs, and torso to prevent pesticide dust or liquid from contacting your skin. Protect your hands and feet with rubber gloves and boots while mixing and applying pesticides. Avoid fabric-lined gloves, since the fabric may absorb pesticides and increase your exposure. Wear sleeves and pant legs of your protective clothing on the outside of gloves and boots. Protect your head and neck from pesticide spray or mist during an application by wearing a hooded jacket, waterproof hat, or helmet. Fabric hats absorb pesticide-laden water, so they must never be worn during a liquid spray application.

Never handle, mix, or apply pesticides without at least minimal protective clothing, including full-length pants and a long-sleeved shirt made from tightly woven cotton fabric. More-hazardous pesticides require wearing waterproof protective clothing; both disposable and reusable types are available and can be worn over regular clothing. Disposables are lightweight and resist tears and punctures. Reusable waterproof clothes consist of woven or nonwoven fabrics coated with or laminated to a waterproof material. The amount of protection offered against pesticide exposure depends on the type of waterproofing used. Neoprene, latex rubber, and polyvinyl chloride (PVC) are materials commonly used for this purpose.

Do not use protective clothing lined with a woven fabric. Although woven linings are comfortable and give the garment strength, they often become wet and contaminated with pesticides, increasing

your risk of exposure. Linings of nonwoven, nonabsorbent materials, such as dacron, are safer.

Use goggles or a face shield to protect your eyes during mixing and while adjusting, cleaning, or repairing contaminated equipment and during most types of pesticide application. Eye protection is not required if pesticides are being injected or incorporated into the soil; pesticides are being applied through vehicle-mounted spray nozzles located below and behind the operator, with the nozzles directed downward; the operator is working in an enclosed cab; or the pesticides being applied are rodenticides or predacides that are not liquid or gaseous.

A pesticide respirator protects the lungs and respiratory tract from airborne pesticides during mixing and application. Many types and styles of respirators have been certified for use with pesticides by the National Institute for Occupational Safety and Health (NIOSH). Base your choice on the type and toxicity of pesticides you are working with, the recommendation or requirement listed on the pesticide label, and the nature of the area where you are working. Filters and cartridges on respirators gradually build up with pesticide residue and must be replaced often. Increased resistance to breathing indicates that the filter's mechanical part may have reached its capacity for trapped particles. Replace respirator cartridges if you experience a pesticide odor or taste or any other irritation. Also, change cartridges following pesticide label instructions and equipment manufacturer recommendations or, lacking

factual information, change them at the end of each workday.

PROTECTING FIELDWORKERS AND THE PUBLIC

Pesticide laws protect fieldworkers and the general public from hazardous pesticide exposures. They designate restricted entry intervals, field posting, and harvest intervals. Worker protection standards mandate training requirements for fieldworkers and protective equipment to be worn. When making any application, always follow the California Department of Pesticide Regulation regulations and pesticide label guidelines. Never apply a pesticide in a vineyard if fieldworkers are present.

Restricted Entry Intervals

The restricted entry interval is the time between a pesticide application and the permitted entrance of anyone into the treated vineyard. Restricted entry intervals are given on pesticide labels, but California regulations are often more restrictive (see Section 6772 California Code of Regulations) (fig. 90.14). The local agricultural commissioner can provide specific information. In all situations where the restricted entry interval on the label differs from California requirements, the longer restricted entry interval applies. A longer period may be indicated on the label, and in these cases, the longer period must be used. For Category II and III pesticides, if no restricted entry interval is specified, people should be kept out of the treated area at least until the spray dries or dust settles.

When two or more pesticides are applied at the same time, a

Figure 90.13 Pesticides must be stored in a separate building away from humans, living areas, food, animal feed, and livestock. The storage area should be well ventilated, well lighted, dry, and secure. Doors and windows must be securely locked. Post signs at all primary entrances warning that the building contains pesticides. *Photo*: J. K. Clark.

Figure 90.14 In California, all Category I pesticides (restricted-use pesticides) have a minimum re-entry interval of 24 hours. A longer re-entry interval may be indicated on the label or prescribed by state regulations. Be sure to understand the correct re-entry interval before making a pesticide application. *Photo*: J. K. Clark.

Figure 90.15 Whenever required by the pesticide label, or by state or local regulations, post a treated area with signs to warn the public of the danger. Signs should be no more than 600 feet apart along usual points of entry and along unfenced areas next to roads and other public rights-of-way. *Photo*: L. J. Bettiga.

new restricted entry interval must be calculated. Compute the new restricted entry interval by adding to the longest period one half of the next longest period. For example, the restricted entry interval is 14 days for Pesticide A and 10 days for Pesticide B. When combined, the new restricted entry interval will be 19 days (14 days plus one half of 10 days). A compound with a restricted entry interval of 10 days, combined with another not having a restricted entry interval, would have a combined interval of 10 days.

Field Posting

Vineyards treated with pesticides having a required restricted entry interval must sometimes be posted with warning signs (fig. 90.15). Regulations require these signs to be of a durable material and printed in English and Spanish. They must contain the word DANGER in letters large enough to be read from a distance of 25 feet. If the restricted entry interval is greater than 7 days, the sign must also name the pesticide that was used and the date that the area may be re-entered. Check pesticide labels and current federal, state, and local laws to determine requirements for posting. Local offices of county agricultural commissioners have this information.

To post a treated area, place signs at usual points of entry into the vineyard and along unfenced areas next to roads and other public rights-of-way. Signs should be no more than 600 feet apart. Signs must be posted before an application is made, but no sooner than 24 hours before the application. They must remain in place throughout the restricted entry interval and must be removed within 3 days after the end of the restricted entry

interval and before workers are allowed to enter the vineyard.

Harvest Intervals

To protect consumers from pesticide residues on agricultural produce, state and federal regulations often establish a harvest interval for pesticide applications. This is the minimum period that must elapse after an application has been made and before the crop can be harvested. Check pesticide labels for this information.

PESTICIDE EMERGENCIES

Even under the most careful conditions, accidents may occur, and any accident involving pesticides must be treated as an emergency because of its great potential for harm to people or the environment. Pesticides diluted with water may be hazardous, but undiluted pesticides are usually even more dangerous. Emergencies may be the result of an accident during mixing, loading, or application, or can result from leaks and spills, fires, or lack of care in storage or handling.

Accidents Involving People

Exposure to a pesticide calls for immediate action. Concentrated pesticides spilled on the skin or clothing can cause serious injury—burns or rashes or, through skin absorption, possible internal poisoning. Pesticides that get into a person's eyes may seriously damage eye tissues; the eyes are also another route of entry to internal tissues of the body. In accidents involving toxic fumes, spray mist, or dust that may be inhaled, the lungs and respiratory tract may be seriously damaged, and the pesticide may move from the lungs to other body tissues. Accidental swallowing of pesticides provides a direct route to internal tissues; the lining of the mouth and digestive system may also be damaged if the pesticide is caustic or contains petroleum distillates.

Prompt first-aid and medical care may reduce the extent of injuries caused by exposure to pesticides. Get the person away from the source of exposure. If possible, read the pesticide label for specific first-aid instructions, especially regarding induction of vomiting. Remove contaminated clothing and flush the skin with clean water. Flush pesticides from the eyes with a gentle stream of water for at least 15 minutes. Artificial respiration or cardiopulmonary resuscitation may be needed if breathing has stopped. Seek medical care at once—provide medical specialists with the name and possibly a label of the pesticide involved. Do not take a container of the pesticide into a health care facility.

Leaks and Spills

Always consider pesticide leaks or spills as emergencies. Concentrated pesticide spills are much more dangerous than spills of pesticides diluted with water, but both types should be dealt with immediately. Leaks or spills can occur during transporting, storing, or using pesticides. When spills occur on public roadways,

immediately contact the California Highway Patrol and the California Office of Emergency Services. These agencies will take charge of coordinating the cleanup and protecting the public. Cleaning up spills involves removing soil and all other contaminated material. Always wear the maximum protective clothing when working around a pesticide spill. Clear the area to prevent others from becoming exposed. Contain the spill with dirt dams or other barriers. Prevent fires by eliminating ignition sources. Put contaminated objects and soil into steel drums or sturdy, scalable containers for transport to an appropriate disposal site. Contact the local county agricultural commissioner for information on disposing of pesticide-contaminated material. Some surfaces can be cleaned of pesticide residues by thorough washing with a commercial preparation or a solution of detergent and soda ash dissolved in water. Use sawdust or cat litter to absorb spilled liquids and all fluids used for washing and rinsing contaminated areas. Place the absorbed material in a scalable container for transport to an appropriate disposal site.

Fires

Fighting pesticide fires requires special care because smoke and fumes generated by burning

pesticides cannot be contained; evacuate areas endangered by fumes. Toxic fumes hamper fire-fighting efforts and require using supplied-air respirators and protective clothing. Always ask the local fire department for help in fighting a pesticide fire and provide fire fighters with the names and labels of pesticides involved. Use water cautiously when fighting pesticide fires; it should be used primarily to cool containers and prevent overheated chemicals from exploding. Do not splash or spread toxic chemicals with high-pressure water. Once the fire is extinguished, contain the runoff with dirt dams and rope off the contaminated area until it has been properly cleaned up. If large amounts of pesticides were involved in the fire, seek assistance from a professional decontamination and disposal company. Small amounts of contamination can be disposed of in the same manner as pesticide spills. Consult the county agricultural commissioner for advice and information on proper disposal methods.

REFERENCES

O'Connor-Marer, P. J. 2000. The safe and effective use of pesticides. 2nd ed. Oakland: University of California Division of Agriculture and Natural Resources Publication 3324.

GLOSSARY OF VITICULTURE AND PEST MANAGEMENT TERMS

abdomen. Posterior of the three main body divisions of an insect, i.e., the head, thorax, and abdomen.

abiotic. Caused by the action of nonliving factors.

abscission layer. Layer of thin-walled cells along which cell separation, or adjunction, occurs to bring about the shedding of a plant part such as leaves, flowers, or fruits.

acidifier. An adjuvant used to lower the pH of (acidify) the water being mixed with a pesticide; an acidulator.

active ingredient (a.i.). Material in a pesticide that kills the pest or performs the desired function.

adjuvant. A material that improves the emulsifying, dispersing, spreading, wetting, or other property of a liquid by modifying its surface characteristics.

adventitious bud. Latent bud in older wood that has remained dormant for more than 1 year.

adventitious root. Root developing from the cambium of a stem.

aedeagus. Male intromittent organ.

aerial roots. Roots developing adventitiously from aerial portions of a vine.

aestivation. To rest, sleep, or be inactive during hot summer months.

agitator. A mechanical or hydraulic device that stirs the liquid in a spray tank to prevent the mixture from separating or settling.

anal. In insects, pertaining to the terminal abdominal segment, which bears the anus.

anal shield. Hard plate on the terminal segment of a caterpillar and certain other immature insects.

anamorph. The imperfect, or asexual, stage of a fungus.

annual. Plant that reproduces from seed and completes its life cycle in one growing season.

antennae. Pair of segmented appendages located on the head above the mouthparts of an insect that usually perform a sensory function.

anther. The part of the stamen that produces and contains pollen, usually borne on a filament.

anthesis. The action or period of flowering.

apical. At the end, tip, or outermost part.

apterous. Wingless.

aquifer. An underground formation of sand, gravel, or porous rock that contains water; the place where groundwater is found.

arm. The permanent divisions of a grapevine arising from the trunk, in the case of head- or cane-pruned vines, or along the cordon, in the case of cordon-pruned vines, that generally bear the spurs and canes retained for fruit production.

ascocarp. Sexual fruiting body of a fungus belonging to the ascomycete group.

ascomycetes. A group of fungi that produce their sexual spores within asci; includes many plant pathogens.

ascospore. Fungal spore resulting from sexual reproduction; borne in an ascus.

ascus. Saclike structure in which ascospores are produced.

asexual. Reproduction without fertilization; parthenogenetic.

attractant. A pesticide that attracts a particular species of animal to a trap or poisoned bait.

avenue. A space at the end of vine rows, usually 20 to 30 feet in width, that should be wide enough for easy turning of vineyard equipment.

axillary buds. Undeveloped portions of the plant located in the upper angle formed by a leaf or branch with the stem.

back siphoning. The process that permits pesticide-contaminated water to be sucked from a spray tank back into a well or other water source.

bacterium. One-celled organism that reproduces by fission.

bait box. Small structure designed to hold poisoned bait so that the target animal must enter to take the bait.

bark. The tough covering of a woody stem or root, external to the vascular cambium, comprised of phloem and periderm tissue; the loose, corky periderm layers that slough off the grape trunk and cordon.

basal. At the base or near the point of attachment.

basal buds. Buds that develop in the axils of bracts at the base of a shoot.

basipetal. Development or movement from the apex toward the base.

berry. An individual fruit of the grape plant.

biotic natural control. Control of pests by the action of living things (parasites, diseases, etc.).

biotroph. An organism that can live and reproduce only on a living host organism.

biotype. Physiological race of a species whose biological characteristics separate it from other individuals of the species.

black light. Ultraviolet light visible to insects.

blade. The expanded portion of a leaf; the lamina.

bleeding. Exudation of sap from the ends of canes and spurs after winter pruning.

bloom. The time of flower opening and pollination, indicated in grapes by shedding of the calyptras (corollas); the waxy, whitish coating on berries that gives a frosted appearance, especially to dark cultivars.

Brix. A measure of the total soluble solid content of grapes, which is approximately the percentage of grape sugars in the juice.

brood. All the individuals that hatch at about the same time from eggs laid by one series of parents and normally mature at about the same time.

brush. The broken ends of the vascular strands when the grape pedicel (cap stem) is pulled from the mature berry; prunings left in the vine row.

bud. A rounded organ at the node of a cane or shoot formed in the axil of the leaf containing undeveloped shoots protected by overlapping scales. Dormant grape buds (also referred to as latent buds or eyes) include three growing points: a primary bud between two less-prominent secondary buds.

budbreak. The stage of bud development in which green tissue becomes visible; bud burst.

bud scales. The outer covering of a bud, impregnated with suberin (waxed substances) and lined with hairs (tomentum) to protect the bud against drying out. The rigid scales guard against mechanical injury.

bud sport. A branch, flower, or fruit that arises from a bud mutation and differs genetically from the rest of the plant.

buffer. An adjuvant that lowers the pH of a spray solution and, depending on its concentration, can maintain the pH within a narrow range even if acidic or alkaline materials are added to the solution.

callus. Parenchyma tissue, which grows over a wound or graft during healing.

calyptra. The fused petals, or corolla, of the grape flower that detaches at the base and falls off during bloom.

cambium. A layer in a vascular plant between the xylem and phloem that produces secondary growth.

cane. Mature (woody or lignified) shoot. *See* **shoot**.

cane pruning. Pruning method in which canes (6 to 15 nodes long) are retained as the fruiting units.

canker. A lesion extending into the vascular tissue on any part of the grapevine.

cannibalistic. Feeding on others of the same species.

cap. *See* **calyptra**.

cap stem. The stem of individual flowers or berries; pedicel.

catch wire. A wire that serves as an attachment for developing shoots. Also used in cordon-trained vines to prevent downward rolling of shoots and crop of young vines.

caterpillar. Larva of a butterfly or moth.

caudal filament. A threadlike structure at posterior end of some insects.

causal agent. Organism that causes disease.

cephalothorax. The anterior portion of the body of certain arthropods, consisting of a fused head and thorax, as in spiders.

certified stock. Grapevine propagation material certified to be free of known virus diseases by the California Department of Food and Agriculture under regulations of the Grapevine Certification and Registration Program.

chasmothecium. Closed perithecium containing asci and ascospores of the powdery mildews, previously called the cleistothecium.

chimera. Mixture of tissues of genetically different constitution in the same part of the plant, resulting from mutation or irregular genetic development.

chitin. A nitrogenous polysaccharide comprising the principal structural material in the exoskeleton of arthropods.

chlamydospore. Thick-walled, asexual resting spore, usually soilborne.

chlorophyll. Green pigment of plants that absorbs light energy and converts that energy into carbohydrates during photosynthesis.

chlorosis. Yellowing or blanching of green portions of a plant, particularly the leaves, that can result from nutrient deficiencies, disease, herbicide injury, or other factors.

chorion. The outer shell of an insect egg.

chrysalis. Pupa of a butterfly or moth.

cleistothecium. *See* **chasmothecium**.

clone. A group of vines of a uniform type reproduced by vegetative propagation from an original mother vine.

codistillation. The volatilization or evaporation and subsequent condensation of two compounds, one of which is generally water.

conidium. A sexual fungal spore.

contact herbicide. An herbicide that acts by killing the green parts of the plant that are directly contacted by the spray.

cordon. Permanent horizontal branches developed from the trunk in grapevines.

cordon wire. A wire on which cordons or permanent branches are trained and tied.

cork cambium. Dividing tissue that is partly responsible for the development of the bark that produces cork or phellem on the outside and a corkskin, or phelloderm, on the inside; the phellogen.

count bud. A dormant bud on a spur or cane, not including basal buds. The first count bud is separated by a quarter-inch or more from the basal buds below. Transitional forms may make it difficult to determine the first count bud.

coxa. Basal segment of insect leg.

crawler. Immature development stage in which an insect has legs and can move, although in later stages the insect may become permanently affixed to one site.

crepuscular. Active at dusk or twilight.

crop load. The amount of fruit borne on vines in relation to the leaf surface, quantified by the ratio of yield to pruning weight.

crop recovery. The crop produced from the new growth following injury by spring frost.

crossarm. A horizontal or slanting crosspiece, usually 12 to 48 inches long, attached at various points on a trellis system to spread the vines, fruiting wood, fruit, or foliage over a greater area.

crown. The point at or just below the soil surface where the main grape stem (trunk) and root system join, as distinguished from the **head**.

crown suckering. *See* **shoot thinning**.

cultivar. A cultivated variety; also, a synonym of **variety**.

cultural control. Making the habitat unfavorable for the pest or favorable for natural enemies.

cutting. A portion of dormant cane, usually 14 to 18 inches long, used for vegetative propagation.

degree-day (DD). The amount of heat that accumulates over a 24-hour period when the temperature is between the lower and upper developmental threshold for an organism.

deutonymph. The third instar of a mite.

developmental threshold. Temperatures between which growth of an organism occurs.

diapause. A period of physiological controlled rest or delay in development during periods of cold.

dieback. Progressive death of a plant part, beginning at the tip of a shoot (or cordon, in grapes).

disbudding. Removal of buds or young shoots shorter than 6 inches.

disease. A continuous dysfunction of cells or tissue caused by biotic or abiotic factors.

disruptive. Treatment or other factors that lessen the ability of beneficial insects to exert a controlling influence on a pest species.

distal. Farthest from the body or main stem.

diurnal. Active during the daytime.

dormancy. A state of reduced physiological activity in plants or other organisms due to internal factors; quiescence. *See* **aestivation** and **diapause**.

dorsal. Top or uppermost.

drop. Abscission of flowers after bloom.

economic injury level. Pest population or damage that causes economic injury to a crop.

economic threshold. Pest population or damage level at which the cost of control equals the crop value gained.

ectoparasite. Parasite that attaches itself to a host and feeds externally.

electrostatic sprayer. A sprayer that uses electrical charges to attract the pesticide liquid or dust to the target surface.

ELISA (enzyme-linked immunosorbent assay). A test that can confirm the presence of specific proteins that is used to detect the presence of certain plant pathogens.

elytra. Thickened, leathery, or horny front wing, characteristic of beetles.

emulsifier. An adjuvant added to a pesticide formulation to permit petroleum-based pesticides to mix with water.

endoparasite. A parasite that feeds and develops within a host's body.

endophyte. An organism that lives in the xylem of a plant.

entomophagous. Feeding on insects, especially wasps that feed larvae to their young.

epidermis. Outermost layer of cells of young or deciduous plant parts.

epinasty. Downward-bending growth of shoot tips or leaves.

epiphyte. An organism that lives on the surface of a plant without causing infection or disease.

eradicant. A substance that eliminates a pathogen.

erinea. Velvety galls composed of tiny plant hairs with round heads caused by eriophyid mites.

erumpent. Bursting out suddenly, as a spore mass.

estivation. *See* **aestivation**.

exclusion. Prevention of one or more animals or species of animals from entering an area.

exoskeleton. External skeleton of insects and other arthropods.

external parasite. *See* **ectoparasite**.

extrafloral nectaries. Specialized cells outside a flower that secrete nectar.

exuviae. Cast skin of an insect or mite. *See* **exoskeleton**.

eye. A compound bud of a grape consisting of primary, secondary, and tertiary buds.

fasciation. Malformation resulting in enlarged, flattened, fused shoots.

feeder roots. Fine roots and root branches with a large absorbing area.

femur. Third segment of an insect leg, located between the trochanter and tibia.

fertilization. The process of applying mineral plant nutrients; the union of sperm cells from the pollen tube with egg cells of the ovary.

field capacity. The water content of a soil after drainage is complete and the water content is momentarily stable.

filament. The stalk supporting the pollen-bearing anther in a flower.

flare-back. Resurgence of a pest species following treatment that suppresses the effect of natural enemy control.

flight. Period of adult moth flying activity that can be used to define part or all of the flying activity of a generation of moths.

forb. A small, broadleaf, flowering plant.

frass. Insect excrement.

French plowing. *See* **row plowing**.

fruit. A mature ovary (berry) or a cluster of mature ovaries.

fruit set. A stage of grape berry development 1 to 3 weeks after blossoming when most of the flowers have fallen and those remaining have begun to develop into berries.

fumigant. A substance that forms toxic vapors that kills pests.

gall. A growth of unorganized plant cells in response to a pathogen or insect.

gibberellin. A naturally occurring growth regulator currently used for bloom thinning and berry enlargement of certain seedless cultivars.

girdling. The removal of a complete ring of outer and inner bark extending to the cambium from a shoot, cane, or trunk; ringing.

glabrous. Smooth and hairless (plant surface).

granulosis virus. Virus particles contained within minute granules.

grape eye. Compound dormant bud of a grapevine.

grass culture. Vegetation management in which volunteer plants, mostly grasses, are allowed to grow without cultivation from late spring until before or beyond harvest.

gravid. Pregnant; bearing eggs or young.

green manure crop. A crop grown and plowed under while still green to improve the soil, especially by adding organic matter.

grub. Thick-bodied larva with well-developed head and thoracic legs, without abdominal prolegs, and usually sluggish, usually in beetles or wasps.

habitat modification. Alteration of the environment where a pest species is found.

hair. Prolongation of an epidermal cell; on a grape stem or leaf, one celled to many celled, living or dead, deciduous or persistent; on a root, one celled, living, short-lived, and restricted to the absorbing zone.

haustorium. A specialized outgrowth of a stem, root, or mycelium (in fungi) that penetrates the host plant and absorbs food.

head. In grapes, the upper portion of a vine, consisting of the top of the trunk and arms, sometimes mistakenly referred to as the **crown**; in insects, the anterior of the three main body segments, i.e., the head, thorax, and abdomen.

head training. Vine training in which a stake supporting the trunk terminates in short permanent arms that bear spurs or canes.

hibernation. Dormancy in an organism's activity cycle, often occurring during winter months. *See* **aestivation** and **diapause**.

honeydew. Sugary, syrupy substance secreted by aphids, mealybugs, and soft scales.

host. Any organism supporting a parasite; a plant on which an insect feeds.

hot spot. Vineyard area where a pest population is substantially larger than in the balance of the vineyard and is at or near the point of causing economic damage.

hydrolysis. Chemical decomposition that involves incorporating one water molecule into another molecule.

hyperparasite. Parasite whose host is another parasite.

hyphae. Single branches or filaments that make up the body or mycelium of a fungus.

indexing. Determining the presence of virus disease in a vine by transferring tissue or inoculum to an indicator plant that reacts with specific diagnostic symptoms.

infection. The process of beginning or producing disease.

inflorescence. The flower cluster of a grapevine.

inoculum. Pathogen part that can infect a host.

instar. Period or stage between molts of insects, the first instar being the stage between hatching and the first molt.

integrated control. Approach that uses all suitable techniques and methods compatibly to maintain pest populations below economic injury levels.

internal parasite. *See* **endoparasite**.

internode. A section of a shoot or cane between two nodes.

interveinal chlorosis. Yellowing between the main veins of a leaf.

larva. Immature stage between egg and pupa in insects having complete metamorphosis; the six-legged first instar of mites.

larvaposition. Depositing live larvae. Compare **ovipositioning**.

latent bud. A bud that has remained dormant for one season or longer.

lateral. A branch of the main axis of a cluster; a side shoot arising from a lateral bud on a primary shoot.

lateral bud. The first bud to form in the leaf axil, which can grow the same season it is formed; a prompt bud.

layering. Replacing a missing vine by burying a long cane from an adjacent vine and allowing it to develop roots, then bringing cane tip up the stake.

leaching. The downward movement of materials, along with water, through a substrate such as soil.

leaf. A flat, thin, expanded organ growing from a shoot consisting of a broad blade, a petiole, and two inconspicuous stipules at the base of the petiole, in which photosynthesis, respiration, and transpiration are concentrated.

leaf scar. The mark left on a cane or stem after a leaf falls.

leaf shingling. The clumping or sticking together of plant foliage caused by the force of a liquid spray.

leghold trap. Device for holding or restraining an animal by the leg.

lenticel. A tiny, pore-like opening surrounded by corky tissue, often prominent as brown spots on grape berries and pedicels, whose main function is gas exchange.

lesion. Localized diseased tissue.

lysimeter. A measuring device that can be used to accurately determine evapotranspiration values of grapevines or other crop plants.

mandibles. Stout, toothlike, lateral upper jaws of chewing insects, used for seizing and biting.

marginal. Relating to the edge of a leaf blade.

maturity. Stage of development in which a fruit has reached the quality for which it is intended.

meconium. Fecal pellet excreted by a larva before pupation.

meristem. Embryonic tissue of a plant from which the cells are capable of active division and differentiation into specialized tissues.

metabolite. A substance produced by or taking part in a metabolic process.

metamorphosis. Change in form during development.

middle. Area between vine rows, not including the berm.

mildew. A fungal disease in which the mycelium and spores are seen as a whitish growth on the infected plant surface.

mixed bud. A bud with both shoot and cluster primordia.

MOG (matter other than grapes). Contaminants such as leaves, canes, permanent wood, or trellis parts in harvested grapes.

mold. Slimy, cottony, or filamentous fungal growth on moist or decaying organic matter or plant surfaces.

molt. In insects and mites, the shedding of skin before entering another stage of growth.

motile forms. Stages in the insect life cycle that are capable of movement.

multiplefeeding bait. Poisonous bait requiring a sustained dosage over a period of time to produce death.

mycelium. Mass of hyphae forming the body of a fungus.

necrosis. The death of plant tissue accompanied by dark brown discoloration.

nocturnal. Active at night.

node. The enlarged portion of a cane or shoot at which leaves, clusters, tendrils, and/or buds are located.

nodosities. Swelling or galls caused by grape phylloxera on the tips of rootlets.

nongame mammal. Any animal not commonly hunted, as specified in the California Fish and Game Code.

nonionic. A compound lacking any appreciable electrical charge.

nontarget species. A species that is not the object of a control method.

nymph. In insects with gradual metamorphosis, stage of development after hatching resembling the adult but lacking fully developed wings and sex organs.

omnivorous. Feeding on many hosts.

opaque. Without any surface luster; not transparent.

ostiole. Dorsal pore of mealybugs.

ovary. The enlarged basal portion of the pistil, which can become a berry. It contains ovules, which develop into seeds. In insects and mites, the egg-producing organ of the female.

overcropping. The production of more crop than the vine can bring to maturity at normal harvest time.

ovigenesis. Formation and maturation of eggs.

ovipositioning. Depositing eggs.

ovipositor. Specialized appendage of insects for egg deposition.

ovisac. Extension of the body wall or a specialized structure produced by a female insect into which eggs are deposited.

own-rooted. A vine grown from a cutting that develops its own root system, as opposed to a vine that is grafted or budded onto a rootstock.

papilla. A minute, soft, projecting body part of an insect.

parasite. An organism that lives in or on a second organism (its host) during at least part of its life cycle, usually causing a disease or death in the host.

parasitoid. An insect whose immature stage parasitizes and kills other insects before emerging as a larva or adult.

parenchyma. Tissue consisting of loosely fitting, thin-walled cells with irregular spaces important in photosynthesis, storage, and wound healing.

parthenogenesis. Reproduction by developing eggs without fertilization.

pathogen. A disease-causing organism.

pathotype. Subgroup within a species; a strain or race.

pedicel. The stalk of an individual flower or berry in a cluster; in insects, a stalk on which an egg rests.

peduncle. The portion of the grape rachis (cluster stem) from the point of attachment to the shoot to the first lateral branch on the cluster.

perennial. Plant whose life cycle generally lasts 2 or more years.

pericarp. The fruit wall from the outer grape berry surface to its inner surface, adjacent to the seeds or seed traces.

periderm. Protective tissue that replaces the epidermis after the growth of the phloem is initiated and that consists of the cork (phellum), cork cambium (phellogen), and phelloderm (corkskin).

perithecium. Flask-shaped fungus structure that contains asci and ascospores, having an opening (ostiole) at the apex from which spores are expelled.

pesticide residue. Traces of pesticide that remain on treated surfaces after a period of time.

petiolar sinus. A cleft in a leaf margin at the attachment of the petiole.

petiole. The leaf stalk attaching a leaf blade to the shoot.

pH. The degree of acidity or alkalinity of a solution measured on a scale from 1 (very acid) to 14 (very alkaline), with 7.0 being neutral.

pheromone. A substance secreted externally by insects that affects the behavior or development of other members of the same species.

phloem. Region of vascular tissue in a plant that is external to the cambium and composed of sieve tubes, companion cells, and parenchyma cells that conduct and store metabolites.

photophase. The light period in a cycle of light and darkness.

photosynthesis. Process by which a plant converts carbon dioxide and water into carbohydrates and oxygen in the presence of chlorophyll.

phytophagous. Feeding on plants.

phytotoxic. Causing injury or death of plants or portions of plants.

pinaculum. In lepidoptera larvae, a flattened, sclerotized plate that bears setae.

pistil. The female part of the flower, consisting of a stigma, a style, and an ovary.

pith. Soft, spongy parenchymatous tissue that occupies the central portion of the stem.

pollination. The transfer of pollen from the anther to the stigma in three phases: release of pollen from the anthers; transfer of pollen to a receptive surface on the stigma; and germination of pollen grains and growth of pollen tubes and entry into the ovule.

polyembryonic. The development of more than one individual from a fertilized egg.

polyhedrosis virus. Virus particles contained in a polyhedric body.

pomace. Crushed grapes after the extraction of the juice or wine.

population density criteria. Population levels selected for pest management sample counts to indicate probable relative abundance of population in the vineyard.

positioning wires. Wires used to direct shoot growth, often used as movable pairs.

postemergence. Typically, herbicides applied after the crop or weeds have emerged.

postplant preemergence. Treatments applied after the grapes are planted, but before the weeds germinate or emerge from the ground.

prebaiting. Placing of nontoxic bait to condition a pest species to eat it before toxic bait is supplied; baiting a trap without setting it to condition pest acceptance of the trap.

predaceous. Feeding as a predator.

predator. An animal that kills and feeds on many other animals (its prey).

preemergence. Typically, herbicides applied before weeds germinate or emerge from the ground.

preplant. Treatments applied before grape planting.

prepseudopupa stage. Third nymphal instar of thrips.

primary inoculum. Spores that initiate disease at the beginning of the season.

primordium. Initial indication of the development of an organ or structure.

prolegs. Appendages that serve as legs on abdomens of caterpillars and other fleshy larvae; false legs.

pronotum. Upper or dorsal surface of the prothorax of insects.

prophyll. The bract or scalelike leaf that is borne at the first or subsequent nodes of a stem.

prothoracic shield. Chitinous plate on the prothorax of a caterpillar just behind head.

prothorax. Forward segment of an insect's thorax, bearing the first pair of legs.

protonymph. Second instar of a mite.

pseudopupa. Larva in a quiescent, pupalike condition.

PTO. Power take-off.

pubescent. Covered with epidermal hairs; in animals, clothed with soft, short, fine, closely set hair.

pupa. Stage between the larva and adult in insects with complete metamorphosis, a nonfeeding and usually inactive stage.

puparium. In flies, the thickened, hardened larval skin within which the pupa is formed.

pycnidium. An asexual, flasklike fungal fruiting body containing pycnidiospores.

rachis. The main axis of the grape cluster stem, including the peduncle, which bears lateral branches containing flowers or berries.

re-entry interval. The period specified by law that must elapse after a pesticide is applied before people can resume work in a treated area.

residual action. The pesticidal activity of a material after it has been applied.

resistance. Developed ability of insect, mite, pathogen, or weed populations to withstand pesticide effects.

rhizome. A rootlike underground stem, with scales at the nodes, producing shoots on the upper side and roots on the lower side.

rhizomorph. A cordlike strand of overwintering or resting tissue.

ringing. *See* **girdling**.

root. Part of the grapevine that grows downward in the soil, lacks nodes and internodes, and provides anchorage, absorption, and storage and conduction of water and minerals.

rooting. A young vine produced from a cutting and grown in the nursery for one season, in which it develops roots and shoots.

rootstock. Specialized material to which fruiting cultivars of grapes are grafted to produce a commercially acceptable vine.

row plowing. Tillage that removes a narrow ridge of soil (berm) and weeds in the vine row.

runway. Path that an animal or animals commonly travel over or through.

sanitation. The removal or destruction of pest breeding, refuge, and overwintering sites, as well as pest food sources or the pests themselves; may include the removal of infected plant parts or the cleaning of infected tools and field equipment.

saprophyte. An organism that feeds on dead or decaying plant matter; a saprobe.

scab. Crustlike disease lesion.

scion. The fruiting cultivar that is grafted or budded onto the rootstock.

sclerotium. Resting mass of fungal tissue, more or less spherical, and dark, hard, and carbonaceous.

secondary inoculum. Inoculum produced during a season from previous infections without experiencing a resting stage.

secondary pest. A pest that normally is not a problem until controls applied for another pest enable it to increase and cause damage.

second crop. Smaller grape clusters borne on lateral shoots that bloom and mature later than the main crop.

sepal. One of the modified leaves of the calyx; the outermost floral organ.

serration. Toothlike indentations at the leaf margin.

setae. Slender, hairlike appendages on insects and mites.

shatter. Detachment of the berries from the grape cluster, either with or without the pedicel.

shelling. Abscission of flowers before or in bloom.

shoot. The current season's succulent, green stem growth that becomes a cane in the fall when the stem matures.

shoot removal. Removal of unwanted shoots on the trunk of a vine below the head; suckering.

shoot thinning. The removal of unwanted shoot growth from the head, cordon, or arms of a vine when the shoots are short, usually 6 to 15 inches long. Compare **disbudding**.

shot berries. Very small, usually seedless berries that fail to develop to normal size.

shoulders. Well-developed laterals at the point of attachment of the grape cluster.

singlefeeding bait. Toxic bait that produces death from one dose.

sinkhole. A hole formed in soluble rock by the action of water that conducts water to an underground passage.

sinus. Cleft or indentation between the lobes of a leaf blade.

smart sprayer. Spray equipment that uses sensors to control output to specific targets, often resulting in reduced chemical usage.

sod culture. Vegetation management in which a ground cover is kept at all times and is usually mowed periodically during the growing season.

sooty mold. A dark (often black) fungus growing on insect honeydew.

spiracles. Lateral breathing pores on the segments of an insect body.

spore. A reproductive fungal body produced by fungi, plants, and some microorganisms.

spur. A short fruiting unit, the basal section of a cane usually cut back to one or two nodes.

spur pruning. Retaining spurs as fruiting units.

stamen. The male part of a flower, consisting of the anther and a filament.

standard rate. Dosage rate of a pesticide commonly recommended for control, usually selected for its effect on target species without consideration of impact on beneficial species.

stigma. The upper surface of the pistil, where the pollen grain is received and germinates.

stipe. Stalklike part of a Willamette mite egg.

stock. *See* **rootstock**.

stolon. A modified stem, creeping and rooting at the tip, that eventually gives rise to new plants.

stomate. A pore bordered by two guard cells in the epidermis of a leaf, young stem, or berries that regulates the inward flow of carbon dioxide and the outward flow of water vapor during transpiration.

striated. Marked with a slight furrow, ridge, or streak.

stylar scar. A small corky area remaining at the apex of a berry after the style dries and falls off following blossoming.

style. The portion of the pistil between the stigma and the ovary.

subdorsal. Below the dorsum and above the stigmata (spiracle).

suberin. A fatty or waxy substance that is deposited in cell walls and functions as a waterproofing agent.

sucker. A shoot arising at or below ground level.

suckering. Removal of shoots arising at or below ground.

surfactant. A material that improves the emulsifying, dispersing, spreading, wetting, or other properties of a liquid by modifying its surface characteristics.

sward. Land covered by planted or resident vegetation.

systemic. Having the ability to spread internally within a plant.

tarsus. Leg segment beyond the insect tibia consisting of one or more segments or subdivisions.

taxonomist. Scientist especially trained in the classification of plants and animals.

teleomorph. The sexual, or perfect, stage of basidiomycete fungi, such as rust fungi, and wood-rotting fungi.

temperature inversion. A condition in which warm air above cooler air near the ground forms a cap that may cause pesticide vapor or droplets to collect and concentrate.

tendril. A slender twining organ on a shoot opposite a leaf that can coil around an object for support.

tetraploid. Grapevine whose cells contain four sets of chromosomes, as compared with a normal diploid vine whose cells contain two sets of chromosomes.

thorax. The second of the three major divisions in the body of an insect, i.e., the head, thorax, and abdomen.

thyacium. External gall-like cyst in abdomen of a host, containing parasitic larvae of Dryinidae wasps.

tibia. Fourth segment of an insect leg, between the femur and tarsus.

titratable acidity. Measure of the organic acid in juice by titration with sodium hydroxide to an endpoint of pH 8.2; in grapes, often expressed as tartaric acid equivalents.

tomentum. A growth of short, matted, woolly hairs on leaves or stems.

translocation. Movement of water, nutrients, chemicals, or elaborated food materials within a plant.

transpiration. Moisture loss in plants as water vapor from the leaf surface and through the stomates.

treatment level. Population level, at any given stage of development or time of the year, when a spray or other management practice will most effectively and economically prevent crop damage in either the current season or the subsequent crop year.

trellis. A permanent support system for a grapevine consisting of a stake and one wire or a stake with multiple wire and crossarm combinations.

trochanter. Second segment of an insect leg, between the coxa and the femur.

trunk. The main stem or body of a vine between the roots and the head.

tuber. A fleshy, usually oblong or rounded thickening of an underground stem, bearing minute scalelike leaves with buds in their axils from which new plants may arise.

tubercle. A knoblike or rounded protuberance.

tuberosities. Swellings caused by grape phylloxera feeding on larger roots.

tunica. An enveloping membrane or layer of body tissue.

tylosis. An outgrowth that originates from an adjacent parenchyma cell that plugs a xylem vessel.

variety. A group of genetically identical plants of common origin within a species that have distinct, uniform, and stable characteristics. *See* **cultivar**.

vascular cambium. A thin sheath of undifferentiating meristematic (dividing) tissue between the bark and the wood that gives rise secondary xylem (to the inside) and phloem (to the outside), resulting in the growth in diameter of stems and roots.

vector. Agent that transmits inoculum, causing disease.

vein. In plants, a strand of vascular tissue in a flat organ such as a leaf; in insects, the thickened, rodlike structure supporting and stiffening the wings.

veinal chlorosis. Yellowing of the main veins of a leaf.

ventral. Lower or underneath.

veraison. The beginning of fruit ripening as indicated by softening of the berry, the beginning of color development, or soluble solids of 7 to 10 Brix.

vermiform. Shaped like a worm.

virion. A single virus particle.

virus. Subcellular disease-causing agent composed of nucleic acid and protein coat that can replicate only inside the living cells of a host.

viscosity. The property of resistance to flow in a fluid.

volatilization. The process by which liquid passes into a gaseous phase.

water sprout. A rapidly growing shoot arising from latent buds on branches or trunks.

wettable powder. An inert powder that holds active material, usually insoluble in water but capable of forming stable suspension in water.

wildlife pest. Any species of wild animal, in any area, that becomes a health hazard, causes economic damage, or is a general nuisance to one or more persons.

wilt. Loss of freshness or turgor of plants because of inadequate water supply or excessive transpiration; a vascular disease interfering with water transport.

wing. In grapes, a well-developed basal cluster branch appearing to be separated from the main cluster.

wing pads. Encased undeveloped wings of nymphs (such as leafhoppers) that appear as two lateral, flattish structures behind the thorax.

witches'-broom. Abnormal, vigorous, brushlike growth often caused by a bud mutation.

xylem. The woody portions of the vascular tissue internal to the cambium that conducts water and minerals, stores food, and supports the trunk, roots, and stems.

yield-to-pruning-weight ratio. A ratio of crop weight to the pruning weight of 1-year-old canes removed at pruning on an individual vine basis, used to assess vine balance.

Index

Note: Entries for which both a common name and a scientific name are given in the text are indexed at the common name, with a cross-reference from the scientific name to the common name. Page numbers with an italic *t*, for example, 548*t*, refer to tables. Entries whose names begin with numerals are indexed at the beginning of the index.

INDEX

transport of, 572–573

See also fungicides; herbicides; insecticide treatments; nematicides; spray applications

Petite Sirah cultivar

Botrytis bunch rot, 101*t*

fasciated clusters (chimera), 31

heat damage, 37

Pierce's disease, 77, 82

powdery mildew, 137

Petri disease, 66*t*, 120, 123–125

pH of soil, 52

Phacelia spp., 502*t*

Phaeoacremonium spp., 120–125

Phaeomoniella chlamydospora, 120–125

Phalaris minor, 530*t*

See also littleseed canarygrass

Phaneroptera nana Fiebre, 179–180

pheasant, 496

pheromone traps

almond moth, 439, 440*t*

driedfruit beetle, 437

European grapevine moth, 350, 351

Indianmeal moth, 439, 440*t*, 442

light brown apple moth, 363

mealybug, 244, 254–255, 261–262

Mediterranean flour moth, 439, 440*t*

omnivorous leafroller, 369, 370–371

orange tortrix, 374, 376

pink hibiscus mealybug, 270

raisin moth, 380, 439, 440*t*

tobacco moth, 439, 440*t*

Phomopsis cane and leaf spot

disease cycle, 128–130

management, 130

management notes, by region, 23, 25

overview, 126–127

sampling, testing, 66*t*

symptoms, 127–128

Phomopsis viticola, 126–130

phosphine fumigation, 444

phosphorous fertilization, timing of, 16, 18, 20

photosystem I inhibitors, 39

photosystem II inhibitors, 39

phylloxera

aerial images, 57–58

description, 192

injury, 192–194

management notes, by region, 17, 19, 21, 23, 25

monitoring, 194–196

nursery stock treatments, 197

overview, 191

replanting options, 200–201

resistant rootstocks, 198–200

in San Joaquin Valley, 197–198

seasonal development, 194

site management, 197–198

spread, 196–197

Phytophthora crown and root rot, 62, 66*t*, 131–132

Phytophthora spp., 62, 131–132

Pierce's disease (PD)

aerial images, 58

causes of similar symptoms, 78–79

disease cycle, 79–80

management, 80–82, 284–285

management notes, by region, 17, 19, 21, 23, 25

overview, 75–76

sampling/testing, 62, 66*t*, 79

symptoms, 76–78

vectors, 75, 76, 79, 80, 81

(*See also* sharpshooters)

pigmentation disorder, 43–44

pigs, 490–491

pin nematode, 456, 457*t*

pine bluegrass, 505

pineapple beetle, 436, 437

pink hibiscus mealybug, 269–270

Pinot gris cultivar, 31

Pinot Meunier cultivar, 110

Pinot noir cultivar

berry cracking, 30

berry shrivel, 45

Botrytis bunch rot, 101, 101*t*

Eutypa dieback, 110

orange tortrix, 374

Pierce's disease, 77, 82

sharpshooters, 285

Willamette spider mites, 408

piston pumps, 545–546

Pisum sativum, 502*t*

See also peas

Planococcus ficus (Signoret). *See* vine mealybug

plant tissue analysis, timing of, 16, 18, 20, 22, 24, 26

plant-back restrictions, 568

Plasmopara viticola, 117–119

Platynota idaeusalis (Walker), 364

Platynota stultana Walsingham. *See* omnivorous leafroller

Plodia interpunctella (Hübner). *See* Indianmeal moth

pocket gopher, 482–486

management note, Coachella Valley, 25

POISON signal word, 564

Polistes apachus Saussure. *See* Apache wasp

Polistes dominulus (Christ). *See* European paper wasp

Polistes fuscatus aurifer Saussure. *See* golden paper wasp

pollination, 5

polyhedrosis viruses, 338, 380, 439

pomace flies. *See* drosophila flies

Portulaca oleracea, 524*t*

See also common purslane

positive displacement pumps, 559

postemergent herbicides, 523

postharvest diseases, 133–136

posting treated areas, 575

potassium fertilization, timing of, 16, 18, 20, 22, 24, 26

INDEX